11-3-64

$ 14.88

1964-65

THE LOWER METAZOA

The Lower Metazoa

COMPARATIVE BIOLOGY
AND PHYLOGENY

EDITED BY Ellsworth C. Dougherty

IN COLLABORATION WITH

Zoe Norwood Brown · Earl D. Hanson · Willard D. Hartman

UNIVERSITY OF CALIFORNIA PRESS

1963   BERKELEY AND LOS ANGELES

University of California Press
Berkeley and Los Angeles, California

Cambridge University Press
London, England

© 1963 by The Regents of the University of California
Library of Congress Catalog Card Number 63–22707
Printed in the United States of America

PREFACE

The present volume traces its origin to the Second Annual Symposium on Comparative Biology of the Kaiser Foundation Research Institute, a meeting almost entirely supported by a grant from the National Science Foundation (G–14066). It was held September 6–9, 1960, at Asilomar, Pacific Grove, California, and September 10, 1960, at the Kaiser Center, Oakland, California. Ellsworth C. Dougherty was expected to be editor of the resulting proceedings, but unforeseen circumstances forced his withdrawal at a crucial time. Editorial work was then undertaken by Dr. B. G. Chitwood, Dr. M. M. J. Lavoipierre, and especially Mrs. Ruth Straus, Editor in the Department of Scientific Publications, Kaiser Foundation Hospitals. Delay due to various difficulties followed, and the Kaiser Foundation Research Institute finally decided to withdraw sponsorship, to return manuscripts to participants, and to release all papers for publication under other auspices at the discretion of the contributors.

At several requests of Symposium participants and other interested persons, Dr. Dougherty and colleagues Mrs. Zoe N. Brown, Dr. Earl D. Hanson, and Dr. Willard D. Hartman undertook to constitute a somewhat comparable volume. This has been accomplished with the result of a book differing only moderately from what the original Symposium would have produced. There have been up-datings or changes of contents of papers by certain workers; a few contributions have been deleted at the decision of the authors; and a few new papers have been inserted. The publication of the volume has been made possible by a generous donation from the Cocos Foundation, Inc., 810 Fletcher Trust Building, Indianapolis 4, Indiana.

ELLSWORTH C. DOUGHERTY
ZOE NORWOOD BROWN
Department of Nutritional Sciences, College of Agriculture
University of California, Berkeley

EARL D. HANSON
Shanklin Laboratory of Biology, Wesleyan University
Middletown, Connecticut

WILLARD D. HARTMAN
Department of Biology and Peabody Museum of Natural History
Yale University, New Haven, Connecticut

CONTRIBUTORS

PETER AX, *Second Zoölogical Institute and Museum, University of Göttingen, Göttingen, German Federal Republic*

ERNEST BALDWIN, *Department of Biochemistry, University College, London, England*

V. N. BEKLEMISHEV, *Institute of Medical Parasitology and Tropical Medicine, Ministry of Public Health, Moscow, U.S.S.R.* (Deceased September 4, 1962)

MARIO BENAZZI, *Institute of Zoölogy and Comparative Anatomy, University of Pisa, Pisa, Italy*

ROYAL BRUCE BRUNSON, *Department of Zoölogy, Montana State University, Missoula, Montana*

R. B. CLARK, *Department of Zoölogy, University of Bristol, Bristol, England*

ELLSWORTH C. DOUGHERTY, *Department of Nutritional Sciences, College of Agriculture, University of California, Berkeley, California*

CADET HAND, *Department of Zoölogy, University of California, Berkeley, California*

EARL D. HANSON, *Department of Biology, Wesleyan University, Middletown, Connecticut*

WILLARD D. HARTMAN, *Department of Biology and Peabody Museum of Natural History, Yale University, New Haven, Connecticut*

H. B. N. HYNES, *Department of Zoölogy, University of Liverpool, Liverpool, England*

J. B. JENNINGS, *Department of Zoölogy, University of Leeds, Leeds, England*

DONALD D. JENSEN, *Department of Psychology, Indiana University, Bloomington, Indiana*

TOR G. KARLING, *Division of Invertebrates, State Museum of Natural History, Stockholm, Sweden*

TAKU KOMAI, *Zoölogical Institute, University of Kyoto, Kyoto, Japan*

KARL LANG, *Division of Invertebrates, State Museum of Natural History, Stockholm, Sweden*

CLAUDE LÉVI, *Laboratory of General Biology, Faculty of Sciences, University of Strasbourg, Strasbourg, France*

G. O. MACKIE, *Department of Zoölogy, University of Alberta, Edmonton, Alberta, Canada*

ARMAND R. MAGGENTI, *Department of Nematology, College of Agriculture, University of California, Davis, California*

EDGAR J. MARTIN, *Laboratory of Comparative Biology, Kaiser Foundation Research Institute, Richmond, California*

BAYARD H. MCCONNAUGHEY, *Department of Biology, University of Oregon, Eugene, Oregon*

W. L. NICHOLAS, *Department of Zoölogy, School of General Studies, Australian National University, Canberra, A.C.T., Australia*

GÜNTHER OSCHE, *Zoölogical Institute, University of Erlangen-Nuremberg, Erlangen, German Federal Republic*

ROBERT W. PENNAK, *Department of Biology, University of Colorado, Boulder, Colorado*

JOHN H. PHILLIPS, *Hopkins Marine Station of Stanford University, Pacific Grove, California*

ADOLF REMANE, *Zoölogical Institute and Museum, University of Kiel, Kiel, German Federal Republic*

AGNES RUTTNER-KOLISKO, *Biological Station of the Austrian Academy of Sciences, Lunz-am-See, Austria*

DIETRICH SCHNEIDER, *Division of Comparative Neurophysiology, Max Planck Institute, Munich, German Federal Republic*

OTTO STEINBÖCK, *Zoölogical Institute, University of Innsbruck, Innsbruck, Austria*

ODETTE TUZET, *Laboratory of Zoölogy and Animal Biology, Faculty of Sciences, University of Montpellier, Montpellier, France*

TOHRU UCHIDA, *Zoölogical Institute, Faculty of Science, Hokkaido University, Sapporo, Japan*

MARIETTA VOGE, *Department of Medical Microbiology and Immunology, School of Medicine, University of California, Los Angeles, California*

CONTENTS

III. Other Disciplines of Comparative Biology

INTRODUCTION

DEPARTMENT OF NUTRITIONAL SCIENCES, COLLEGE OF AGRICULTURE,
UNIVERSITY OF CALIFORNIA, BERKELEY

By comparison with most other animal groups, the lower Metazoa are relatively neglected. There remains an immense amount of fundamental taxonomic, morphological, and physiological work to be done before we have a reasonably clear picture of their biology. Somewhat more advanced in these connections is the rich and busy discipline of "protozoölogy."[1] Also in the animal sciences there are thriving studies of such advanced forms as vertebrates, arthropods, molluscs, and echinoderms, to name most. But between the "protozoa" and these higher metazoa are diverse assemblages, many of which have been relatively little explored. One must except, to be sure, the parasitic groups, which annoy man enough to be rewarded with a wealth of attention; but, for free-living members of most major taxa that loosely can be called the lower Metazoa, there are comparatively few investigators.

When the meeting that formed the basis of what, after much delay, has become this volume was conceived in 1960, it was not my expectation to see emerge an encyclopedic tome treating all the lower Metazoa equally. Rather I strove for a sampling of work in different disciplines, with a consequent cross-fertilizing of ideas. My reasons for being interested in the lower Metazoa were, first, that for almost a decade and a half much of my own research had been done with certain of them, special concern having thus been evolved; and, second, that I was, and remain, much intrigued with the unresolved questions of their origin *vis-à-vis* the "Protozoa" and of their interrelationships. It was evident, from scanning the literature of recent years, that there was a group of distinguished European phylogeneticists and another group of American and that the latter, at least, had relatively little knowledge of what the former were writing.

---

[1] Protozoölogy actually comprehends the study of a *pot pourri* of forms, some of which are shared amicably with the botanists; perhaps a happier alternative would be to eliminate, at the level of unicellular forms and the multicellular algae, the animal-plant distinction and to use instead of a unifying term such as "protist," with words "animal" and "plant" left for the Metazoa and Metaphyta respectively.

So it seemed a felicitous notion to bring together the principal students—those consenting—from both sides of the Atlantic and elsewhere for first-hand discussions. Invitations were extended to the leading authorities, but, of course, could not all be accepted.

A prime feature of the meeting was a round table discussion where opposing views were argued on the origin of the Metazoa and allied problems. For suggesting this we are endebted to Dr. Earl D. Hanson. Otherwise the persons invited were free to talk about any subject, including ones transcending the lower Metazoa, provided that the latter organisms were basic to the discussion. It was originally hoped to see represented the taxa (phyla) Porifera, Mesozoa, Platyhelminthes, Rhynchocoela (Nemertinea), Coelenterata (Cnidaria), Ctenophora, Acanthocephala, Aschelminthes, and Entoprocta. In this volume one or more aspects of all groups save the last are treated, and the list has been extended to the Ectoprocta with the insertion of Dr. Dietrich Schneider's paper, which was not on the original program.

Although the book that is finally emerging largely coincides with the addresses at the meeting, several papers were withdrawn because of delay in publication. But a number of contributions offered in substitution have been included. The original tenor of the meeting has thereby been largely retained. A detailed summary and synthesis based on the diversity of papers that follow would be beyond the scope of a short introduction. Rather than offering further, necessarily superficial review of the contents of this volume, I feel it more useful to take this opportunity to formulate a generalizing idea, much of which the meeting brought into focus.

The concept revolves about the time-honored problem of homology *vs.* analogy in biology. For the most part we know perfectly well what we mean when we use these terms. The wing of a bird is homologous with the pectoral fin of a fish, but merely analogous (convergent in function) with the wing of a butterfly, in the latter instance because the similarly named bird and butterfly appendages are flying organs without phylogenetic connection as usually reckoned. But I should like to interject a concept that, if it has any virtue at all, may help resolve some of the argumentation about the significance of homology *vs.* analogy in the never-never land between protist and metazoön (and in other biological domains as well).

As a working hypothesis I suggest that most of the crucial evolutionary "ideas," both structural and biochemical, were evolved very early, and, once realized, have, by a sort of "principle of genetic parsimony," never really been discarded even though we may lack, at our present stage of knowledge, either morphological or physiological evidence of certain features in the life cycle of a given organism today. What has primarily happened is that, where a basic attribute is not expressed, genetic information has been merely shuffled about and put to other use, but remains in the genome of the organism and, under appropriate situations, is ready for utilization—given time to be genetically mobilized, of course.

This concept can lead to seemingly far-fetched speculations. For example, I wonder if the sort of genetic information that enables serial replication to give, say, a string of bacteria is not called upon (with added genetic ammunition, of course) to make possible serial replication at much higher levels: cestode strobilization; metamerism generally; and so forth. If the living world is looked at through the eyeglass of such a principle of genetic parsimony, many things that seem convergent or parallel (and are so in the sense they are generally conceived) have an element of homology. If you recoil at conceiving of *homology* between linear sequences of bacteria and cestode strobili, we can perhaps compromise with a different word—*metalogy,* let us say.

For ultimate testing of the concept of metalogy, those that must be asked are not we more or less orthodox invertebrate zoölogists (who are in no position—so far as I can see—to test such a hypothesis), but the geneticists and molecular biologists. They are the ones that might ultimately provide the DNA blueprints, if such exist. The question really is: is novel genetic information, once acquired, too precious to be thrown away; may it perhaps be shifted about and put to seemingly different use, but, like the genie in the bottle, remain to emerge again in its earlier form and so engineer the repetition of conditions that by most usual conventions would be termed non-homologous?

If this is a valid idea, then a great deal of the argumentation on homology *vs.* analogy in phylogeny at the metazoan level really misses the mark. The answers lie not in relatively recent (I mean 600,000,000-year-old) events, but two billion or more years earlier when basic genetic ideas were first really formulated; thereafter they have kept cropping up—*inter alia* to bedevil today the phylogeneticist trying to make sense out of a metalogy that is far more archaic than he may imagine.

More than a year ago I went to a doctoral oral examination on some serpentine gymnostomatous ciliates. If I had not been forewarned, I should have thought that at one point I was seeing slides depicting the anterior end of gastrotrichs and, from the view of the posterior end of the same animalcules, of nematodes. It made me ask myself: are these mere examples of convergence (in the traditional sense) or are they metalogous—that is, have our modern aschelminths brought into use genetic information that was fashioned two billion or more years earlier by organisms much further down the evolutionary scale?

I. Comparative Morphology and Phylogeny

A. GENERAL ORIGIN AND AFFINITIES

1 ◆ Homologies and the Ciliate Origin of the Eumetazoa

EARL D. HANSON

DEPARTMENT OF BIOLOGY, WESLEYAN UNIVERSITY,
MIDDLETOWN, CONNECTICUT

The elucidation of phylogeny is dependent on the identification of homologies (Remane, 1956). In an earlier paper (Hanson, 1958), reviewing the problem of the phylogenetic origin of the Eumetazoa, it was shown that the acele Turbellaria share many similar features with certain gymnostomatous ciliates. On the basis of these similarities—homologies were, at that time, specifically avoided—it was concluded that there could exist a phylogenetic relationship between aceles and ciliates such that a ciliate-like form was ancestral to both groups. This conclusion, based simply on similarities, has been criticized as having an insufficient basis for phylogenetic speculations (Grimstone, 1959; Nursall, 1959; Dr. Rudolph Jander, through personal discussions). The purpose of this presentation is to reëxamine the data presented in the paper just alluded to, and determine if any of the similarities noted there are indeed homologies.

The most significant analysis of the problem of homologies is that of Remane (1956). This eminent morphologist has developed criteria that can be used to identify homologous structures and at the same time exclude parallelisms and convergences that have been mistaken for homologies. The major part of this paper will be devoted to an examination of the Remanian criteria of homology and their application to the possible ciliate origin of the acele Turbellaria. First, however, there must be presented, at least briefly, arguments in favor of the primitive nature of acele organization, as opposed to its interpretation as being secondarily reduced, for, if the Acoela are not the most primitive of the free-living flatworms, there would be no point in comparing them to the ciliates for phylogenetic purposes.

This paper was written while the author was a fellow of the John Simon Guggenheim Foundation for 1960–1961.

The Primitive Nature of the Acoela

This problem can be approached by listing three features typical of forms usually widely accepted as showing structural and functional reductions. These are often parasitic forms (*e.g.,* cestodes) or sessile forms (*e.g.,* tunicates).

    1. Reduction is the result of adaptation to a special mode of life.

    2. Not all characters of the organism are reduced; certain are of continuing significance to the biology of the organism and hence are preserved without reduction and often evolve to a more specialized level.

    3. Embryologically there is often evidence of reduction through the transitory appearance of embryonic structures that are suggestive of a more complex ancestral form.

Taking these three points in order, we see, first, that there is no evidence that the simplicity of the aceles relative to other Turbellaria is the result of adaptation to a mode of life conducive to the reduction of body parts. Aceles are herbivores, carnivores, and ecto-commensals. There are also benthic and pelagic forms. All of these forms, pursuing very different modes of living, show a characteristic acele organization, and to argue that in all cases the postulated reduction is an adaptatively significant change is simply not convincing.

Next, we note that those favoring the secondary reduction of acele characters argue that *all* major structures—epithelium, gut, excretory apparatus, genitalia, nerve net, contractile fibers, etc.—are reduced. Not a single organelle system remains that is not affected. This is not the case in well-established examples of reduction.

Third, there is only one embryonic character in the Acoela that suggests the possibility of reduction, and that is the occurrence of cellular blastomeres in the early cleavage. These cell boundaries disappear when the young worm hatches or shortly thereafter. Another explanation for this phenomenon is, however, possible—namely, that this is the only way the fertilized egg can develop. Such a suggestion will be inconceivable to those convinced by the biogenetic law that metazoan embryogenesis must always recapitulate something, and that the cells in early acele embryos are such a recapitulation. This point is discussed again later in the context of the origin of acele embryogenesis; further details are therefore deferred until that discussion.

In brief, no convincing argument for reduction is possible. To compare acele structures with their counterparts in other turbellarians and then simply "interpret" the differences as reduction is to argue without explicit criteria. When, however, such criteria are used, as above, the conclusion in favor of reduction of structures remains unfounded. On the other hand, to argue for the primitive nature of these structures is to argue for a lack of excessive specialization. Excessive specialization can result in highly complex structures or in much simplified ones. The first are relatively obvious and do not constitute a problem in the Acoela. The second are the same as reduction and can be recognized by the criteria suggested above. In the case of the Acoela, lack of fulfillment of these criteria and the absence of structures of obvious evolutionary complexity exclude the possibility of considering acele structures as highly evolved relative to other Turbellaria. The Acoela are properly considered as the most primitive flatworms.

The Criteria of Homology

As Remane has pointed out, though we accept descent from a common ancestor as the *explanation* of homologies, we do not as a rule, and cannot in the case of the higher taxa, use a breeding analysis to test for this genetic propinquity. The test of homology, despite its explanation, is not genetic. Remane proposes that homologies be identified primarily on morphological grounds, ethological and serological studies being other, supporting lines of evidence. Furthermore, specific morphological criteria are proposed for the purpose of this identification. Rather than repeat those criteria here, a modification of them is presented since it is in this modified form that they are used in this paper. The modifications relate essentially to the scope of application of the criteria and to the formulation of the subsidiary criteria. Regarding the scope of application, it appears that homologies are present not only in structures, but also in functions or processes. For we know that the ability to develop anew *both* structures and processes is passed from parent to progeny. Or, to put it another way, genes control structures and also functions. Hence, accepting the genetic explanation of homologies, it follows that, if we expect certain relationships between structures evolved from a common genetic source, we also expect the same for processes. Indeed, the criteria for homology, as proposed here, are such that they may apply to any gene-controlled phenomenon of sufficient complexity to make comparison meaningful. Thus included are structures, functions, and also ethological and serological studies. Such an approach has already been developed by Waterman (1961) from Remane's criteria.

　　1. In the first, and major, criterion there are three major relationships of homologous entities.

　　　a. Positional relationship. Homologous structures or functions occupy a similar position in the system of which they are a part.

　　　b. Compositional relationship. Homologous structures or functions are composed of constituent parts similar in number, shape, or function performed, and in relation to other constituent parts.

　　　c. Serial relationships. Homologous structures or functions can be arranged serially so that the least similar or extreme members of the series are joined by intergrading forms connected at each step by positional and compositional relationships.

　　Then there are three subsidiary criteria. Here certain changes from Remane's thinking are incorporated, but, nevertheless, the fundamental approach is clearly dependent on him. These criteria are useful in the absence of clear establishment of the major criterion.

　　2. Homologies are probable in structures and functions similar in placement and composition that appear in forms already known, by the major criterion, to possess homologies. [The appearance of such structures or functions in forms known not to possess homologies establishable by the major criterion, renders homologies improbable.]

3. Homologies are probable in structures and functions occurring in a large number of nearly similar forms, whose similarity is unlikely except as the result of descent from a common ancestor.

4. The possibility of homology exists if different structures or functions of suspected homology all have a similar distribution in nearly similar forms; this possibility increases with the addition of more parts or processes of similar distribution.

Those familiar with Remane's criteria will recognize criteria 3 and 4. Criterion 2 is the converse of his final criterion, here given in brackets. The present order is thought to reflect a decreasing probability of identification of homologies.

To those unfamiliar with these criteria, their derivation, and their significance for the study of homologies, a study of the original works of Remane (1955, 1956) is strongly recommended.

Physiological homologies.—Perhaps some general comments are in order on the application of these criteria to functions, for the concept of homology is readily associated with morphological entities, but not so commonly with physiological ones. Its application is, however, similar in both areas: in studying morphological entities the placement of structures is observed in relation to the whole body and the composition of these structures is seen through appropriate dissections. Similarly, a given physiological function is seen in its contribution to the total body function, and the composition of this function is understood as a series of particular subprocesses.

More specifically, if we take as the major function of any organism the perpetuation of its kind, we can see within any generation the many interdependent processes that lead from immaturity to maturity and thence to reproduction. This applies to the so-called cell-generations of microörganisms and to the embryogenesis of multicelled systems. The temporal sequence of these events in one organism can be compared with the same events in other organisms, and in this way the positional relationship of homologies can be examined. Further, processes such as gamete formation can be examined in terms of their subparts, such as pre- or postzygotic reduction, meiotic behavior, differentiation of gametic structures, etc. From such data, taken from different organisms or groups of organisms, the processes can be examined comparatively and the compositional relationships evaluated. The relationship of serial array can be studied by comparing functional position and composition as just outlined. In this manner the detailed complexities of function at the cellular, tissue, or organ level can be examined as evolved relationships pertinent to the concept of homology.

Homologies and microscopic structures.—The concept of homology has been developed almost exclusively from data derived from multicellular, macroscopic forms. The question now arises as to whether this same concept is meaningful and useful to microscopic organisms lacking cellular subdivisions. This is especially important in our present case where the acellular or unicellular ciliated protozoa are being examined for possible homologous relationships to aceles—forms considered to be clearly related to larger, multicelled forms.

The relative simplicity of protozoa, and of protistan forms in general, has three important consequences for the study of homology. To begin with, it makes difficult the precise definition of positional relations. In forms with no well-defined plane of symmetry or anterior-posterior polarization, it is difficult to compare the relative locations of cell-organelles. Furthermore, the absence from most protists of such things as endoskeletal articulations, innervations, and circulatory tracts, which are of great help in comparing the location of metazoan appendages, for example, render it that much more difficult to make meaningful comparison of positional relations in microscopic forms. Physiologically there does not seem to be so great a problem because the temporal location of sequential activities (*e.g.,* in cell division) does have the time axis for relative orientation.

Next, the relative simplicity of these forms is also seen in their organelles. Lack of complexity here renders difficult the evaluation of the compositional relationship. Furthermore, it can be recalled that this is not just an optical problem of needing more resolving power. One of the great contributions of electron microscopy is the revelation of a protoplasmic fine structure that is extraordinarily ubiquitous—cytoplasmic membrane systems, mitochondrial cristae, ciliary and flagellar cross-sections, and so on. Here, then, we must concern ourselves with structures more complex than the basic protoplasmic elements. Attention must be directed to structural specializations that are evolved from this common protoplasmic foundation. The comparative anatomy of organelles such as nuclei, contractile vacuoles, cortical fiber systems, and various other cytoplasmic elements will have to be studied. It may well be that, with further low-powered electron microscopy especially, the relative simplicity of organelles will not be so great a difficulty as it at present seems.

A parallel problem exists in the elucidation of the nature of many protistan processes; for here again, attention must be directed to functional specializations above the level of those activities that are of almost universal occurrence in protoplasm. The Emden-Meyerhof scheme, the Krebs cycle, and paths of fatty acid and protein synthesis were elucidated from data taken from bacteria, yeast, pigeon breast muscle, and many other sources and represent a major advance in establishing the unity of life. Our present concern, however, is with the diversity of life that has been evolved with these common metabolic patterns. So here, in the pursuit of functional homologies, we are concerned with special nutritional requirements, with the functioning of cell organelles, with their mode of formation, with total cell activities such as growth rates, and with the reproductive and sexual processes of cell bodies. Unfortunately, in many of the Protista these more highly evolved processes are as yet unknown or only fragmentarily known. So what promises to be a valuable complement to morphological homologies is all too often unavailable at present.

And then, finally (and a most important problem), relative simplicity has been taken to imply a relative lability of structure (Grimstone, 1959). The argument is a genetic one: simpler structures need relatively few genes for their expression; fewer genes mean that a single mutational change can have quite marked effects; hence, simply through mutation pressure simpler structures are more readily modified, lost, and also formed, even several times over and independently of one another, than in more complex structures made of tissues and organs. Two criticisms, however, should be raised with regard to this argument. First, it may be premature to assume that simpler structures need relatively fewer genes for their expression. In terms of specific cases there are in the Protozoa only two analyzed instances of structural variants. One of these concerns the form of trichocysts in *Paramecium aurelia* (Preer, 1959) and is dependent on a single gene difference from the normal type. The other, also in *Paramecium aurelia,* is not completely analyzed (Hanson, unpublished), but on present evidence is caused by a single gene with variable expression and penetrance, which affects gullet morphology. These seem to offer insufficient grounds for any general conclusions regarding the complexity of genetic control of visible organelles in these forms. Furthermore, we know that a single gene is responsible for a single amino acid, as in the hemoglobin molecule (Ingram, 1957), or for the presence or absence of a whole molecule, as, for example, in enzyme formation (Ryan, 1952). From this, if we knew how many different kinds of protein form an organelle such as a flagellum or a contractile vacuole, or a trichocyst or gullet, we might get an estimate of the underlying genetic complexity of protozoan structure. But we simply do not know. And finally, regarding this point of underlying genetic complexity, one must realize that even in complex organisms, such as the laboratory mouse, single genes are known that can drastically modify a structure despite the known involvement of many other genetic loci in the formation of this structure (Dunn and Gluecksohn-Waelsch, 1953). Hence, it is premature to imply that relatively simple structures, such as cell-organelles, rest on a simple genetic foundation that renders them evolutionarily labile.

The second criticism of the genetic argument for structural lability is the following. The stability of a structure is not just a question of the inherent variability of genetic factors; the effect of selective pressures must also be considered. Recently it has been proposed that in connection with certain proteins, such as cytochrome c and ribonuclease, the genes controlling them in various organisms are homologous and "*do* appear to have survived happily through long periods of time, some well exceeding the span of the fossil record" (Anfinsen, 1959, p. 213). If a biological entity continues to play a vital role in the organism, there seems good reason for it to be evolutionarily conservative rather than plastic. Relative simplicity does not necessarily mean structural instability. The same line of reasoning would apply to functional entities.

At this point should be mentioned the probably very long evolutionary history of ciliates and aceles. Despite the lack of fossil evidence, it is not improbable that these forms first arose in the Pre-Cambrian. If they diverged from a common ancestor at that time, they have had many hundreds of millions of years to diverge even further, *if such were the selective pressures.* But, as has just been noted and as is well known, natural selection can achieve evolutionary stability as well as evolutionary change. (Note the possibility of extraordinary stability in fossil radiolarians. Simpson—1949, p. 194—reports that these marine protozoa are reputed to have existed since the Pre-Cambrian without one type ever becoming extinct!)

From the foregoing, the following points should be borne in mind. Organisms lacking cellular subdivisions commonly present an organization in which structural positional relations are hard to define. Functionally the problem is not so difficult, since a temporal sequence offers a useful way of comparing the relative position of various activities. Regarding the details of the composition of a structure or function, protistan organisms present special problems. The level of organization that is most useful for identifying homologies is that of cell-organelles and the cell-body itself. This is an area better known morphologically than physiologically. Hence, regarding compositional relationships, structure will, on the whole, be more useful than functions—the reverse of the situation for positional relations.

From this it is clear that the establishment of the serial relationships in any given case will be difficult, depending as it does on the first two relationships. Add to this the long historical period available for evolutionary change, if it is going to occur even at a slow rate, and we see that the application of the Remanian criteria to the acellular or unicellular Protista will rarely supply conclusive answers.

Nonetheless, there is nothing that invalidates an attempt to establish homologies. We are simply warned of the possible difficulties and should therefore take advantage of all possible information in such a study. This we are going to do in using both structural and functional data.

Ciliate-Acele Homologies

We can now proceed to an outline of the possible application of the criteria of homology to the general structure and function of the ciliates and aceles. There is no space here for great detail; for that the earlier paper on this topic is referred to (Hanson, 1958). There it was pointed out that since the ciliates are such a multifarious group, it would be easy to extract enough isolated characters to parallel the salient features of acele biology. A more critical approach would demand that acele characters be derivable from a single, relatively homogeneous group of ciliates. In answer to this point it was further remarked that all the major acele characters were derivable from certain gymnostome genera (*i.e., Remanella* and *Dileptus*). In this sense the gymnostomatous ciliates are the living forms closest to an archetype of the ciliates and aceles. They can therefore be compared to the aceles on the one hand and the higher ciliates on the other.

Before we proceed, however, one further important point must be made regarding the gymnostomes and their key position as a group showing homologous relations to both aceles and the other ciliates. This is the problem of ciliate-acele similarities being the result of convergence rather than true homologies. Remane (1956, p. 86) has pointed out the convergent similarities in such protozoan and metazoan forms as the flagellate *Leptodiscus* and the medusa *Homoeonema,* the ciliate *Stentor* and the rotifer *Ptygura,* and also the suctorian *Dendrosoma* and the polyp *Syncoryne.* In these cases it is easy to see the convergence—the similarities are restricted to superficial structural features. This is typical for all cases of convergence, including, for example, the classic one of sharks, ichthyosaurs, and porpoises. Convergences can be identified in the context of the Remanian criteria. Convergent similarities do not fulfill the serial relationship, and they rarely fulfill the compositional relationship. Furthermore, they can often be identified by the converse of the first subsidiary criterion; that is, similarities appear unaccompanied by demonstrable homologies. In this sense the spotty distribution of hemoglobin (Baldwin, 1937) and of quinone-tanned proteins (Grimstone, 1959) among various animal phyla, and of macronuclei in ciliates and foraminifers (Grimstone, 1959), can all be seen as non-homologous, convergent characters. The problem of convergence all but disappears when investigations compare the total biology of organisms, for under such a scrutiny isolated or superficial similarities are clearly seen against the background of many dissimilarities (or lack of homologous relationships). This emphasizes the importance of extending the concept of homology to processes as well as parts—of comparing the *total* biology of organisms and not just their morphology or development; the more numerous the similarities that can be established, the greater the probability of homology. It is my contention, in the case of ciliate-acele comparisons, that the similarities are so far-reaching and the differences so adequately explicable that convergence is rendered highly improbable. We here consider first structural, then functional comparisons.

General body organization.—The general body organization of ciliates and aceles presents certain broad similarities. Some of these characters, for example, acele bilateral symmetry, anterior-posterior polarization, and ventral mouth, are common to the majority of the Eumetazoa. Such characters, however, are by no means widespread in the Protista, and it is therefore significant that they are all found in the ciliates—with especially good examples in the gymnostomatous ciliates. Complete ciliation is another permanent character significantly held in common by ciliates and aceles. Furthermore, internally, the syncytial acele body, essentially devoid of internal cell membranes except around the gametes, is broadly similar to that of ciliates. Its subdivisions, using Westblad's (1948) effective terminology, of outermost epicytium, innermost endocytium, and intermediate ectocytium, seem similar to the outermost ciliate ectoplasm, innermost, sol-like endoplasm, and intermediate gel-like endoplasm, respectively.

The final aspect of general body organization concerns the nuclear material. This material in its most typical form seems quite dissimilar in the two groups; *i.e.,* the polyploid macro- and diploid micronuclei of ciliates *versus* the many diploid acele nuclei. In terms of location, the former lie in the inner endoplasm of the ciliates, the latter are scattered throughout all the acele body layers. In terms of composition, the typical macronuclei are in a class by themselves. The diploid micronuclei and acele somatic nuclei, however, may not be so dissimilar, since preliminary work (Hanson, 1961) indicates that the absence of centrioles and aster fibers and the presence of a nuclear membrane during division, all typical of ciliates, are found characteristic of the somatic nuclei of at least certain aceles.

The final relationship of the major criterion demands that homologs be arrayed in a series joining the most dissimilar forms by intergrading intermediates. In the earlier paper on this topic it was suggested that the multinucleate situation in certain gymnostomes was intermediate to the typical ciliate situation and that found in the Acoela. Raĭkov (1958, 1959), having studied certain gymnostomes in great detail, has concluded that the nuclear situation found there is indeed primitive. Basically it consists of forms with many diploid micronuclei and many macronuclei of very low ploidy. These latter are incapable of division and are derived directly from micronuclei. Furthermore, he concludes that the primitive nuclear condition for the ciliates is a form possessing many diploid nuclei. Also, there is Lwoff's (1923, 1936) description of *Stephanopogon mesnili,* a gymnostome with only two nuclei, neither of which is a macronucleus. The series suggested by these forms is the following. At one end of the series are the aceles with their many, widely distributed nuclei. Next, ideally, there would appear a form with many diploid nuclei, not widely dispersed but lying centrally. The gymnostome *Stephanopogon* is suggestive of this organization with its monomorphic nuclei lying in the inner endoplasm. The next grade is represented by the forms studied by Raĭkov, especially his beautiful series in *Trachelocerca.* These are gymnostomatous ciliates with many diploid micronuclei, which can divide to form more such nuclei and can also differentiate into small macronuclei of low ploidy level that are incapable of division. Finally, to complete the series, there is the typical ciliate situation, exemplified by the remaining gymnostomes and non-gymnostomatous ciliates. Here, as is well known, the nuclei are usually few in number, both types are capable of division, and the macronuclei arise from the micronuclei only at times of sexual reorganization.

Now, relative to the Remanian criteria of homology, what conclusions are possible? Positionally, there are similarities at each step in the series, the greatest problem arising between the widely dispersed nuclei of the aceles and the more centrally located ones of the lower ciliates. Compositionally, the presence of diploidy throughout is a significant similarity and the appearance of the macronucleus as a differentiation of diploid nuclei in the gymnostomes reveals that this type of nucleus evolved within the ciliates, and its absence from the aceles is understandable on that basis. Regarding the detailed structure of diploid nuclei in ciliates and aceles, more work is needed, especially on acele somatic nuclei, but there are indications that the similarities already mentioned do exist. Finally, regarding the serial relationship, the series just outlined presents the real possibility of a continuum joining the extremes of aceles and higher ciliates.

Organelles.—The term "organelle" applies to both aceles and ciliates, for there are no true organs in these forms since there are no cellular aggregates forming tissues that perform certain functions. All too often, biologists overlook this point and mistakenly refer to tissues and cells in the aceles. For example, the so-called nerve-net is simply a differentiation of peripherally located cytoplasmic fibrils; there are not nuclei associated with these fibrils. The same is true for the so-called muscles; these are simply contractile fibrils of differentiated cytoplasm—no nuclei are associated with them in the sense of a muscle cell.

Looking for specific organelles, we find in the aceles no organelles for circulation, excretion, or respiration. The same is true for the ciliates except for the possible excretory role of the osmoregulatory contractile vacuoles, but even these are missing in certain marine forms.

The *feeding organelles* consist, in both groups, of a mouth and food vacuoles. In the higher ciliates the mouth evolves a complex ciliation, whose homologous relationships have been important in revising the taxonomy of the ciliates (Corliss, 1956). And again the gymnostomes, as the name implies, with their relatively simple mouth opening directly on the cell-body surface, resemble the aceles and offer an intermediate stage between the aceles and more complicated ciliates. In both groups there is no digestive cavity, ingested matter lying in the food vacuoles. Egestion is by the mouth in aceles, by the anal pore in certain more complex ciliates, and seems to be unstudied in the gymnostomatous ciliates. Regarding the feeding structures, then, they are located in roughly similar places; their composition is too simple to make meaningful comparisons except in terms of mouth or cytostome structures, the gymnostome mouths being somewhat intermediate between the simple mouths of the aceles and the more complicated buccal apparatus of the more complex ciliates. In this sense a serial relationship is suggested. Since the major criterion is only suggested here, it seems that these comparisons are better treated by the second subsidiary criterion (*i.e.,* similarities found in many different forms).

The *contractile fibrils* are always located peripherally in the ciliates and usually so in the aceles, the exceptions in the latter being the fibrils that pass dorsoventrally. In the aceles the peripheral contractile fibrils lie at the base of the epicytium. In the gymnostomes, such as *Dileptus,* where contractile fibrils are present, their exact location is unknown. In other ciliates (*e.g., Stentor*) the contractile elements are at the base of the ectoplasm. In terms of fine structure, the acele contractile fibrils appear striated (Westblad, 1942). Their fine structure is unknown in the gymnostomes, but in other ciliates (again *Stentor,* Dierks, 1926) it is reported as striated. More work on the gymnostomatous ciliates is needed to see if they can again play the role of the intermediate form. If so, the similarities in placement and fine structure and the presence of a serial array would all indicate a possible fulfillment of the major criterion of homology.

The *secretory* and *extrusible elements* of aceles and ciliates offer an especially rich area for comparative studies since both groups are heavily supplied with these structures. Unfortunately, however, among the Acoela different authorities have used different techniques and consequently different classifications for these so-called glands; comparative comments are therefore difficult. Furthermore, the fine structure studies made by means of electron microscopy on certain ciliate trichocysts are so far completely lacking for the aceles. What we can say now is simply that seemingly comparable structures are placed in the ectoplasm in the ciliates and in the epicytium in the aceles. As to the composition of these elements we can point out that, in both groups, apparently toxic substances can be released or thread-like materials ejected. Beyond this, detailed comparisons are of doubtful value at present. In summary, it is clear that here again there are, at least superficially, similar entities of widespread distribution, similarly placed and with some similarity in structure. Whether detailed study will demonstrate the presence of a serial array still remains to be seen, but the possibility of fulfilling the major criterion seems to be present.

The *coördinatory* and *sensory organelles* are a special problem. In the Acoela these organelles comprise the so-called nerve-net—a system of paired longitudinal fibrils with scattered, connecting cross fibrils, a statocyst, eye-spots in many forms, and some presumably tactile elements. The nerve-net is located at the base of the epicytium in most forms, except anteriorly, where it is concentrated near the statocyst, which lies in the ectocytium. The tactile elements seem to lie in the epicytium (Westblad, 1940). The position of the eye-spots is probably also epicytial. This system contrasts with the so-called neuromotor system of ciliates, which is clearly ectoplasmic in most forms, and, from electron micrographs of *Paramecium,* for example, seems to be a product of the kinetodesmata or ciliary roots. In some of the more complex forms, structures distinct from the cilia and more deeply placed seem to represent the neuromotor system and are tentatively identified as homologs of the kinetodesmatal system of other ciliates. Thus in both groups there are ciliary root hairs, and there are also more internally located structures. This suggests a possible independent evolution in both groups of the deeper lying elements. Whether they both arose from the ciliary root hairs is difficult to say, especially in the aceles. Again, careful work is needed on the gymnostomes, for they are relatively unstudied in this regard. Eye-spots are lacking in the simplest aceles, and hence these entities probably evolved within the group. Whether or not the acele statocyst and the Müller's vesicles of gymnostomes are homologous is still open to question. The tactile elements are poorly identified in the Acoela. That these organisms respond to touch is known; the same is true for the ciliates and many other forms. This character has a widespread distribution not coextensive with other characters being studied here and so, on the basis of the second subsidiary criterion (criterion 3), is not helpful for the problem of homology.

The *reproductive organelles* of aceles are far more complex than in ciliates and contain two features completely missing from the latter. These are cellularized gametes and a permanent male gonopore. The difference in complexity of genitalia between the simpler and the more complex Acoela indicates that much of the evolution of these structures occurred within this group. Indeed, the common features of the whole group are the permanent gonopore, lying caudally or on the posterior ventral surface, and the gametes, lying in double longitudinal rows with the spermatogonia in the lateral rows and the oögonia in the medial rows. In comparison, the ciliates' gametic material differs in position, number, and composition of elements. Single male and female gametic nuclei develop in each ciliate from the micronucleus during conjugation, and only in *Ophryoscolex* is a gamete—the male one—cellularized. With this organelle system the possibility of structural homology seems remote.

In conclusion, concerning the possibility of structural homologies between aceles and ciliates, on present evidence—and the incompleteness of that evidence must be admitted—there are no instances of clear-cut fulfillment of the major criterion. It is suggested here, however, that the nuclear material, and possibly the contractile, and the secretory-extrusible organelles may all fulfill the three relationships of that criterion. The feeding organelles fit better the requirements of the secondary subsidiary criterion, as do also certain features of general body organization. The sensory-coördinatory elements are different in both groups, but might possibly have had a common start from kinetodesma-like structures. The reproductive organelles are structurally quite different in the two groups.

Functional homologies.—The contractile, secretory-extrusible, and coördinatory-sensory elements have not been studied physiologically in the aceles and only partly in the ciliates. Hence their comparison for possible homologies is now not possible.

Concerning metabolism and nutrition only general comments can be made. Though no specific studies on such functions as biosynthetic pathways have been carried out on aceles, it is safe to conclude that they partake of the same general systems as do other animal organisms. But this is also to say that these similarities are so generally distributed that they are not useful here, in that they are common to all protozoa and metazoa. Nutritionally the aceles are chemoheterotrophs. The same is true of the ciliates and other animalistic protozoa. Hence this similarity is also too general to be of much critical importance.

Looking at feeding, we see that it is holozoic, by means of a permanent mouth, in both ciliates and aceles. This mode is found nowhere else in the Protista except possibly in certain of the more complex zoöflagellates and is, indeed, universal in free-living metazoa. Digestion is carried on in the food vacuoles in both the Acoela and ciliates. Egested material is eliminated orally in the aceles and by the anal pore in at least some forms of ciliates, such as *Paramecium*. The presence or absence of an anal pore in gymnostomes seems to be undetermined. These general similarities, then, are possibly significant under the second subsidiary criterion.

The aceles reproduce, typically, only sexually. The recent report of asexual reproduction by fission in *Amphiscolops langerhansi* (Hanson, 1960) and the earlier report of architomy in *Convoluta* sp.? (Marcus and McNae, 1954), in all probability, represent a process evolved within the aceles since both of these are quite complex forms and asexual processes are so far unknown in the simpler forms. The sexual process in the aceles is the typically eumetazoan one of gametogenesis with prezygotic reduction divisions, fertilization, and subsequent development of the zygote. None of these processes is known in great detail. Oögenesis of *Polychoerus caudatus* has been described in some detail (Gardiner, 1898), including some important observations on reduction divisions. Essentially nothing is known of spermiogenesis. Copulation has been reported for a variety of forms. In all cases sperm are exchanged between the copulants; in the simpler forms "the sperm mass is fastened somewhere on the body of the counterpart by means of cement glands" (Westblad, 1948), in others it is inserted into the body of the partner by a penis. Fertilization is internal; zygotes are released through the mouth. Cleavage is spiral and leads to embryogenesis and the hatching of small, immature worms.

In that ciliates undergo a differentiation and prezygotic reduction of gamete nuclei, in that they are hermaphroditic, producing both male and female gamete nuclei and exchanging the male one with their partners in conjugation, and in that fertilization is internal, a sequence of important events similar to that found in the Acoela is supplied. No other protozoa have sexual processes so similar to that of the Eumetazoa. The basic difference between the aceles and the ciliates is in the presence of embryogenesis in the former and its absence in the latter. Since embryogenesis is possible only when gametes are cellularized, this cellularization of egg and sperm is, then, the basic difference. How such cellularization occurred in the aceles is, of course, a major problem. We turn to it again further on. As for homologies in the reproductive processes, it can be said only that a general similarity in patterns of sequence of events is present with some similarity in details, but with an important difference regarding the fate of the zygotic material.

To summarize this outline of functional homologies we must first remark on the lack of much information, especially regarding acele physiology. Certain nutritional and feeding similarities have been noted. These would meet, at best, only the subsidiary criteria. Except for the similarities in the sexual processes up to the point of fertilization, no definite suggestion of homologies emerges. The absence in the ciliates of a counterpart to acele embryogenesis is especially to be noted.

Conclusions and Comments

In no case is the major criterion of Remane completely fulfilled. In four instances, however, the data come close to meeting the requirements of the criterion. These are relative to the nuclei, the contractile organelles, the secretory extrusible elements, and the processes of the sexual phenomena. Similarities fulfilling the second subsidiary criterion are the general body organization (*i.e.,* bilateral symmetry, anterior-posterior polarity, subdivisions of the body such as acele epicytium and ciliate ectoplasm, etc.) and complete body ciliation; feeding organelles; and the feeding process.

Note here, that if homologies fulfilling the major criterion are eventually established between aceles and ciliates, these latter similarities, having the same distribution as the major criterion homologies, would then fulfill the first subsidiary criterion. This would strengthen the argument for genetic relationships between the Ciliophora and Acoela.

There are still to be considered those entities that show little evidence of possible homology. These are the acele nerve-net and ciliate neuromotor system; the cellularized gametes and genitalia of the aceles, especially the male gonopore, all of which are absent from the ciliates; the acele embryogenesis, also absent from ciliates.

Concerning the differences in the sensory-coördinatory structures, one can only repeat what was said earlier, that in both the more complex ciliates and aceles a fibrillar system has evolved internal to the level of the ciliary kinetodesmata. It has been argued that in the ciliates this neuromotor system is indeed the homolog of the fibrillar infraciliature of the lower ciliates. Whether or not this is true of the aceles will depend on more information. Especially important is the study of certain key gymnostomes. This problem may resolve itself as a possible homology; it may not. At present no decision is possible.

The greatest barrier to accepting a phylogenetic relationship between the ciliates and aceles concerns the differences between sexual processes and structures in these forms. As has been argued before (Hanson, 1958, pp. 36–37), the key step here has been the appearance of cellularized gametes in the aceles. By this advance both sexual reproduction and embryogenesis are achieved—both are features of the greatest evolutionary importance and both represent new features relative to the ciliates. It is argued here that because of the evolutionary advantages of cellularized gametes, forms possessing them will capitalize on this feature and will be expected, therefore, in this special respect to differ from forms lacking them. The argument is presented in three steps: first, the genetic-evolutionary advantages of cellularized gametes; next, very briefly, the developmental-evolutionary advantages; and, finally, the particular significance of all this to ciliate-acele phylogeny.

From a genetic-evolutionary point of view sexuality and reproduction are two different things. Sexuality refers to any process leading to the possibility of new genotypes through fertilization (see, especially, Waddington, 1939). Reproduction is biological increase in number. Ciliate conjugation is a sexual process; it is not a reproductive process—most textbooks to the contrary. New genotypes arise in ciliates, apart from mutation, only as a result of sexual reorganization of nuclear material and then are preserved in clones asexually by fission—the only way one protozoön makes more protozoa. Hence in natural populations of ciliates, as in all asexually reproducing forms, genetic variability is restricted since asexual processes are the only means of propagating genotypes. On the other hand, in aceles, except for the rare cases of asexual reproduction, fertilization accompanies the formation of each new individual, and each new individual exists in addition to the parent that produced it. Here the possibility of new genotypes and increase in number— sexuality and reproduction—proceed as a unified process. And since each sexually produced acele is formed from a separate pair of gametes, there is possible a greater genetic variability in acele populations than in ciliate populations. The importance of this in the light of modern population genetics can scarcely be overestimated (Dobzhansky, 1950). The key difference between the ciliates and aceles, which permits the latter to reproduce sexually and hence achieve a greater total potential genetic variability, is the presence of cellularized gametes.

Now add to this genetic-evolutionary feature the developmental-evolutionary advantages of embryogenesis, and one can see the enormous significance of the consequences of cellularized gametes. For such epigenetic phenomena add a vast new dimension to the opportunistic selections of evolution (De Beer, 1940). In the ciliates development is normally restricted to fission, budding, and reorganization during sexual processes; there is no embryogenesis from a relatively undifferentiated zygote. The presence of the zygote and its subsequent developmental plasticity open up great new fields for evolutionary experimentation (*e.g.,* neotenous development). I am here proposing, therefore, that acele embryogenesis is a new evolutionary feature since it is absent in the ciliates and their probable forebears, the zoöflagellates. It recapitulates nothing. We can simply say that cleavage and the formation of cells during early acele embryogeny occurs in this fashion because such is the only way for this material to develop. The syncytial phenotype of the adult reappears when the nucleo-cytoplasmic condition of the adult is restored through much embryonic cleavage. It is true this is not an "explanation" in the sense of describing the mechanism of cleavage and showing it to be a necessary consequence of zygote organization. Such an explanation is lacking for cleavage in all forms. The problem we must face is this: can we see any reason for postulating the evolutionary innovation of embryogenesis? The answer is, yes, and has already been given; it is that embryogenesis along with increased genetic variability, both resulting from cellularization of gametes, endows the organism so provided with evolutionary advantages not present in forms lacking cellularized gametes.

The point of all this for our present discussion is straightforward: the advent of sexual reproduction through cellularized gametes achieves such significant new evolutionary advances that one might expect very rapid evolutionary developments thereafter. Specifically one could expect the rapid refinement of sexual characters so as further to capitalize on the evolutionary advances resulting from cellularized gametes. The result could be evolution of genitalia more rapidly than other structures and the elimination, through competition, of those closely related forms not evolving such a reproductive system. We would then expect that the aceles would show their greatest specializations in the organelles relating to sexual phenomena, and that the break with related forms would be sharpest relative to these organelles. This is precisely what we have found in comparing ciliates and aceles from a phylogenetic point of view.

Summary

1. Phylogenies are dependent on the prior establishment of homologies. In this light acele-ciliate similarities need reëxamination to see if homologies can be found.

2. The relatively simple nature of the Acoela is discussed in the light of three criteria to decide whether these forms are considered to possess a reduced or an original simplicity. It is concluded that they are primitively the simplest of the Turbellaria.

3. The criteria of homology used are adapted from Remane. Whereas Remane emphasized the predominant role of structures in the study of homology, in this paper functions as well as structures are included in the criteria of homology.

4. Furthermore, the special problems arising from the application of these

criteria to acellular or unicellular protists is discussed. It is concluded that certain important difficulties exist in such an application; nevertheless, with these difficulties in mind, the study of homologies can be usefully prosecuted.

5. Certain gymnostomatous ciliates are important in showing characters intermediate between aceles and other ciliates. Upon applying the criteria of homology this position is reëmphasized relative to many ciliate-acele comparisons.

6. Although no clear-cut instance of homology (fulfillment of the three relationships of the major criterion) is found between the aceles and ciliates, four instances suggestive of the major criterion are described. Other similarities fulfilling certain of the subsidiary criteria are also found.

7. In two areas homologies are unlikely. These are discussed in some detail, especially that concerning the presence of cellularized gametes and embryogenesis in aceles and the absence of these features in ciliates. It is concluded that the acele features are of such striking evolutionary advantage—genetically and developmentally—that significant evolution would continue along these lines in the aceles and thus explain the sharp difference found between aceles and ciliates regarding this character.

REFERENCES

Anfinsen, C. B.
    1959   The Molecular Basis of Evolution. Wiley, New York.
Baldwin, E.
    1937   An Introduction to Comparative Biochemistry. Macmillan, New York.
Corliss, J. O.
    1956   On the evolution and systematics of ciliated protozoa. Syst. Zool. 5:68–140.
De Beer, G. R.
    1940   Embryos and Ancestors. Oxford Univ. Press, London.
Dierks, K.
    1926   Untersuchungen über die Morphologie und Physiologie des *Stentor coeruleus* mit besonderer Berücksichtigung seiner kontraktilen und konduktilen Elemente. Arch. Protistenk. 54:1–91.
Dobzhansky, T.
    1950   Heredity, environment and evolution. Science 111:161–166.
Dunn, L. C., and S. Gluecksohn-Waelsch.
    1953   Genetic analysis of seven newly discovered mutant alleles at locus T in the house mouse. Genetics 38:261–271.
Gardiner, E. G.
    1898   The growth of the ovum, formation of the polar bodies, and the fertilization in *Polychoerus caudatus*. J. Morph. 15:73–110.
Grimstone, A. V.
    1959   Cytology, homology and phylogeny—a note on "organic design." Amer. Nat. 93:273–282.
Hanson, E. D.
    1958   On the origin of the Eumetazoa. Syst. Zool. 7:16–47.
    1960   Asexual reproduction in acoelous Turbellaria. Yale J. Biol. Med. 33:107–111.

1961   *Convoluta sutcliffei,* a new species of acoelous Turbellaria. Trans. Amer.
          micr. Soc. 80:423–433.

Ingram, V. M.
1957   Gene mutations in human haemoglobin: the chemical difference between
          normal and sickle cell haemoglobin. Nature 180:326–328.

Lwoff, A.
1923   Sur un Infusoire cilié homocaryote à vie libre. Son importance taxono-
          mique. C. R. Acad. Sci., Paris 177:910–913.
1936   Le cycle nucléaire de *Stephanopogon mesnili* Lw. (Cilié homocaryote).
          Arch. Zool. exp. gén. 78:117–132.

Marcus, E., and W. MacNae.
1954   Architomy in a species of *Convoluta.* Nature 173:130.

Nursall, G.
1959   On the origin of the Eumetazoa. Trans. roy. Soc. Can. (Sec. 5) 53:1–5.

Preer, J. R., Jr.
1959   Nuclear and cytoplasmic differentiation in the protozoa. Pp. 3–20 in:
          Developmental Cytology. D. Rudnick, Ed. Ronald Press, New York.

Raïkov, I. B.
1958   Der Formwechsel des Kernapparates einiger niederer Ciliaten. I. Die Gat-
          tung *Trachelocerca.* Arch. Protistenk. 103:129–192.
1959   Der Formwechsel des Kernapparates einiger niederer Ciliaten. II. Die Gat-
          tung *Loxodes. Ibid.* 104:1–42.

Remane, A.
1955   Morphologie als Homologienforschung. Verh. dtsch. zool. Ges., Tübingen
          (1954) (Zool. Anz., Suppl. 18): 159–183.
1956   Die Grundlagen des natürlichen Systems der vergleichenden Anatomie
          und der Phylogenetik. 2d ed. Geest und Portig, Leipzig.

Ryan, F. J.
1952   Adaptation to use lactose in *Escherichia coli.* J. gen. Microbiol. 7:69–88.

Simpson, G. G.
1949   The Meaning of Evolution. Yale Univ., New Haven.

Waddington, C. H.
1939   An Introduction to Modern Genetics. Allen and Unwin, London.

Waterman, T. H.
1961   Comparative physiology. Pp. 521–593 in: The Physiology of Crustacea.
          Vol. II. Sense Organs, Interaction, and Behavior. T. H. Waterman, Ed.
          Acad. Press, New York, London.

Westblad, E.
1940   Studien über skandinavische Turbellaria Acoela. I. Ark. Zool. 32A, no.
          20:1–28.
1942   *Idem.* II. *Ibid.* 33A, no. 14:1–48.
1948   *Idem.* V. *Ibid.* 41A, no. 7:1–82.

2 ◆ The Evolution of the Metazoa from Colonial Flagellates vs. Plasmodial Ciliates

ADOLF REMANE

ZOOLOGISCHES INSTITUT UND MUSEUM,
UNIVERSITÄT KIEL, KIEL

Today zoölogy is divided into two camps as regards the origin of the Metazoa. Until recently the leading morphologists of the last hundred years have derived the Metazoa from colonial flagellates; but now a new view, promulgated by Hadži (1944, 1953), Steinböck (1952, 1958), and Hanson (1958), proposes that a multinucleated plasmodial form, like the ciliates, was the ancestral type of the Metazoa and connects these ciliates directly with the turbellarians, especially the Acoela. This new hypothesis has begun to invade textbooks. We are thus confronted with the question: are these new views better founded than the older theory of the origin of the Metazoa from colonial flagellates?

The problem of whether multicellularity originated in a plasmodium or a colony of cells exists only for the zoölogists, not for the botanists. There is no doubt that in plants the multicellular forms are evolved from cellular colonies. In many lines of algae there exists today all the steps between unicellular species, cell-colonies, and multicellular plants. The different answer of botanists and zoölogists to the same problem is explained by the fact that, in the animal kingdom, there is a wide gap between the protozoa and the simplest free-living metazoa. Metazoan derivation, therefore, must be a theoretical problem.

In discussing the possibilities of bridging the existing gap, we begin with the protozoa. There are many trends leading to complex plasmodial or multicellular organisms. Cellular colonies exist in many orders of flagellate protozoa—*e.g.,* the Phytomonadida (*Volvox, Gonium, Eudorina,* etc.), Chrysomonadida (*Synura, Dinobryon*), Dinoflagellida, Protomonadida (many genera).

The form of these colonies is highly variable—bush or tree-like, chain-like, or plate-like. The most interesting cell colonies are the free-swimming spheres, because the first ontogenetic stages of many metazoa have spherical cell-assemblages (that is, the blastula). Not only the Phytomonadida, with the famous *Volvox,* have genera of such a type, but also the Chrysomonadida (for example, *Synura*), and also the zoöflagellates. A good example of the latter is *Sphaeroeca* Lauterborn, belonging to the choanoflagellates (fig. 2-1). The derivation of the Metazoa from cell-colonies in no way necessitates a *Volvox*-like ancestral form (see Hanson, 1958), but only a flagellate colony; for this purpose colonies of zoöflagellates like *Sphaeroeca* are the best examples.

Plasmodial protozoa with many nuclei exist in the Rhizopoda (*e.g.,* the ameba *Pelomyxa* and the heliozoön *Actinosphaerium*). Most of the Foraminifera are multinucleate in at least part of their life cycle. In the Ciliata there are several multinucleate genera with a number of macro- and micronuclei (*Dileptus, Remanella*). Flagellates with many nuclei are comparatively rare; I know of them only among the parasitic and symbiotic flagellates (*Calonympha, Opalina,* etc.). No one has tried to derive the Metazoa from multinucleated Rhizopoda even though the plasmodium of many foraminifers is divided into many chambers separated by complicated septa. But the division of this plasmodium into chambers is not correlated with a regular distribution of nuclei. Several chambers have many nuclei,

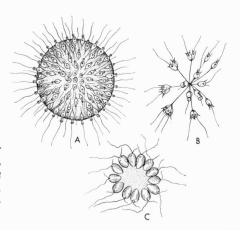

FIGURE 2-1. Swimming colonies of choanoflagellates (A,B) and chrysomonads (C). A, *Sphaeroeca volvox* Lauterborn; B, *Astrosiga radiata* Kent; C, *Volvochrysis polyochla.* (A,B, after Hollande, 1952b; C, after Hollande, 1952a.)

others none. The chambers of the Foraminifera, therefore, are not cells of the metazoan type. In any case, those favoring the origin of the Metazoa from a plasmodial protozoön all consider a ciliate or a protociliate as the starting point.

I might at this point add that the term "proto," given to a hypothetical ancestral form, is justified because a remote ancestor can scarcely be identical with known recent forms. Haeckel designated many hypothetical ancestors in this way. But such a terminology is dangerous, for a hypothetical form must differ from recent species in its group and therefore its postulated organization is inevitably uncertain. A hypothetical form without clear characteristics allows no solid basis for discussion. Only after an exact characterization (for example, stating whether presumptive protociliates have macro- and micronuclei, and whether there is copulation or conjugation), would it be possible to carry out a meaningful discussion.

The existing genera of protozoa supply evidence for both theories, but the derivation of the Metazoa from plasmodial ciliates presents many serious difficulties.

1. Fertilization in all known ciliates is a result of conjugation. In metazoa it follows copulation and is achieved in the same manner as in many flagellates, rhizopods, and plants. Hadži (1953) has tried to bridge this marked difference between the Ciliata and Metazoa in the following manner. He compares the two ciliate

conjugants with two hermaphroditic aceles in the process of mating. The stationary micronucleus is compared to the egg of the Acoela and the migrating micronucleus to the sperm. In this view, the internal fertilization and copulation of the turbellarians is directly derivable from conjugation in ciliates. And the great similarity in sexual processes in plants and metazoa would be a convergence originating in some other way. The above mentioned comparisons by Hadži are highly misleading. The migrating micronucleus is in no way a sperm. Hadži mentions the situation in the ciliate *Cycloposthium*.[1] The individuals of this genus mate by apposing the ciliated anterior parts of the body. In this extraordinary situation the migrating micronucleus, surrounded by a layer of cytoplasm and with a connecting fiber, passes freely from the peristomial region of one conjugant to the other. But the derivation of the sperm cells of the Metazoa from a migrating micronucleus with a thin layer of cytoplasm is, in my opinion, quite impossible. The sperm cells of the Metazoa are not merely haploid nuclei with a minute amount of cytoplasm, but rather are complicated structures with mitochondria, centrosomes (absent in the ciliates), fibrils, acrosomes, etc. These sperm cells resemble certain zoöflagellates very closely, as has been demonstrated by Tuzet (1950) and others.

2. The fertilization of eggs is external in all the primitive Metazoa. Internal fertilization is a secondarily evolved process, as is shown by many evolutionary lines. We know of no evolutionary line in which internal fertilization is transformed into external.

3. A further difficulty for the derivation of the Metazoa from plasmodial protozoa is that the majority of metazoa show a cellular, not a plasmodial, organization. A hypothesis of plasmodial origin would demand that all these metazoa must have acquired their cellular status secondarily and independently in many lines. This process is called "cellularization" by Steinböck (1952, 1958).

Several ontogenetic processes, in animals and in cellularized plants, are known to transform a plasmodium into a mass of cells. Arthropod development, with its superficial cleavage, is an example; we find similar processes in a few cnidarians (for example, *Eudendrium*). All these ontogenetic processes, which proceed from a plasmodium into cellular structures, are surely derived from primitively cellular organizations. In distinction from these ontogenetic processes, we know of no evolutionary process that demonstrates with certainty the transformation of a plasmodium into a cellularly organized animal.

We must not forget that the plasmodial ciliates have no typical centrioles—structures characteristic of metazoan cells. Also, the cells of the Metazoa contain Golgi apparatus and mitochondria; hence, cellularization must achieve not only a distribution of the more fluid cytoplasm around each nucleus, but also a normal distribution of all the typically formed elements of the cell. Further, the ciliated epithelium, in the light of the plasmodial theory, must be not a primitive tissue, but the terminal stage of an evolution beginning with a plasmodium.

Difficulties in deriving metazoan organization from a plasmodium are therefore much greater than in its derivation from colonies of typical flagellate cells. Cell

---

[1] This genus, cited by Hadži as possibly demonstrating the transformation of a migrating micronucleus into a sperm cell, consists of a very specialized ciliate of the order Entodiniomorphida—commensal in the stomach of mammals. It is always dangerous to choose specialized recent species for connecting ancient phyla.

colonies can be transformed into primitive metazoa by the process of differentiation of the cells in form and function, a process visible in all trends of organic evolution. One apparent difficulty seems to be that meiosis is postzygotic in many algae and flagellates (postreduction; zygotic meiosis), while in metazoa and ciliates it is prezygotic (prereduction; genetic meiosis). But this difference is not found in all flagellates. We know several genera with prereduction (*Notila, Urinympha, Rhynchonympha, Macrospironympha*) and the same for several heliozoa (*Actinosphaerium, Actinophrys*). Both types of reduction exist, therefore, within these natural groups.

Now let us consider the problem from the other side—that is, the metazoan. We first examine the simplest metazoa and the possibility that these forms arose from the Protozoa. (We omit from consideration *Salinella*—a monodermic form with a central cavity, since it has not been reported after the first description by Frenzel (1892). We also omit the parasitic Mesozoa, not knowing whether their relatively simple organization is primitive or reduced by parasitism.)

We have not one but many forms of simple metazoa: the cnidarian *Protohydra* Greef (a genus without tentacles, with simple gonads, and having no skeleton); sponges of the asconoid type with very primitive tissue; *Xenoturbella* Bock; the aceles; rotifers like *Rotaria* Scopoli without a gonoduct; and bryozoans like *Monobryozoon* Remane.

All these simple forms differ greatly among themselves. *Protohydra* and the ascon sponges represent phyla that are clearly histologically primitive; the aceles, *Rotaria,* and *Monobryozoon* are simple forms within phyla also containing much more differentiated members.

In the last century biologists often declared that simple animals are primitive. The intensive study of homologies and affinities has shown that many simple forms are retrogressive and not primitive. The so-called Archiannelida, containing the families Nerillidae and Dinophilidae (the latter including the very simple genus *Diurodrilus*), are now considered to be degenerated polychetes. The duckweeds (Lemnaceae), with the genus *Wolffia,* a globular little plant without roots, are the simplest flowering plants, but they are surely not primitive phanerogams; on the contrary, the complicated Magnoliaceae and Nymphaeaceae are the primitive angiosperms. In the same way, morphologically simple mites (Acarina) are not so primitive arachnoids as are the complicated scorpions! Among insects, the very simple wing venation of aphids, certain small flies, and braconid wasps is not a criterion of primitiveness. Instead the dragonflies (Odonata) and Palaeodictyoptera, which show a very complicated wing venation, are the primitive forms. Only after a careful study of homologies and affinities is it possible to declare a structurally simple organism primitive.

Returning to the above-mentioned simple animals, one may confidently state that no biologist regards *Protohydra*[2] as the most primitive metazoön. The absence of tentacles and probably the absence of a gonophore generation are secondarily degenerate attributes. And *Monobryozoon* is surely not primitive; it is merely a simplified bryozoön.

Before taking up the famous Acoela, we ought to discuss whether the different simple metazoa favor the possibility of several independent origins of metazoan

---

[2] Even though *Protohydra* is not primitive, the whole phylum Cnidaria, to which it belongs, is surely primitive.

phyla from protozoa. The majority of zoölogists claim a monophyletic origin. Only the Porifera are often derived independently from protozoa and named Parazoa. The new studies of Tuzet (1948) make it highly improbable that the Porifera are an isolated offshoot from protozoa. This viewpoint is not fully proved, but the diphyletic origin of the Porifera and other metazoa seems unlikely and the monophyletic origin of all metazoa seems better founded. In consequence, only one of the many simple metazoa can represent the ancestral form, at least for the Eumetazoa.

Are the aceles the primitive metazoan forms, transitional from ciliates to the Metazoa? The facts alleged for this view are several. The aceles are plasmodial organisms with many possibly isopotent nuclei. There are many similarities in the structure of ciliates and aceles. For instance, the body of both is covered with cilia and the cytostome of the Ciliata resembles the mouth of the Acoela (Steinböck, 1952, 1958). Hadži (1950, p. 124; 1953, p. 150) derives the entoderm

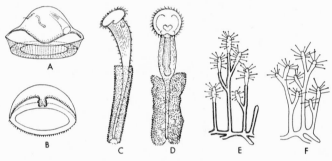

FIGURE 2-2. Similarities without phylogenetic significance in protozoa and metazoa. Medusa-like forms: A, the dinoflagellate *Craspedosoma;* B, a Hydromedusa. Rotifer-like forms: C, the ciliate *Stentor,* a widely distributed genus of ciliate protozoa; D, the rotifer *Ptygura.* Polyp-like forms: E, a suctorian (Protozoa, Ciliata); F, a hydropolyp (*Coryne* sp.). (After Remane, 1956.)

(endocytium) of the turbellarians from the digestive endoplasm of the ciliates, the protonephridia from the contractile vacuoles, the rhabdites of the Turbellaria from the trichocyst, etc. Do these similarities represent homologies or only analogies? Only the proof of homology enables us to establish affinities. That superficial similarities are not convincing is demonstrated by many such similarities between very different protozoa and metazoa—for example, between the flagellate *Medusochloris* and the medusa *Craspedotella,* between the suctorians and polyps, and between stentors bearing vibratile lobes and rotifers such as *Ptygura* (fig. 2-2).

In paramecia, the cytopharynx and digestive endoplasm with vacuoles is very similar to the esophagus and syncytial intestine of the rotifer genus *Habrotrocha,* described by Burger (1948) and Schulte (1954) (fig. 2-3). These similarities with rotifers also exist in the hymenostomatous ciliates or Trichostomata, but in the gymnostomatous ciliates or Pleurostomata, which are regarded by some as ancestral to the Acoela (Hanson, 1958). All these similarities are analogous, not homologous. The same considerations apply to similarities between the ciliates and aceles. No criterion of homologies is given. The contractile vacuoles have no in-

ternal cilia or terminal flame bulbs so characteristic of protonephridia. (In the
Acoela protonephridia are entirely wanting!) The ciliated body surface is not a
special character of ciliates and turbellarians, but is widespread in primitive metazoa
and their larvae. Rhabdites and trichocysts are quite different in structure, as demonstrated by electron microscopy (Pedersen, 1959), and also in their origin; in the
Turbellaria they arise from glands, in the Ciliata from infraciliary corpuscles. No
intermediate form bridges the great gap in these superficial similarities. We can
bridge every gap with fancy, but a useful discussion is only possible if we construct
the bridge not from fancy but with facts.

Further, the plasmodial organization of the Acoela is of very doubtful status. Ax,
in his paper in this volume, gives many examples of cellular organization in the
aceles; within a single genus there often exist species with a syncytial and others
with a cellular outer layer. Reisinger (1959), in a careful experimental study of

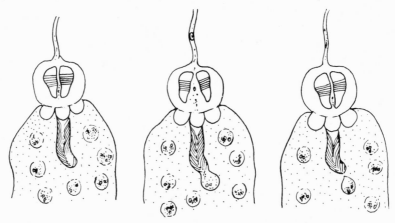

FIGURE 2-3. *Habrotrocha* sp. A rotifer with a stomach and formation of
vacuoles containing food particles, very like *Paramecium*. (After Schulte,
1954.)

tissues without internal cell boundaries, came to the conclusion that in turbellarians
cellular tissue is the primitive condition. A syncytial tissue can be transformed into
cells by stimuli (for example, mechanical stimuli) and the cellular gastric epithelium
of *Otomesostoma* loses its cellular character after infection by parasitic protozoa.
After the expulsion of the parasites this epithelium regains its cell boundaries.
Reisinger states (1959, p. 641) that the syncytial tissues of the turbellarians are
"lediglich strukturdynamisch bedingte Ausprägungen eines *latent dauernd vorhande-
nen zelligen Aufbaues.*" [3] The most convincing evidence for this is the cellular
ontogeny of the Acoela. Not only the genera *Polychoerus* (Gardiner, 1895) and
Convoluta (Bresslau, 1909), but also the recently investigated genera *Otocelis* and
Aphanostoma (Reisinger, 1959), begin ontogeny with typical cell divisions of a
slightly modified spiral cleavage type (duet-cleavage) and only after a period of
typical cellular organization do the cell boundaries in the tissues, or in some tissues,
become invisible. Therefore, turbellarian tissues lacking visible cell boundaries are

---

[3] "Solely morphogenetically limited expressions of a latent, persistent, omnipresent cellular
organization."

syncytial, not plasmodial. I cite again Reisinger (1959, p. 641): "Vor diesen *ganz klaren Tatsachen* muss fürderhin derjenige seine Augen verschliessen, der weiterhin darauf besteht, bei Turbellarien von plasmodialen Strukturen zu sprechen. Das 'Archihiston' (Steinböck 1958) ist genausowenig ein Plasmodium wie die als Ekto-, Meso- und Entoplasmodien bezeichneten Körperschichten der Acölen, denn sie alle entstehen *durch Fusion unsprünglich wohl individualisierter Embryonalzellen, sind also Syncytien;* z. T. wie unsere Versuche erwiesen haben, sogar unter Beibehaltung einer latenten Cellularisation." [4]

In this connection the electron-microscope investigations of Bargmann and Knoop (1959) are valuable. They state that the placental tissue of many mammals, hitherto considered to be syncytial, is in reality cellular. They further point out that the mesenchyme with a continuous network of fibrocytes, hitherto considered to be syncytial, is clearly subdivided by cellular boundaries when investigated by electron microscopy.

Concerning the supposed plasmodial organization of the Acoela I present the following summary. The aceles are not plasmodial, but syncytial. They are only partly syncytial, since many species show certain tissues as cellularized. The syncytial structures of turbellarians have so far been investigated only by light microscopy. The electron-microscope work of Bargmann and Knoop shows cell boundaries in mammalian tissues hitherto reported as syncytial, and the experimental studies of Reisinger, demonstrating subdivision of so-called syncytial tissue of turbellarians into cells, make it very doubtful whether these tissues are even syncytial in the strict sense of the word. I conclude, therefore, that the assumption of a plasmodial aceloid as the primitive metazoan has a very tenuous scientific basis.

Not only do the foregoing facts make the plasmodium theory of the origin of the Metazoa highly improbable, but the theory has certain untenable consequences. If it is accepted, we are forced to derive all cellular metazoa and all other simple metazoa from an aceloid plasmodial organization.

Let us consider the attempt of Hadži to derive the Cnidaria and the Ctenophora from the turbellarians. Hadži (1923) proposes that the ctenophores originated from neotenic polyclad larvae. There is no doubt that neotenic processes, or persistence of juvenile characters, can produce new evolutionary branches. The Cladocera and two families of the so-called archiannelids—the Nerrillidae and Dinophilidae—are examples. In explaining a phylogenetic development as neotenic, it is required that the ontogenetic development of the groups in question be identical; one of the group persists in the larval stage with the acquisition of gonads, the other develops further into the complicated structures of the adult organism. This inevitable situation is not seen when comparing polyclads and ctenophores. The cleavage of the embryo in these two groups is quite different. Polyclads have a typical spiral cleavage into quartets and a 4-d cell, nearly identical with what are observed in annelid development (Surface, 1907; Kato, 1940). The ctenophores show a special cleav-

---

[4] "In view of these completely obvious facts, he that still persists in referring to plasmodial structures in the Turbellaria must, in this regard, have closed his eyes. The 'archihiston' (Steinböck, 1958) is no more a plasmodium than are the acele body layers (designated as ecto-, meso-, and endoplasmodium), for they all arise through the fusion of initially completely individualized embryonal cells and, therefore, are syncytial—as our studies have, in fact, shown—even to the point of retaining a latent cellularization."

age not found in any other phylum. The larvae of polyclads (Müller- and Goette-larva) have no special characters in common with the ctenophores that might enable us to suggest a special phylogenetic affinity between the two phyla. The fertile stage of the primitive ctenophore *Pleurobrachia* has four gastric pockets with gonads and is, therefore, much nearer to the cnidarian body type in structure than to the larvae of polyclads.

The derivation of the Cnidaria from higher turbellarians such as the temnocepha-lids is equally ill-founded. The Temnocephalidae are epizoötic or ectoparasitic platyhelminths, once considered as a separate class, but now known as a special family of the suborder Dalyelliina (order Neorhabdocoelida). Their organization is the same as in the typical dalyelliine turbellarians. The gonads are differentiated into germarium and vitellarium; the testes are isolated; the genital ducts are very complex, with seminal vesicles, penis, etc. There is a brain with differentiated nerves. Also present are typical protonephridia and a complicated pharynx (pharynx doliiformis). The only similarity between the Temnocephalidae and Cnidaria (especially Anthozoa) are the tentacles of these worms, but in the Temnocephalidae the tentacles lack entodermal tissue, canal, and nematocysts. The similarity, therefore, is so tenuous that the establishment of a definite homology and close phylogenetic affinity is unthinkable. The enormous differences in the internal anatomy exclude a derivation of the Anthozoa from these highly specialized turbellarians. There exists no intermediary form connecting these fundamentally different groups.

Finally, returning to the comparison of the two rival theories concerning the origin of the Metazoa, I consider the *flagellate* derivation from flagellate colonies to be much better founded than the plasmodium theory, which connects the ciliates with the aceles. There is no scientific reason to replace the older cell-colony theory with a plasmodium theory. The discussion of these theories raises a last question: are phylogenetic theories subjective views? Can any man propose his own phylogeny, or can we get definitive scientific solutions? If we look at the more intensively studied groups (for example, the vertebrates), we can conclude that, after much investigation, the phylogeny of the classes and orders is now well established. But the road leading to this end has been very long.

Phylogenetic reconstruction begins with the recognition of similarities. But affinities based only on similarities are dangerous. In the 18th century Bonnet (1769) placed the ostrich with the mammals (*partim avis partim quadrupes*), the snakes with the eels, etc. In the African deserts we find in the family Euphorbiaceae plants that are very similar to the Cactaceae of the New World. But in these instances similarities are in no way an indication of phylogenetic connection. The next step is the separation of the similarities into those recognizable as homologies, analogies, or parallelisms. A worth-while phylogenetic theory can only be proposed after an intensive study of taxonomy, comparative anatomy, and ontogeny based on the scientific use of homologies. If we avoid this long road and bridge all steps with fancy, we can scarcely expect to arrive at reliable solutions. And even after critical study of homologies the facts may still not convincingly favor a given theory, but may suggest two or three hypotheses. In such instances we can only treat the problem as a continuing challenge and constantly seek to refine our knowledge and render our discrimination more acute.

REFERENCES

Bargmann, W., and A. Knoop
    1959   Elektronenmikroskopische Untersuchungen und Plazentarzotten des Menschen (Bemerkungen zum Synzytiumproblem). Z. Zellforsch. 50: 472–493.

Bonnet, C.
    1769   Contemplation de la Nature. 2d ed. Rey, Amsterdam.

Bresslau, E.
    1909   Die Entwicklung der Acoelen. Verh. dtsch. zool. Ges. Frankfurt a. M. (1909):314–324.

Burger, A.
    1948   Studies on the moss dwelling bdelloids (Rotifera) of eastern Massachusetts. Trans. Amer. micr. Soc. 67:111–142.

Franzén, Å.
    1956   On spermiogenesis, morphology of the spermatozoön and biology of fertilization among invertebrates. Zool. Bidr. Uppsala 31:355–482.

Frenzel, J.
    1892   *Salinella*. Arch. Naturgesch. 58(1):66–96.

Gardiner, E. G.
    1895   Early development of *Polychoerus caudatus* Mark. J. Morph. 11:155–177.

Hadži, J.
    1923   O podrijetlu, srodstvenim odnosima i sistematskoj poziciji ktenoforâ. Rad jug. Akad. Znan. Umj. 228:53–62. [In Croatian.] [Also: Über den Ursprung, die Verwandtschaftsverhältnisse und die systematische Position der Ktenophoren. Bull. int. Acad. Yougoslav. 15–18:53–62.]
    1944   Turbelarijska Teorija Knidarijev. (Turbellarien-Theorie der Knidarier.) Slov. Akad. Znan. Um., Ljubljana. [In Slovenian with German summary.]
    1949   Problem mezoderma in celoma v luči turbelarijske teorije knidarijev. (Problems of mesoderm and coelom elucidated by the Turbellarian theory of Cnidaria.) Razpr. Razred. prir. Odsek Slov. Akad. Znan. Um., Ljubljana 4:5–84. [In Slovenian with Russian and English summaries.]
    1950   Uporedivanje spolne faze infuzorija sa spolnim plođenjem kod turbelarija. Rad Jug. Akad. Znan. Umj. 280:31–53. [In Croatian.] [Also: a comparison of the sexual phase of infusorians with the sexual reproduction of the turbellarians. Bull. int. Acad. Yougoslav. (n.s.) 3:17–24.]
    1951   Izvajanje knidarijev iz turbelarijevin nekatere posledice tega izvajanja. (Die Ableitung der Knidarien von den Turbellarien und einige Folgerungen dieser Ableitung.) Razpr. (Dissertationes) Razred. prir. med. Vede Slov. Akad. Znan. Um. 1:107–126. [In Slovenian with German summary.]
    1953   An attempt to reconstruct the system of animal classification. Syst. Zool. 2:145–154.

Hanson, E. D.
    1958   On the origin of the Eumetazoa. Syst. Zool. 7:16–47.

Hollande, A.
    1952a   Classe des Chrysomonadines (Chrysomonadina Stein, 1878). Traité Zool. 1, fasc. 1:471–578.

1952b   Ordre des Choanoflagellés ou Craspédomonadines (Choanoflagellata S. Kent, 1880, Craspedomonadaceae Senn, 1900). *Ibid.* 1, fasc. 1:579–598.

Hyman, L. H.
1942   The transition from the unicellular to the multicellular individual. Pp. 27–42 in: Levels of Integration in Biological and Social Systems, Vol. VIII, Biological Symposia. R. Redfield, Ed. Cattell, Lancaster, Pennsylvania.

Kato, K.
1940   On the development of some Japanese polyclads. Jap. J. Zool. 8:537–574.

Moment, G. B.
1958   General Zoology. Houghton Mifflin, Boston.

Pedersen, K. J.
1959   Some features of the fine structure and histochemistry of planarian subepidermal gland cells. Z. Zellforsch. 50:121–142.

Reisinger, E.
1959   Anormogenetische und parasitogene Syncytienbildung bei Turbellarien. Protoplasma 50:627–643.

Remane, A.
1955   Morphologie als Homologienforschung. Verh. dtsch. zool. Ges., Tübingen (1954) (Zool. Anz., Suppl. 18):159–183.
1956   Die Grundlagen des natürlichen Systems, der vergleichenden Anatomie und der Phylogenetik. 2d ed. Akad. Verlagsges., Leipzig.
1958   Zur Verwandtschaft und Ableitung der niederen Metazoen. Verh. dtsch. zool. Ges., Graz (1957) (Zool. Anz., Suppl. 21):179–195.
1960   Die Beziehungen zwischen Phylogenie und Ontogenie. Zool. Anz. 164: 306–337.

Schulte, H.
1954   Beiträge zur Ökologie und Systematik der Bodenrotatorien. Zool. Jb. (Syst.) 82:551–617.

Steinböck, O.
1952   Keimblätterlehre und Gastraea-Theorie. Pyramide 2:13–15.
1958   Zur Phylogenie der Gastrotrichen. Verh. dtsch. zool. Ges., Graz (1957) (Zool. Anz., Suppl. 21):128–169.

Surface, F. M.
1907   The early development of a polyclad *Planocera inquilina* Wh. Proc. Acad. nat. Sci. Philad. 59:514–559.

Tuzet, O.
1948   La place des Spongiaires dans la classification. C. R. XIIIᵉ Congr. int. Zool., Paris (1948):429–432.
1950   Le spermatozoïde dans la série animale. Rev. suisse. Zool. 57:433–451.

3 ◆ The Early Worm: A Planula

CADET HAND

DEPARTMENT OF ZOÖLOGY,
UNIVERSITY OF CALIFORNIA, BERKELEY

It is my contention that the early worm was a planula, or a planuloid organism, and that the planula did not come from early worms. As a corollary, I contend, moreover, that the Hydrozoa are the most ancient class of the celenterates, that the primitive symmetry of the phylum is radial, and that the bilaterality of the Anthozoa is an advanced and adaptive character referable only to this group and not derived from an ancestry of bilateral flatworms.

Hadži (1944, 1953) and others (Steinböck, 1937; Remane, 1954 and earlier; Jägersten, 1956; Alvarado, 1956; Marcus, 1958) have expressed a point of view quite the contrary of that just outlined. They have argued that the Cnidaria are primitively bilateral and that the Anthozoa are the most ancient class of celenterates. Hyman (1959) and Hand (1959) have discussed the two contrasting points of view and maintained that the evidence supports the traditional view of the Cnidaria as a pre- and not post-flatworm development in metazoan phylogeny.

Still another possibility has been examined by Greenberg (1959), who, in a series of arguments concerning ancestors, embryos, and symmetry, has concluded that the Cnidaria and Platyhelminthes have origins so discrete that they do not even have a common planuloid in their ancestry.

Much phylogenetic discussion seems to be declarative and circumlocutory, and one hopes to avoid this. Emotion, too, sometimes seems to substitute for reason. At present there is no unequivocal way to substantiate our arguments, and we must rely on such data as we can accumulate from comparative morphological and embryological studies, from biochemical and serological studies, and from the fossil record and zoögeography. Not all of these are useful sources of data when one seeks the origin of the Cnidaria, but many are; and, when one examines the facts available and considers these, as well as the necessary truth that any ancestry must consist of a lineage of at least temporarily successful forms, then some conclusion to our problem should be possible. One regrets that phylogeny is not, by and large, an area open to the experimental approach. I should like now to review some of the evidence that, I believe, points to the Cnidaria as an early and pre-flatworm phylum.

Phylogenetic speculation has culled much of its factual material from the area of comparative embryological studies, and, if the flatworms are the ancestors of the celenterates, some evidence for this may be looked for in their embryologies. Throughout the free-living flatworms we find spiral cleavage present; this pattern persists through certain phyla—the nemertines, annelids, molluscs, and minor relatives—and is used as phylogenetic evidence of their common lineage. No celenterate, however, shows spiral cleavage; in fact, within the phylum a wide variety of patterns occurs, suggesting to me and to others that, as this group evolved, it was, in essence, experimenting with cleavage patterns. It is hard to accept that the celenterates abandoned spiral cleavage, a pattern of obvious success, as the turbellarian theory demands. Another profound difference between the two groups may be noted; namely, that the embryological axes of Cnidaria are the adult axes, and are not modified as in the Platyhelminthes. It could be argued that the cnidarian mode is a simplification, a dropping out of certain steps as compared to the flatworm pattern, but there is no evidence to support this.

Greenberg (1959) has critically discussed the embryologies of these two groups, pointing out that some of the simplest flatworms may have a cleavage pattern that cannot fairly be called spiral. Nevertheless, he concludes that, over-all, flatworms and celenterates have such "radically different" early embryologic patterns that a derivation of one from the other is untenable. I do not feel that we must necessarily look to different protozoan ancestors for these two phyla. Although there is an attractive cogency in Greenberg's arguments, I do not find them sufficiently compelling to rule out as an alternative possibility the hypothesis that there was a common planuloid ancestor for worms and celenterates, evolved from protozoa and in turn leading to our modern phyla.

When we consider the germ layers, their functions, and the modes of origin of the body layers, I believe we must again choose the celenterates as more primitive than the flatworms. As evolution proceeded from acellular to cellular, the organisms must have remained functionally complete. That is, nutritive, reproductive, and presumably locomotive activities had to be maintained. On entirely speculative grounds it seems easiest to imagine an initial separation of ectoderm and endoderm, without any necessity for the development of a mesoderm. It is a moot point whether or not mesoderm exists in the celenterates. Among certain anthozoa the mesoglea does possess cells, and, in this, resembles certain types of connective tissue; however, the mesoglea of hydrozoa and scyphozoa is essentially free of cells. At the gross level at least, the mesoglea of some celenterates looks more like the dermal membrane of higher metazoa than like either the parenchyma of flatworms or mesoderm and connective tissue. It is unfortunate that both mesoglea and dermal membranes seem to be structures whose embryological origins are not known. It would be curious, however, if the essentially noncellular mesoglea of celenterates were either the direct precursor or the antecedent of mesoderm as we know it.

Intimately related to the development of a third body layer must be the role it has played. In the celenterates this layer varies from a simple cementing substance to a highly elastic and supportive structure. Never is it involved in such obviously mesodermal activities as reproduction or the development of muscles. There are fluids and spaces for supportive functions or possible activities related to circulatory and excretory systems, and here analogies to flatworm parenchyma may be drawn. Related to the necessity of a third layer is, also, the size of the animal. As is well demonstrated in many very small metazoa, the smaller the organism, the less well developed or the fewer and smaller the mesodermal structures (*i.e.,* absence of celom and blood vessels and of circulatory system). In the celenterates the origin of the mesoglea is not evident, but it is clear that its origin is not highly determinate and specific, as in flatworms. Now, taking the points just mentioned together, if we can accept that the primitive or ancestral celenterates must have been very small, a matter to be discussed shortly, it is again easier to accept the Cnidaria as a primitively diploblastic phylum rather than one originating from a triploblastic group.

The question of the size of unknown ancestral animals, like phylogenetic questions, must deal more with the speculative than the factual, but let us continue. The celenterates are an old group and, at the time of their emergence as an identifiable line, were almost certainly accompanied by hordes of other organisms. These organisms must have included the celenterates' food and quite possibly their predators. Both the turbellarian theory and the more traditional ideas look to these early animals as being "planuloid" in general form. Now, nematocysts characterize the Cnidaria, while rhabdoids characterize the Platyhelminthes. It is interesting that nematocysts or nematocyst-like structures occur in certain protists, namely dino-flagellates, cnidosporidians, and possibly ciliates (cnidotrichocysts); whereas rhabdoids at best seem analogous only to some sorts of trichocysts. Notably, too, rhabdoids are not known to occur in the presumably most primitive Turbellaria, although, as Ax has pointed out, we must question here what is the primitive turbellarian. These facts suggest that the Cnidaria are more closely allied to the acellular organisms than to flatworms. If we now can accept nematocysts as a primitive cnidarian feature, we might ask what their functions may have been. Nematocysts may be divided into three functional categories: adhering, entangling, and penetrating; they serve the animal for defense and food gathering. It is not possible to say what, precisely, was the primitive use of nematocysts, but certain observations about the modern distribution of types are possible. For example, the Hydrozoa possess the most varied nematocysts, while the Schyphozoa and Anthozoa possess more limited ones. It is interesting, too, that the Hydrozoa, as a group, are more varied in body form than is either of the other two classes. These facts suggest to me that the Hydrozoa are the older group. We also should note that the Hydrozoa have simple guts possessing no nematocysts, whereas the Scyphozoa and Anthozoa have divided guts with nematocysts. The Hydrozoa seem, as small animals, to be specialized as predators upon smaller food organisms, while the Anthozoa and Scyphozoa seem specialized for catching and digesting relatively large food organisms. Indeed, what can be the function of nematocysts within the gastrodermis other than to deliver a final quieting and killing dose of toxin to some still struggling prey? The turbellarian theory asks one to accept the idea that the Anthozoa were the first cnidarians; that they evolved with divided guts and, I suppose, with gastrodermal nematocysts. These early celenterates must have been feeding upon relatively large and active food. The fossil record, although the evidence is weak, does not support this; nor, I believe, does common sense. In the absence of acceptable homologs of nematocysts in the flatworms, and in view of their presence in various protists, I feel we must interpret the Cnidaria as a group stemming from small original forms. These hypothetical ancestral forms may well have been planuloid, their guts simple, and their prey small. As larger food organisms came onto the phylogenetic scene, the celenterate gut was pressed to evolve, and such complexities as compartmentalization of the gut and gastrodermal nematocysts became successful evolutionary changes.

Very basic to our arguments is the problem of the primitive symmetry of the Cnidaria. Traditionally we have held that the group is radial; the turbellarian theory, by contrast, argues for their being initially bilateral. Radiality, I believe, has three explanations among modern animal groups; namely, it can be primitive, or associated with sessility, or consequent upon planktonic existence. As to its primitive nature, one can point to the development of most organisms. The early ontogenetic stages, such as blastulae and gastrulae, are morphologically radial, and it is only later that bilaterality appears. Many individual protists are radial, as are certain multicellular protistan colonies. Radial protists are those that have a free-swimming, planktonic existence, or those that are sessile. It is the creeping-crawling benthic protists that tend toward bilaterality. That radiality is associated with sessility is nearly a biological axiom. The sponges, celenterates, and echinoderms should serve as evidence here. That a planktonic way of life should be associated with radiality is not so easy to explain. We may be arguing in circles to cite the medusae of cnidarians or the colonial forms of such pelagic hydroids as *Velella* and *Porpita,* since their radiality is here presumed to be phylogenetically primitive. The ctenophores, a group whose symmetry is best described as biradial, provide, perhaps, a better argument for a relationship between planktonic existence and radiality. I think, too, that the externally radial form of a few rotifers and, generally, of trochophores and certain other larvae, as well as the more fundamental radiality of most planktonic protists, supports my contention. As to why most planktonic organisms are not radial, I can say that they are forms stemming from bilateral ancestors and that more strongly swimming (nektonic) organisms presumably have retained their bilaterality because its advantages are greater than those of radiality. Yet, the maintenance of radial form by the colonial hydroids *Porpita* and *Velella,* by medusae and ctenophores, and by the floating anemone *Minyas,* or the pelagic sea cucumber *Pelagothuria,* serves as evidence for me that a planktonic existence and radial body are related in those groups whose ancestry is radial. From these ideas I suggest that the Cnidaria are a radial phylum, the radiality being acquired first as a primitive feature, and then reinforced by their variously sessile and planktonic ways of life.

Greenberg (1959) has essentially agreed with what has just been stated, but he has pointed out that the differences in symmetry are so "deep-rooted" that they "would seem to emphasize the improbability of common ancestry." I do not feel that the improbability is necessarily emphasized any more than I feel that the possibility exists that a common ancestry could be involved. I certainly agree with Greenberg that the Protometazoa must have been planuloid, but, to my way of thinking, the evolution of radial, biradial, and spiral cleavage patterns and their related symmetries could just as well have occurred among planuloids, rather than as steps in the evolution of Protometazoa from Protozoa, as Greenberg suggests.

If the Cnidaria are a radial phylum, how then do we account for the bilaterality of the Anthozoa? First let me ask, how bilateral are the Anthozoa? Where are the anterior end, the left and right sides, or the dorsal and ventral surfaces? As a *convention,* students of the Anthozoa have termed the side that possesses the first pair of directive mesenteries as ventral. I emphasize, this is a convention. The mesenteries develop as couples along the longitudinal axis and on opposite sides. "Ventral" having been defined, "left," "right," and "dorsal" may also be identified. "Anterior" and "posterior" can also be distinguished, since the aboral end of some planulae carries a tuft of specialized cilia and tends to be at the front, or anterior, as far as direction of movement is concerned. The axes of bilaterality, then, seem to be useful analogs or terms that we use to describe developing or adult anthozoa, and not necessarily homologs of these features in bilateral organisms. If we examine planula larvae, we find they are not differentiated externally into dorsal and ventral surfaces except possibly for the larvae of some corals and the zoanthella larvae of some zoanthids. Unfortunately, we do not have developmental studies to tell us whether or not the longer "ventral" cilia are related to the "ventral directives." I would rather believe that the ventral cilia are adaptations to a creeping life, as are the ventral cirri of some protists, than that they are ancestral reminiscences of bilateral ancestors.

The Anthozoa are a sessile group. Their way of life requires that water be forced into the celenteron in order that they may expand, and in turn it is against this contained water that the body musculature operates. Food and water pass into the celenteron, and indigestible wastes are expelled. The cilia of the throat are highly organized into incurrent areas, the siphonoglyphs, and excurrent areas. This organization is required first to inflate the polyp and second to maintain a turgid and functioning body while food intake and elimination are occurring. The compartmentalization of the body by mesenteries enlarges the digestive surfaces to handle the large food objects of anthozoa; as a purely celenterate feature, endodermal longitudinal muscles have developed. The mesenteries, in order to accommodate food objects and the varying forms of the animal, need both longitudinal and transverse muscles, and it is little wonder that as an epitheliomuscular system these occur on opposite faces of the mesenteries. Such a complex system demands organization, and the presence of the siphonoglyph and the organization of muscles and mesenteries give to the Anthozoa their seeming bilaterality. Nowhere in the Turbellaria do we find analogs or homologs of this organization around the longitudinal axis, or of endodermal musculature. Such features must be interpreted as cnidarian adaptations to larger size and sessility, rather than as an incomplete disguise of a once bilateral organism. Pantin (1960) has concluded on similar grounds that the bilaterality of the Anthozoa is a functional adaptation, not an ancestral reminiscence.

If the Cnidaria stem from flatworms and if the Anthozoa are the more ancient class, it is completely enigmatic to me that the sessile Anthozoa are not wholly hermaphroditic. Hermaphroditism and sessility clearly seem to be related—as, for example, in barnacles, bryozoans, and tunicates; but, although monecious anthozoa do occur, the majority are diecious. These facts seem more logically to mean that the Anthozoa can better be interpreted as stemming from diecious ancestors than from the monecious flatworms.

What, then, do the Cnidaria stem from? I have presented elsewhere (Hand, 1959) some of my reasons for assuming that this group originated from planuloid organisms. On embryological grounds I would argue that some flagellate, not ciliate, gave rise to planuloids. These planuloids would be endowed with the same radial symmetry as that seen in some volvocines. As nutritive and locomotory functions became more separate, the mouth developed as a posterior structure. The planktonic planuloid evolved into a tentacled actinuloid and with its nemato-cysts, a protistan inheritance, gave rise to medusae.

A planktonic way of life and radial ancestry clearly mark the Cnidaria. Sessility developed as an innovation of budding juvenile stages—the actinulae—and estab-lished in the Hydrozoa a trend toward the diphasic life history of this group. It seems best to interpret the medusa as the primitive adult, since in those hydroids that possess gonads one can almost always find clearly medusoid features associated with the gonads. The Scyphozoa, still favoring the medusa as the adult, have developed a larva with a compartmented gut. This larva not only foreshadows its adult, but makes an interesting ancestral type for the Anthozoa, as might alter-natively the sessile and precocious Stauromedusae. By the device of loss of the free medusae, as among many hydroids too, the sessile phase became the definitive adult of the Anthozoa. The compartmentalization of the gut of scyphozoa and anthozoa is an adaptation to larger body size and to the large food entities ingested by these organisms. The low frequency of occurrence of hermaphroditism in the Anthozoa argues against an ancestry from monecious flatworms, and the bilaterality of anthozoa is best interpreted as necessary adaptations related to larger size, the hydrostatic skeleton, and development of endodermal musculature.

The fossil record suggests that medusoid and hydroid body forms evolved be-fore anthozoan polyps. Certainly there is no evidence in the embryologic patterns of cnidarians that these organisms are derivable from flatworms. From the discus-sion and facts presented here and by Hyman (1959), Greenberg (1959), and Pantin (1960), I conclude that the Cnidaria are a primitively radial phylum; that the Hydrozoa are the most ancient class, and that the bilaterality of the Anthozoa is an advanced and adaptive character referable only to this group and not derived from an ancestry of bilateral flatworms. Thus I must conclude, too, that the early worm was a planula and not that the planula came from early worms. Like Hyman (1959, p. 753), I feel that "It is impossible to bypass the Cnidaria in the evolutionary story."

REFERENCES

Alvarado, R.
    1956   On the origin and evolution of the coelomates [*sic*] Metazoa. Proc. 14th Int. Congr. Zool., Copenhagen (1953):146–150.
Greenberg, M. J.
    1959   Ancestors, embryos, and symmetry. Syst. Zool. 8:212–221.
Hadži, J.
    1944   Turbelarijska Teorija Knidarijev. (Turbellarien-Theorie der Knidarier.) Slov. Akad. Znan. Umt., Ljubljana. [In Slovenian with German sum-mary.]
    1953   An attempt to reconstruct the system of animal classification. Syst. Zool. 2:145–154. [This paper includes a bibliography of most of Hadži's earlier papers relevant to this subject.]

Hand, C.
  1959   On the origin and phylogeny of the coelenterates. Syst. Zool. 8:191–202.
Hyman, L. H.
  1959   The Invertebrates. Vol. V: Smaller Coelomate Groups. McGraw-Hill, New York, Toronto, London.
Jägersten, G.
  1956   On the early phylogeny of the Metazoa. The bilaterogastraea theory. Zool. Bidr. Uppsala 30:321–354.
Marcus, E.
  1958   On the evolution of the animal phyla. Quart. Rev. Biol. 33:24–58.
Pantin, C. F. A.
  1960   Diploblastic animals. Proc. Linn. Soc. London 171:1–14.
Remane, A.
  1954   Die Geschichte der Tiere. Pp. 340–422 in: Die Evolution der Organismen. Vol. II. Heberer, G., Ed. 2d ed. Fischer, Stuttgart.
Steinböck, O.
  1937   Eine Theorie über den plasmodialen Ursprung der Vielzeller (Metazoa). 4th Int. Congr. Cytol. (1936) (Arch. exp. Zellforsch. 19):343.

4 ◆ Origin and Affinities of the Lower Metazoa: The "Aceloid" Ancestry of the Eumetazoa

OTTO STEINBÖCK

ZOOLOGISCHES INSTITUT,
UNIVERSITÄT INNSBRUCK, INNSBRUCK

In the following comparison of the "aceloid" to the "planuloid," I shall present not only my own ideas, but also those of my friend Jovan Hadži, who was unfortunately not in a position to accept the invitation to take part in the meeting at which this paper was read, but whose cordial greetings I nevertheless had the pleasure to convey to all those present, both "friend" and "foe."

My conceptions on the descent of the Eumetazoa from ciliate antecedents were not formed at my desk, nor at a drawing board with ruler and compass; they suggested themselves when I studied (Steinböck and Reisinger, 1931) the Acoela of Greenland in their living state for months and, for more than a year, subjected the microscopic preparations to histological investigation. I was wholly strengthened in my conception when Hadži, *independently of me,* and as an expert on the Cnidaria, came to the same conclusion. I was also convinced by the results of my regeneration experiments on the acelous turbellarian *Amphiscolops* sp., which I carried out for the specific purpose of experimentally supporting my theory. The most important experimental results, which are of interest to us in this connection, I have dealt with in a separate study (Steinböck, chap. 8 in this volume).

In the course of my studies, it became increasingly clear that Haeckel's (1872, 1874, 1895) hitherto prevailing gastrea theory, which at his time was an ingenious and audacious construction, cannot be right, for the following reasons: (1) the theory demands of nature a roundabout course in attaining a higher organization from the Protozoa by way of a loose cell-colony (phylogenetic—morea; ontogenetic—morula), the cellular state (blastea, blastula), and, finally, the diploblastic gastrea; and (2) it is not only roundabout, but a blind alley as well. All attempts to understand the origin of the Bilateria from the sessile hydrozoan or anthozoan polyp have remained pure hypothetical constructions. For instance, there is not one known organism that connects the Cnidaria to the Annelida; and the known forms that account for the origin from the Protozoa (Flagellata) come from the plant realm (*Eudorina, Volvox,* etc.).

It is quite different for the acele theory. The Acoela are principally plasmodial and are organized very similarly to the Ciliata. There is a compact outer layer (*Deckschichte*) resembling the ectoplasm of the Ciliata. At the base of the *Deckschichte* lies the nervous system, then comes the epithelio-muscular layer, which lies in a looser mass of nuclei and cytoplasm transitional to the digestive plasmodium (*verdauendes Plasmodium*), this latter corresponding to the entoplasm of the Ciliata. The mouth opening is in primitive representatives very simple— just a slit—whereas the Ciliata have a much more complicated cytopharynx. In the immature aceles one can see only uniform nuclei, but they alter during the genesis of the gametes. Which nuclei in the plasmodium become gametes is decided, as regeneration experiments show, by the respective position of the germ nuclei as a whole. The nuclei grow remarkably quickly; the chromatin becomes clearly visible, and finally the nuclei surround themselves with cytoplasm and a delicate egg-membrane.

Evolution to the higher Turbellaria can only be roughly outlined, but there are a number of examples that may serve as excellent models. First, the outermost layer is completely separated from the underlying plasmodium by means of a basal membrane, thus reinforcing the body wall and thus becoming an "epithelium." For the time being (*e.g., Proporoplana,* Reisinger, 1935) it remains plasmodial, however, and only later becomes cellular. The epithelio-muscular layer comes to lie below the basal membrane, as does the nervous system. Tissue located toward the interior is still able to form a uniform plasmodium (*e.g.,* the Kalyptorhynchia), but the part concerned with digestion segregates the mesenchyme from the remaining archihiston, thereby definitely producing "ectoderm" and "entoderm." *Thus, in our opinion, the mesenchyme is not formed by the "primary germ layers" of the gastrea theory, but, in the course of phylogeny, the germ layers segregate from the primary total plasmodium, the "archihiston."*

Personally, I consider all mesenchymal and mesodermal tissues in general to be mesenchyme, in the broad sense (Steinböck, 1954–56, p. 319). Mesenchyme, strictly speaking, is a multistructural tissue containing cavities to varying degrees, whereas a mesoderm occurs in the form of epithelia (endothelium, mesothelium, etc.). Starck (1955) presents a similar point of view.

Mesenchyme, in the strict sense, in all metazoa, insofar as it occurs as a corresponding system of organs at all, forms the main part of the muscular system, and, very often, also the skeletal system, the nephridia, the blood vascular system, and the celom with its mesenteries, etc. In primitive groups lacking a germinal path (*Keimbahn*), the mesenchyme, as can be proved by experiment, is also the source of the gametes, which thus demonstrates the primitive nature of this tissue. In addition, the mesenchyme, in most animal groups, including man, plays a decisive part in regeneration (Steinböck, 1954–56).

The opening into the digestive lumen becomes progressively complicated, proceeding from the apharyngeal state of the primitive Acoela, through the pharynx simplex, finally arriving at the most varied pharyngeal types (Remane, 1950a; Ax, chap. 14 of this volume). The now cellular gut, which during digestion may still reversibly pass over into the aceloid state (Steinböck, 1927, 1958b), tends frequently to a very extensive formation of diverticula in all directions. It is an interesting fact that the intestine may also assume skeletal functions by extending anteriorly a blind branch that assumes a structure similar to a roll of money (*i.e.,* chorda-like—*Otoplana intermedia* Dupl.—von Hofsten, 1918; Steinböck, 1958a; Ax, 1957, 1960).

The evolutionary development of the nervous system, from the simplest situation in the lower Acoela, has progressed far to attain the level of the higher aceles, and, in the case of the higher Turbellaria, has led to the formation of a rope-ladder-like nervous system, which in the Tricladida shows much similarity to that of primitive Annelida.

The seemingly confusing abundance of sexual discharge ducts of the higher Turbellaria, which is a special development within this group, may be followed in sequence from the simplest conditions in the Acoela up to the most complicated duct-systems of the higher Turbellaria.

Thus, clear lines of evolutionary development may be shown within the Turbellaria, from forms that by themselves point to the organization of the Ciliata, to the various higher turbellarian groups. Those who, without prejudice and with freedom from the fetters of the gastrea theory, search for the roots of this genealogical tree necessarily arrive at the Ciliata. With the exception of the nuclei and the sexual apparatus, everything exists in the Ciliata in anticipation of what is also found in the Acoela, where there is higher development because of the generally greater body mass.

The question remains, however, as to whether the so-called "silver line system" is an excitation-conducting system (von Gelei, 1937, 1939; Klein, 1928). As far as I can see, only the American research workers give a positive reply to this question (*cf.* Hyman, 1940, p. 167–69, and fig. 13, p. 66). But, even if it were not possible to prove the existence of such a nervous system, one would not need to use excessive imagination or erect a perplexing construction to see that the nervous system of primitive aceles could have originated in organisms derived from the Ciliata.

It stands to reason that the present-day Ciliata, which have an evolutionary history of hundreds of millions of years, do not exactly correspond to those forms that we—Hadži and I—and Hanson (1958) consider to be the predecessors of the Proacoela. Above all, the existence of generative and vegetative nuclei is nothing original and is a special mode that may have led the Ciliata into the blind alley of their evolutionary development. Personally, I believe that the immediate progenitor of the Proacoela was a universally ciliated, bilateral, diecious, bottom-dwelling prociliate that had numerous equivalent totipotent nuclei, as is still true today for the Acoela (and higher forms) and as is consistent with general theoretical considerations of sexuality (Hartmann, 1956). The parting of the ways may have been at that stage where separation into generative and somatic nuclei began—*i.e.,* the beginning of the Ciliata in the present sense of the word. Decisive factors for their development were probably, among other things, the "remaining small" of the Ciliata on the one hand and the "growing large" of the Proacoela on the other.

Nothing certain can be said, of course, about sexual conditions in the "aceloid." If we proceed from a stage of conjugation, we may say that the pro-acele or "aceloid" may have been created when the stationary nucleus surrounded itself with cytoplasm for the first time and thus became an unfertilized ovum, or when the syncaryon did not immediately form new nuclei, but surrounded itself with cytoplasm and a membrane and thus became a fertilized ovum. This would correspond to "internal fecundation." If, however, the unfertilized ovum was separated from the body and deposited in water and only then was visited by migratory nuclei (=sperm), this would be "external fecundation." Such an entirely conceivable process is all that is needed for protozoa to become metazoa.

The Cnidaria

If it is true that the Turbellaria are descended from the Prociliata, the Cnidaria must somewhere and somehow have originated from these forms, unless their direct descent from the Protozoa is to be assumed (but for that there is no indication whatsoever). In our opinion, such a special development characterizes the Porifera (Spongiaria) in spite of Tuzet's view (1949, and chap. 10 of this volume)[1] but this group will not be further dealt with here, because its rather doubtful position does not touch upon the core of our problem.

It is, of course, not possible to say exactly where the ancestors of the Cnidaria have branched off. My friend Hadži was previously (1953, 1958) more inclined to believe in a derivation at a somewhat higher stage of organization (Rhabdocoela), but we agree that the Archicnidaria still possessed a rich mesenchyme (=mesohyl of Hadži) with ovaries, a well-developed external epithelium, and intestine. It is difficult to judge the extent to which they already had other, more highly developed organ systems. Since we intend to reconstruct as little as possible, and, on the other hand, wish to prove as much as possible on the basis of living models, we must here point out the trend of the Turbellaria toward sessility. The caudal plates of many of the Macrostomida and other Turbellaria, the adhesive organs of the Micropharyngidae living on rays, and the Bdellouridae living as commensals on *Limulus* must be judged from this point of view. Above all, however, it is the Temnocephala, with their semi-sessile life and with the formation of a foot disk and well-developed tentacles, that make the potentialities of the Turbellaria clearly discernible.

According to the opinion expressed long and vigorously by Hadži (1949b), which is in best agreement with that of the paleontologists (Schindewolf, 1930, and other papers) and to which recently also Jägersten (1955, 1959) has come to agree, the Anthozoa, which are in principle of bilateral structure, are the most primitive of the Cnidaria living today. We must therefore search here for points of correspondence with the Turbellaria. Hadži deals with this problem very thoroughly, and, as it seems to me, very successfully in a book now in preparation, the manuscript of which he has been kind enough to place at my disposal. Only three problems can be dealt with now. (1) The mesenchyme (mesohyl, mesoglea): Hadži points out that it would be contrary to all experience if the sessile mode of life were to cause the development of a thick mesenchymal layer from a delicate, structureless, thin membrane of the supporting lamella in the allegedly more primitive Hydrozoa. Furthermore, the "mesoglea" corresponds to the mesenchyme of the turbellarian ancestors, which, in adapting to the sessile state, has transformed its internal structures into a solid skeleton-forming tissue with heavy fibers. This,

[1] See also Tuzet, Loubatières, and Pavans de Ceccatty, 1952; Tuzet and Pavans de Ceccatty, 1953, 1955; and Czihak, 1958.

with respect to its potentialities, is quite possible. (2) The homology of the digestive tract of the Cnidaria with that of the Turbellaria: this was discussed by Hadži (1949a) in the chapter, "Are the peripheral parts of the gastrovascular system of anthopolyps homologous with the intestinal diverticula of the Turbellaria?" He answered this question, with full justification, in the affirmative. The various intestinal configurations within the Turbellaria, as expressions of the response to equally varied morphological and physiological situations, as well as the experimentally determined knowledge of the immense plasticity of the turbellarian body in regeneration, clearly show that a procnidarian, which has gone over to the sessile state, is capable of forming functionally adapted, longitudinal anthozoan enteric pouches for the enlargement of the digesting surface—e.g., the purely hypothetical (bilatero)gastrea. (3) Axial conditions with respect to sessility: in this case, also, the Turbellaria satisfy all possible demands. I agree with Hadži (1946b) that the "aceloid" had a simple mouth aperture approximately in the middle of the ventral surface, similar to that of many of the Acoela living today. Since, however, the plasticity of these animals permits the mouth aperture to be shifted in the course of evolution to either the anterior or posterior end, it is theoretically not difficult to assume that the first of the Procnidaria became sessile with the mouth aperture at the fore end (or near it) and attached themselves to the substratum at the other end (models: Acoela—*Proporus, Hofstenia, Hallangia;* other Turbellaria—*Prosthiostomum, Prorhynchus, Dallyellia*), or, *vice versa*, that the fore end with the frontal gland became the point of attachment with a mouth aperture at the rear end (or near it) (models: Acoela—*Diopisthoporus;* other Turbellaria—*Cestoplana, Cylindrostomum, Opistomum*). It is a natural assumption that the Procnidaria became attached at the rear end and that the tentacles grew at the fore end as assumed by Hadži (1949a, p. 80) with reference to the Temnocephala. Adherents to the strictest form of phylogenesis will, however, by referring to the planula, insist that the "procnidaroid" also became attached at the aboral pole (*i.e.,* the fore part), for which, also, as just shown, possible models are available. In view of my scepticism (which does not mean total rejection) with respect to phylogenetic interpretations of the larval stages, I should like to put the question for discussion as to whether the structure of the anthozoan larva (fig. 4-1) necessarily leads us to conclude the existence of similar axes in the ancestor.

The great majority of the Turbellaria, among them the most primitive ones, develop without larvae, hence, those with larvae are remarkable exceptions. Very well known and, above all, misinterpreted, are the larvae of some few, by no means primitive, polyclads, to which must be added the quite aberrant Luther-larva of *Rhynchoscolex* (Reisinger, 1924). From the fact that larvae generally are a rare exception among the lowest Eumetazoa, the conclusion may be drawn that, in general, *all larvae are secondary formations.* This also agrees well with our opinion that swimming is a mode of life derived from bottom dwelling. In our example—the Cnidaria—it may therefore be assumed with full justification that larvae have occurred only *after* the evolution of sessility, which may be easily understood from a biological point of view.

The phylogenetic significance of larvae has, up to the present day, been considerably overestimated. Since the discovery of the plankton, with its abundance of hitherto unknown microscopic forms, came just at the height of morphologically oriented theories of evolution, this led, consciously or unconsciously, to the notion that life had originated from the pelagic mode and that its simpler metazoan forms, *i.e.,* larval forms, must represent the most primitive structural forms.[2] It must once again be emphasized that *swimming about freely is a secondary phenomenon.* In our opinion, *life originated on the bottom of the sea.* Larvae are secondary forms, which rose from the bottom at more or less early stages of ontogeny and went over to swimming as a "pelagial propagation phase" (Burdon-Jones, 1956, p. 70) and, because of limited cellular mass, developed organs exclusively serving the purpose of swimming. Such specializations need have nothing to do with their adult structural plan, and are able temporarily to modify it considerably. As far as I know, Reisinger (1924, p. 27) was the first to express the irrefutable idea that all pelagic larvae would have to be of similar appearance as a result of their formation from a limited number of very similar components in every case. Gar-

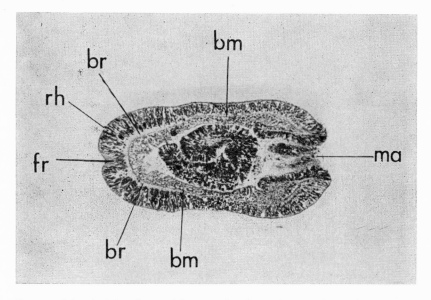

FIGURE 4-1. *Actinian larva.* Photograph of a microscopic section (kindly sent by Prof. Jägersten, Uppsala), ca. × 200. br, brain calotte; fr, frontal organ; ma, mouth aperture; bm, basement membrane; rh, rhabdites.

stang (1922), Hadži (1955), Ivanov (1937), and de Beer (1954) also treat the larvae as derived forms, "so that the notion of the larva as a secondary character compared to other stages of ontogenesis may be looked upon as a dominant viewpoint in contemporary embryology" (Zakhvatkin, 1956, p. 36).

I therefore believe it quite possible that the anthozoan larva, with sensory cells and nerve-calotte at the aboral pole where it attaches, nevertheless had ancestors whose mouth *and* brain were at the anterior. But it also seems possible that, in the case of the larva, which is free-swimming, the larval nervous center and the organs in the larval main axis have shifted, compared with the sessile form. In the larva the anterior end and the frontal organs are incorrectly interpreted, on the

---

[2] This overestimation of the plankton was misleading also in other fields. Thus, in limnology, it led to a neglect of the soil fauna in favor of the plankton, which has its effects to some extent up to the present day.

basis of the biogenetic law, as being primitive. The assumption that the axes are shifted is, however, not one that was invented by myself at random. I was able to prove such a shifting on the basis of a good example in the course of a regeneration experiment with the acele *Amphiscolops* (Steinböck, 1954). The possibility of shifting the axis in the planula larva seems to me a convincing argument for the caution with which not only the previous ontogenetic stages (cleavage) must be judged with respect to the "biogenetic law," but also the later ones. This applies particularly to all the lower phyla.

Beyond the foregoing problems, it is necessary to examine the organization of the planula and its turbellarian origin from the point of view of adherents of the

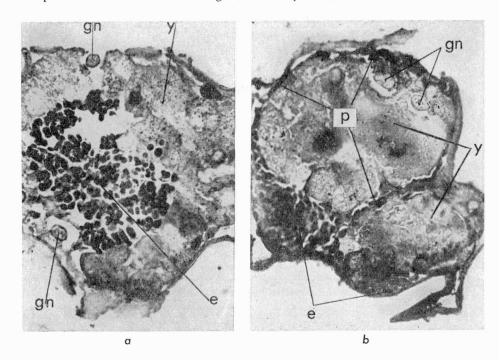

FIGURE 4-2. *Geocentrophora sphyrocephala* (de Man): *a*, Pleroplast, laid Jan. 17, 1958, and fixed Jan. 28, 1958; *b*, Koiloplast, laid Dec. 26, 1957, and fixed Jan. 13, 1958. e, embryo; gn, giant nucleoli; p, periderm; y, yolk. (Photo. B. Hauser, Innsbruck.)

gastrea theory and the "biogenetic law," for the larva has (Jägersten, 1959, fig. 3; and here, fig. 4-1) a thick outer layer with a "basiepidermal" nerve-calotte and, on the fore end, a frontal organ, which is a "characteristic structure of the Turbellaria" (Hyman, 1951, fig. 2). Also a comparatively thick layer of tissue exists between the ecto- and entoderm (fig. 4-2, *a*), which may perhaps correspond to mesenchyme (=archihiston). In any case, agreement with the acele Turbellaria is exceedingly good (fig. 4-2, *b*). Also, living models are available for this comparison, and this must carry more weight than the hypothetical construction of the (bilatero)gastrea. The question now arises whether we are confronted with cenogenesis, palingenesis, or an uninterpretable stage. Regardless of the point of view, the result of this discussion seems to be the following: *the early worm is not a planula larva, but the planula larva is a reminiscence of the early worm!*

The Euplatyhelminthes

There is rare unanimity with respect to the close relationship of the Euplatyhelminthes (*i.e.,* the Turbellaria, Trematoda, and Cestoda), especially with respect to the Trematoda. If there were only a few species, they would surely be considered an order of the Turbellaria. The problem of the cestodes is more difficult, because here the problems of metamery (segmentation), corm- or zooid-formation, etc., arise; but these cannot be dealt with here. Today, the general opinion is that the Cestodaria are not the ancestors of the Eucestoda, and that the ancestral forms are to be found among the Trematoda, or, more probable still, among the Turbellaria.

The Rhynchocoela (Nemertinea)

Morphological and histological data, it is almost universally agreed, make obvious the relation of the Rhynchocoela to the Turbellaria. Since, however, they possess a proboscis, a blood vascular system, and an intestine with a terminal anal aperture, the nemertines are a distinct group. It is, therefore, justifiable that they be placed as a subgroup with the Platyhelminthes under the higher taxon Euplatyhelminthes (Claus, Grobben and Kühn, 1936).

The proboscis can be derived easily from the turbellarian ancestors and has its counterpart with the Kalyptorhynchia. Terminal intestine and anus are a matter of course in such elongated animals. The turbellarian *Tabaota curiosa* Marcus, with its "poro anal transitorio," perhaps shows how the anus has been formed (*cf.* Steinböck, 1958a, p. 154, fig. 12). In all animals possessing it, including human beings, the blood vascular system is a system of tissues of distinctly mesenchymal origin. Hence, the fact that it exists in the Rhynchocoela is not indicative of a fundamentally new organ system, for it is already functionally anticipated by the liquid-filled spaces in the mesenchyme of the Euplatyhelminthes as well as by occasional occurrences of "lymphatic vessels" (*e.g.,* Paramphistomidae, Trematoda). Friedrich (1935), in several very interesting nemertines, describes celomic spaces with which nephridia connect as protonephridia *and* metanephridia. He interprets them as the remains of an involution of annelid ancestors with extensive celomic spaces. *Why "remains"? Why so much "retroformation" and so much "retrogression" in evolution?* I venture to declare that here we have cavities that must be described as "celoms" and are spaces formed originally within the nemertine mesenchyme. This is, indeed, confirmed by the facts that: (1) these cavities cannot be definitely distinguished from the blood vessels themselves; (2) the terminal chambers, into which the nephrostomata protrude, are, according to Friedrich, apparently separate from the blood vessels; and (3) these chambers are formed ontogenetically by cavitation in the mesenchyme and, therefore, mesenchymal cells form the walls (as in humans). *In this case the "biogenetic law" ought to be applied!* The "rhynchocelom" is formed in exactly the same manner (Friedrich, 1935). Hardly anybody would have this cavity derived from the celom of the Annelida.

Remane (1955; *cf.* the Remane-Steinböck discussion—Steinböck, 1958b) derives the Platyhelminthes from a hypothetical "archicelomate" with one unpaired and two paired celomic cavities, from which metanephridia lead to the outside, and with a blood vascular system and terminal intestine. Marcus (1958) and Jägersten (1959) seem to support him. For these scientists the Acoela are the terminal forms in a regression from the "archicelomate." As thus the core of our acele theory has been touched, it is necessary to deal with this hypothesis separately. Remane's conception also demands the following: comparatively highly organized animals (evolved from the archicelomate) approach the state of the polynuclear Ciliata by regression, but also evolve further to the level of the Annelida! Furthermore, it follows that *regression* from celomate ancestors led to the ovariate Turbellaria, and then, by renewed *evolution,* there developed the large groups of lecithophore Turbellaria (the main part of this group) as well as the classes of the Trematoda and Cestoda (and, in my opinion, also the Aschelminthes)! This is, it seems to me, an impossible phylogenetic development with no known parallel elsewhere. It can and even must be demanded that proponents of the regression theory explain this "way back" and prove, especially within the Turbellaria where a sufficient number of living models exist, that the evolution from the Acoela to higher Turbellaria is wrong. This latter view has been accepted as correct by the great majority of two generations of research scientists, beginning with their senior, von Graff.

The Aschelminthes (Amera, Nemathelminthes)

The origin of this large group is still contested. Whereas the majority of research workers derive it from Platyhelminthes, Remane (1954), Marcus (1958) and (probably) also Jägersten (1959) have recently expressed or implied the belief that it originated from Remane's archicelomate by regression or have considered it to be regressed from the Annelida (*cf.* the discussion between Remane and Steinböck, mentioned above). I have discussed this earlier, in 1957 at Graz (Steinböck, 1958a). With regard to the affinity of the Turbellaria and the Gastrotricha, I want only to add the statement of Franzén (1955) that *the sperms of these groups agree as to their structure.* And finally: *he who here does not recognize clear homologies as well as numerous similarities,* to which Remane (1932) *summa summarum* also attributes great importance, must be one denying the foundations on which the concept of homology rests.

Since there is little doubt of the kinship between the Gastrotricha, Rotatoria, Nematoda, Kinorhyncha, and probably also the Priapulida (*cf.* Remane, 1935–36), further treatment of them is omitted here. Thus, a discussion of the lower Metazoa ends.

General Discussion

An examination, in the light of the two phylogenetic theories under discussion, of the adult stages of the organisms in question reveals an enormous difference in the supporting evidence for each theory. The acele theory leads in a natural way—

and always substantiated by models—into the total range of the lower Eumetazoa with satisfactory understanding of the genesis of the higher Eumetazoa.

On the other hand, the gastrea theory is not able to use a single living adult form as a model, from the colony-forming plant-like Protista (*Volvox*) right up to the sessile Cnidaria (the medusa is nearly without exception considered to be a secondarily derived form), and from the latter to the Annelida and the so-called "Deuterostomia" (better "Notoneuralia," Ulrich, 1950), a fact that has recently been admitted by Remane (1960). Thus, the gastrea theory has lost its most essential evidence, for it is the study of the adult forms upon which the outstanding successes of paleontology are based, and it is the comparative anatomy of extant adult animals that is needed to assure a satisfactory natural system. Thus, the gastrea theory has nothing left as a proof for its correctness but ontogeny, to which, however, Remane (1950b) ascribes only an auxiliary role.

As already emphasized, I believe that ontogeny has only a very limited value for phylogenetic questions. It is without doubt possible, in advanced stages of embryonic development, especially in the higher taxa and by using the most critical examination, to learn many essential facts concerning phylogenetic relationships. But such conclusions become all the more doubtful, the earlier the stages that are investigated. This applies especially to segmentation of eggs (cleavage). Thus the Cnidaria, Haeckel's "Gastraeadae," show an "ameboid cleavage," as I would term it, and in the case of *Pennaria tiarella* (Hargitt, 1904) plasmodial, irregular, radial, and even spiral phenomena have been observed. Hyde (1894) describes in *Aurelia marginalis* Ag. (Scyphozoa) not only equal and unequal, as well as regular and irregular cleavage, but also two modes of formation of germ layers, *viz.* invagination *and* delamination. Such "exceptions" to "normal" development are described in great numbers in the standard work by Korschelt and Heider (1890–93, 1902–10, 1936), which adheres strictly to the gastrea theory. If, however, original papers are consulted, a more confusing abundance of "exceptions" is found, which *by far* exceed the "standard." Clarification is impossible solely by means of the gastrea theory. Let us, therefore, try to attain this aim by studying the development of the Turbellaria.

The development of the Acoela has, unfortunately, been relatively little studied, and we know nothing at all in this respect about the most interesting primitive species. What is well known is only the cleavage of *Convoluta roscoffensis* von Graff (Bresslau, 1909), which cannot, however, be considered as primitive. In this case cleavage is into an unequal duet, which leads to a complete epiboly of the macromeres by hardly smaller micromeres *without the formation of cavities.* Thus, no "blastocele" and no "blastopore" is formed. This cleavage is, in my firm opinion, not *the* rigid scheme for all Acoela, as is usually supposed. I believe that much more frequently a more or less irregular cleavage occurs, such as was found by Gardiner (1895) in *Polychoerus caudatus* Mark and later by Hyman (1937) in *Amphiscolops langerhansi* von Graff. If, as in *Convoluta,* macromeres exist, they contain the yolk substance and, surrounded by the micromeres by epibolic growth, they penetrate into the interior where the digesting plasmodium forms. This process is a so-called gastrulation, but without any phylogenetic implications.

Remane (1954) and Ax (1956) believe the Macrostomida to be a pivotal group within the Archoophora, the embryonic development of which thus acquires great importance. According to Seilern-Aspang (1957), it does not, however, develop in the expected "spiral-quartet 4d" pattern—rather, cleavage is very irregular. Duets or quartets may occur; or the blastomeres may form some other pattern. Within the lecithophoric Turbellaria a loosening of the blastomeres gradually takes place until finally there is "blastomeric anarchy." I have been able to prove that the course of development is not strictly determined (Steinböck and Ausserhofer, 1950) with *Prorhynchus stagnalis* M. Schultz, in which the early development may be in the form of a full germ (pleroplast), or a hollow germ (koiloplast). As my student B. Hauser has observed (unpublished), the ovum of *Geocentrophora sphyrocephala* (de Man) also develops irregularly, as pleroplast or as koiloplast, and both forms can occur at the same temperature. Spiral cleavage I have attributed to the best possible utilization of space in a hard-shell egg, and we can refer to a very instructive case of facultative spiral segmentation in a hard-shell egg in the case of *Gonionema murbachi* M. (Hydrozoa) (Perkins, 1902). A classical example for the utilization of space in a hard-shell egg was given by Bigelow (1902) in the cleavage of *Lepas* (Cirripedia). As soon as spiral cleavage becomes hereditary, it may continue as spiral even though the blastomeres do not lie against the wall of the egg at all, or contain a soft mass of yolk as in the first cleavage of *Prorhynchus stagnalis* (Steinböck and Ausserhofer, 1950).

If early larval development is present, the surface is increased both by the formation of cavities in the interior and by the increase of the volume for the purpose of reducing the rate of sinking (and probably also for increasing the number of cilia). The cells contain more yolk, which persists into the larva and is then conveyed into the interior of the stereoblastula by the micromeres; this corresponds to epiboly. Here is the beginning of the "invagination gastrula" of the gastrea theory! This event—invagination—may take place later, but comparatively rarely, in those forms with an eggshell. If one studies the individual animal groups in an unprejudiced and critical manner as to the mode of their development, one arrives at the conclusion that epiboly is by far the *most frequent* mode, as is stated also by Korschelt and Heider (1902–1910, p. 219): "epiboly is very widespread as to its occurrence." The picture develops even more completely in favor of epiboly if one considers that in many cases "epibolic gastrulation" is mentioned only in order to satisfy the conceptions of the gastrea theory.

Hence, as arguments against the (bilatero)gastrea theory: not only are concrete, adult forms lacking to support the theory, but also what seems to be its strongpoint, ontogeny, finds an exceedingly simple and ontomechanical alternative explanation. Finally, I wish to express my deepest conviction that *it is impossible for nearly the whole animal realm, with its immense diversity of form, to have originated from sessile forms; there is no evidence to support the theory that it did so.*

REFERENCES

Ax, P.

    1956   Die Gnathostomulida, eine rätselhafte Wurmgruppe aus dem Meeressand. Abh. math.-nat. Kl. Akad. Wiss. Lit., Kiel (1956):531–562.

    1957   Ein chordoides Stützorgan des Entoderms bei Turbellarien. Z. Morph. Ökol. Tiere 46:389–396.

    1960   Die Entdeckung neuer Organisationstypen im Tierreich. Ziemsen, Wittenberg.

Bigelow, M. A.
1902 The early development of *Lepas*. Bull. Mus. comp. Zool. Harv. 40:61–144.

Bresslau, E.
1909 Die Entwicklung der Acoelen. Verh. dtsch. zool. Ges., Frankfurt a. M. (1909)19:314–324.

Burdon-Jones, C.
1956 Nachtrag: Enteropneusta. Handb. Zool. 3, 2d half, no. 9:57–79.

Claus, C., K. Grobben, and A. Kühn.
1936 Lehrbuch der Zoologie. Springer, Berlin.

Czihak, G.
1958 Morphologie und Entwicklungsgeschichte der Wirbellosen (1945–1956). Fortschr. Zool. 11:1–34.

De Beer, G. R.
1954 The evolution of Metazoa. Pp. 24–33 in: Evolution as a Process. Huxley, J., *et al.*, Eds. Allen and Unwin, London.

Franzén, Å.
1955 Comparative morphological investigations into the spermiogenesis among Mollusca. Zool. Bidr. Uppsala 30:399–456.

Friedrich, H.
1935 Studien zur Morphologie, Systematik und Ökologie der Nemertinen der Kieler Bucht. Arch. Naturgesch. (N.F.) 4:293–375.

Gardiner, E. G.
1895 Early development of *Polychoerus caudatus* Mark. J. Morph. 11:155–176.

Garstang, W.
1922 The theory of recapitulation: a critical re-statement of the Biogenetic Law. J. Linn. Soc. (Zool.) 35:81–101.

Gelei, J. von
1937 Ein neues Fibrillensystem im Ectoplasma von *Paramecium;* zugleich ein Vergleich zwischen dem neuen und dem alten Gittersystem. Arch. Protistenk. 89:133–162.

1939 Ein Vergleich der Ciliaten und der Strüdelwürmer. Mém. Soc. zool. tchécosl. [Věstník českosl. zool. Společ.] 6–7:155–182. [This work has many references to von Gelei's papers on the "silver-line" system.]

Hadži, J.
1949a Problem mezoderma in celoma v luči turbelarijske teorije knidarijev. (Problems of mesoderm and coelom elucidated by the Turbellarian theory of Cnidaria). Razpr. Razred. prir. Odsek. Slov. Akad. Znan. Um., Ljubljana, 4:5–84. [In Slovenian with Russian and English summaries.]

1949b Die Ableitung der Knidarien von den Turbellarien und einige Folgerungen dieser Ableitung. C. R. XIIIe Congrès int. Zool., Paris:448–449.

1950 Upoređivanje spolne faze infuzorija sa spolnim plođenjem kod turbelarija. Rad jug. Akad. Znan. Umj. 280:31–53. [In Croatian.] [Also: A comparison of the sexual phase of infusorians with the sexual reproduction of the turbellarians. Bull. int. Acad. Yougoslav. (n.s.) 3:17–24.]

1953 An attempt to reconstruct the system of animal classification. Syst. Zool. 2:145–154.

1955 K diskusiji o novi sistematiki živalstva. (Zur Diskussion über das neue zoologische System.) Razpr. (Dissertationes) Razred. prir. Vede Slov. Akad. Znan. Um. 3:175–207. [In Slovenian with German summary.]

1958 Zur Diskussion über die Abstammung der Eumetazoen. Verh. dtsch. zool. Ges., Graz (1957) (Zool. Anz., Suppl. 21):169–179.

Haeckel, E.
  1872   Die Kalkschwämme. Eine Monographie. Reimer, Berlin.
  1874   Die Gastraea-Theorie, die phylogenetische Classification des Thierreichs
          und die Homologie der Keimblätter. Jena. Z. Naturw. 8:1–55.
  1895   Systematische Phylogenie. Reimer, Berlin.
Hanson, E. D.
  1958   On the origin of the Eumetazoa. Syst. Zool. 7:16–47.
Hargitt, C. W.
  1904   The early development of *Pennaria tiarella* McCr. Arch. EntwMech. Org.
          18:453–488.
Hartmann, M.
  1956   Die Sexualität. 2d ed. Fischer, Stuttgart.
Hofsten, N. von
  1918   Anatomie, Histologie und systematische Stellung von *Otoplana inter-
          media* du Plessis. Zool. Bidr. Uppsala 7:1–74.
Hyde, I. H.
  1894   Entwicklungsgeschichte einiger Scyphomedusen. Z. wiss. Zool. 58:531–
          565.
Hyman, L. H.
  1937   Reproductive system and copulation in *Amphiscolops langerhansi* (Tur-
          bellaria Acoela). Biol. Bull. 72:319–326.
  1940   The Invertebrates. Vol. I: Protozoa through Ctenophora. McGraw-Hill,
          New York, Toronto, London.
  1951   *Idem*. Vol. II: Platyhelminthes and Rhynchocoela—the Acoelomate
          Bilateria. McGraw-Hill, New York, Toronto, London.
Ivanov [Iwanov], A. V.
  1937   Allgemeine und vergleichende Embryologie.
Jägersten, G.
  1955   On the early phylogeny of the Metazoa. Zool. Bidr. Uppsala 30:321–354.
  1959   Further remarks on the early phylogeny of the Metazoa. *Ibid*. 33:79–108.
Klein, B. M.
  1928   Die Silberliniensysteme der Ciliaten. Weitere Resultate. Arch. Protistenk.
          62:12–260.
Korschelt, E., and K. Heider
  1890–
  1893   Lehrbuch der vergleichenden Entwicklungsgeschichte der Wirbellosen
          Thiere. Fischer, Jena.
  1902–
  1910   *Idem*. 2d ed. Fischer, Jena.
  1936   Vergleichende Entwicklungsgeschichte der Tiere. Rev. E. Korschelt.
          Fischer, Jena.
Marcus, E.
  1958   On the evolution of the animal phyla. Quart. Rev. Biol. 33:24–58.
Perkins, H. F.
  1902   The development of *Gonionema murbachii*. Proc. Acad. nat. Sci. Philad.
          54:750–790.
Reisinger, E.
  1924   Die Gattung *Rhynchoscolex*. Z. Morph. Ökol. Tiere. 1:1–37.
  1935   *Proporoplana jenseni* nov. gen. nov. spec., ein morphologisch bedeut-
          samer Turbellarientyp. In: Ergebnisse einer von E. Reisinger und O.
          Steinböck mit Hilfe des Rask-Ørsted Fonds durchgeführten Reise in
          Grönland 1926. Vidensk. Medd. dansk naturh. Foren. Kbn. 90:13–84.

Remane, A.
1929–
1933   Rotatoria. Bronn's Klass. 4, sect. 2, book I [1929. Lieferung 1:1–160;
1932, Lieferung 2:161–288; 1932, Lieferung 3:289–448; 1933, Lieferung
4:449–576].

1935–
1936   Gastrotricha und Kinorhyncha. *Ibid.* 4, sect. 2, book 2, pt. 1:1–385.
[1935, Lieferung 1:1–160; 1936, Lieferung 2:161–385.]

1950a   Porifera-Coelenterata-Vermes-Tentaculata. Handb. Biol. 6, pt. 3 [Lie-
ferungen 28/29]:97–160.

1950b   Entstehung der Metamerie der Wirbellosen. Verh. dtsch. Zoologen, Mainz
(1949) (Zool. Anz., Suppl. 14):16–23.

1954   Die Geschichte der Tiere. Pp. 340–422 in: Die Evolution der Organismen. Vol. 2. Heberer, G., Ed. 2d ed. Fischer, Stuttgart.

1960   Die Beziehungen zwischen Phylogenie und Ontogenie. Zool. Anz. 164:
306–337.

Schindewolf, O. H.
1930   Über die Symmetrieverhältnisse der Steinkorallen. Paläont. Z. 12:212–
263.

Seilern-Aspang, F.
1957   Die Entwicklung von *Macrostomum appendiculatum* (Fabricius). Zool.
Jb. (Anat.) 76:311–330.

Starck, D.
1955   Embryologie. Thieme, Stuttgart.

Steinböck, O.
1927   Monographie der Prorhynchidae (Turbellaria). Z. Morph. Ökol. Tiere
8:538–662.

1955   Regeneration azöler Turbellarien. Verh. dtsch. zool. Ges., Tübingen
(1954) (Zool. Anz., Suppl. 18):86–94.

1954–
1956   Zur Theorie der Regeneration beim Menschen. Forschungen Forscher
Tirol. Ärztesch. (Med. Fak. Univ. Innsbruck) 4:315–351.

1958a   Zur Phylogenie der Gastrotrichen. Verh. dtsch. zool. Ges., Graz (1957)
(Zool. Anz., Suppl. 21):128–169.

1958b   Schlusswort zur Diskussion Remane-Steinbock. *Ibid.* (1957):196–218.

Steinböck, O., and B. Ausserhofer
1950   Zwei grundverschiedene Entwicklungsabläufe bei einer Art (*Prorhynchus
stagnalis* M. Sch.) Turbellaria. Arch. EntwMech. Org. 144:155–177.

Steinböck, O., and E. Reisinger.
1931   *Nemertoderma bathycola* nov. gen. nov. spec. In: Ergebnisse einer von
E. Reisinger und O. Steinböck mit Hilfe des Rask-Ørsted Fonds durchgeführten zoologischen Reise in Grönland 1926. Vidensk. Medd. dansk.
naturhist. Foren. Kbn. 90:13–84.

Tuzet, O.
1949   La place des Spongiaires dans la classification. C. R. XIII Congrès intern.
Zool., Paris (1948):429–432.

Tuzet, O., R. Loubatières, and M. Pavans de Ceccatty
1952   Les cellules nerveuses de l'Éponge *Sycon raphanus* O.S. C. R. Acad. Sci.,
Paris 234:1394–1396.

Tuzet, O., and M. Pavans de Ceccatty
1953   Les cellules nerveuses et neuro-musculaires de l'Éponge: *Cliona celata*
Grant. *Ibid.* 236:2342–2344.

1955   Les lophocytes de l'Éponge *Pachymatisma johnstoni* Bow. *Ibid.* 237:
        1447–1449.

Ulrich, W.
1950   Über die systematische Stellung einer neuen Tierklasse (Pogonophora,
        K. E. Johansson) den Begriff der Archicoelomaten und die Einteilung
        der Bilaterien. S. B. dtsch. Akad. Wiss. (1949), no. 2:1–25.

Westblad, E.
1949   *Xenoturbella bocki* n. gen., n. sp., a peculiar, primitive turbellarian type.
        Ark. Zool. (ser. 2) 1:11–29.

Zakhvatkin, A. A.
1956   Vergleichende Embryologie der niederen Wirbellosen. Dtsch. Verlag.
        Wissensch., Berlin.

5 ◆ A Critique of the Enterocele Theory

WILLARD D. HARTMAN

DEPARTMENT OF BIOLOGY AND PEABODY MUSEUM OF NATURAL HISTORY,
YALE UNIVERSITY, NEW HAVEN, CONNECTICUT

Speculations on phylogenetic events not recorded in the strata of the past are useful in bringing to mind important structural relations, but they often prove incapable of providing definitive answers to the questions we like to ask. The absence or fragmentary nature of the fossil record constrains the phylogeneticist to reconstruct the early history of animal evolution on the basis of homologies of adult and developmental structures.

Remane (1956) has formulated a useful set of criteria that must be satisfied in establishing homology. In brief, the chief criteria state that homology is evidenced through (1) establishment of positional similarities, (2) demonstration of special similarities of form, and (3) existence of intermediate forms (either morphological or ontogenetic) that bridge otherwise dissimilar structures occupying different positions. The certainty of homologies based on these criteria increases with the grade of complexity of the structures. Waterman (1961) has applied Remane's criteria to physiological comparisons that provide the potentiality of adding another dimension to phylogenetic hypotheses.

At relatively low levels of organization, however, it has been argued that assumed homologies based on descriptive criteria may lead to false assumptions because of the increased likelihood that fundamentally unrelated animals may be expected to have simple structures, as Greenberg (1959) has suggested. Grimstone (1959) has also called attention to the presumptive difficulty of distinguishing, at lower levels of organization, between similarities resulting from common ancestry and those arising through independent origins. And Pantin (1951) is likewise of the opinion that we must expect organisms to arrive independently at the same solutions to common functional problems; in his view, this is because the number of possible answers is severely restricted by limitations in the number and kind of the parts and properties available in nature.

Remane (1956) is cognizant of the difficulties involved in distinguishing between homology in the evolutionary sense, and independent origin, when simple structures are compared, and he has proposed three auxiliary criteria as an aid in differentiating such cases. The probability of the homology of simple structures grows if (1) the structure in question occurs in a large number of otherwise closely related forms and (2) further similarities of like distribution occur in closely related forms; but the probability of homology decreases (3) with the frequency of the occurrence of these similarities in presumptively unrelated forms.

In this discussion of the enterocele theory I propose to state the major tenets of the hypothesis, to apply Remane's criteria for homology to them, to attempt to determine whether the homologies are more likely to give evidence of phylogenetic relationship or of convergent evolution, and to examine alternative hypotheses.

The Enterocele Theory

The enterocele theory of the origin of the body cavity of celomate animals stresses the similarity between the peripheral parts of the gastrovascular cavity of celenter-

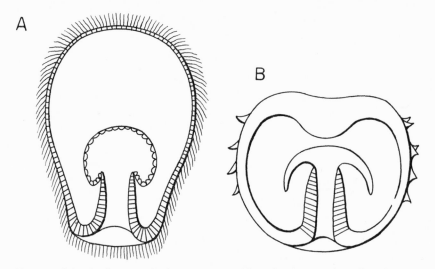

FIGURE 5-1. A. Larva of *Astropecten* with celomic pouches forming at internal end of archenteron. B. Cydippid larva with gastrovascular canals arising as outgrowths of the gastrovascular system. (After Mechnikov, 1874.)

ates (Cnidaria and Ctenophora) and the celom. All bilateral animals are regarded as celomate and as having arisen from an archicelomate ancestor, from which two lines have evolved: the Protostomia and Deuterostomia.

Early theorists[1] compared existing celenterates with celomate animals showing an enterocelous origin of the body cavities. Thus, Mechnikov (1874) pointed to the similarity in development of the echinoderms and the origin of the gastrovascular canals of ctenophores (fig. 5-1). Sedgwick (1884) believed that "all the most important organ systems of the Triploblastica are found in a rudimentary condition in the Coelenterata." He felt that the gastral pouches of medusae and the Anthozoa foreshadow the body cavities of enterocelous phyla and regarded the method of celom formation found in the Protostomia and vertebrates as an em-

---

[1] Historical details on the enterocele theory are given by Remane in chap. 6.

bryonic abbreviation of the enterocelous method. In the latter view he followed Lankester (1875), who supposed that the splitting of the mesoblast is only a delayed formation of the lumen of an enterocelous pouch.

Remane (1954) has given a more general exposition of the enterocele theory. He traces the celom back to the four gastral pockets of a radially symmetrical "Urpolyp," from which the existing classes of celenterates have also stemmed. Transformation to a celomate type required an elongation and eventual subdivision of the "Urmund" to form mouth and anus. The original four enteric pouches then took up positions along the gut as an anterior, unpaired protocele (axocele); median, paired mesoceles (hydroceles); and a posterior, unpaired metacele (somatocele). These pouches eventually pinched off from the gut; the metacele divided in two, and the celomate archetype (fig. 5-2) was achieved, with five celomic sacs.

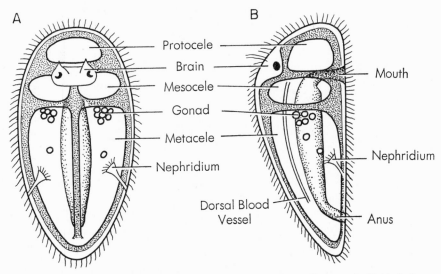

FIGURE 5-2. Remane's reconstruction of the celomate archetype. A. Dorsal view. B. Lateral view. (After Remane, 1954.)

Evidence for such an ancestral archicelomate form comes from certain similarities between the lophophorate protostomatous phyla (Phoronida, Ectoprocta, and Brachiopoda, joined by some authors to form the phylum Tentaculata) and the deuterostomatous phyla Echinodermata, Hemichordata, and Pogonophora. Hyman (1959) has noted that these two groups of phyla share a triregionated body, of which the protosome is suppressed except in hemichordates and pogonophores. The mesocele is generally separated from the metacele by a strong septum. The lophophore of phoronids, ectoprocts, and brachiopods arises from the mesosome and is provided with extensions of the mesocele, as are the tentaculate arms of pterobranchs. It is probable also that echinoderms originally had a pair of tentacle clusters bearing extensions of the mesocele. The tentacles of pogonophores, however, belong to the protosome. Articulate brachiopods share an enterocelous method of celom formation in common with the deuterostomatous phyla under consideration. Lack of cephalization further characterizes the lophophorate protostomes and the lower deuterostomes.

The phoronids resemble the echinoderms and hemichordates in having the nervous system located in an intraepithelial position. According to Silén (1954), the nerve cells and most of the fibers of phoronids are located among the bases of epidermal cells and are bounded within by a limiting membrane. Localized concentrations of cells and fibers form tracts and one of these, the circumoral ring, is closed by associative neurons. An extension of the nervous system of phoronids into the gut epithelium is, however, restricted to the ectodermal parts of the gut; the remarkable sensory system found in the esophagus and stomach of enteropneusts and echinoderms is absent in phoronids. Likewise, a celomic motor system is absent in phoronids where the muscles are innervated from motor cells situated outside the basal membrane. Thus, although in general organization of the nervous system the phoronids bear comparison with deuterostomes, there are significant differences. Silén concludes that, in regard to their nervous system, the phoronids occupy an isolated position among animals. This may be related to the fact that all the main portions of the adult phoronid nervous system arise anew following the curious metamorphosis of the larva.

In spite of many resemblances between lophophorate celomates and deuterostomes, the former have trochophore larvae and are protostomatous, in contrast to the latter phyla, which have dipleurula-like larvae and are, of course, deuterostomatous. Remane regards the lophophorate phyla as representing an early offshoot of the protostomatous line, which, in common with the deuterostomes, arose from the postulated archicelomate ancestral form.

The remainder of the protostomatous phyla are grouped by Remane as the Spiralia, since typical members share the well-known and characteristic spiral mode of determinate cleavage, with the mesoderm and endoderm arising from further division of a quartet of macromeres at the vegetal pole. The lack of segmentation and the hint of a mesocele in the tentacle apparatus of sipunculids give evidence for the simplicity of these forms, but it is impossible to say with certainty whether this simplicity is primary or secondary. Remane (1950) suggests that the metamerism of annelids is derivable from the triregionated condition in the archicelomate form (fig. 5-3) by suppression of the protocele and mesocele and constriction of the metacele into three or more larval segments, as described by Ivanov (1928). Post-larval segments of varying number are then added posteriorly from a preanal budding zone. Molluscs and arthropods also represent offshoots of the spiralian line.

One of the most controversial aspects of the theory of animal phylogeny developed by Remane is his disposition of the Platyhelminthes, Rhynchocoela, and the aschelminth complex. These groups are interpreted as celomate animals that have lost the celom secondarily. The hydrostatic functions of the celom are replaced in platyhelminths and nemertines by parenchyma and in the aschelminths by a pseudocele. The platyhelminths and nemertines clearly belong to the Spiralia, as is evidenced by the spiral cleavage patterns of their embryos and by trochophore-like larvae. Secondary simplicity of the platyhelminths is suggested by the complicated reproductive systems so widely distributed among the group. The aschelminth complex is joined to the Spiralia by way of the rotifers, which are regarded as neotenic trochophore larvae.

This, then, is an outline of the course of evolution of bilateral animals as developed by Remane (1954) and accepted by Marcus (1958).

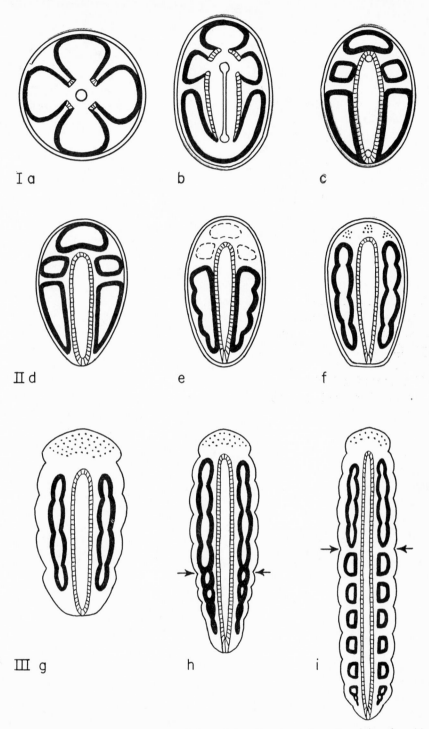

FIGURE 5-3. Remane's concept of the origin of metamerism. I. origin of archi-metamerism from a radial plan: *a*, celenterate with four gastric pouches and mouth; *b*, division of the mouth to form mouth and anus; *c*, separation of the gastric pouches to form celomic cavities. II. Origin of deuterometamerism by retrogression of protocele and mesoceles (*d-f*). III. New formation of tri-tometameres: *g*, condition found in larvae of heteronomous polychetes and crustaceans before secondary metameres appear; *h-i*, same, following appearance of secondary post-larval metameres shown posterior to the arrows. (After Remane, 1950 and 1954.)

REMANE'S CRITERIA FOR HOMOLOGY AND THE ENTEROCELE THEORY

Let us now apply Remane's (1956) criteria for descriptive homology to the enterocele theory. The characters to be compared are the epithelialized linings of the gastric pockets of cnidarians and ctenophores on the one hand and, on the other, the similar linings of the celomic pouches of larval echinoderms, hemichordates, and pogonophores. Remane's first criterion, similarity of position, is at first sight fulfilled. The gastric pockets of anthozoa and medusae, the gastrovascular canals of ctenophores, and the celomic rudiments of echinoderms, hemichordates, and pogonophores all occur as outpocketings of the gut. The gastric pockets of celenterates, however, are arranged radially around the celenteron, whereas the celomic sacs of the other groups mentioned take up a bilateral orientation on each side of the gut, with the exception of the protocele, which is preoral. Further, while it must be admitted that the development of the gastrovascular canals of ctenophores bears a resemblance to those of enterocelous celomates—in each case outpocketings of the archenteron being involved—the development of the gastric pouches of cnidarians takes place in quite another way—namely, by ingrowth of septa that secondarily subdivide the celenteron into peripheral pockets (see, for example, Gemmill, 1921).

The second criterion, the occurrence of special characteristics, is said by Remane to increase in significance with the grade of complexity and conformity of the structures being compared. Presumably the ciliated nature of the epithelia lining the pouches and the occurrence of pores to the outside represent special features of the pouches, worthy of comparison. Sedgwick (1884) and Beklemishev (1960) regard the excretory pores of cnidarians and the anal pores of ctenophores as homologs of the celomopores of celomates. Sedgwick carried the homology to an extreme in seeing a relationship between the excretory pores and gastrovascular canals of medusae and the excretory organs of annelids and vertebrates and between the subgenital pits of scyphozoa and the tracheae of arthropods. Gill slits were also traced back to pores of the gastrovascular cavity of celenterates.

Remane's third criterion states that dissimilar structures occupying different positions can be homologized if intermediate forms are demonstrable. Such intermediates may occur in the ontogeny or adult morphology of the organisms concerned. This criterion has relevance here in that the body cavities of adult echinoderms, hemichordates, and pogonophores may be related to the gastric pouches of celenterates by way of the celomic rudiments that bud off the archenteron of the larva in enterocelous celomates.

Summing up so far, we find that, on a descriptive level, a homology between the structures under discussion is supported by a similarity in position and form. The gastrovascular cavities of celenterates are pouches of the gut, as are the larval celomic sacs of the enterocelous phyla. The latter may be regarded as an intermediate stage between the former and the condition existing in adult enterocelous celomates, in which celomic sacs have separated from the gut. We have noted, however, that the positional similarity is not complete and that relatively few special characteristics reinforce the homology. Further, since cavities of common form and mode of origin are widely distributed in the animal kingdom, we must apply Remane's auxiliary criteria as well.

Remane's first auxiliary criterion states that the probability of homology increases if the structure in question occurs in a large number of otherwise closely related forms. Gastric pouches occur in all scyphozoa, anthozoa, and ctenophores. They are absent only in hydrozoa among celenterates. Similarly, celomic pouches of enterocelous origin are distributed generally among the deuterostome phyla Echinodermata, Hemichordata, and Pogonophora. The question of whether or not these two assemblages of animals are otherwise closely related is discussed further on.

According to Remane's second auxiliary criterion, the probability of the homology of simple structures grows with the presence of further similarities of similar distribution in closely related forms. The additional similarities between celenterates and enterocelous celomates mentioned by Remane (1954) include: (1) the ciliated epithelium lining the gastric pouches on the one hand and the celomic sacs on the other; (2) the excretory activities performed by the walls of each; (3) the fact that the gonads are housed in the walls of the sacs in each case; (4) the occurrence, in celenterate larvae, of an aboral sensory area, which may be homologized with the brain of certain celomates.

Pantin (1960) has pointed out further similarities between celenterates and certain enterocelous phyla.[2] Among these the most remarkable is the intraepithelial position of the nervous system. The work of Pantin and his associates (*e.g.,* Pantin, 1952) on sea anemones has demonstrated that a nerve network occurs in both ectoderm and endoderm and that a complete sensory and motor system exists in each. Nervous elements, however, are absent from the mesoglea. Two similar nerve nets exist in the Scyphozoa and *Velella*. Pantin points out the uniqueness of the two-dimensional nervous system of celenterates, but, as he notes, a close approach to it is found in echinoderms and hemichordates. The nervous system of the latter phylum is especially comparable to that of celenterates—although it even lacks the sensory discrimination and diversity of response found in some forms of the latter group. The nervous system of enteropneusts, as described by Bullock (1945), is an intraepithelial plexus of scattered sense cells, ganglion cells, fibers, and synapses separated from internal structures by a limiting membrane. Motor axons seemingly penetrate the limiting membrane to pass inwards to the muscles, but no internal concentrations of nervous tissue are known to occur. The dorsal and ventral cords and the few additional cords found represent local concentrations of fibers and neurons; but there is no evidence that these cords constitute a central nervous system. A nerve fiber layer exists in the pharynx, esophagus, and stomach, but seems to be absent in the intestine except in the posterior end of some genera. Ventral and dorsal cords may occur in the gut as well as in the epidermis. Silén (1950) has reported a diffuse, one-layered plexus of motor neurons in the ventral mesentery.

The nervous system of echinoderms is essentially like that of enteropneusts, being an intraepithelial and subepithelial plexus of primary sense cells, ganglion cells, and fibers distributed both at the base of the epidermis and in the epithelium of parts of the gut (Smith, 1937). Localized aggregations of fibers and ganglion cells form cords as in enteropneusts. The sensory and motor systems, however, are separated by a limiting membrane. In starfish the chief motor system consists

---

[2] Pantin does not draw any phylogenetic conclusions from these similarities.

of fibrillar centers in the celomic epithelium, but these communicate with the sub-epithelial plexus of the sensory system through interspaces of the limiting membrane. Thus the ectoneural system of asteroids is composed of both sensory fibers and association fibers, whereas in enteropneusts (Knight-Jones, 1952) motor functions are also incorporated into the epithelial system. This is suggested by the fact that the epidermal nervous system of *Saccoglossus* differs from that of *Marthasterias* in that the through-conduction paths of the former are superficial and the deeper fibers are irregular, whereas in the latter the deeper layers are organized into bundles and the superficial layers are irregular. Other motor nerves in asteroids occur in the epithelial wall of celomic sinuses following the hemal system and at the bases of the epithelial plexus of the ectoderm in the arms. In spite of some differences in detail, the nervous systems of hemichordates and echinoderms show a striking similarity in general organization and both are more like the nervous system of celenterates than that of any other invertebrates. In all three groups the nervous system lacks morphological centralization and lacks or has few complex sense organs.

Further similarities between celenterates and echinoderms as noted by Pantin (1960) follow. (1) A collagenous connective tissue is invaded by cells forming calcareous secretions in the Alcyonacea and echinoderms. These groups share this characteristic only with the calcareous sponges. (2) In the Anthozoa there is hydrostatic inflation of the gut from the exterior; a parallel is seen in the enteroceles of echinoderms, hemichordates, and pogonophores. The celom of protostomes is never inflated in this way, but excretes to the exterior. (3) A mesenchymal migration of genital cells occurs only among celenterates and deuterostomes. Among echinoderms and hemichordates the germ cells seem to arise from mesoderm, often from the walls of the celom, but they then migrate to the surface to form gonads with their own cavities and ducts to the exterior. This is in striking contrast to the association of the gonads with the celom in protostomes. (4) Finally Pantin, like Sedgwick (1884) and Beklemishev (1960), points to the openings from the gut to the exterior in both celenterates and deuterostomes. The marginal pores of the Scyphozoa, the cinclides and terminal pores of tentacles and base in the Anthozoa, and the anal pores of the Ctenophora are compared to the gill slits and intestinal pores of the Hemichordata and the celomoducts of the celomates in general.

The third auxiliary criterion suggested by Remane states that the probability of homology of characters decreases with the frequency of their occurrence in certain unrelated forms. It seems to me that each of the similarities cited by Remane in support of the enterocele theory may be criticized in this light. First, cavitation is a common phenomenon in the ontogeny of animals. Such diverse structures as the archenteron, celomic cavities, neural tubes, lenses, otocysts, and various glands and sensory structures among invertebrates all form by identical methods: infolding or outpocketing of epithelial sheets, or secondary cavitation. Furthermore, the method of formation in specific instances is subject to regulation under experimental conditions. Thus Townes and Holtfreter (1955) have shown that a neurocele may form by secondary cavitation as well as by infolding; Hörstadius (1928) has shown that celomic sacs in *Astropecten* may form by secondary cavitation within a mass of mesenchyme cells (fig. 5-4, B, C) following sagittal sectioning of the larva; Runnström (1925) has shown that the celomic rudiments may regenerate from ectoderm in *Paracentrotus* (fig. 5-4, A). If enveloping tissues are present, hydrostatic inflation of cavities may occur in a wide variety of epithelia or tissue masses.

Since cavity formation is widespread in the development of animals, occurs in a limited number of ways, and is subject to considerable regulation under experimental conditions, it is necessary to consider seriously the possibility of convergence in the development of the gastric pouches of celenterates and the body cavities of celomate animals. Remane's criterion of similarity of position fails to make the homology more certain. No intermediate forms connect the celenterates with radially arranged gastric pockets and the celomates with bilaterally arranged celomic cavities. Such an alteration in polarity is supposed to be related to the elongation of the mouth apparent in the Anthozoa and Ctenophora, with its even-

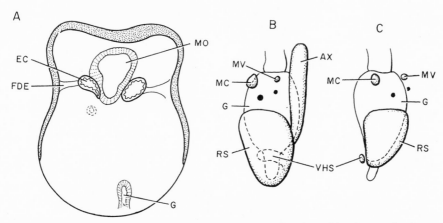

FIGURE 5-4. Regulatory formation of celomic pouches in echinoderms. A: Larva of *Paracentrotus lividus* following exposure to potassium-free sea water, showing celomic rudiments forming from ectoderm. EC, ectodermal celomic rudiment; FDE, dorsal ectoderm folding inward; G, gut rudiment; MO, mouth opening. (After Runnström, 1925.) B,C: Celom formation in right halves of sagittally sectioned embryos of *Astropecten aurantiacus*. (B, dorsal view; C, view from left side.) AX, axocele; G, gut rudiment; MC, mesenchymal celomic rudiment; MV, mesenchymal madreporic vesicle; RS, right somatocele; VHS, ventral horn of right somatocele. (After Hörstadius, 1928.)

tual subdivision into mouth and anus to form the hypothetical archicelomate. As Pantin (1960) has pointed out, however, the elongation of mouth and pharynx in sea anemones may be explained on a functional basis as a valve for retaining sea water within the celenteron. Thus the bilateral or biradial symmetry among the Anthozoa may well be secondary and of an origin quite independent of the bilaterality of celomate groups.

We may also point out the sporadic occurrence of enterocelous methods of celom formation among diverse animal groups. The chetognaths exhibit this method of celom formation, but are otherwise very different from deuterostomes. Tardigrades have body cavities of enterocelous origin, but otherwise show relationships to the Onychophora. Articulate brachiopods have an enterocelous type of celom formation, although in other structures this group of lophophorate celomates is least like the deuterostomes of the three phyla of this assemblage. Early reports of enterocely in the gastropod *Paludina* have been shown to be erroneous (Raven, 1958).

The fact that in both celenterates and deuterostomes the gastric pouches are lined by ciliated epithelium is unlikely to constitute evidence of homology, in view of the widespread occurrence of ciliated cavities among animals.

The excretory functions performed by cells lining the gastric pouches of celenterates and the body cavities of enterocelous celomates seem to be of little significance in establishing homology, since the gut may perform this function in a wide variety of animals, including entoprocts, nematomorphs, and some nematodes, annelids, and arthropods.

The fact that the gonads of both anthozoa and ctenophores lie in the walls of the gastric pouches and discharge their products into the pouches actually differentiates them from echinoderms and hemichordates, in which the gonads open directly to the outside. A more cogent comparison here is the similar migration of the germ cells through the mesenchyme in the groups being compared, as Pantin (1960) has pointed out.

Aboral sensory areas are widely distributed among pelagic larvae and usually contribute to the nervous system of the adult; however, in echinoderms and hemichordates, which really lack a central nervous system, such concentrations of nervous tissue as do occur in the adult actually develop quite independently of the larval sensory areas.

On the basis of this application of Remane's criteria of descriptive homology to his arguments in favor of the enterocele theory, we may conclude that, although similarities do exist, these concern characteristics at a simple level of organization that are distributed widely among animals. The problem of distinguishing between genetic relationship and convergence is therefore difficult. Some of the similarities suggested by Pantin are less open to attack on this point. Intraepithelial nervous systems are restricted to celenterates, nonchordate deuterostomes, and phoronids among lophophorate celomates. Hydrostatic inflation from the exterior, as in anthozoa and some deuterostomes, contrasts sharply with the celom of protostomes, which secretes to the exterior. Cells secreting calcareous skeletal elements in a matrix of collagen are found only in sponges, aside from octocorals and echinoderms. The mesenchymal migration of germ cells characteristic of celenterates and echinoderms leads to a new gonadal cavity, opening to the exterior, in the latter; while in protostomes the celom serves as a gonadal cavity.

THE FUNCTION OF THE CELOM

Celomic cavities as well as gastric pouches of anthozoa function chiefly as hydrostatic skeletons. Chapman (1958) has described the general similarity of hydrostatic skeletons in diverse animals, pointing out that they provide a fluid mechanism by which the several parts of the body musculature can be antagonized. In animals of cylindrical form, whether they are sea anemones, annelids, sipunculids, or sea cucumbers, in all of which there is no bulk movement of fluid from one part of the system to another, arrangement of the muscles into circular and longitudinal components is a universal feature. A similar condition exists among the flatworms and nemertines, where the parenchyma, with its fluid-filled spaces of limited extent, and the gut contents serve to antagonize the muscles. Special conditions exist among other animals. Thus in the Scyphozoa the subumbrellar circular muscles are antagonized by the elasticity of the mesoglea. In ctenophores, if a system of meridional and latitudinal muscles antagonized by the mesoglea were present, it would exert pressure on the gastrovascular system and inhibit feeding. Instead, there exists a series of radial muscles operating in antagonism to unique looped muscles in such a way that the gastrovascular system is freed from compression. Among ectoprocts, which are often provided with rigid, box-like skeletons, several different hydrostatic mechanisms have evolved to provide for eversion and contraction of the lophophore. In the water vascular system of echinoderms there is movement of fluid from one part of the system to another, and here the longitudinal and circular muscles are localized in the tube feet and ampullae respectively.

For the purposes of our present discussion it is sufficient to note the occurrence of a common plan of antagonistic longitudinal and circular muscles associated with the hydrostatic skeleton of diverse animals of cylindrical shape, and the departures from this plan in certain instances to meet special functional problems. The fact that animals of cylindrical shape but of diverse relationship have arrived at a common type of hydrostatic skeleton suggests that this plan has developed independently several times during the course of evolution and casts doubt on a phylogenetic interpretation of the observed descriptive homologies.

Pantin (1960) has emphasized the significance of the two-dimensional nature of the muscular system of the Cnidaria, a plan that differentiates this group functionally from bilateral metazoa. The entire muscular system of a sea anemone is located in the ectoderm and endoderm and is based upon a two-dimensional network of muscle fibers attached only to the outer surface of the mesoglea. The cell body may or may not extend to the surface of the epithelium concerned. Even when the muscle sheet is folded to form the retractors or the marginal sphincter, the epithelium is carried with it, and the two-dimensional network is retained in sharp contradistinction to triploblastic animals, the muscles of which are built up of three-dimensionally packed fibers and give a greater flexibility of movement. It must be conceded that a mesenchymal muscle system could have been added to the celenterate mesogleal plan during the course of evolution. Indeed, the ctenophores constitute an intermediate group in this regard, although it is uncertain whether their mesenchyme is ectodermal or endodermal in origin.

A further peculiarity of the muscular system of sea anemones is the spatial separation of the longitudinal and circular fibers. The former are found only in the mesenteries, whereas the latter occur in the column wall (Batham and Pantin, 1951). This arrangement, which facilitates rapid retraction of the disc, is unique among animals with a comparable hydrostatic mechanism.

EVALUATION OF THE DESCRIPTIVE DATA

Having explored a series of descriptive homologies between celenterates and the deuterostomatous phyla, we are in a position to evaluate the data for their significance in formulating evolutionary hypotheses. The difficulties involved in the transition from descriptive to explanatory comparisons in this instance may be appreciated when it is recognized that both the celenterates and the echinoderms have had an independent history since Pre-Cambrian times. Hydrozoa and scyphozoa are known through scattered fossil remains as far back as the Cambrian period; medusae have been reported from Pre-Cambrian strata. The Anthozoa are known from the Ordovician, at least. The report by Glaessner and Daily (1959) of a Pre-Cambrian octocoral is highly questionable. The fossil record of echinoderms also extends back into Cambrian time.

The certain fossil history of the hemichordates begins with remains of an Upper Cretaceous pterobranch. Many authors also accept an affinity between certain graptolites and pterobranchs; if correct, this would project the known history of the Hemichordata back to the Cambrian as well.

Our analysis of the descriptive homologies between the groups in question suggests a relationship chiefly on the basis of the structure of the gut pouches and their associated special characteristics, and of the level of organization of the adult nervous system. Do these characters give evidence of genetic continuity between the celenterates and deuterostomes by way of a hypothetical intermediate form at some remote time in the past? Or are they simply examples of convergent evolution?

Considering, first of all, the possibility that the gastric pouches of celenterates are forerunners of the celom, we have already noted the widespread distribution of cavities among animals and their common modes of formation through hydrostatic dilatation of epithelia or mesenchymal masses. Picken (1960) points out that the capacity of celomic cavities for regulatory regeneration suggests that they are not the discrete morphological entities for which phylogeneticists hope. Following experimental removal of the celomic cavities from embryos of echinoderms, new rudiments may develop from ectoderm, mesenchyme, or endoderm (Hörstadius, 1928, 1939; Runnström, 1925). Picken concludes that "it must be accepted as a minimal datum that individual cells are empowered to associate and form coherent cell layers, which may in turn form vesicles; the movement of coherent sheets is but one mode of morphogenesis." The erratic distribution of enterocely among animal phyla bears out the insignificance of the method used to achieve the final result, a body cavity.

We have also noted the wide distribution, among animals, of hydrostatic mechanisms acting in antagonism to the body musculature. Animals of diverse relationship have comparable arrangements of muscles operating against fluid-filled cavities. Developmental and physiological data thus lead us to conclude that a convergent evolution of the cavities of celenterates and deuterostomes is highly probable. Support for a phylogenetic interpretation of the data must come from a detailed comparison of special characteristics. The ciliated epithelia lining the cavities and the presence of pores from the cavities to the exterior are characters cited in support of a phylogenetic relationship between the groups. The first may be passed by as being nonspecific and hence without significance. The second bears further examination. Do the cinclides, excretory pores, and anal pores of cnidarians and ctenophores bear a phylogenetic relationship to the celomopores and gill slits of deuterostomes? Insofar as they represent evaginations of the gastrovascular system on the one hand and of the celomic pouches or gut on the other, these structures are comparable. (Cinclides are formed as either ectodermal invaginations or endodermal evaginations, according to Stephenson, 1928.) Also, in all cases the openings serve for the passage of water or other materials from the interior to the outside. A strong case can be made, however, that these structures are homoplastic, and at best we may say that they do not contradict the enterocele theory.

Pantin (1960) has made the interesting observation that the hydrostatic mechanism of anthozoa, echinoderms, and hemichordates is inflated from the exterior in
all cases. But this functional similarity is not borne out on a morphological level,
since the hydrostatic inflation of anthozoa takes place through the mouth and
pharynx, whereas, in the other two groups, celomopores are the site of intake of
water.

In summary, we may conclude that, although it is possible to ascribe a phylogenetic significance to the descriptive homologies between the cavities in question,
it is highly probable that the resemblances are owing to convergence, on the basis
of the arguments put forward here. Yet, the descriptive homologies do not contradict
the enterocele theory, and we must consider further evidence.

Turning now to the resemblance in the adult nervous system among celenterates,
echinoderms, and hemichordates, we have noted its intraepithelial position in all
these groups, the absence of concentrations of nervous tissue in a subepithelial
position, the absence of morphological centralization of the nervous system, and
the scarcity of complex sense organs. The nervous systems of these groups of
animals thus share a common plan of organization, although differences in detailed
structure do exist, as already mentioned. There is no reason to doubt that the
nervous systems in these groups are basically primitive and not secondarily simplified, in spite of the sessile or sluggish nature of the animals, since a comparable
simplification of the nervous system is not apparent in other animals of similar
habits (except for the phoronids, as mentioned). But that these primitive systems
are related phylogenetically must remain open to question, since the detailed resemblance that would allow an unequivocal evolutionary interpretation of the
homologies is lacking.

The secretion of calcareous skeletal elements in a matrix of collagen by cells of
octocorals, on the one hand, and of echinoderms, on the other, can be interpreted
in a convergent sense as easily as in one denoting common phylogenetic origin. The
mesenchymal migration of germ cells is similar in celenterates and echinoderms,
but the end result of the migration differs, for in celenterates the gonads develop in
the walls of the gastrovascular cavity, into which they free their products, and in
the echinoderms they take up a position away from the gut and open directly to
the outside.

In evaluating the descriptive homologies between celenterates and deuterostomes
we find that some of the characters have a high probability of being convergent
and that others can be interpreted as being either convergent or significant of
phylogenetic affinity. In no case is it possible to establish a homology firmly in an
evolutionary sense. We must conclude that, although interesting structural and
functional comparisons can be made between the groups, a close phylogenetic relationship between them is improbable on present evidence.

Primary and Secondary Segmentation

It should be pointed out that an important link in Remane's (1954) account of the
phylogeny of celomate animals has been shown to be highly questionable. In relating the protostomes to an archicelomate ancestor, Remane has cited Ivanov's (1928,
1944) hypothesis of the independent origin of primary and secondary segments

in annelids and arthropods. In this way Remane has been able to compare the metacele of the archicelomate form to the primary segments of annelids and to argue that elongation of the latter forms is a secondary condition. Anderson's (1959) study of the development of *Scoloplos armiger,* however, has led him to regard the successional formation of segments in annelids as primitive, a conclusion that Manton (1949) had reached earlier from her studies of the Onychophora and Crustacea. Anderson found that every trunk segment in *Scoloplos* contains a pair of 4d mesodermal somites and that these develop in strict succession, the mesoderm segmenting before the ectoderm. The same condition holds in *Arenicola cristata,* and Anderson believes that further investigation of polychete development will confirm that this is the primitive mode of segment formation in polychetes generally. Heteronomy, involving the development of primary segments that show simultaneous ectodermal and mesodermal determination of their segmentation, has been demonstrated unequivocally only in the Serpulidae and Nereidae, where it may be interpreted as an adaptive response to a planktonic larval life much as in crustaceans where the naupliar segments may arise in a different manner from the post-naupliar ones (Manton, 1928).

Eupomatus, the polychete studied by Ivanov, has little yolk in the egg and has a planktonic larva in which ability to feed at an early stage of development is a functional necessity; thus the appearance of primary segments is related to the rapid development of functional segmental larval organs of ectodermal origin. Other serpulids with yolky eggs and lecithotrophic larvae likewise show a development of three primary segments even though these are now functionally unnecessary. An analogous condition exists in the Crustacea (Manton, 1928). Anderson argued that, if Ivanov's assumption of the primitiveness of polychetes with three primary segments is correct, some trace of these segments will be apparent in the development of all polychetes. *Scoloplos,* with lecithotrophic larvae, shows no trace of primary and secondary segmentation.

Manton (1949) has remarked that "a larva with primary segments only does not represent an adult ancestor with few segments, but only the larva of an ancestor, and the formation of a post-trochophore by secondary metamerism does not necessarily represent the phylogenetic origin of a many-segmented animal from one with few segments. These ontogenetic stages can only represent phases in the ontogeny of the ancestral line. Many larval features have no phylogenetic significance and may be interpreted as specializations correlated with larval habits of life. Thus processes appertaining primarily to larval developments need very cautious interpretation." She offered two approaches to an understanding of primary and secondary metamerism: (1) that the primary segments appear in association with precociously developed ectodermal structures essential to larval existence, and (2) that the first-formed ectoderm and mesoderm of a larva may be sufficient to supply only the anterior segments essential to early larval life, but that the formation of posterior segments may require new ectoderm and mesoderm which arise together from a growth zone. Manton has also pointed out that an increase in yolk content of the eggs of malacostracan crustaceans does not lead to an obliteration of primary and secondary metamerism, in spite of the absence of a functional need for it in forms in which the early larvae are suppressed. She suggests that the general occurrence of heteronomy, at least of the mesoderm in arthropods, is correlated with the possession at some phylogenetic stage of specialized larvae that were characterized by primary and secondary metamerism to meet larval functional needs. Since the Onychophora show a successional formation of somites from anterior to posterior end, with no evidence of heteronomy, she concluded that specialized larvae were absent from their ancestors and that the absence of primary and secondary metamerism is primitive.

According to the data presented by these authors, Remane's argument for relating protostomes to his celomate archetype is based on a secondary adaptive condition occurring in certain polychetes and crustaceans and therefore is of questionable phylogenetic significance.

Alternative Hypotheses

The most widely held alternative hypothesis of the origin of the celom is the gonocele theory originally suggested by Hatschek (1878). As restated by Goodrich (1945), this theory holds that the paired celomic sacs have been derived from the paired gonadal sacs or genital follicles found in flatworms, nemertines, rotifers, etc. The epithelial covering of these sacs eventually grew faster than the gonad itself and formed a fluid-filled cavity that acquired excretory and hydrostatic functions. The development of metameric segmentation is regarded as an adaptation to rapid movement and is related to the regular repetition of organs already apparent in flatworms and nemertines. The origin of the celom is thus linked with the origin of segmentation in the gonocele theory. But this is consequently difficult to apply to the lower deuterostomes and lophophorate phyla, for there is no evidence that the latter animal groups were derived from forms with a well-developed metameric segmentation; on the contrary, the triregionated condition found among them seems to be primitive.

Another major criticism of the theory is that the germ cells of celomates frequently arise quite independently of the celomic linings and only secondarily become associated with the celom. This is true even among annelids (Davydov, 1959), in which, if the gonocele theory were valid, one would expect a closer parallel to the condition in flatworms and nemertines. In the polychete genus *Spio* the germ cells appear precociously in the trochophore independently of the mesoderm bands (Ivanov, 1928) and later migrate posteriorly to become associated with the celomic cavities of post-larval segments. In polyclads with entolecithal development, on the other hand, the gonads seem to be derived from descendants of the mesentoblast (Hyman, 1951). Goodrich (1945) does not feel that this objection is fatal to the gonocele theory, however, since the germ cells in polychetes and other celomate phyla do finally take up a position in the wall of the celomic cavity, which he persists in regarding as a gonadal sac. He states further that the gonocele theory is in harmony with the view that the "celomesoderm" gives rise to the gonads; but Ivanov's studies of annelid development are in direct opposition to this generalization. Hyman (1951) questions the significance of the linear arrangement of gonads among certain turbellarians. She points out that the gonads in these forms develop after intestinal branches have formed and that the only space left for the former is that between the intestinal branches. Hence it is more probable that the linear arrangement of gonads in a turbellarian and the similar array of celomic pouches in an annelid represent convergent developments than that they represent characters of phylogenetic significance.

Several authors have attempted to unite the enterocele and gonocele theories into a unified concept. For example, Jägersten (1956) derives all metazoa from an imagined creature, the *bilaterogastrea,* a ciliated benthonic form with bilateral symmetry, a brain, epitheliomuscular cells, an elongate mouth, an intestine, and paired gonads. Following the development of three pairs of intestinal pouches in which the gonads become localized, such a postulated form can serve as an ancestor for both the celenterates and the celomates. The Cnidaria are derived from the bilaterogastrea by way of an octocoral-like solitary polyp that lacked a skeleton and was provided with eight tentacles and eight septa, six of which bore gonads. Jägersten strongly emphasizes the primitive features of the Anthozoa and insists that the Cnidaria are basically bilateral in symmetry. It is, however, difficult to imagine how the perfect radial symmetry of most of the Hydrozoa and Scyphozoa can have evolved by way of a bilateral ancestor without evidencing any traces of this heritage. It seems more likely that the bilateral symmetry of the Anthozoa is a secondary functional adaptation associated with the hydrostatic skeleton of these animals. As Pantin (1960) has pointed out, the sleeve-like pharynx of sea anemones acts as a valve to retain sea water and, "since the sleeve necessarily collapses laterally under pressure, an axis of bi-radial symmetry can become almost inevitable." Given a biradial pharynx, a similar arrangement of the septa would also seem to be inevitable, since the primary septal muscular elements are the transverse muscle sheets that serve for opening the mouth to admit food and for controlling the water-volume of the body. The retractor muscles associated with the septa have evolved within the Anthozoa, as is suggested by their absence or weak development in primitive actiniarians and in cerianthids.

The bilaterogastrea is readily transformed into a protocelomate through (1) subdivision of the elongate mouth into mouth and anus by a median fusion of the free margins, (2) separation of the three pairs of gonad-sheltering intestinal pouches from the gut, and (3) the connection of the pouches to the exterior by way of celomoducts. Jägersten's theory thus arrives at the same end point as Remane's version of the enterocele theory and unites with this hypothesis a modified interpretation of the gonocele theory. It removes the difficulty faced by Remane, who has to postulate a secondary subdivision of the somatocele, and it separates the origin of the celomic pouches from the origin of annelid-like metamerism, in contrast to the gonocele theory. Yet, it must be remembered that the creature conjured up by Jägersten to enable the enterocele and gonocele theories to coexist "lies in the realm of fantasy," to borrow one of Hyman's pithy phrases.

Beklemishev (1960) has also pointed out that altered versions of the enterocele and gonocele theories may be united, since the peripheral parts of the gastrovascular systems of the Anthozoa and Ctenophora house the gonads, as do the celomic cavities of celomates. He regards the Deuterostomia as animals having a level of organization comparable to that of the Ctenophora, as evidenced by the epithelialization of the peripheral parts of the endoderm and mesoderm (phagocytoblast of Beklemishev) and by the similar organization of the nervous system. Beklemishev notes that in annelids and molluscs the mesoderm is set aside precociously as the 4d cell by consequence of determinate cleavage. Since the 4d cell has an origin in common with the endoderm in these forms, the development of the celom in annelids and molluscs may be compared to that in deuterostomes.

Nevertheless, Beklemishev regards the origin of the celom of annelids, arthropods, and molluscs, on the one hand, and of deuterostomes, on the other, as homoplastic rather than homophyletic. He sets forth the hypothesis that the several groups of Bilateria derived independently from celenterates at different levels of organization. The Scolecida (Platyhelminthes, Mesozoa, Rhynchocoela, Acanthocephala, and the aschelminth complex) arose from celenterates with histological differentiation at the level of the planula, without an epithelialized gut and with nervous elements restricted to the ectoderm. The Priapulida are the only representatives of this group with a celom, and this has presumably arisen independently of the celom of all other animals, according to Beklemishev (see also Shapeero, 1961). The Trochozoa (Mollusca, Annelida, Arthropoda, Sipunculoida, and Entoprocta) arose from celenterates with an epithelialized central but nonepithelialized peripheral phagocytoblast and without nervous elements to the phagocytoblast. The Deuterostomia (Echinodermata, Pogonophora, Hemichordata, and Chordata) stemmed from celenterates at the level of the existing Anthozoa and Ctenophora with an epithelialized central and peripheral phagocytoblast. The echinoderms and hemichordates have nervous elements associated with the ectoderm, gut, and celomic epithelia. The Actinotrochozoa (Phoronida and Ectoprocta), and presumably also the brachiopods, have most probably developed a celom independently of all these groups, according to Beklemishev.

Beklemishev's views fail to explain the common occurrence of trochophore-like larvae among Scolecida and Trochozoa; his derivation of deuterostomes from celenterates with an organization like the Anthozoa and Ctenophora is open to the same criticisms as are other versions of the enterocele theory.

Lemche (1960) has revived a version of the cyclomerism theory of Sedgwick (1884) and Lang (1904), in which he proposes that the celenterates, flatworms, and the higher Spiralia may have arisen from a common Pre-Cambrian ancestor. His evidence is based in part on the fossil record. Through a comparison of the biradial arrangement of the septa of tetracorals with the radiating, septum-like muscle-scars of monoplacophorans, he has concluded that metamerism originated gradually from cyclomerism. According to Lemche, the monoplacophorans show an approach to teloblastic growth through a slight differentiation between an anterior region and a main, posterior one. The similarities in septal arrangement, as well as his comparisons between the musculature of cnidarians and the Spiralia, are more plausibly interpretable as convergences than as homologies.

Vandebroek (1952) has placed emphasis on early morphogenetic factors in the embryo in espousing still another variation of Sedgwick's version of the enterocele theory. He describes three methods of closure of the blastopore among the Metazoa: (1) gastroraphy, characteristic of protostomes, in which blastopore closure takes place by the medial union of two lateral lips, leaving mouth and anus as persistent openings; (2) nototeny, characteristic of chordates, in which the blastopore closes by an elongation of the dorsal lip; and (3) isochily, found in echinoderms and enteropneusts, in which the blastopore closes by equal ingrowth from all sides. Vandebroek argues that the protostomes and chordates have arisen from a common ancestral stock. Their celomic pouches are homologous, since their mesoblastic rudiments are situated on either side of the blastopore in the advanced gastrula stage and give rise to a large number of metameres. Although the nervous systems of the two groups are not homologous, they have a periblastoporal origin in both instances, and the adult system in each is longitudinal. These common characteristics of the nervous systems of protostomes and chordates have led Vandebroek to unite these groups as the Tenoneuria, which must be set off from the Cycloneuria—the echinoderms, hemichordates, and chetognaths—which have a basically annular disposition of the nervous system. In the enteropneusts, for example, the first appearance of the nervous system is in the form of diffuse rudiments in the proboscis and collar, at the base of each of which transverse nerve rings soon develop. The dorsal and ventral cords develop later. The first neural structures are thus far removed from the blastopore, in contrast to the situation in the Tenoneuria. The developing nervous system of enteropneusts does not arise as a result of induction by underlying tissues. An isolated pregastrular animal half of an enteropneust can acquire a triregionated form and nervous elements in the proboscis, in the total absence of mesoblast and endoblast, according to Vandebroek. In amphibians an isolated pregastrular animal half fails to develop a nervous system.

Vandebroek reinforces his arguments in favor of a wide gap between Tenoneuria and Cycloneuria by citing basic differences in the morphogenesis of the embryos in the two groups. He points out that in echinoids two cortical polar gradients are the chief factors influencing early morphogenesis, while in *Tubifex* and in amphibians, taken as examples of the Tenoneuria, a deep plasmo-vitelline gradient with its center at the vegetal pole exists, coupled with a second deep gradient in *Tubifex* and a dorsal cortical gradient in amphibians.

With these differences in mind, Vandebroek has traced the Tenoneuria and Cycloneuria back to different groups of cnidarians. He regards the cerianthids as the most likely ancestors of the Tenoneuria, thus following the theory of Sedgwick as developed by van Beneden (1891), in which the gastric pouches of these anthozoa are homologized with the celomic sacs of onychophorans and cephalochordates. He derived the Cycloneuria from a medusoid form, swimming with its blastoporal surface downward, and with the nervous system developed far from the mouth. He envisaged such a creature as having elongated along the oral-aboral axis and as having developed a new mouth. The change in proportions would have brought the basitentacular nerve fibers into the peculiar annular position that they occupy in enteropneusts. The only factual basis for such a remarkable transformation is the common occurrence of a diffuse nervous system in cnidarians, echinoderms, and enteropneusts, and the occurrence of isochily in certain cnidarians that gastrulate by invagination.

Vandebroek's theory is of interest in that it brings to bear on phylogenetic questions the hypotheses of certain embryologists about the basic factors involved in early morphogenesis. In supporting a closer relationship between echinoderms and hemichordates than between the latter and chordates, he reinforces a conclusion based on larval similarities and on the simple level of organization of the nervous system in the first-mentioned groups. In using such similarities to divorce these organisms widely from the chordates, he overlooks the detailed similarity between the gill slits of hemichordates and those of cephalochordates, structures that must be assumed to be convergent if his theory is accepted. The different methods of blastopore closure described by Vandebroek seem readily derivable from one another by differential growth processes. An intermediate condition between isochily and nototeny is seen in the closure of the blastopore of the cephalochordates, where ingrowth occurs around the entire perimeter of the blastopore, although ingrowth of the anterior lip is somewhat precocious and more extensive. A transformation from a medusoid form to an enteropneust, as postulated by Vandebroek, seems highly improbable, and the derivation of other celomates from cerianthids is open to the same criticisms as is Remane's account of the enterocele theory.

Ziegler's (1898) theory that the celom represents the expanded inner end of a nephridium finds little support today. Not only does it fail to account for the celom in enterocelous forms, but species-specific differences in the ontogeny of nephridia among annelids (*e.g.,* ectodermal in *Pheretima,* mesodermal in *Tubifex*) fail to give consistent support to the theory on the basis of present evidence. Ziegler pointed out that active mesenchyme formation occurs at the inner end of the archenteron in *Antedon,* echinoids, and certain ophiuroids. This suggested to him that the celomic cavities of echinoderms may have been formed originally through the appearance of a cavity in a mass of mesenchyme cells. The enterocelous method of celom formation might have resulted from a delayed separation of mesenchyme cells from the archenteron, and the enterocele would then be cenogenetic. As evidence of this he cited the example of *Ophiothrix fragilis,* in which two small compact masses of cells separate from the endoderm, and cavities form in these secondarily. He admitted, however, that this can be interpreted as a reduced type of enterocely rather than the reverse, although the former interpretation is fatal to his theory.

A variant of the nephrocele theory has been suggested by Faussek (1899), who regarded the celom as an excretory space that appears in the embryo to meet the needs of the developing organism. This hypothesis is in turn related to the schizocele theory, in which the celom is regarded as a new formation in the phylogeny of animals. Instead of being related to the gonads of flatworms or the gastric pouches of celenterates, celom formation is interpreted as involving the appearance of a series of spaces in the mesenchyme as a result of the accumulation of fluid. Such a mode of formation of the celom is seen only in phoronids among existing animals.

Such a theory is attractive in divorcing the origin of the celom from questionable precursors and treating it rather as a new structure developed to meet the need of bilateral animals for a hydrostatic skeleton that could also serve excretory functions and to provide a suitable site for the development of the germ cells. It is perhaps significant that it is the phoronids that exhibit a mesenchymal origin of the celom. These animals seem to be an early offshoot of the protostome line, and they share the triregionation of the lower deuterostomes, on the one hand, and a trochophore-like larva of the protostomes, on the other. Their relatives, the brachiopods, exhibit both enterocely and schizocely, although among inarticulates the mesoblast cells proliferate from the lateral walls of the archenteron (Yatsu, 1902) and celom formation in these forms may be regarded as a delayed type of enterocely. The brachiopods suggest how closely related schizocely and enterocely are during early developmental stages. There need only be a still earlier segregation of presumptive mesoderm in the form of a 4d cell to relate the schizocely of annelids and allied protostomes to the retarded separation of the mesoderm seen among echinoderms, hemichordates, and pogonophores. Under experimental conditions cavity formation by the outpocketing of epithelial sheets or by secondary cavitation of cell masses is often interchangeable. This leads us to a vital point: for the foregoing reasons it should not be surprising to find an erratic scattering of enterocely and schizocely among the animal phyla in spite of the general tendency of lower deuterostomes to be enterocelous and of protostomes to be schizocelous.

Conclusion

I have attempted to restrict this discussion to data provided by existing animals. On the basis of descriptive and experimental embryology it is apparent that the several types of celom formation are rather closely related. More or less precocious separation of the mesoderm from the endoderm during development can lead to schizocely or enterocely. The lophophorate celomates, with their flexibility in methods of celom formation, their deuterostome-like body regionation, and their protostome-like embryos, exhibit a level of organization intermediate between the two main lines of celomate animals. Yet their lack of cephalization suggests that they too are also secondarily modified—for a sedentary existence, as Hyman (1959) has pointed out. There is no direct evidence of their exact ancestry.

I am inclined to agree with Hyman (1959) when she says that questions as to the origin of the Bilateria and as to which mode of celom formation is primitive are unanswerable on the basis of present information. This is not surprising in view of the fragmentary nature of the fossil record of the early history of the Metazoa and in view of the difficulty in distinguishing between convergence and hereditary relationship when simple levels of organization are under discussion. Specific theories of the origin of the celom on the basis of current knowledge may be useful in highlighting important structural and functional affinities, but they fail to provide a definitive answer to the question at the present time. A more fertile approach to the problem would seem to lie in still more penetrating studies of the development and physiology of the celom, since the details of Pre-Cambrian evolution may never be known to us.

REFERENCES

Anderson, D. T.
   1959   The embryology of the polychaete *Scoloplos armiger*. Quart. J. micr. Sci. 100:89–166.
Batham, E. J., and C. F. A. Pantin
   1951   The organization of the muscular system of *Metridium senile*. *Ibid*. 92: 27–54.
Beklemishev, V. N. [Beklemischev, W. N.]
   1960   Grundlagen der vergleichenden Anatomie der Wirbellosen. Vol. II. Dtsch. Verlag Wissensch., Berlin.
Beneden, É. van
   1891   Recherches sur le développement des *Arachnactis*. Arch. Biol. 11:115–146.
Bullock, T. H.
   1945   The anatomical organization of the nervous system of Enteropneusta. Quart. J. micr. Sci. 86:55–111.

Chapman, G.
   1958   The hydrostatic skeleton in the invertebrates. Biol. Rev. 33:338–371.
Davydov, K. N. [Dawydoff, C.]
   1959   Ontogenèse des Annélides. Traité Zool. 5, fasc. 1:594–686.
Faussek, V.
   1899   Über die physiologische Bedeutung des Coeloms. Trav. Soc. Nat. St.-
             Pétersb. [Leningr.] 30:83–84.
Gemmill, J. F.
   1921   The development of the sea anemone *Bolocera tuediae* (Johnst.). Quart.
             J. micr. Sci. 65:577–587.
Glaessner, M. F., and B. Daily
   1959   The geology and late Precambrian fauna of the Ediacara Fossil Reserve.
             Rec. S. Aust. Mus. 13:369–401.
Goodrich, E. S.
   1945   The study of nephridia and genital ducts since 1895. Quart. J. micr. Sci.
             86:113–392.
Greenberg, M. J.
   1959   Ancestors, embryos, and symmetry. Syst. Zool. 8:212–221.
Grimstone, A. V.
   1959   Cytology, homology, and phylogeny—a note on "organic design." Amer.
             Nat. 93:273–282.
Hatschek, B.
   1878   Studien über Entwicklungsgeschichte der Anneliden. Ein Beitrag zur
             Morphologie der Bilaterien. Arb. zool. Inst. Univ. Wien 1:1–128.
Hörstadius, S.
   1928   Über die Determination des Keimes bei Echinodermen. Acta zool., Stockh.
             9:1–191.
   1939   The mechanics of sea urchin development, studied by operative methods.
             Biol. Rev. 14:132–179.
Hyman, L. H.
   1951   The Invertebrates. Vol. II: Platyhelminthes and Rhynchocoela—the
             Acoelomate Bilateria. McGraw-Hill, New York, Toronto, London.
   1959   *Idem.* Vol. V: Smaller Coelomate Groups. McGraw-Hill, New York,
             Toronto, London.
Ivanov [Iwanoff], P. P.
   1928   Die Entwicklung der Larvalsegmente bei den Anneliden. Z. Morph.
             Ökol. Tiere 10:62–161.
   1944   [Primary and secondary metamery of the body.] J. gen. Biol., Moscow
             5:61–95. [In Russian with English summary.]
Jägersten, G.
   1956   On the early phylogeny of the Metazoa. The bilaterogastraea theory. Zool.
             Bidr. Uppsala 30:321–354.
Knight-Jones, E. W.
   1952   On the nervous system of *Saccoglossus cambrensis* (Enteropneusta).
             Phil. Trans. B236:315–354.
Lang, A.
   1904   Beiträge zu einer Trophocöltheorie. Jena Z. Naturw. 38:1–376.
Lankester, E. R.
   1875   On the invaginate planula, or diploblastic phase of *Paludina vivipara*.
             Quart. J. micr. Sci. 15:159–166.
Lemche, H.
   1960   A possible central place for *Stenothecoides* Resser, 1939 and *Cambridium*

Horny, 1957 (Mollusca Monoplacophora) in invertebrate phylogeny. Rep. 21st int. geol. Congr. (pt. 22: Proc. int. paleont. Un.):92–101.

Manton, S. M.
1928   On the embryology of the mysid crustacean, *Hemimysis lamornae*. Phil. Trans. B216:363–463.
1949   Studies on the Onychophora. VII. The early embryonic stages of *Peripatopsis* and some general considerations concerning the morphology and phylogeny of the Arthropoda. *Ibid*. B233:483–580.

Marcus, E.
1958   On the evolution of the animal phyla. Quart. Rev. Biol. 33:24–58.

Mechnikov [Metschnikoff], E.
1874   Studien über die Entwicklung der Medusen und Siphonophoren. Z. wiss. Zool. 24:15–83.

Pantin, C. F. A.
1951   Organic design. Advanc. Sci., London 8:138–150.
1952   The elementary nervous system. Proc. roy. Soc. B140:147–168.
1960   Diploblastic animals. Proc. Linn. Soc. Lond. 171:1–14.

Picken, L. E. R.
1960   The Organization of Cells and Other Organisms. Oxford Univ., London.

Raven, C. P.
1958   Morphogenesis: the Analysis of Molluscan Development. Pergamon, London.

Remane, A.
1950   Die Entstehung der Metamerie der Wirbellosen. Verh. dtsch. Zoologen, Mainz (1949) (Zool. Anz., Suppl. 14):18–23.

Remane, A.
1954   Die Geschichte der Tiere. Pp. 340–422 in: Die Evolution der Organismen. Vol. 2. G. Heberer, Ed. 2d ed. Fischer, Stuttgart.
1956   Die Grundlagen des natürlichen Systems, der vergleichenden Anatomie und der Phylogenetik. 2d ed. Geest und Portig, Leipzig.

Runnström, J.
1925   Regulatorische Bildung von Cölomanlagen bei Seeigelkeimen mit gehemmter Urdarmbildung. Arch. EntwMech. Org. 105:114–119.

Sedgwick, A.
1884   On the origin of metameric segmentation and some other morphological questions. Quart. J. micr. Sci. 24:43–82.

Shapeero, W. L.
1961   Phylogeny of Priapulida. Science 133:879–880.

Silén, L.
1950   On the nervous system of *Glossobalanus marginatus* Meek (Enteropneusta). Acta zool., Stockh. 31:149–175.
1954   On the nervous system of *Phoronis*. Ark. Zool. (ser. 2)6:1–40.

Smith, J. E.
1937   On the nervous system of the starfish *Marthasterias glacialis* (L). Phil. Trans. B227:111–173.

Stephenson, T. A.
1928   The British Sea Anemones. Vol. I. Ray Soc., London.

Townes, P. L., and J. Holtfreter
1955   Directed movements and selective adhesion of embryonic amphibian cells. J. exp. Zool. 128:53–120.

Vandebroek, G.
1952   La classification générale des Metazoaires supérieurs et les recentes données embryologiques. Ann. Soc. zool. Belg. 83:131–142.
Waterman, T. H.
1961   Comparative physiology. Pp. 521–593 in: The Physiology of Crustacea. Vol. II. Sense Organs, Integration, and Behavior. T. H. Waterman, Ed. Acad. Press, New York, London.
Yatsu, N.
1902   On the development of *Lingula anatina*. J. Coll. Sci. Tokyo 17:1–112.
Ziegler, H. E.
1898   Über den derzeitigen Stand der Cölomfrage. Verh. dtsch. zool. Ges., Heidelberg (1898)8:14–78.

6 ◆ The Enterocelic Origin of the Celom

ADOLF REMANE

ZOOLOGISCHES INSTITUT UND MUSEUM,
UNIVERSITÄT KIEL, KIEL

Celomic cavities characterize many phyla of the Bilateria. With the advent of phylogenetic studies their importance for the study of evolutionary affinities was recognized, and their origin has been discussed by many authors. There are four principal theories bearing on this problem.

1. The *enterocele theory* proposes that the celom is derived from gastric pockets such as those found in many cnidarians and ctenophores. Leuckart (*fide* Heider) was the first to compare celenterate gastric pockets and celomic cavities. Many outstanding morphologists (for example, Heider, 1913, 1914; Hertwig and Hertwig, 1882; Sedgwick, 1884; Bütschli, 1921; Naef, 1931; Marcus, 1929, 1958; Jägersten, 1955, 1959; Alvarado, 1955, 1956) have accepted this view. The theory postulates the following stages: (*a*) archenteron with undivided cavity, (*b*) archenteron with enteric pockets in communication with the central cavity, and (*c*) interruption of the communication; the enteric pockets thus become isolated and therefore celoms.

2. The *gonocele theory* (Hatschek, 1878; Bergh, 1885, 1889; Lang, 1881, 1904; Meyer, 1890; Goodrich, 1895, 1945) suggests that gonads are the source of the celom. Hollow gonads grow and are transformed into celomic cavities by the following evolutionary steps: (*a*) compact isolated gonads; (*b*) hollow gonads; and (*c*) restriction of the definitive germ-cell-forming area to a part of the gonad wall, the rest of the wall becoming the normal epithelium of the celom.

3. The *mesenchyme-schizocele theory* (Faussek, 1889; Hadži, 1949; Steinböck, 1958). The starting point is a mesenchymal tissue, probably homologous to the mesoglea of the celenterates. Fluid-filled spaces originate within this mesenchyme and are surrounded by flat epithelial cells, thus giving rise to the celom. The stages are: (*a*) typical mesenchymal tissue, (*b*) mesenchyme with spaces, (*c*) spaces surrounded by cells, and (*d*) celomic cavities with typical epithelia. In Hadži's and Steinböck's view, the mesenchyme is the product of a multinucleated plasmodium ("archihiston").

4. The *nephrocele theory* (Ziegler, 1898) proposes that celomic cavities are expanded regions of the flame bulbs (terminal organelles) of protonephridia.

We must discuss carefully the proposals of the four theories, their degree of probability, and their consequences. It is better to avoid terms like "definitely rejected" or "definitely dead" or "fantastic nonsense," such as we find in a recent textbook regarding one of these theories. These problems are very complex, and only after a thorough study of much material would it be possible to give a definitive answer.

The Enterocele Theory

The following are facts that favor the enterocele theory.

1. The typical celomic cavity is limited by a ciliated epithelium with basement membrane. This organization is present in the deuterostome Echinodermata as well as in protostome phyla (for example, many of the Polychaeta, Sipunculoida, Brachiopoda). A derivation from the celenterate gastric pockets with their ciliated epithelium, as seen in many of the Cnidaria, such as the Anthozoa or the Ctenophora, poses no difficulties. All the other theories need a secondary transformation of mesenchyme, gonads, or differentiated protonephridial cells into a typical ciliated epithelium. Such processes are not known in any of the well-established phylogenetic lines. In phylogeny there exist some processes that are of general occurrence and others that seem to be unique in the evolution of a family or order. And, when one comes to a theory that depends on reconstructed processes for which there are *no* demonstrable examples, it is surely reasonable to assume that the latter has a lesser probability than a theory founded on processes of general occurrence and demonstrable in the well-established phylogeny of many phyla.

2. The celomic epithelium harbors the gonads in many phyla of the Protostomia (for example, the Annelida, Mollusca, Bryozoa, Brachiopoda, and Sipunculoida) and in the Vertebrata and Pogonophora among the Deuterostomia. The gametes are discharged into the celomic cavity. We find an identical situation in gastric pockets of the Anthozoa, Scyphozoa, and Ctenophora. The isolated gonads of many Bilateria are derived from typical celomic structures as demonstrated in the Mollusca, the Arthropoda, the clitellates, and many others.

3. The celomic epithelium and the epithelium of the enteric pockets contain excretory products.

4. During ontogeny, the celomic epithelium and the mesoderm bands are derived from the entoderm, except in a few secondarily altered species. In many phyla the celomic cavities are typical enteric pockets of the embryo, at least in some genera. These genera demonstrate ontogenetic transformation of such pockets into celomic cavities.

The transformation of enteric pockets with ciliated and muscular epithelium into typical celomic cavities is simple. The communication with the central gastric cavity is reduced. Many embryonic stages of the Bilateria pass through phases in which the rudimentary form of the celomic cavities is really that of enteric pockets.

DIFFERENCES AMONG PROPONENTS OF THE ENTEROCELE THEORY

Authorities differ in the derivation of the Bilateria from a celenterate with gastric pockets. These differences do not affect the enterocele theory proper, but only the number of the enteric pockets or other characteristics. Heider, in reconstructing the "sphenula" as ancestor of the Bilateria, mentions only one pair of enteric pockets, one on each side (fig. 6-1). The metagastrea of Naef also contains only one pair of enteric pockets, whereas Sedgwick, in his corallula theory, in accordance with the numerous gastric pockets in many Anthozoa and the numerous celomic cavities of the Annelida, proposes a great number of pockets for the ancestors. Bütschli and I have chosen four pockets, because the tetraradiate type is very common among the Cnidaria and also visible in the first gonad-bearing stages of the ctenophores (figs. 6-2 and 6-3). Jägersten assigns six pockets to the bilaterogastrea. This number is often seen in the primitive Bilateria, which Ulrich (1952) has designated the Archicoelomata. I hold the extreme numbers of pouches to be improbable. The connection of actinians and annelids by Sedgwick is too direct and entails many far-

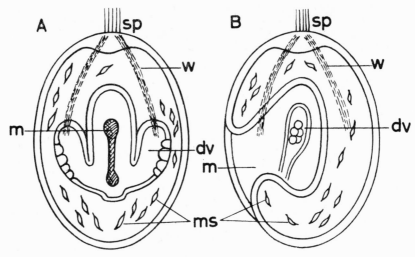

FIGURE 6-1. The ancestor (= sphenula) of the Bilateria reconstructed by Heider, 1915. A, ventral view; B, side view. dv, enteric pocket = celomic diverticulum with gonads; m, slit-like mouth in the process of dividing into mouth and anus; ms, mesenchyme cells; sp, apical plate; w, bands of cilia. (From Heider, 1914.)

fetched interpretations (for example, derivation of parapodia from tentacles). The assumption of only one pair of pockets is inadequate because of the presence of three pairs in many primitive Bilateria. The difference between four or six pockets is not of great importance; six are more probable if we start from the Bilateria, but four are more probable relative to the primitive tetraradiate type of the Cnidaria and Ctenophora and possibly also of the Porifera.

I omit here the problem of the symmetry of the ancestor of the Bilateria—whether it was basically bilateral or radial—and avoid the problem as to whether this ancestor ever passed through a sessile stage, which, though not impossible, is improbable.[1]

---

[1] Sessile habits are not irreversible in phylogeny. We know many species that are secondarily free-living, such as the attached cnidarian *Lucernaria,* which is capable of creeping on its oral surface by means of its tentacles. Aboral sense organs derived from the apical plate are present in the Ctenophora and many of the Bilateria, but only poorly represented in some larvae of

Problems Concerning the Enterocele Theory

The enterocele theory presents certain difficulties. The celom does not always develop from enteric pockets. Even in those phyla in which this mode of formation is typical there are many species that form their celomic pockets in another way. In the whole stem of the Protostomia we find an enterocelic celom only in brachiopods; and in the Tardigrada (Marcus, 1929), embryonic expansions of the entoderm. In many phyla of the Protostomia the celom starts from one or a few primordial

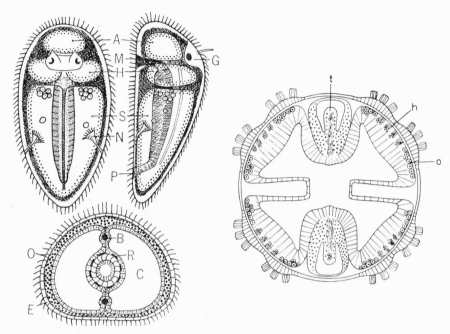

FIGURE 6-2. The ancestor of the Bilateria reconstructed by Remane. Dorsal view, side view, and cross section. A, anterior celomic cavity (protocele, axocele); B, dorsal blood vessel; C, celomic cavity; E, epidermis; G, apical plate with brain and sense organs; H, second celomic cavities (mesocele, hydrocele); M, mouth; N, nephridium; O, muscle layer derived from the celomic epithelium; P, anus; R, blood vessels between gastrodermis and celomic epithelium; S, third celomic cavities (metacele, somatocele.)

FIGURE 6-3. The first mature stage of the ctenophore *Pleurobranchia pileus* with four gastral pockets, each with gonads in the peripheral part of the gastrodermis. h, testis; o, ovary; t, basal part of the tentacle within the tentacle pocket.

mesoderm cells (= *Urmesodermzellen*). These produce the mesoderm bands, which hollow secondarily to form the celomic pockets. In many cases two teloblasts produce the mesoderm bands. This is the teloblastic method of mesoderm formation found in annelids, molluscs, and crustaceans. In other instances mesoderm bands are derived from many cells that migrate into the region of the blastopore. This is exemplified by the "derived mesoderm band method" of arthropods, especially

the Cnidaria. These larvae are attached to the bottom in the region of this aboral organ, which is therefore reduced in the adult. This fact makes it improbable that the Bilateria have passed through a stage of aboral attachment.

insects, and the lamellar method of vertebrates (Hyman, 1940, 1951). There are
many modes of mesoderm and celom formation during ontogeny. Which of these
different modes is the primitive one? The enterocele theory prefers one of them.
What are the reasons for this preference? The problem is discussed by Ziegler
(1898) and very critically by Korschelt and Heider (1909, p. 302). The following
facts are important.

The formation of celomic mesoderm is different even in obviously natural groups
(for example, the Enteropneusta). Figure 6-4 shows this: enterocelic origin from
one to three gastric pockets, migration of cells of mesenchymal character, which secondarily form the celomic sac, and so on. Many different processes are also known

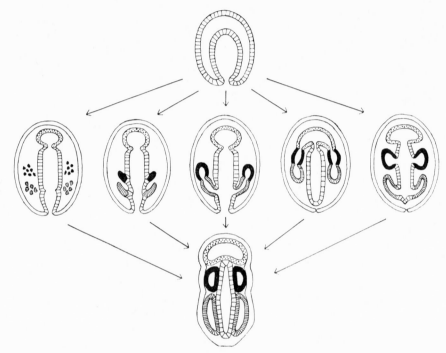

FIGURE 6-4. Different modes in the formation of the celomic cavities within the
Enteropneusta. (After Remane, 1956.)

in the Echinodermata and other groups. There is no doubt that these phyla are
natural groups and must be derived from a specific, common ancestor. The different
ontogenetic modes of celom formation cannot be the recapitulation of phylogenetically different modes of formation. These facts demonstrate that the primary
ontogenetic processes producing the celom and the surrounding mesoderm are,
phylogenetically considered, very easily modified.

We find this situation not only in the development of mesoderm, but also in
the formation of ciliated chambers of the Porifera, of entoderm and neural structures generally, and, in the chordates, of the sclerotome, notochord, amnion, etc.
In the Porifera, invagination (*Plakina, Oscarella*), migration of cells, and differentiation of isolated cells produce chambers with choanocytes. The neural tube of
the Chordata is formed by invaginations, migration with secondary formation of

the central channel, or by a few neuroblasts as in the Copelata (=Larvacea). The variability of these processes within clearly natural groups excludes the possibility that these different modes of ontogenetic formation indicate different phylogenetic origins.

An ontogenetic process can further be differentiated into several isolated sub-processes in space and in time. The ciliated area of the larva of many poriferan species is transformed directly into the choanocyte epithelium of the adult animals. In other species it is destroyed, and cells of the mesenchyme form the choanocyte epithelium. We find an analogous situation in the formation of entoderm, mesoderm, and other entities (Siewing, 1960; Weygoldt, 1960). It is generally accepted that these complications are secondary developments; therefore they are not supportive of our considerations here.

No author has held the primitive origin of the celomic mesoderm to be from one or a few cells corresponding to the few mesentoblast cells as seen in the Annelida and other forms. Heider has explained this reduction of the mesoderm germ to one or few cells as being the precocious segregation of the mesoderm in a blastula or gastrula having only a few cells. The same explanation is reasonable for the formation of the entoderm from one or a few cells (*Urentodermzellen*) as found in the Pantopoda and several of the Crustacea, or for the few neuroblasts and chordoblasts of the Copelata. This view seems to be generally accepted. I have found no author proposing that the primordial mesoderm cell represents a phylo-genetically significant stage.

Thus there are two ontogenetic processes, but achieving possibly one and the same phylogenetic end, that is, formation of the celom. 1. Entodermal epithelium → invaginated enteric pocket → celom with celomic epithelium and formation of mesenchyme, musculature, etc. (Invagination.) 2. Entodermal epithelium → migration of many cells → mesenchymal mesoderm → secondary hollows therein → formation of a secondary epithelium lining these hollows. (Migration.)

The second process is not only more complicated, but also contains an event not yet known to occur as an evolutionary sequence: the development, from a typical mesenchyme, of a characteristic ciliated epithelium with basement membrane. Furthermore, in vertebrates, in which the evolutionary development of the neural tube, amnion, and other structures is known, it is stated that the ontogenetic invagination occurring in these structures recapitulates their phylogeny. The close ontogenetic connection between body musculature and enterocelic pockets supports this view. Hence, comparing the two ontogenetic processes, there is good evidence that the first process represents the actual phylogenetic situation. The probability for the second process is much less. We know many examples of evolutionary segregation of an organ from an epithelial layer, and we know many ontogenetic processes that achieve this same thing. But I do not know any example of evolutionary development, within a mesenchymal tissue, of an organ formed, ontogenetically, by folding of an epithelial layer that is not part of that organ. Therefore it is very improbable that the ontogenetic formation of the celom from pockets of the entoderm layer is a secondary process whose evolutionary development was achieved by another process.

Hence, I maintain that the difficulties of the theory of enterocelic origin of the celomic cavities are fewer than those arising from other points of view.

CRITICISMS OF THE ENTEROCELE THEORY

Now I have to discuss some objections to the enterocele theory. Hyman (1959, p. 750) holds that, if we accept the enterocele origin of the celom, the Anthozoa must be regarded as the basic cnidarians. "This is in itself implausible since they are anatomically the most complicated members of the phylum. The statement of Alvarado (1956) that the Anthozoa are the most simple cnidarians is incomprehensible. If the Anthozoa are taken as the basic cnidarians it becomes very difficult to account for the origin of medusae. We are asked to believe that Scyphozoa and Hydrozoa are evolved from Anthozoa by some sort of retrogressive process, something that is highly improbable since their polypoid phases lead the same kind of sessile existence as do anthozoans and their medusoid phase is far more active than any anthozoan."

These criticisms of Hyman's arise from certain principles for reconstructing

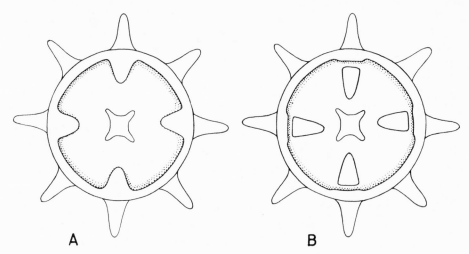

A   B

FIGURE 6-5. A. Typical cnidarian with four gastric pockets. (After Hyman, 1940.) B. The same with connecting channels between the pockets (ring channels, septal stomata), characteristic of the cnidarians.

phylogenetic lines—but principles that are not shared by many other scientists. No further discussion is possible before examining these precepts.

One presumptive principle is that simple organisms are primitive; complicated ones, derived. Since the Hydrozoa are simpler, they are primitive; the Anthozoa are complicated, therefore derived. The evolution of animals and plants, it is true, is in the great lines an evolution from simple to complicated organisms, but there are many exceptions—and not only in parasites. For instance, no botanist doubts that the very simple duckweeds, the Lemnaceae, are not primitive but derived from complicated plants like the Araceae. No zoölogist doubts that the mites, or Acarina, the simplest arachnids, are derived from the more complicated Araneae. Hydrozoa appear simple only if we compare the polyps; the medusae of the Hydrozoa, with their sense organs, nerve rings, etc., are more complicated than the anthozoans, though Hyman claims that the medusae (Trachylina) are the primitive forms. (see fig. 6-5.) Therefore a derivation of anthozoa from hydrozoa demands very great reductions—of the whole organization of the medusa. Without the assumption of reduction we can neither derive hydrozoa from anthozoa, nor anthozoa from hydrozoa. It is necessary in any case to explore whether a simple structure is primitive or not. Ignoring this necessity has led to much useless argumentation.

A second troubling principle is the following: recent classes, orders, and phyla are treated as if derived from other recent taxa. Yet it is self-evident that all recent classes, orders, etc., are derived animals, each descended from an ancestral form that is similar to the recent group in some structures, but different in others. True, there are many "living fossils" today—the Onychophora, *Neopilina, Latimeria,* the Dipnoi, and others. But no one of these living fossils is primitive in *all* structures of its body, though primitive in many. Therefore it is scarcely possible to derive the total organization of one recent taxon from another.

Yet there do exist several exceptions—for example, the class Trematoda of the Platyhelminthes is derivable from the recent class Turbellaria, especially from the recent order Neorhabdocoela, suborder Dalyelliina. But in this example the trematodes are overemphasized because of their numerous species and their practical significance to mankind. In a strictly systematic treatment the Trematoda would be only a family within the Dalyelliina.

It is necessary to investigate the possible homologies of all structures and to reconstruct the archetype (="systematischer Typus," Remane, 1956, p. 140) of every family, order, and class, as postulated by Naef (1931). The archetype of a taxon contains all the essential structures of that taxon. The identification of such structures derives from their dispersal as homologs throughout the taxon in question; and, hence, such a distribution demands that they must be evolved from a common ancestor. In the class Pterygota, wings with complicated venation are distributed in such a manner that, despite numerous wingless groups (Aphididae, Cimicidae, Anoplura, etc.), wings can be attributed to a common ancestor with certainty. The archetype is therefore a most critically reconstructed ancestral type (Remane, 1956—see also papers of 1950, 1954, 1955). Comparisons between these archetypes enables us to reconstruct phylogenies with the greatest possible confidence, especially if fossil forms are scanty. Several authors do not follow this necessary procedure; they collect disparate similarities within a group without testing for homologies or establishing an archetype, and then they present this assemblage of various similarities as proof of affinities. This procedure is very old. Sanders, in the 18th century, proposed a connection of the hummingbirds with the Sphingidae (Lepidoptera) because both have similar colors, a similar tongue for feeding from flowers, a similar pattern of flight, etc. This approach achieves no rational phylogenetic reconstruction.

If one uses the concept of homologies and archetypes, it is improbable that the ancestor of the Cnidaria was an anthozoön or a hydrozoön. Rather, it is probable that it had no ectodermal stomodeum, but had gastric pockets, because the latter are present in all classes today. The young hydromedusa has four gastric pockets; they are transformed into the radial canals. Four gastric pockets are also characteristic for many scyphozoan polyps and medusae (Lucernarida, Charybdea), and eight or more pockets are found in the Anthozoa.

Four typical gastric pockets are also present in the first mature stage of the ctenophores. If we accept the enterocele theory, there is no need to derive the Bilateria from the Anthozoa, specifically from the Ceriantharia, for we only postulate an ancestor with enteric pockets lined with a ciliated epithelium, gonads, etc. This condition is seen in recent classes of ctenophores and cnidarians.

Many authors oppose the foregoing conclusion since in textbooks turbellarians without celoms stand at the beginning of the Bilateria, and the phylum Platyhelminthes, as a whole, has no celom. The archetype of the Platyhelminthes is discussed elsewhere (see Ax, chap. 14 of this volume). Suffice it to say here, I am convinced that in several characters the Turbellaria are primitive (nervous system, ciliated epidermis), but in other characters they are surely not primitive (internal fertilization and structure of spermatozoa, which are unlike the free spermatozoa of many Bilateria, as Franzén, 1956, has demonstrated). Is the absence of the celom in the Turbellaria primitive or secondary? That is a key question. The close connection of the Turbellaria with the Annelida, Mollusca, and Sipunculoida is demonstrated by the very special spiral-quartet 4d cell type of development. In these lines the celom often is reduced by mesenchyme and musculature, as in the Mollusca, which did not come from turbellarians, but from forms with expanded celomic cavities and six to seven pairs of nephridia, as demonstrated by *Neopilina* and, in the Annelida, by the Dinophilidae, Hirudinea, Myzostomata, etc. (Jägersten, 1955).

Several genera of the Mollusca are, in many respects, turbellarian-like (for example, *Pseudovermis, Rhodope,* etc.). These genera are not missing links between Turbellaria and Mollusca, nor between Mollusca and Turbellaria, but they demonstrate that a turbellarian-like organization can be derived from a more highly organized animal with an extensive celom.

Hyman (1959) doubts that the gastric pockets of the Cnidaria are homologous with the celom of the Bilateria. She mentions that the formation of these pockets is variable—in some instances the septa grow from the peripheral layer into the interior, and in other instances the pockets grow outwards. This is true, and both modes are seen in the Bilateria (ingrowing septa in the Brachiopoda, outgrowing pockets in most other phyla). Both are also encountered in the Cnidaria. Distinguishing between an ingrowing and an outgrowing process in ontogeny is often very difficult. For this purpose we need vital staining as Vogt (1925) has done for the investigation of cell movements in the vertebrate embryo. Such investigations have not been undertaken for the gastric pockets in cnidarians and metazoa. Besides this, it is not evident that different ontogenetic processes establish correspondingly different phylogenetic histories. I remember that some authors have denied the common derivation of the lung lamellae in the air-breathing scorpion and the gill lamellae of *Limulus,* because the latter are outgrowths of the legs and the former are septa between ingrowing air-pockets. But ontogenetic study has revealed developmental processes intermediate to these extremes so that the homology now seems well established. It is surely possible that gastric pockets have been produced several times from the entoderm. But the fact that the Cnidaria and Ctenophora have gastric pockets makes it more probable that they are primitive structures in the evolution of the Metazoa.

Comparison of the Enterocele and Other Theories

Now, contrasting the possible theories, we find, first, that the nephrocele theory of Ziegler is very improbable. There exist neither ontogenetic processes nor known evolutionary changes that favor this theory, and I know no author that supports it. The gonocele theory of Lang, accepted and defended by Goodrich, is, in its strictest formulation, not well founded. In all the many forms in which we know the ontogeny of the germ cells, we find the celom and its epithelium not formed by germ- but by somatic cells, and the primary germ cells migrate into the celomic epithelium (*Sagitta,* Vertebrata). We know many groups that reduce celomic cavities to a gonadal structure (for example, Hirudinea, Myzostomata, *Dinophilus,* Arthropoda, Mollusca), but no taxon in which the gonad is expanded into a typical celom.

There remains for discussion the mesenchyme theory, which proposes that a mesenchymal schizocele evolved into a cavity lined by a typical ciliated epithelium. The first step of this process is demonstrable. We know several cases in which a schizocele is formed within a mesenchyme. The best example is the so-called lymph system of several trematodes (for instance, the Paramphistomidae, Cyclocoelidae). In these families there exists a system of channels filled with fluid, containing free cells, and lined by flattened mesenchymal cells. But the next step postulated by the theory, the transformation of a mesenchymal tissue into a typical ciliated epithelium, is without known example. A further difficulty for the mesenchyme theory is the enterocelic origin of the celom in the ontogeny of many of the Bilateria. A secondary mesenchyme formation, utilizing the entoderm and its epithelium, is very difficult to explain by this theory.

There remains the following problem: it is possible that celomic cavities have arisen by many different processes, an enterocelic origin in some of the Bilateria, a mesenchymal origin in others. This is unlikely. The view that the ancestors of the Bilateria had celomic pockets of enterocelic origin is not yet definitely established, but it is better founded than any other possibility.

A final answer depends on whether the Bilateria are monophyletic or polyphyletic. Today many biologists incline to the polyphyletic view and regard the Bilateria as comprising two (Protostomia and Deuterostomia) or four (Beklemishev, 1958–1960) independent branches. Comparing the evidence for the monophyletic and polyphyletic hypotheses, it seems to me that monophyly is better founded. In all the major branches of the Bilateria we have a set of common structures: an intestine with mouth and diverticula, a typical circulatory system with dorsal and ventral vessels, celomic cavities that receive the gametes from the gonads lying more or less in their walls, nephridia, and mesodermal muscles of body wall and intestine that are derived from celomic structures or mesoderm bands. Most of these characters are not sufficiently complex to permit their definite establishment as homologous on the basis of the criteria of homology (Remane, 1956). But the similar distribution of all these characters not dependent on a special mode of life increases the probability of their homology—though not proving it—and therefore also renders probable the monophyly of the Bilateria. Despite this conclusion many biologists have abandoned the monophyletic concept and accept a polyphyletic one. (See fig. 6-6 for schematic representation of various types of relationship.) A polyphyletic origin can only be established if, despite the fact that seemingly homologous structures characterize two or more lineages, there are series of living or, better, fossil connecting forms between two lineages and unrelated forms at a lower grade. This condition is in no way realized in the Bilateria, and therefore today the monophyletic view seems to be much better founded than the polyphyletic.

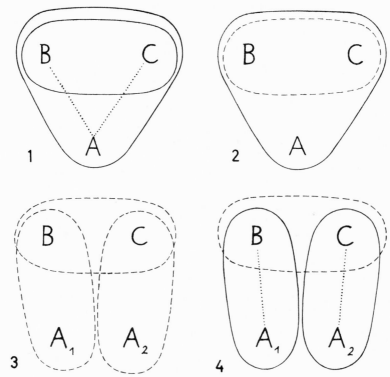

FIGURE 6-6. Diagram illustrating the problems of monophyly *vs.* diphyly.
1. Two groups (families, orders, or higher taxa), B and C, are connected
by common characters, which are definitive homologies (solid, encircling
line); they are also connected by definitive homologies with A. Monophyletic origin is the only possible view. 2. The same situation, but the
similarities connecting B and C are only *possible* homologies (broken
line). Monophyly is probable but not definitely proved. 3. B and C have
similarities that are possible homologies, but *B* has also such similarities
with the group A_1 and C with the group A_2. Monophyly and diphyly are
possible until the problem of homologies is cleared. 4. The same situation
as in 3, but the similarities of B with A_1 and of C with A_2 are definitive
homologies. Diphyletic origin is proved.

REFERENCES

Alvarado, R.
    1955   Sobre el origen y evolución de los metazoos coelomados. Bol. Soc. esp.
               Hist. nat. (Secc. Biol.) 52:147–154.
    1956   On the origin and evolution of the coelomates [*sic*] Metazoa. Proc. XIV
               intern. Congr. Zool., Copenhagen (1953):146–150.
Beklemishev, V. N. [Beklemischew, W. N.]
    1958–
    1960   Die Grundlagen der vergleichenden Anatomie der Wirbellosen. Vols. I
               and II. Dtsch. Verl. Wiss., Berlin.
Bergh, R. S.
    1885   Die Exkretionsorgane der Würmer. Kosmos 17:97–122.
    1899   Nochmals über die Entwicklung der Segmentalorgane. Z. wiss. Zool. 66:
               435–449.

Bütschli, O.
1921   Vorlesungen über vergleichende Anatomie. Vol. I. Englemann, Leipzig.

Faussek, V.
1899   Über die physiologische Bedeutung des Cöloms. Trav. Soc. nat. St.-Pétersb. 30:83–84.

Franzén, Å
1956   On spermiogenesis, morphology of the spermatozoön and biology of fertilization among invertebrates. Zool. bidr. Uppsala 31:355–480.

Goodrich, R. S.
1895   On the coelom, genital ducts and nephridia. Quart. J. micr. Sci. 37: 447–510.
1945   The study of nephridia and genital ducts since 1895. *Ibid*. 86:113–392.

Hadži, J.
1949   Problem mezoderma in celoma v luči turbelarijske teorije knidarijev. (Problems of mesoderm and coelom elucidated by the turbellarian theory of Cnidaria.) Razpr. Razred. prir. Odsek Slov. Akad. Znan. Um., Ljubljana 4:5–84. [In Slovenian with Russian and English summaries.]

Hatschek, B.
1878   Studien über Entwicklungsgeschichte der Anneliden. Ein Beitrag zur Morphologie der Bilaterien. Arb. zool. Inst. Univ. Wien 1:277–404.

Heider, K.
1913   Entwicklungsgeschichte und Morphologie der Wirbellosen. Pp. 176–332 in: Die Kultur der Gegenwart. Hinneberg, P., Ed. 3, sect. 4, pt. 2. no. 2. Teubner, Berlin, Leipzig.
1914   Phylogenie de Wirbellosen. Pp. 453–529, *ibid.*, 3, sect. 4, pt. 4. Teubner, Berlin, Leipzig.

Hertwig, O., and R. Hertwig.
1882   Die Coelomtheorie. Jena. Z. Naturw. 15:1–150.

Hyman, L.
1940   The Invertebrates. Vol. I: Protozoa through Ctenophora. McGraw-Hill, New York, Toronto, London.
1951   *Idem*. Vol. II: Platyhelminthes and Rhynchocoela—the Acoelomate Bilateria. McGraw-Hill, New York, Toronto, London.
1959   *Idem*. Vol. V: Smaller Coelomate Groups. McGraw-Hill, New York, Toronto, London.

Jägersten, G.
1955   On the early phylogeny of the Metazoa. Zool. Bidr. Uppsala 30:321–354.
1959   Further remarks on the early phylogeny of the Metazoa. *Ibid*. 33:79–108.

Korschelt, E., and K. Heider.
1909   Furchung und Keimblätterbildung. VI. Kapitel. In: Lehrbuch der vergleichenden Entwicklungsgeschichte der wirbellosen Thiere. Fischer, Jena.

Lang, A.
1881   Der Bau von *Gunda segmentata* und die Verwandtschaft der Plathelminthen mit Coelenteraten und Hirudineen. Mitt. zool. Sta. Neapel. 3: 187–251.
1904   Beiträge zu einer Trophocöltheorie. Jena. Z. Naturw. 38:1–376.

Marcus, E.
1929   Zur Embryologie der Tardigraden. Zool. Jb. (Anat.) 50:333–384.
1958   On the evolution of the animal phyla. Quart. Rev. Biol. 33:24–58.

Meyer, E.
1890   Die Abstammung der Anneliden, der Ursprung der Metamerie und die Bildung des Mesoderms. Biol. Zbl. 10:296–308.

Naef, A.
  1931   Phylogenie der Tiere. In: Handbuch der Vererbungswissenschaft. Baur,
          E., and M. Hartmann, Eds. Lieferung 13. Borntraeger, Berlin.
Remane, A.
  1950   Entstehung der Metamerie der Wirbellosen. Verh. dtsch. Zoologen,
          Mainz (1949) (Zool. Anz., Suppl. 14):16–23.
  1954   Die Geschichte der Tiere. Pp. 340–422 in: Die Evolution der Organismen.
          Heberer, G., Ed. Vol. 2. 2d ed. Fischer, Stuttgart.
  1955   Morphologie als Homologienforschung. Verh. dtsch. zool. Ges., Tübingen
          (1954) (Zool. Anz., Suppl. 18): 159–183.
  1956   Die Grundlagen des natürlichen Systems der vergleichenden Anatomie
          und der Phylogenetik. 2d ed. Akad. Verlags., Leipzig.
  1960   Die Beziehungen zwischen Phylogenie und Ontogenie. Zool. Anz. 164:
          306–337.
Sedgwick, A.
  1884   On the origin of metameric segmentation and some other morphological
          questions. Quart. J. micr. Sci. 24:43–82.
Siewing, R.
  1960   Über mehrphasige morphogenetische Vorgänge und deren Bedeutung für
          die Keimblätterlehre. Zool. Anz. 164:368–381.
Steinböck, O.
  1958   Zur Phylogenie der Gastrotrichen. Verh. dtsch. zool. Ges., Graz (1957)
          (Zool. Anz., Suppl. 21):128–169.
Ulrich, W.
  1952   Vorschläge zu einer Revision der Grosseinteilung des Tierreichs. Verh.
          dtsch. zool. Ges., Marburg (1951) (Zool. Anz., Suppl. 15):244–271.
Vogt, W.
  1925   Gestaltungsanalyse am Amphibienkeim mit örtlicher Vitalfärbung.
          Vorwort über Wege und Ziele. I. Teil, Methodik und Wirkungsweise der
          örtlichen Vitalfärbung mit Agar als Farbträger. Arch. EntwMech. Org.
          106:542–610.
Weygoldt, P.
  1960   Mehrphasige Gastrulationen bei Arthropoden. Zool. Anz. 164:381–385.
Ziegler, H. E.
  1898   Über den derzeitigen Stand der Cölomfrage. Verh. dtsch. zool. Ges.,
          Heidelberg (1898) 8:14–78.

7 ◆ The Evolution of the Celom and Metameric Segmentation

R. B. CLARK

DEPARTMENT OF ZOÖLOGY,
UNIVERSITY OF BRISTOL, BRISTOL

Two concepts of fundamental importance in metazoan morphology are those of the celomate condition and metamerism. The evolution of a secondary body cavity and of segments seems to have been essential steps in the development of increasingly complex structural organization in the larger animals. Despite the crucial positions these concepts hold in morphological theory, there is still no generally accepted definition of either, and there is considerable disagreement about the evolution of both types of body organization. An examination of any recent general discussion of metazoan morphology (*e.g.,* Hyman, 1951, 1959; de Beauchamp, 1959, 1961) will reveal the great range of interpretations that have been placed on the nature and origin of the celom and segments. This confused and confusing situation is due, of course, to the fact that no direct evidence is afforded by paleontology (and in the nature of things it is most improbable that any such evidence will ever be forthcoming); we are forced, instead, to rely on the circumstantial evidence derived from embryological and comparative anatomical investigations. Herein lies a danger, and too often embryologists have relied excessively on Haeckel's biogenetic theory of recapitulation, and anatomists on a mere juggling of existing morphological types in order to fit them into a tidy sequence. In either event, the tendency has been to obscure the argument with details of the structure and development of existing animals.

What has generally been lacking from discussions of the evolution of the celom and metamerism is a consideration of the selective advantages of these types of body organization. Segmented animals and animals with a secondary body cavity have enjoyed enormous success. This is attributable, to a considerable extent, to the structural plasticity conferred on them by the possession of segments or a celom (witness the structural variety of arthropods and vertebrates compared with non-segmented groups). But the evolutionary potential of a structure can never account for its first appearance; clearly it must be of selective advantage in the organisms and under the circumstances in which it first evolves.

Another general point that seems to have been too little considered is whether the celomic cavity and metameric segmentation are monophyletic or polyphyletic. As long ago as 1886, Bateson pointed out that if, as then seemed possible and now seems almost certain, metameric segmentation has been evolved within the Protochordata-Chordata, the metamerism of the Annelida-Arthropoda must have been independently evolved. This being so, we have two alternatives: either metamerism in the two phyla is convergent and has been evolved in response to similar selective pressures, or it has been evolved quite independently and in response to different selective pressures. In the former case, we must consider the selective advantage of metamerism that would have been applicable equally in the primitive chordates and in protoannelids; in the latter case, we must seek the different advantages that metamerism conferred on chordates and on annelids. Similar considerations arise when we turn to the origin of the celom.

Whether or not the evolution of metamerism is indissolubly linked with that of a celom is a third matter of considerable theoretical importance, and is rarely discussed. The linking or separation of the evolution of these two types of organization seems generally to be a matter of convenience to a theory rather than a subject for examination and justification. If, as in several theories of the origin of metamerism, segments first evolved as segmented celomic cavities, then either the celom of non-segmented celomates has been independently evolved, or it has been derived from a segmented celom by regressive evolution, leaving no trace of its primitively segmented nature. Either solution is theoretically possible, but it is important that the full implications of a theory should be considered, since they must obviously affect its assessment. This is rarely done.

The present position of theories of celom and segment origins, so far as there can be said to be a position in such a controversial field, is as follows. The celom is held to be monophyletic, but is to be distinguished from similar cavities such as a pseudocele or hemocele. Its origins are doubtful. In the form in which they are generally stated, the two most widely held theories (the gonocele and enterocele theories) are virtually incompatible, but there are serious difficulties in accepting either except for limited groups of animals in which the embryological evidence favors one or the other theory. Metameric segmentation is usually regarded as having been independently evolved in chordates and annelids, though in most theories the two phyla are treated as if they were strongly convergent in this respect and the evolution of metamerism is discussed in terms more appropriate to a monophyletic than a diphyletic origin. It is commonly supposed to have evolved by the segmentation of the musculature of animals in which the gonads and possibly other structures, including celomic pouches, already showed a pseudometameric repetition, and that this happened as an adaptation to undulatory swimming movements.

Current theories of both celom and segment origins can be criticized in both detailed and general terms. The chief difficulties faced by theories concerning the origin of the celom spring from the insistence upon a monophyletic origin, whereas the embryological evidence suggests to the unprejudiced eye a diphyletic if not a polyphyletic origin. Linking the evolution of the celom with that of segmentation (as in several current theories) leads to difficulties in accounting for the existence of non-segmented celomates. Most theories of the origin of metamerism either offer little, if any, functional justification for this important evolutionary step (Remane, 1950; Jägersten, 1955; Marcus, 1958), or, if the evolution of segments is related to pseudometamerism and swimming (Goodrich, 1946; Hyman, 1951, 1959), conceal half the problem within the term "pseudometamerism" and ignore the fact that undulatory swimming has no obvious connection with segmentation. All long, narrow animals swim in precisely the same way whether they are segmented or not (Taylor, 1952) and there is no shred of evidence to suggest that segmented animals do so any more effectively than unsegmented ones merely because they are segmented.

For all its defects, however, the locomotory theory of the origin of metamerism, is useful in that it suggests a functional interpretation and directs attention to the musculature. In fact, segmentation of the musculature is fundamental to our concept of metamerism. Unless the musculature of an animal has a segmental organization, the animal is regarded as, at best, pseudometameric. Although there have been several attempts to interpret the celomate and metameric types of organization in mechanical terms (Thiele, 1902, 1910; de Beauchamp, 1911; Marchie Sarvass, 1933; Zenkevich, 1945), this type of analysis has never been discussed in detail or its implications fully examined. In consequence, the mechanical attributes of the secondary body cavity and of segments have never been given the consideration they warrant.

In examining the functional significance of a secondary body cavity and of the segmentation of the musculature and other organ systems and in drawing conclusions that relate to the evolution of the celomate and metameric types of organization, we have one great advantage. When we consider locomotion and its influence on the form of animals, we are concerned chiefly with the interaction of the mechanical and physical world upon the organism, rather than with purely biological influences. The principles of dynamics do not change, and an examination of the mechanism of locomotion in an existing animal provides information that is immediately applicable to any other organism that moves in the same way and has fundamentally the same structure. So long as the argument rests on mechanical considerations, therefore, we deal with certainties that can be verified by experimentation, and not, as in most of the classical theories, with possibilities or probabilities.

The following account is necessarily brief. Space does not permit the marshaling of a body of supporting evidence that will be presented elsewhere (Clark, 1964), and I consider here only the major evolutionary trends that can be discerned. Many important details and several important subsidiary issues are therefore ignored for the present. Similarly, the bibliographic references give no more than hints to the scattered but extensive literature that is pertinent to this enquiry.

The Role of the Musculature and the Fluid Skeleton in Locomotion

In order to consider the relationship between structure and locomotory ability, we must examine the performance and structure of existing animals without prejudice to their evolutionary status. The potentialities of a postulated ancestral organism may be as well exemplified among modern forms by a secondarily reduced member of an advanced phylum as by an animal that has retained a primitive structure. If, however, any clear picture is to emerge from this analysis, it is important to select and consider modern animals in which there is a minimum of irrelevant complication introduced by special adaptations, and it is essential to appreciate the significance of such complications as exist before they can safely be discounted.

The earliest Metazoa are likely to have been composed of a relatively small number of cells and to have fallen in the size range of the larger ciliates and smaller acele turbellarians, that is, of the order of 1 mm. in length. They are likely to have been ciliated externally and to have been motile. At some stage, early or late in their evolutionary history, they are likely to have had a solid body, and, like both ciliates and aceles, they are likely to have had or evolved modest powers of changing their shape by means of peripheral contractile elements. So much seems to be common to most current theories of metazoan origins and represents a relatively uncontroversial series of postulates about the structure of a primitive and ancestral eumetazoan. I now add a further postulate that these animals tended to increase in size in the course of evolution.

Among modern animals, the Acoela, as much as any, approximate in essential features to the postulated primitive form and, furthermore, the size range of the Tubellaria, from a millimeter or so to several inches, corresponds with that of early metazoa and their immediate descendants. The locomotory abilities of the Turbellaria therefore offer us some clues as to the mechanical problems and potentialities of small acelomate animals.

The smallest aceles swim by cilia as our postulated primitive animals are supposed to have done, but cilia are ineffective locomotory organs except in very small organisms, and most turbellarians are too large to swim by ciliary action though they may creep on the substratum by this means. Even so, ciliary locomotion has severe limitations and, in the Tricladida and Polycladida, the much more powerful forces of muscular contraction are used, first to supplement and then to supplant ciliary beat as a means of locomotion. The musculature of the body wall, feebly developed in the Acoela and used in them only to produce relatively minor changes of shape, is correspondingly larger and more important in the Tricladida and Polycladida.

The muscle fibers of the body wall are organized in circular and longitudinal layers, and both layers are essential to the occurrence of reversible changes of shape (fig. 7-1). (Theoretically, other arrangements of the body-wall musculature could produce the same result, but would demand greater complexity of nervous control and coördination than the circular and longitudinal layers that exist in the vast majority of worms—Chapman, 1958.) Contraction of the longitudinal muscles shortens the animal and, since its volume remains constant, causes a compensating increase in diameter and stretching of the circular muscles. Muscles are incapable of exerting a thrust, so that recovery of the original length is possible only by contraction of the circular muscles. Thus the circular and longitudinal muscles are antagonists and act upon each other by the transmission of fluid pressures through the contents of the body enclosed by the muscular body wall, which therefore behave as a "fluid skeleton." Ideally, the fluid skeleton should be totally incompressible and infinitely deformable—a fluid in fact—but a loosely packed, mesenchymatous tissue may serve—and does so in turbellarians and nemerteans.

Worm-like animals with a body-wall musculature disposed in circular and longitudinal layers are capable of a great range of changes of shape (fig. 7-2). The structure of turbellarians and nemerteans may be complicated by the existence of a layer of diagonal muscle fibers, but, so far as we know, they do not intervene in locomotory movements and the locomotory repertoire of these worms illustrates the potentialities of animals of this grade of structure. Apart from undulatory swimming, which is common to all long, thin animals, three types of muscular locomotion are employed by acelomate worms. All three foreshadow types of locomotion that occur in celomate animals.

Pedal locomotory waves

Waves of contraction pass along those longitudinal muscles of the body wall that are in contact with the ground. The rest of the musculature plays a static role, and extension of a contracted part of the longitudinal musculature is by contraction of

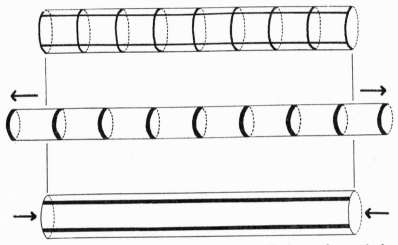

FIGURE 7-1. Antagonistic circular and longitudinal muscles, and the hydrostatic skeleton. Contraction of the circular muscles causes extension of the worm and a decrease in its diameter. Recovery to the original dimensions is possible only by contraction of longitudinal muscles.

other parts of the ventral longitudinal muscles (fig. 7-3). Minimal demands are made upon the fluid skeleton since, at least in theory, the internal fluid pressure remains constant and tensions are transmitted within the ventral longitudinal musculature. Forward movement of any part of the worm occurs when the muscles immediately anterior to it contract. This part is then affixed to the ground while the longitudinal muscles are extended.

Pedal locomotory waves of considerable complexity may be generated. Presumably they represent specialized developments and elaborations of this type of locomotion that are not likely to have occurred in the more primitive animals. The waves may pass along the ventral surface of the animal in the same direction as, or in the opposite direction to that of locomotion, they may extend across the entire width of the body or be confined to its edges, they may be in phase or out of phase in different parts of the body, and so on (Olmsted, 1917, 1922). Pedal locomotory waves are employed by some triclads and more particularly by polyclads (Lehnert, 1891; Crozier, 1918), but they are by no means confined to acelomate worms.

This type of locomotion is especially characteristic of gastropod and amphineuran molluscs, in which waves of the greatest complexity are found (Parker, 1911; Olmsted, 1917). In most, the waves are confined to the sole of the foot, which in this respect is mechanically equivalent to the entire body of the turbellarian, and the visceral mass is an irrelevant passenger. Pedal locomotion has also been observed in actinians, and in these the muscular waves are confined to the base of the pedal disc (Parker, 1917). The celenteric contents, which may in theory

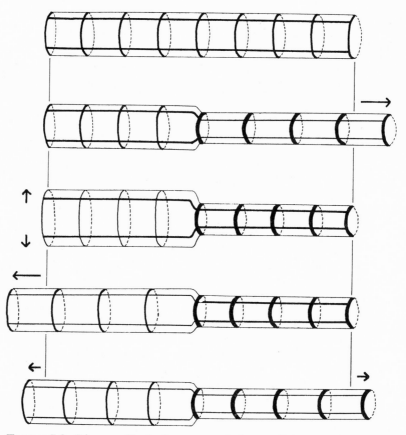

FIGURE 7-2. Diagram illustrating some of the possible consequences of contraction of the circular musculature of one half of a worm. The various ensuing changes in shape depend upon the behavior of the remaining body-wall muscles. (After Chapman, 1958.)

act as a fluid skeleton and do so act in some circumstances, can serve this function only so long as the mouth of the anemone remains closed and its volume constant. This does not happen when the animals are creeping in this manner. Here we have additional evidence that a fluid skeleton plays no necessary part in this type of locomotion.

Leech-like movements

The looping motions characteristic of leeches are also employed by some triclads (Gamble, 1893; Pearl, 1903) and, with slight modification, by malacobdellid nemerteans. The sequence of events during one locomotory cycle is as follows (fig. 7-4). The posterior end of the body is attached to the substratum by a sucker that is permanent in leeches, temporary in triclads. The body is then extended by contraction of the circular muscles so that the anterior end is thrust forwards and, in turn, fixed to the substratum by the anterior sucker. The posterior sucker is detached, the longitudinal muscles contract, drawing up the posterior end of the

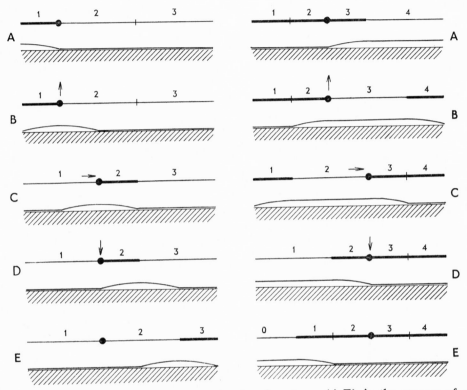

FIGURE 7-3. Pedal locomotory waves, showing five stages (A-E) in the passage of a locomotory wave along the ventral surface of the animal, which is in contact with the substratum, and the behavior of arbitrarily delimited, longitudinal muscle fibers associated with it. On the left, *direct locomotory waves* in which the wave travels along the body in the same direction as the direction of locomotion; on the right, *retrograde locomotory waves* which pass along the body in the opposite direction to that of locomotion. Arrows indicate the stages at which a fixed point on the ventral surface of the animal is detached from the substratum (stage B), moved forward (stage C), and reaffixed (stage D) during the passage of the wave. (After Parker, 1911.)

worm, and the posterior sucker is fixed to the substratum again, immediately behind the anterior one. The cycle is then repeated. There are generally some additional complications to this type of movement (*e.g.,* differential contraction of dorsal and ventral longitudinal muscles causes arching of the body, which permits the posterior sucker to be fixed close behind the anterior one so that the stride is approximately equal to the extended length of the worm) but, in essence, locomotion is produced by alternate and antagonistic contraction of the longitudinal and circular body-wall muscles, alternately thrusting the body forward against a fixed point provided by the posterior sucker and dragging it forward against the anterior fixed sucker (Herter, 1929).

Much more powerful locomotory forces can be generated by this means than by pedal waves, for both the longitudinal and circular musculature are actively engaged instead of only a fraction of the longitudinal muscle layer—that on the ventral surface of the worm. Another major difference between the two types of locomotion is that, since longitudinal and circular muscle coats act antagonistically, forces are transmitted through the fluid skeleton. But, although leech-like looping

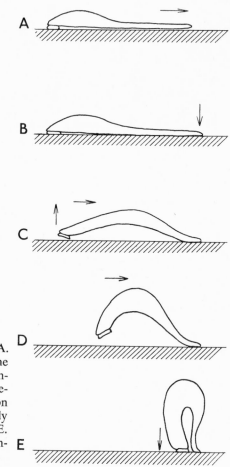

FIGURE 7-4. Locomotory cycle of a leech. A. Elongation of the body by contraction of the circular muscles. B. Maximum extension, anterior sucker affixed. C. Posterior sucker removed, body begins to shorten by contraction of longitudinal muscles. D. Shortening of body by contraction of longitudinal muscles. E. Posterior sucker affixed immediately behind anterior sucker. (After Herter, 1929.)

involves the use of a fluid skeleton, this method of locomotion does not make exacting demands upon it. A wave of contraction passes along the circular musculature, putting the contents of the worm under radial compression, which is compensated for by elongation of the animal and a redistribution of its contents. Contraction of the longitudinal muscles places the contents under longitudinal compression and causes radial expansion. Each operation is progressive and is completed before the other begins. Under these circumstances a loose parenchymatous tissue serves adequately as a fluid skeleton, and this type of locomotion is particularly characteristic of leeches, in which the celom is largely occluded by botryoidal tissue, and of acelomate worms. Although the existence of a patent secondary body-cavity to serve as a fluid skeleton is clearly not essential to this type of movement, celomate animals are, of course, also able to move in this way, as are some holothurians and caterpillars. Among acelomates, most nemerteans are incapable of leech-like movements, not because of any deficiency of the musculature and fluid skeleton, but because they lack suckers or the ability to make temporary ones, and hence cannot achieve sufficient adhesion between themselves and the substratum for looping. *Malacobdella* is exceptional in that it possesses a posterior sucker and does perform a modified type of looping (Eggers, 1935).

Peristaltic locomotory waves

This type of locomotion (Gray and Lissmann, 1938) has something in common with both pedal locomotion and looping. The entire body-wall musculature and the fluid skeleton are involved in it (fig. 7-5). A wave of contraction passes, generally backwards, along the circular muscles of the body. This causes elongation of the region of the body affected by the wave of muscle activity. It is immediately followed by a zone of longitudinal muscle contraction and this, in turn, by another wave of circular muscle contraction. Several such cycles appear along the length of the body at the same time. Adhesion between the worm and the substratum is provided at the points where the longitudinal muscles are maximally contracted. As in looping, the whole of the body-wall musculature contributes locomotory forces, but, whereas in looping one phase of the cycle is completed before the next phase begins, in peristaltic locomotion longitudinal and circular muscle contraction occurs simultaneously in different parts of the body and several cycles may be exhibited at once.

Multiple peristaltic waves make severe demands on the fluid skeleton. They involve the rapid transmission of pressure changes, without damping, from one part of the body to another, and one part of the fluid skeleton is under radial compression while adjacent parts are under longitudinal compression. A parenchymatous tissue is insufficiently plastic to be suitable, and this type of locomotion is normally found only in animals with a true fluid skeleton in the form of a celom, pseudocele, or hemocele. Nemerteans are exceptional, for they sometimes move in this way (Eggers, 1924). It is significant that the mesenchyme tissue of these worms is largely gelatinous and, unlike that of turbellarians, contains relatively few cells (Prenant, 1922). It therefore approximates a true fluid skeleton, but, even so, locomotion by peristalsis is relatively inefficient in nemerteans for a variety of reasons, and they rely chiefly upon cilia.

A feature of peristaltic locomotory waves (and of looping, though that is less significant) is that, since they involve contraction of the circular muscles, the cross-sectional shape of the moving animal is circular. The circular muscles are not involved in pedal locomotion, and the worm can be very much flattened, thus presenting a large area to the ground and increasing locomotory efficiency in that way. This is impossible for animals employing peristaltic locomotory waves, which are consequently ill-adapted for creeping over the substratum. But peristaltic waves are ideally suited for moving through the ground because the entire body wall is effectively a locomotory surface. Furthermore, localized dilatations of the body produced by contraction of the longitudinal muscles wedge the momentarily stationary points of the body firmly against the sides of the burrow and so permit greater forward thrusts to be generated (fig. 7-5).

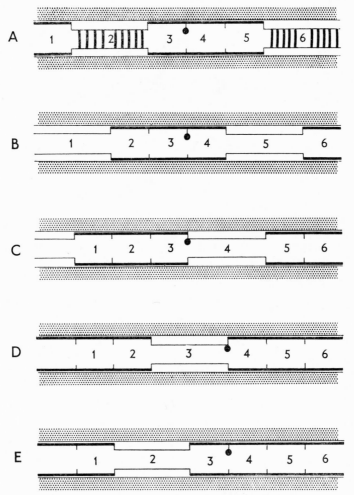

FIGURE 7-5. Peristaltic locomotory waves, showing five stages
(A-E) in the passage of a peristaltic wave along the body of an
animal burrowing through the substratum (heavy stippling). The
circular musculature is contracted in long, narrow regions of the
body (as in regions 2 and 6 of stage A), the longitudinal muscles
are contracted in short, fat regions (as in regions 1, 3, 4, and 5
of stage A) where the body is wedged against the walls of the
burrow. The peristaltic waves move in the opposite direction to
the direction of locomotion (*i.e.,* are *retrograde*) and a fixed
point on the body of the animal remains stationary until a phase
of circular muscle contraction reaches it (stages C and D).

The great majority of unsegmented, worm-like animals with a spacious secondary
body cavity and complete layers of circular and longitudinal body-wall muscles
employ peristaltic locomotion and live in burrows or tubes in the substratum. None
of them are capable of very effective locomotion over the surface. Only animals
with a true fluid skeleton or a close approximation to one can display peristaltic
locomotion, and they alone can burrow by use of the body-wall musculature.

Although unsegmented celomate worms can construct a burrow and move along it by peristaltic locomotory waves, none, except for a few specialized forms, are capable of sustained locomotory activity. They are virtually all sedentary animals. One does not have to search far for an explanation. Contraction of any of the muscles causes compensatory changes in all other muscles in the body wall and affects the conditions under which they operate (fig. 7-6, A). Although the possession of a true hydrostatic skeleton is essential for the most effective use of the body-wall musculature, a patent celom extending uninterrupted from one

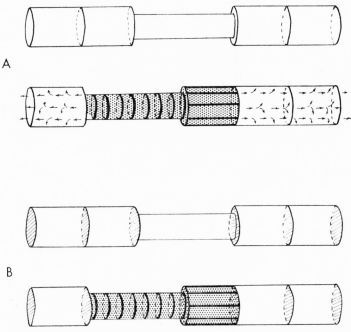

FIGURE 7-6. Diagram illustrating the essential mechanical difference between non-septate and septate worms during the passage of locomotory waves along the body. In a non-septate worm (A), as one region of the body is shortened by contraction of the longitudinal muscles, and an adjacent region is elongated by contraction of the circular muscles, the increase in fluid pressure in these regions (stippled) is dissipated and transmitted to all other parts of the body wall. In a septate worm (B), the pressure changes are ideally localized within the segments undergoing change of length.

end of the worm to the other is not suited to the performance of localized actions such as are involved in peristaltic locomotion. When the celom is subdivided by septa, however, the behavior of the musculature in each segment does not appreciably influence the performance of muscles in other parts of the body (fig. 7-6, B) (Newell, 1950). For the effective use of a compartmented celom it is necessary, of course, that the body-wall muscles be organized on a segmental basis, and, with them, the nervous system and, indirectly, other organ systems. The possession of complete metameric segmentation permits a worm not only to burrow by means of peristaltic movements, but also to burrow almost continuously. Witness the habits of such metamerically segmented animals as earthworms and capitellid and lumbrinereid polychetes compared with echiuroids, sipunculids, and many sedentary polychetes.

The Evolution of Celomate and Metamerically Segmented Animals

With this knowledge of the locomotory capabilities of animals of different grades of morphological organization, we can state the types of habitat that are available to them, and hence, we are able to reconstruct the evolutionary sequence of the appearance of various levels of morphological complexity. It is not to be supposed that this approach necessarily yields information about the phyletic interrelationships of existing animals; for that, the detailed studies of embryologists and comparative anatomists are essential. But it does provide a broad context within which these detailed investigations must be viewed, and which must be taken into account when the phyletic implications of embryological and anatomical investigations are considered.

We may suppose that the early triploblastic Metazoa were small and that they swam or crept over the substratum by means of cilia. With an increase in the size of the animals, cilia became ineffective first for swimming and then, also, for creeping. The more powerful forces of muscular contraction supplemented and replaced those of ciliary beat. I suppose contractile elements to have been present in the body wall of the early, pelagic Metazoa and to have permitted slow and feeble changes of shape such as we observe in modern ciliates and acele turbellarians. The muscles became more highly developed and better organized as muscular locomotion superseded ciliary, and the development of a strong longitudinal musculature, in particular, permitted both swimming by undulatory movements and creeping on the substratum by pedal locomotory waves. Although the circular body-wall muscles play a static role in locomotion of these kinds, they are essential to the occurrence of reversible changes of shape and must have undergone a development similar to that of the longitudinal muscles.

The rich food supply in the form of detritus on the surface of the substratum would have favored the exchange of a planktonic for a benthic existence in some, at least, of the early Metazoa, and these animals must have included those of larger size in which, perforce, more effective locomotory devices were evolved. The modern animals most nearly corresponding in gross structure, locomotory techniques, and range of habitats to the primitive Metazoa at this stage in their evolution are clearly the Turbellaria, and it is likely that adaptations similar to those of rhabdoceles, triclads, and polyclads, including the carnivorous habit, appeared as soon as the population of macroscopic animals living on the sea bed became sufficiently large to support predators. The ability of smaller and less specialized microphagous animals and detritus feeders to burrow into the substratum would have afforded them an escape from predation without excluding them from the rich food supply on the surface.

The only substantial improvement in locomotory ability over that in the solid-bodied worms involves the use of powerful contractions of both longitudinal and circular body-wall muscles, and demands the existence of a true fluid skeleton in the form of a secondary body cavity. The evolution of this was an essential prerequisite to burrowing into the substratum, for while very small organisms can live as an interstitial fauna, macroscopic animals must exert considerable thrust against the substratum as they burrow, to push aside the particles composing it.

The solid-bodied worms possessed a muscular organization of great potential value, but the full realization of its potentialities, the exploitation of a new environment hitherto unexplored by macroscopic animals, coupled with the possibility of escaping from predation by penetrating into the substratum, all depended upon the evolution of a true fluid skeleton. This represented an explosive evolutionary situation, and the stage seems to have been set for an outburst of radiative evolution. Any fluid-filled cavity that is mechanically opposed to the body wall can serve as a hydrostatic skeleton. Incipient secondary body cavities in the form of lacunae in the mesenchyme, cavities in the gonads, or gastric pouches may well have become hypertrophied, modified, and pressed into service. The bewildering array of minor, and some major, celomate phyla of uncertain and disputed affinities may well have been the result, and there is certainly no reason to suppose that the celom is homologous throughout the animal kingdom. The gonocele, schizocele, and enterocele theories may thus all be correct within different groups of animals.

Because, however, changes in fluid pressure are freely transmitted to all parts of the body wall through the celomic fluid in animals with a secondary body cavity, such animals are condemned to a relatively sedentary existence. Sustained burrowing is possible only if the celom is subdivided by septa and the body-wall musculature is segmented. The evolution of metamerism clearly must have been an early development among the celomate but unsegmented worms. A metameric organization of the musculature entails a segmental organization of the nervous system, and the subdivision of the celom entails a serial repetition of the other organs. With this evolutionary advance we arrive at a protoannelid having the same fundamental structure as an oligochete, though lacking such oligochete adaptations as a reduced reproductive system, the occupation of fresh-water and terrestrial habitats, and, in the first instance, chetae.

At every stage in this evolutionary sequence, animals have abandoned a subterranean existence and returned to the surface of the substratum or to the waters above it. The molluscs represent a group of celomates (segmented or not, depending on the interpretation placed on the Monoplacophora) that have done so. With this change of habitat, peristaltic locomotory waves ceased to be an effective means of transport, and the animals reverted to pedal locomotion exactly comparable to that of their flatworm ancestors. The celom, having lost its hydrostatic function, has become vestigial. The leeches are segmented worms that have more recently abandoned the burrowing habit, and septa and, indeed, much of their segmental organization, as well as the celom, is virtually lost.

The most primitive polychetes, the "errant" worms, on the other hand, have retained much of their segmental organization although, for the most part, they do not live in burrows. They are generally versatile animals that can crawl on the substratum, swim, or burrow. The use of the parapodia as lateral segmental appendages suggests that they were evolved as an adaptation to movement over the surface of a substratum on which obstacles in the form of algal or animal growths or an extremely uneven surface precluded the use of pedal locomotory waves, or in a surface ooze of such a consistency as to be unsuitable for locomotion by either pedal or peristaltic locomotory movements. The development of lateral parapodial lobes has resulted in acute modifications of the body-wall musculature, which no longer forms two concentric layers of longitudinal and circular muscle, and an extrinsic and an intrinsic parapodial musculature have been developed. The tendency within this group to crawl by means other than peristaltic movements results in a reduction or loss of the septa, though they are often retained at least in a modified form, so that the turgor of individual segments is maintained to provide reasonably rigid insertions for the parapodial muscles (Clark, 1962). Many polychetes, however, have reverted to a sedentary existence and have suffered a severe reduction or loss of septa and much of the segmental organization of the musculature. Since powerful muscular activity is necessary for the construction of a burrow and for moving inside it, the celom remains patent. They therefore come to resemble the unsegmented celomate worms very closely in both habit and structure.

The Crustacea, with the evolution of a hard exoskeleton and true skeletal muscles, naturally do not employ peristaltic locomotory movements of the body wall. Furthermore, not only is the celom vestigial, having lost its prime function as a hydrostatic organ, but much of the segmental organization, save that of the musculature and, in part, the nervous system, is lost or substantially modified.

I have so far neglected an important group of segmented celomates, the Chordata, in this discussion. It is clear that chordate metamerism has arisen independently of that of annelids, and there is no reason to suppose that it is in any way related to peristaltic locomotory waves or to burrowing (Berrill, 1955). The characteristic feature, and the key to an understanding of the evolution of the chordates, is the notochord, which seems to have preceded segmentation in order of first appearance. Chordates emerged from a protochordate stock as swimming animals, and locomotory forces were generated by undulatory motions of the body as in other animals of comparable shape. But, unlike those of invertebrates, the locomotory movements of chordates are not produced by waves of contraction passing along the longitudinal muscles of the body wall, but by torsional forces applied to the axial notochord (Gray, 1953). Because of the comparative rigidity of the notochord, flexures can be transmitted smoothly along the body of the animal only if the musculature is organized into myotomes (Nursall, 1956).

The fact that the axial structures of invertebrate worms are completely flexible permits them to generate similar locomotory waves by the contraction of unsegmented longitudinal muscles, although, of course, segmentation of the musculature does not debar an invertebrate from swimming in this way. Sinusoidal swimming movements are generated solely by the longitudinal musculature; hence a fluid skeleton is not implicated in this type of locomotion. The presence or absence of a celom is therefore irrelevant and it is evident that undulatory swimming is available to all long, narrow animals that possess sufficiently powerful longitudinal muscles, whatever their evolutionary status.

Conclusions

The fact that the celom is severely reduced in all animals in which it does not serve a hydrostatic function is strong evidence that its chief and original function was mechanical and not physiological. If this is so, it can only have evolved to permit strong, antagonistic contractions of circular and longitudinal muscles, and this implies a burrowing habit. The morphological nature of the secondary body cavity is unimportant so long as it can serve this mechanical function. Consequently there is no reason why the celom should not have been evolved more than once and from different morphological origins, as, indeed, embryological evidence suggests has been the case.

Metameric segmentation, on the other hand, has been evolved at least twice, in annelids and chordates, and represents quite different adaptations in the two phyla. In the annelids it is an adaptation to sustained burrowing through the substratum, in chordates an adaptation to swimming with an axial notochord. In the absence of a notochord, animals without a segmented musculature can perform swimming movements, and many invertebrates do so. Metamerism, particularly of the celom, as in annelids, carries with it the serious disadvantage that most of the internal organs must be replicated in each segment. Any change in the locomotory habit of these animals has been promptly followed by the loss of septa and a substantial reduction of the metameric organization of the body.

Other types of metamerism, in the sense of a serial repetition of organ systems, exist, as, for instance, in the cestodes. There is no convincing logical justification for excluding cestode segmentation from the definition of "metameric segmentation;" as Hyman (1951) points out, zoölogists are generally reluctant to regard the segmentation of cestodes in the same light as that of annelids, and rightly so. There are, in fact, several different types of metamerism. All represent adaptations of approximately, but not identically, the same type in response to different evolutionary demands. Metamerism of various sorts has been evolved as an adaptation to burrowing (annelids), swimming (chordates), reproduction (cestodes), and metamerism of particular organ systems, as an adaption to the needs of providing for excretion or nervous control in very long, thin animals like nemerteans.

The evolution of the celom has been strongly convergent and that of metamerism has been divergent, notwithstanding the superficial similarities between segmented animals of different origins.

REFERENCES

Bateson, W.
    1886   The ancestry of the Chordata. Quart. J. micr. Sci. 26:535–571.
Beauchamp, P. de
    1911   Conceptions récentes sur l'anatomie et l'embryologie comparées des Vers et des groupes voisins. Les théories du trophocœl. Bull. Sci. Fr. Belg. 46: 106–146.
    1959   Généralités. Traité Zool. 5, fasc. 1:3–11.
    1961   Généralités sur les Métazoaires triploblastiques. *Ibid.* 4, fasc. 1:1–19.
Berrill, N. J.
    1955   The Origin of Vertebrates. Clarendon, Oxford.
Chapman, G.
    1958   The hydrostatic skeleton in the invertebrates. Biol. Rev. 33:338–371.
Clark, R. B.
    1962   On the structure and functions of polychaete septa. Proc. zool. Soc. Lond. 138:543–578.
    1964   Dynamics in Metazoan Evolution. Clarendon, Oxford.

Crozier, W. J.
1918 On the method of progression in polyclads. Proc. nat. Acad. Sci. 4:379–381.

Eggers, F.
1924 Zur Bewegungsphysiologie der Nemertinen. I. *Emplectonema*. Z. vergl. Physiol. 1:579–589.
1935 Zur Bewegungsphysiologie von *Malacobdella grossa* Müll. Z. wiss. Zool. 147:101–131.

Gamble, F. W.
1893 Contributions to a knowledge of British marine Turbellaria. Quart. J. micr. Sci. 34:433–528.

Goodrich,E.S.
1946 The study of nephridia and genital ducts since 1895. *Ibid*. 86:113–392.

Gray, J.
1953 Undulatory propulsion. *Ibid*. 94:551–578.

Gray, J., and H. W. Lissmann
1938 Studies in animal locomotion. VII. Locomotory reflexes in the earthworm. J. exp. Biol. 15:506–517.

Herter, K.
1929 Vergleichende bewegungsphysiologische Studien an deutschen Egeln. Z. vergl. Physiol. 9:145–177.

Hyman, L. H.
1951 The Invertebrates. Vol. II: Platyhelminthes and Rhynchocoela—the Acoelomate Bilateria. McGraw-Hill, New York, Toronto, London.
1959 *Idem*. Vol. V: Smaller Coelomate Groups. McGraw-Hill, New York, Toronto, London.

Jägersten, G.
1955 On the early phylogeny of the Metazoa. The bilaterogastraea theory. Zool. Bidr.Uppsala 30:321–354.

Lehnert, G. H.
1891 Beobachtungen an Landplanarien. Arch. Naturg. 57:306–350.

Marchie Sarvass, A. E. du
1933 La Théorie du Coelome. Thesis, Utrecht.

Marcus, E.
1958 On the evolution of the animal phyla. Quart. Rev. Biol. 33:24–58.

Newell, G. E.
1950 The role of the coelomic fluid in the movements of earthworms. J. exp. Biol. 27:110–121.

Nursall, J. R.
1956 The lateral musculature and the swimming of fish. Proc. zool. Soc. Lond. 126:127–143.

Olmsted, J. M. D.
1917 Notes on the locomotion of certain Bermudan mollusks. J. exp. Zool. 24:223–236.
1922 The role of the nervous system in the locomotion of certain marine polyclads. *Ibid*. 36:57–66.

Parker, G. H.
1911 The mechanism of locomotion in gastropods. J. Morph. 22:155–170.
1917 Pedal locomotion in actinians. J. exp. Zool. 22:111–124.

Pearl, R.
1903 The movements and reactions of fresh-water planarians: a study in animal behaviour. Quart. J. micr. Sci. 46:509–714.

Prenant, M.
    1922   Recherches sur le parenchyme des Platyhelminthes. Essai d'histologie comparée. Arch. Morph. gén. exp., fasc. 4:1–474.

Remane, A.
    1950   Die Entstehung der Metamerie der Wirbellosen. Verh. dtsch. Zoologen, Mainz (1949) (Zool. Anz., Suppl. 14):16–23.

Taylor, G.
    1952   Analysis of swimming of long and narrow animals. Proc. Roy Soc. A214: 158–183.

Thiele, J.
    1902   Zur Cölomfrage. Zool. Anz. 25:82–84.
    1910   Über die Auffassung der Liebeshöhle von Mollusken und Anneliden. Zool. Anz. 35:682–695.

Zenkevich, L. A.
    1945   The evolution of animal locomotion. J. Morph. 77:1–52.

8 ◆ Regeneration Experiments and Phylogeny

OTTO STEINBÖCK

ZOOLOGISCHES INSTITUT,
UNIVERSITÄT INNSBRUCK, INNSBRUCK

In general it may be said that ability to regenerate, which is exceedingly high in the case of many of the Ciliata, decreases with increasing complexity of organization. It would, however, be quite wrong, on this basis, to draw conclusions regarding the phyletic position of an animal, for within the most kindred groups—even species—there exist forms that regenerate well, badly, and even not at all. Thus, many of the Turbellaria—*Amphiscolops, Euplanaria,* and others—are among the animals that regenerate best of all, whereas other, such as *Dalyellia* and *Prorhynchus,* are practically unable to regenerate even small parts of the body.

Arguing from the Turbellaria, I have stated (1954, 1955, 1958) that it is the "archihiston" (=mesenchyme), above all, that has regenerative powers. As I have shown, this applies, on the whole, throughout the entire animal world, including human beings, in whom the mesenchyme still has very remarkable regenerative powers despite the constantly repeated statement in textbooks that mammals are capable of only scanty wound healing. But even admitting that, in general, no definite information may be obtained from regeneration regarding questions of phylogeny, I believe it possible, in certain instances, to draw positive phylogenetic conclusions from the process of regeneration.

The modern proponents of the gastrea theory (Remane, 1954, 1958, 1960; Marcus, 1958; Jägersten, 1955, 1959) consider the Turbellaria to be the most regressed descendants of the hypothetical Archicoelomata, which possessed one unpaired and two paired celomic spaces with metanephridia, a system of blood vessels, anal canal (rectum), and anus. In what manner this regression has taken place is not explained in detail. The terminal link of this chain of regression is supposed to be the Acoela, the organization of which, however, shows so much agreement with the Ciliata that one may, in my estimation, be fully justified in deriving them from the latter. To investigate the regeneration of these aceles, let us consider *Amphiscolops* sp., which I have studied in Spain for three summers. The following few experimental observations prove that *Amphiscolops* is among those animals possessing the greatest regenerative powers.

If this animal (fig. 8-1) is cut up in any of a great variety of ways, the parts will, in a short time, assume shapes that are like the shape of the original animal. This is done by regulation of form alone—*i.e.*, without the formation of a "regeneration cone."

1. *Regeneration experiment, R-142,1.9.1953.* An animal was cut through from front to rear just short of complete separation (fig. 8-2,A). (Often separation occurs as a consequence of the vigorous motion of the lateral parts.) After the lapse of 49 minutes, the two parts had already become completely fused (fig. 8-2,B), and after 3 hours and 56 minutes only a slight unevenness was visible (fig. 8-2, C).

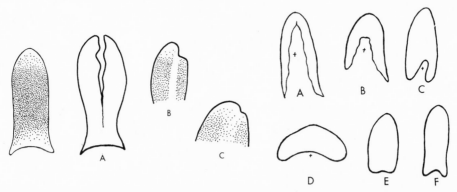

FIGURE 8-1. *Amphiscolops* spec. The body size differs very much (f. *castillonensis* 1.5–3 mm., f. *gerundensis* 2–4 mm., *cf.* Steinböck, 1954). The body shape also differs, particularly the two small tails. The species lacks a statocyst. The dots represent zooxanthellae (f. *castellonensis*) and zoochlorellae (f. *gerundensis*). (Original figure.) NOTE: The species could not be determined as the individuals were not mature during the regeneration experiments (July–Aug.).

FIGURE 8-2. A. Cut from front to rear (4/5 of the body). B. After 49 minutes; clear of algae—less scar is visible. C. After 3 hours, 56 minutes there is a slight trace of a scar. (After Steinböck, 1954b, partly modified.)

FIGURE 8-3. A. The whole entoplasmodium has been removed (= area marked +). B. Confluence and shortening of the lateral parts takes place immdiately following the operation. C. After 31 minutes the excised area is being filled, and the lateral parts are even more shortened. D. After 6 hours the piece has broadened. E. After 19 hours, 27 minutes the two bulges at the rear are not the tails, but the remains of the lateral parts. F. After 31 hours, 12 minutes form regulation with two new tails is completed. (After Steinböck, 1954b, partly modified.)

2. *R-155,4.9.1953.* If one excises the greatest possible quantity of entoplasmodium, starting from the rear and moving toward the front to include the brain, but avoiding separation of the lateral parts despite their vigorous movements (fig. 8-3, A), a confluence or a filling up of the excised area, or both, is observed to follow immediately upon the excision and is accompanied by a shortening of the lateral parts (fig. 8-3,B). Figure 8-3,C, shows the animal 31 minutes after the operation. Subsequently, however, the two lateral ends do not become tails; they are first rounded off (fig. 8-3,D) and new tails are formed (fig. 8-3,E,F).

3. *R-143,1.9.1953.* The wounds inflicted on this specimen were as bizarre as possible (fig. 8-4). The fragments of tissue that extend posteriorly are drawn in within an almost incredibly short time by ameboid motions. (See legend, fig. 8-4, B-F.) After 41 hours, 32 minutes, new tails again protrude visibly.

4. *R-181,12.9.1953.* A center part (fig. 8-5,A-C) burst under my eyes 17 hours, 50 minutes after the operation, the fluid entoplasmodium squirting out from the covering layer, whereas the latter shrank like the skin of a sausage (fig. 8-5,D). A large part of the entoplasmodium still cohered with the outer material and was even enlarged by pieces of protoplasm coming into contact with it and immediately adhering to it. Thus, after 27 minutes the situation shown by figure 8-5,E, was apparent. A few minutes later, the entoplasmodial mass separated from the other material and floated independently, performing lively circular motions (fig. 8-5,F). Form regulation with appearance of new tails was observed (fig. 8-5,G and H).

5. *R-285,7.9.1955.* Also, "punching out" gave surprising results. Thus, I "punched out" a protoplasmic column from the last fifth of the body (fig. 8-6,A) by means of a glass capillary 157 μ in diameter. After 12 hours the piece

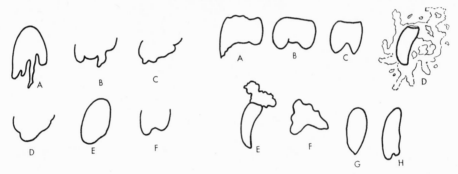

Figure 8-4. A. The lobate wound. B. After 5 minutes the lobes are withdrawn by ameboid motions. C. After 12 minutes (all times are from the *beginning* of the experiments). D. After 20 minutes. E. After 22 minutes. F. The rear after 41 hours, 40 minutes. (After Steinböck, 1954b, partly modified.)

Figure 8-5. A. Cross piece from the middle of the body. B. After 4 hours, 26 minutes. C. After 17 hours, 44 minutes. D. After 17 hours, 50 minutes: the release of the entoplasmodium. E. After 19 hours, 23 minutes: concentration of the aggregated and contracted plasmodium at the site of release. F. The detached plasmodium freely swimming in lively circular motions. G. The same after 42 hours, 22 minutes. H. After 67 hours: elongated with incipient tails. (After Steinböck, 1954b, partly modified.)

looked like a mushroom (fig. 8-6,B). After a total of 133 hours, it assumed a bilateral shape and the tails had already become visible (fig. 8-6,E). Furthermore, the brain had already become clearly differentiated.

6. *R-176,11.9.1953. Shifting of axes.* A cross piece out of the middle of the body (fig. 8-7,A) remained nearly immobile, in distinct contrast to the behavior of most other parts. For about 30 hours after the operation this part moved, when stimulated, in the direction of original main axis (fig. 8-7,B). After these 30 hours the right narrow end had broadened somewhat, and, when stimulated, the piece now moved somewhat uncertainly in a direction deviating by about 45° from the original main axis (fig. 8-7,C). After 71 hours shifting of the axis by 90° had been nearly completed, the right lateral part had become the front, and the left had become the rear end with two tails (fig. 8-7,D).

From this and about 350 other experiments the conclusion may be drawn that, in the case of *Amphiscolops,* (1) the entire plasmodial tissue including the "digesting plasmodium," is totipotent, and (2) together with, perhaps before, re-

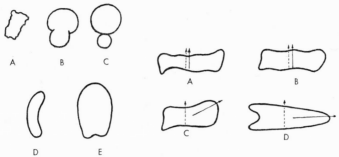

Figure 8-6. A. "Punched out" piece immediately after having been blown out of the capillary. B. After 12 hours: "mushroom." C. The stalk of the "mushroom" becomes independent; the volume of the main part diminishes. D. After 121 hours: asymmetrically circular movements. E. After 133 hours: bilaterally symmetrical, two tails.

Figure 8-7. A. The third piece of a quartered animal, immediately after the operation. B. After 3 hours, 48 minutes movement still takes place in the direction of the main axis. C. After 29 hours, 53 minutes the right side enlarges and will become the new anterior end; the piece moves, somewhat uncertainly, at an angle of 45° to the original axis. D. After 71 hours elongation occurs in the direction of the original cross axis; movement in the same direction. (Dotted arrows = the original main axis; solid arrows = direction of movement.) (After Steinböck, 1954b, partly modified.)

generation in the strictest sense, a typically ameboid form regulation, or morphallaxis (Morgan, 1901) plays a decisive part.

On the basis of these experimentally determined facts I believe it to be impossible that such members of the Acoela, being animals with extensive regenerative and form-regulating capabilities, should be the regressed descendants from celomate antecedents, which are of a far higher organization. The Acoela must therefore be considered to be primitive turbellarians.

Appendix

A comparison between the acele digestive plasmodium and the syncytia of the intestines of the Gastrotricha and Rotatoria (Remane, 1958) is, after what has been said, entirely inadmissible, for the latter have no parallels with the former. Indeed, if one attempts regeneration experiments on gastrotrichs and rotifers, the differences between these forms and the aceles will be obvious.

In this connection a comparison of regenerative powers, which must be interpreted as phylogenetic, may be fitting. Remane (1954, p. 360) and Marcus (1958, p. 32) favor the celomate origin of the Turbellaria because, among other things, the Hirudinea, as undoubted celomates, apparently evolved a platyhelminth-like parenchyma. An inspection of the highly developed triclad mesenchyme, which probably suggested this comparison, immediately makes the parenchyma of the Hirudinea appear to be a uniquely evolved tissue, the regenerative power of which is nearly nil,[1] although the Annelida, in general, regenerate very well.

---

[1] The results obtained by Glushkevich (1908) with *Protoclepsis tessellata* (O. F. Müller) are not convincing and require checking (*cf.* Korschelt and Heider, 1936).

REFERENCES

Glushkevich [Gluschkiewitsch], T. B.
1908   Regeneration des Vorder- und Hinterendes von *Clepsine tessellata*. Arch. EntwMech. Org. 25:1–6.

Jägersten, G.
1955   On the early phylogeny of the Metazoa. Zool. Bidr. Uppsala 30:321–354.
1959   Further remarks on the early phylogeny of the Metazoa. *Ibid.* 33:79–108.

Korschelt, E., and K. Heider
1936   Vergleichende Entwicklungsgeschichte der Tiere. Rev. E. Korschelt. Fischer, Jena.

Marcus, E.
1958   On the evolution of the animal phyla. Quart. Rev. Biol. 33:24–58.

Morgan, T. H.
1901   Regeneration. Macmillan, New York, London.

Remane, A.
1954   Die Geschichte der Tiere. Pp. 340–422 in: Die Evolution der Organismen. G. Heberer, Ed. 2d ed. Fischer, Jena.
1958   Zur Verwandtschaft und Ableitung der niederen Metazoen. Verh. dtsch. zool. Ges., Graz (1957) (Zool. Anz., Suppl. 21): 196–218.
1960   Die Beziehungen zwischen Phylogenie und Ontogenie. Symposium Bremen: Ontogenie und Phylogenie. Zool. Anz. 164:306–337.

Steinböck, O.
1954   Sobre la misión del "Plasmodio digestivo" en la regeneración de *Amphiscolops* (Turbellaria Acoela). Publ. Inst. Biol. apl. 17:101–117.
1955   Regeneration azöler Turbellarien. Verh. dtsch. zool. Ges., Tübingen (1954) (Zool. Anz., Suppl. 18):86–94.
1958   Zur Theorie der Regeneration beim Menschen. Forschungen Forscher Tirol. Ärztesch. (Med. Fak. Univ. Innsbruck) (1954–56)4:315–351.

9 ◆ Hoplonemertines, Myxinoids, and Vertebrate Origins

DONALD D. JENSEN

DEPARTMENT OF PSYCHOLOGY,
INDIANA UNIVERSITY, BLOOMINGTON

During the last century man's probable ancestors have been recognized in a number of vertebrate groups: primates, insectivores, reptiles, amphibians, lobe-finned fish, early jawed fish, and jawless fish. But with the myxinoid jawless fish, clearly the most ancient vertebrate group, with relatives probably appearing in the Ordovician (Jarvik, 1960, p. 90; Stensiö, 1958, p. 415), the line of ancestors ends. No satisfactory probable ancestor of the myxinoids[1] has been recognized. At present the most popular hypotheses of vertebrate origins derive the vertebrates from lower chordates (Gregory, 1951; Berrill, 1955; Romer, 1959). These views encounter difficulty in the evidence that the lower chordates (cephalochords, tunicates, etc.) are degenerate rather than primitive, for these groups lack homologs for most vertebrate nervous and sensory structures, appear to be more closely related to the petromyzont jawless fish than to the more ancient and primitive myxinoids (Garstang, 1954), and lack any clear relation to the still more primitive groups of the lower Metazoa. These difficulties are of greatest importance if another more reasonable hypothesis is available—that is, if a group can be recognized that does possess homologs for most major vertebrate structures, including sensory and nervous features, does appear to be more closely related to the myxinoids than to other vertebrate groups, and does have clear affinities with the lower Metazoa. Such a group appears to exist in the *hoplonemertines,* an order of the phylum of ribbon worms (Rhynchocoela). The evidence available is consistent with the hypothesis that hoplonemertines are the ancestors of the myxinoid jawless fish, which in turn gave rise to other chordate groups (Jensen, 1960).

Prepared while the author was a National Science Foundation Postdoctoral Fellow at the Zoölogical Laboratory, State University of Groningen, The Netherlands, 1958–1960.

[1] In this discussion *myxinoids* and *petromyzonts* are synonymous, respectively, with *pteraspidomorphs* and *cephalaspidomorphs* (Stensiö, 1958), but reference is made to living rather than fossil representatives of the two groups of jawless fish.

This hypothesis is historically related to the views of Hubrecht, the Dutch zoölogist that early (1883, 1887) argued for the nemertine affinities of the vertebrates, but without specifying relations between groups smaller than phyla and without providing homologs for many vertebrate structures. To differentiate the hypothesis being offered from the nemertine hypothesis of Hubrecht, it will be termed the *hoplonemertine hypothesis*.[2]

Homologies and Derivations

Let us now evaluate the hoplonemertine hypothesis by comparing the biological characteristics of the hoplonemertines and the myxinoid jawless fish and by seeking homologs of, and derivations for, vertebrate structures in structures of hoplonemertines or closely related nemertines. We can begin by comparing the embryology of the two groups.

Embryology

Grobben (1908) differentiated the Metazoa into the *Protostomia* and *Deuterostomia* on the basis of a single embryological character, the relation of the blasto-

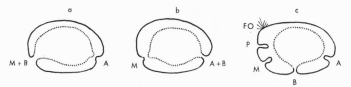

FIGURE 9-1. Embryological patterns of protostomes (1*a*), deuterostomes (1*b*), and hoplonemertines (1*c*). A, anus; B, blastopore; FO, frontal organ; M, mouth, P, proboscis. (Fig. 9-1*c* after Bürger, 1897–1907.)

pore to the adult mouth and anus (fig. 9-1). Nemertines were classed as protostomes, in which the blastopore is said to become, or to be associated with, the mouth, while the anus, if present, develops independently (fig. 9-1*a*). Myxinoids and other chordates were classed as deuterostomes, in which the blastopore is said to become, or be associated with, the anus, while the mouth develops independently (fig. 9-1*b*). Grobben spoke of the different fate of the blastopore as a "deep chasm" separating the protostomes and the deuterostomes. If this be so, the hoplonemertines seem to bridge that chasm. In this group the blastopore neither becomes nor is closely associated with mouth or anus, and both mouth and anus develop independently (fig. 9-1*c*).

In other embryological characters, nemertines and deuterostomes are similar.

---

[2] This terminology does not differentiate the present hypothesis from the view of Macfarlane (1918, pp. 419–452), who suggested that the petromyzont jawless fish were derived from the polystyliferous hoplonemertines. Macfarlane's view, which differs from that here presented in a number of ways and which was unknown to me until Nov., 1961, seems to have had little influence; it is not cited in the more recent reviews of the nemertines. A detailed discussion of Macfarlane's views is in preparation.

Nemertines may show equal cleavage, which is typical of certain lower chordates, or unequal cleavage in which the so-called micromeres are larger than the macromeres (Hyman, 1951, p. 506), which is the opposite of the typical protostome condition. Nemertines and lower chordates seem to be similar in the amount of regulation possible in embryos, regulation occurring until after the third cleavage in both groups (Hörstadius, 1937; Wilson, 1900, p. 149; Conklin, 1932). Nemertines typically show spiral cleavage, but so do several deuterostome groups, both typically, as in certain echinoderms, and occasionally, as in cephalochordates (Conklin, 1932).

These embryological similarities are all consistent with the hoplonemertine hypothesis and at variance with the protostome-deuterostome dichotomy of Grobben. Let us turn, then, from early embryology to the study of particular organs of hoplonemertines and myxinoids and consider first the proboscis apparatus typical of the entire nemertine phylum.

NEMERTINE PROBOSCIS APPARATUS

This apparatus (fig. 9-2) is a complex organ lying above the digestive tract and typically functioning in the capture of prey. It is composed of an invaginated por-

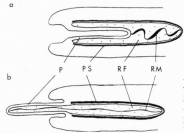

FIGURE 9-2. Nemertine proboscis apparatus, schematic, shown retracted (2a) and everted (2b). P, proboscis; PS, proboscis sheath; RF, rhynchocelomic fluid; RM, retractor muscle.

tion of the body wall, the *proboscis,* which is inserted at the end of a short cavity, the *rhynchodeum,* and normally lies within a muscular tube, the *proboscis sheath.* The space between the proboscis and the proboscis sheath is filled with a watery fluid, the *rhynchocelomic fluid,* and the anterior end of the proboscis and the posterior portion of the proboscis sheath are connected by a flat muscular band, the *retractor.* When the muscular sheath contracts, hydraulic pressure on the rhynchocelomic fluid rapidly everts the proboscis to expose its sticky, glandular external surface. The retractor functions to pull the everted proboscis back into the proboscis sheath.

Hubrecht (1883) suggested that the vertebrate notochord was homologous with a part of the nemertine proboscis apparatus—that is, to the proboscis sheath. Consistent with this suggestion are the mesodermal origins of both structures, their position above the digestive tract, and their typical extension nearly the length of the body. But, if we section the myxinoid notochord, we find indications that it is a compound structure, composed (fig. 9-3a) of an outer fibrous *notochord sheath* surrounding gelatinous *notochord contents* in which lies a flat, fibrous strand of tissue running nearly the length of the notochord, the *notochord strand* ("Strang" in Pietschmann, 1933–1955, p. 164; Cole, 1905–1926). The three components of the notochord resemble not one but three components of the proboscis apparatus

FIGURE 9-3. Comparison of myzinoid notochord (*3a*) and nemertine proboscis apparatus (*3b*). Schematic. NC, notochord contents; Nsh, notochord sheath; NSt, notochord strand; PS, proboscis sheath; RF, rhynchocelomic fluid; RM, retractor muscle.

(fig. 9-3*b*): the fibrous notochord sheath resembles the muscular proboscis sheath; the vacuolated, gelatinous notochord contents resemble the rhynchocelomic fluid; and the flat notochord strand resembles the flat retractor muscle. To transform the nemertine structures into a notochord would require only that the muscular tissues of the sheath and retractor become non-contractile and that the rhynchocelomic fluid increase in viscosity. This increase may have taken place without great modification of the rhynchocelomic fluid, since cells that could become more numerous and vacuolated are to be found floating in it.

The modification of parts of the proboscis apparatus, which functions in prey capture, into a stiffening structure, which functions to prevent shortening of the body during fish-like locomotion, might at first glance seem unlikely. There is, however, evidence in the pelagic polystyliferous hoplonemertines that the proboscis apparatus, without losing its function in prey capture, also serves as a stiffening structure for locomotion. These nemertines swim actively by dorsoventral flexions of the body (Coe, 1926, p. 92; 1943). Such a mode of swimming, while differing from the locomotion of fish in the direction of undulation, also requires a stiffening organ, and the thick proboscis sheath of these forms serves that function.

Now, if the notochord is homologous to, and derived from, the proboscis sheath, rhynchocelomic fluid, and retractor, what has happened to the other part of the proboscis apparatus, the eversible proboscis itself? To answer this question adequately, the proboscis of hoplonemertines must first be described in greater detail.

While in many nemertines the proboscis is a simple eversible tube, in the hoplonemertines it typically has two parts: the *muscular proboscis,* which is eversible, and the *glandular proboscis,* which is not (fig. 9-4). Between these two parts is found a muscular bulb surrounding a solid body, the *stylet base,* which may support a sharp, tooth-like structure, the *stylet barb.* The barb is single in the monostyliferous hoplonemertines and multiple in the polystyliferous. When the hoplonemertine proboscis is everted (fig. 9-4*b*), the sharp stylet barb is exposed so that it can puncture the body wall of prey, the poisonous secretions of the glandular proboscis pouring out meanwhile to subdue the prey.

In myxinoids there are a number of structures, associated with the anterior

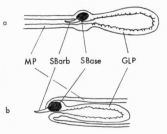

FIGURE 9-4. Hoplonemertine proboscis, retracted (*4a*) and everted (*4b*). Schematic. GLP, glandular proboscis; MP, muscular proboscis; S. Barb, stylet barb; S. Base, stylet base.

end of the notochord, that resemble components of the hoplonemertine proboscis. First, the *glandular hypophysis* is associated with the anterior end of the notochord. It, like the glandular proboscis, is formed by an anterior medial ectodermal invagination. In the hoplonemertines this invagination proceeds toward and then into the proboscis sheath (fig. 9-5a), but in the myxinoids the invagination halts near the anterior end of the notochord. It is suggested, therefore, that the glandular hypophysis is a vestige of the glandular proboscis that has not invaginated into the proboscis sheath. Second, the first pair of *muscular somites* are associated with the anterior end of the notochord. Still more remarkably, the first pair of somites in certain vertebrates are closely associated with the glandular hypophysis, being confluent with it and with each other (Goodrich, 1917; Wedin, 1955). This remarkable association suggests that the muscular somites are homologous with the muscular proboscis, which has invaginated laterally along the proboscis sheath rather than into it (fig. 9-5b). Subdivision of the muscular cavities could then produce the lateral rows of somites found in the myxinoids (fig. 9-5c). Third, the *skeletal cartilage* of myxinoids is associated with the anterior end of the notochord. The cartilage that surrounds the anterior end of the notochord, the so-called *notochordal cartilage,* is one of the first to develop in myxinoids. This, like the stylet base of hoplonemertines, is a supportive matrix, and it seems likely that the

FIGURE 9-5. Derivation of vertebrate notochord and head structures (5c) from the hoplonemertine proboscis apparatus (5a), with a hypothetical intermediate (5b).

stylet base has increased in size and ramified to form the cartilage skeleton of the myxinoids (shown in black in fig. 9-5c). Associated with certain cartilages of myxinoids, which lie superficially in the buccal cavity, are *horny teeth.* Because such teeth of myxinoids are associated with cartilage, and the stylet barb of hoplonemertines is associated with the stylet base, which is the homolog of cartilage, it seems likely that the horny teeth and stylet barb are also homologous.

In summary, the proboscis apparatus of hoplonemertines offers homologs for the notochord, the glandular hypophysis, the muscular somites, the skeletal cartilage, and the horny teeth of myxinoids and provides a phylogenetic explanation for the curious relations among these structures in terms of relations of presumptively homologous structures in the hoplonemertine proboscis apparatus (*cf.* Adelmann, 1922).

SECONDARY STOMODEUM

In most nemertines the proboscis apparatus opens to the exterior by the rhynchodeum and the foregut opens to the exterior separately by the *primary stomodeum,* a more ventrally placed longitudinal slit (fig. 9-6a). In the eumonostyliferous hoplonemertines and the closely related genus *Malocobdella,* the proboscis apparatus and the foregut have a common opening to the exterior, the secondary stomodeum (fig. 9-6b). In *Malocobdella* both the primary stomodeum and the secondary

FIGURE 9-6. Relations of hoplonemertine proboscis
apparatus and digestive tract in most nemertines
(6a) and in eumonostyliferous hoplonemertines
(6b). FO, frontal organ; P, proboscis; S_1, primary
stomodeum; S_2, secondary stomodeum.

stomodeum develop, but at different times in the embryonic sequence (fig. 9-7,*a-d*).
The primary stomodeum and rhynchodeum develop, but both then close over, and
the former disappears while the latter develops, joining the foregut and the
proboscis apparatus to the exterior. Now, in the myxinoids there is an opening to
the foregut that is associated with the homolog of one part of the proboscis apparatus. This is the nasopharyngeal duct, on the dorsal wall of which lies the glandular
hypophysis. The nasopharyngeal duct develops very much as does the secondary
stomodeum of *Malocobdella* (fig. 9-8, *a-c*). Both involve ectodermal invaginations
that close over, perforate into a pharynx that is probably ectodermal in origin, and
later reopen to the exterior as laterally directed slits (von Kupffer, 1899; Dean,
1899). On the basis of similar relations to homologous structures and similar
development, the secondary stomodeum of hoplonemertines and the nasopharyngeal duct of myxinoids are here considered homologous.

Myxinoids possess still another medial opening to the foregut, the more ventrally
located *mouth*. In view of its position we might suppose that the myxinoid mouth
is homologous with the primary stomodeum of hoplonemertines, which for some
reason failed to close over during embryonic development. When we examine the
early development of the myxinoid mouth, however, we see that it does not appear
earlier than the nasopharyngeal duct, as we should expect if it were homologous
with the primary stomodeum. Instead, it develops at the same time as does the
more dorsal nasopharyngeal duct. Moreover, it develops by the same embryonic
process as that producing the nasopharyngeal duct—namely, a lateral expansion of
the foregut, which perforates to form a laterally directed, slit-like opening to the
exterior. The foregut of myxinoids shows not merely two such lateral expansions,
but a whole series, which perforate at about the same time to produce not only
the nasopharyngeal duct and mouth, but the pharyngeal gill slits as well (Stockard, 1906; Dean, 1899). On the basis of embryological similarities, it is thus possible to consider the secondary stomodeum as homologous with the three types of
foregut openings in myxinoids, all of which develop from lateral expansions of
the foregut. The most anterior of these expansions perforates as the medial nasopharyngeal duct; the next most anterior perforates as the medial mouth; the next
few are suppressed and fail to perforate; and the more posterior expansions per-

FIGURE 9-7. Stages in the development of the secondary stomodeum of *Malocobdella*. P, proboscis; S_1, primary stomodeum; S_2, secondary stomodeum.
(After Brinkmann, 1917.)

forate on either side as the lateral gill slits. All the foregut openings of the myxinoids thus seem to be serial homologs of the single secondary stomodeum of the hoplonemertines.

The formation of respiratory gills by multiple lateral perforations of the hoplonemertine pharynx may at first glance seem an improbable modification of an ingestive structure. There is evidence, however, that the pharynx of some nemertines possesses a respiratory function as well as an ingestive one, water being pumped in and out of the heavily vascular pharynx for respiratory purposes (Wilson, 1900, p. 109). Gills may well have developed as modifications allowing straight-through flow of water and more efficient respiration.

Digestive and Circulatory Systems

If the anterior portions of the myxinoid and hoplonemertine digestive tracts are homologous, we might expect the remainder to be similar. The more posterior portions of the digestive tracts of myxinoids and of certain eumonostyliferous hoplo-

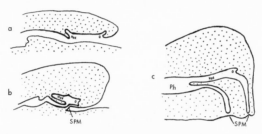

FIGURE 9-8. Stages in the development of the mouth and nasopharyngeal duct of *Bdellostoma*, a myxinoid. Npd, nasopharyngeal duct; O, olfactory organ; Ph, pharynx; SPM, secondary pharyngeal membrane. Body tissues and egg membranes are stippled. (After von Kupffer, 1899.)

nemertines are similar, being basically straight tubes from pharynx to anus, while possessing prominent ventral glandular structures: the gastric diverticulum of hoplonemertines and the liver of myxinoids. The two digestive tracts thus seem to be homologous.

Just above the digestive tract and just below the notochord lies a major vessel of the myxinoid circulatory system. There is a similar structure associated with presumptively homologous structures in hoplonemertines. Above the digestive tract of hoplonemertines and closely associated with the proboscis sheath—the homolog of the notochord sheath—is a major vessel of the hoplonemertine circulatory system. This system resembles the myxinoid circulatory system in being semi-closed and in possessing ameboid blood cells resembling white corpuscles and red blood cells reportedly containing hemoglobin. The two systems differ greatly in complexity, but not in basic structure, and may be considered homologous.

A striking difference in the circulatory systems is the pumping mechanism. In myxinoids, circulation is produced by action of the ventral heart, several accessory hearts, and the gill musculature (Johansen, 1960). In hoplonemertines, the major pumping structure seems to be the contractile proboscis sheath, inside of which the dorsal vessel runs for part of its length. One can guess that other means of transport were unnecessary until the proboscis sheath became non-contractile during the transformation into notochord.

SENSE ORGANS

We have found homologs for a considerable number of myxinoid structures, for notochord, glandular hypophysis, muscular somites, cartilage, horny teeth, nasopharyngeal duct, mouth, gills, digestive tract, and circulatory system. Now let us seek homologs for the sensory organs of myxinoids, structures that are not represented in the lower chordates.

The *labyrinths,* or ears, of myxinoids develop as paired ectodermal invaginations at the level of the anterior end of the notochord. The receptor cells—the organ of Corti—bear short, bristle-like cilia. The *cerebral organs* of nemertines (fig. 9-9a) develop as paired ectodermal invaginations at the level of the anterior end of the proboscis sheath, the homolog of the notochord sheath. The receptor

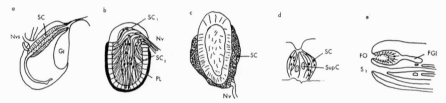

FIGURE 9-9. Sense organs of hoplonemertines: 9a, cerebral organ of *Drepanophorus spectabilis* (after Bürger, 1897–1907); 9b, inverse retina eye of *Drepanophorus spectabilis* (after Böhmig, 1929); 9c, direct retina eye of *Geonemertes agricola* (after Böhmig, 1929); 9d, "onion-shaped" organs of *Nectonemertes* (after Cravens and Heath, 1907); 9e, frontal organ of *Prosadenoporus badiovagatus* (after Bürger, 1897–1907). FGl, frontal glands; FO, frontal organ; Gl, glands; Nv, nerve; Nvs, nerves; PL, pigment layer; S_2, secondary stomodeum; SC, sensory cells; SupC, supporting cells.

cells of the cerebral organs also bear short, bristle-like cilia. The myxinoid labyrinths, which possess one semicircular canal, are more complex than the sack-like nemertine cerebral organs, but resemble them during early embryonic development. The similar position, histology, and embryology of the labyrinths and cerebral organs support their homology.

Vertebrates typically possess two types of eye: the inverse retina eye, exemplified by the vertebrate *paired eyes,* and the direct retina eye, exemplified by the *pineal eye* of many vertebrates. In myxinoids the pineal eye is rudimentary (Conel, 1929, 1931), but petromyzonts (the other extant jawless fish) and a number of vertebrates of other groups possess it. The paired eyes of myxinoids are particularly primitive, lacking completely the eye muscles and accessory structures associated with paired eyes of other vertebrates. In hoplonemertines, eyes of both the inverse and direct retina types are reported; the *lateral eyes* resemble the vertebrate paired eyes in their tendency to occur in pairs, in the presence of an outer pigment cup adjacent to inverse retinal elements, and in the presence of two types of retinal cell, one rod-like and one cone-like (fig. 9-9b). The inverse retina eyes of myxinoids and of hoplonemertines seem to be homologous. In *Geonemertes agri-*

cola, a eumonostyliferous hoplonemertine, eyes of the direct retina type are reported (fig. 9-9*c*) that resemble the pineal eye in structure and seem to be homologous with the vertebrate pineal eye (Southgate, 1959).

Vertebrates possess *neuromast organs,* functioning in taste and the lateral line system. These organs typically have distinctive sensory cells placed centrally within supporting cells (Dahlgren and Kepner, 1908, p. 263). Larval petromyzonts have neuromasts that differ from the typical vertebrate pattern in having the sensory cells dispersed among the supporting cells. In certain pelagic polystyliferous hoplonemertines, "onion-shaped" sense organs occur on the head and body surface, histologically resembling neuromasts; but in these organs the sensory cells tend to lie peripherally to the supporting cells (fig. 9-9*d,* after Cravens and Heath, 1907). The relative positions of the sensory cells in these sense organs of hoplonemertines, jawless fish, and higher vertebrates form a sequence consistent with the hopolonemertine hypothesis. On the basis of histological similarity, the neuromast organs of vertebrates and the "onion-shaped" organs of hoplonemertines are considered homologous.

Frontal Organ

The only anterior sense organ of the myxinoids for which a homolog has not yet been presented is the *olfactory organ.* It develops from the anterior edge of the *neural plate,* which is left outside when the neuropore closes during the transformation of the neural plate into a closed, ciliated *neural tube* (Kleerekoper and van Erkel, 1960, p. 213). The embryonic origin of the olfactory organ explains the close relations of this organ and the neural tube.

There is a nemertine structure whose embryology parallels that of the vertebrate neural plate. This is the flask-shaped *frontal organ* (fig. 9-9*e*), which in *Geonemertes agricola,* a eumonostyliferous hoplonemertine, originates from a flat plate of ciliated ectodermal cells and invaginates as a longitudinal groove to form a ciliated tube that remains open at its anterior end (Böhmig, 1929, p. 79). The frontal organ opens onto the secondary stomodeum in hoplonemertines; the olfactory organ of myxinoids opens onto the nasopharyngeal duct, the homolog of the secondary stomodeum. Associated with the frontal organ of hoplonemertines are prominent glands that discharge into the lumen of the frontal organ; associated with the neural tube of myxinoids is the *subcommissural organ,* which secretes Reissner's fibers into the lumen of the neural tube (Olson, 1958). On the basis of similar position, embryology, and association with homologous structures, the frontal organ of hoplonemertines is considered homologous to the olfactory organ and neural tube of myxinoids, the myxinoid structures being derived by elongation of the frontal organ back above the proboscis apparatus or notochord and by the closing of the neuropore.

Solid Nerves and Ganglia

The nervous system of myxinoids does not develop solely from the neural plate. On either side of the neural plate is found a series of ectodermal placodes from which develop the ganglionic masses and solid nerves of the myxinoid nervous system. The material of the large *lateral placodes* near the primordia of the

FIGURE 9-10. Schematic diagrams of vertebrate (10*a*) and nemertine (10*b*) nervous systems, commissures shown stippled. AP, alar plate; BP, basal plate; CO, cerebral organ; DG, dorsal ganglion; DRE, direct retina eye; DSN, dorsal spinal nerve; FO, frontal organ; HN, head nerves; IRE, inverse retina eye; L, labyrinth; LS, lateral stems; MCN, mixed cranial nerves; MPN, motor proboscis nerves; NH, neurohypophysis; O, olfactory organ; SPN, sensory proboscis nerves; SomN, somite nerves; VN, vagus nerve.

labyrinths seems to provide ganglionic material for the brain, and the *neural crest placodes* seem to provide this material for the spinal cord. The ganglionic material eventually integrates with that from the neural tube and comes to lie on the floor and sides of the neural tube as the nuclei of the basal and alar plates (fig. 9-10*a*). These plates are peripheral in position in the neural tube of myxinoids, but tend to lie more internally in the neural tubes of other vertebrates (Jansen, 1930, p. 503).

Near the primordia of the cerebral organs of nemertines, the presumptive homologs of the labyrinths, occur a pair of prominent *ectodermal masses* from which develop the solid brain ganglia and solid nerves of the nemertine nervous system (fig. 9-10*b*). Similarities in embryonic development and relations to homologous structures suggest that the lateral placodes of myxinoids are homologous with ectodermal masses of nemertines. Moreover, there is remarkable correspondence in the organization of structures derived from these placodes. The nemertine dorsal ganglia are sensory in function; so are the dorsal alar plates of myxinoids. From the dorsal ganglia and commissure of nemertines arise nerves to the frontal organ, eyes, mouth region, and cerebral organs; the dorsal alar plates and dorsal commissures of myxinoids connect to the presumptively homologous olfactory organ, eyes, mouth region, and labyrinths, respectively. From the dorsal ganglia and commissures of nemertines arise sensory nerves to the proboscis; from the optic chiasma, an anterior sensory commissure of the myxinoid brain, arises the infundibulum or *neural hypophysis,* which is associated with the glandular hypophysis, the homolog of the glandular proboscis. The nemertine ventral ganglia are motor in function; so are the ventral basal plates of the myxinoid brain. From the nemertine ventral ganglia and commissures arise nerves to the proboscis; from the ventral basal plates of myxinoids arise nerves to the anterior somites, homologs of the muscular proboscis. In nemertines there are lateral nerves that arise from both dorsal and ventral ganglia and extend into the body mass; in myxinoids the vagus nerves are both sensory and motor in function and extend into the body mass. In sum, the similarity in organization of the myxinoid and nemertine brains suggests that the myxinoid brain was derived by amalgamation of the nemertine solid brain and the frontal organ. The spinal cord can then be understood as a backward extension of the fused structure with replication of lateral placodes to form the neural crest placodes, from which spinal nerves develop as serial homologs of vagus and anterior somite nerves. The development of the spinal cord seems to be related to the innervation of the more posterior somites and to the development of fish-like locomotion by lateral undulations of the body.

Discussion

In the eumonostyliferous nemertines we have found presumptive homologs and derivations for a large number of myxinoid and vertebrate organs: the notochord, composed of notochord sheath, notochord contents, and notochord strand; the glandular hypophysis; the muscular somites; the skeletal cartilage and horny teeth; the nasopharyngeal duct, mouth, and gill slits; the digestive tract with liver and anus; the circulatory system with a dorsal vessel and red and white blood cells; paired eyes and pineal eye; the labyrinths; the neuromast organs; olfactory organ, neural tube, alar and basal plates of the brain and spinal cord; the sensory, mixed, and motor nerves; and the neural hypophysis. Now let us turn from the search for homologs and derivations to the interpretation of those we have found.

First, there is evidence of phylogenetic affinity between hoplonemertines and myxinoids. There are too many detailed and interrelated homologies to be reasonably explained by convergence. Similarities in one or two organs could justifiably be explained by convergence, but the similarities found in organ after organ and between whole sets of organs cannot reasonably be so explained. Second, neither group seems to be greatly degenerate. To be sure, the myxinoids lack the pineal eye and may have non-functional lateral eyes (Worthington, 1905), but the olfactory organ and labyrinths show little evidence of reduction. Both groups include sensitive, motile, active organisms. Third, the myxinoids are obviously more complex than the hoplonemertines in almost every organ system. These three interpretations—affinity, progressive rather than degenerative evolution, and greater complexity of the myxinoids—strongly support the hoplonemertine hypothesis that the myxinoids evolved from forms similar to existing eumonostyliferous hoplonemertines.

The hoplonemertine hypothesis can be combined with a number of hypotheses regarding the origins of various chordate groups (fig. 9-11). Jarvik (1960) derives the petromyzonts from the myxinoids, and Garstang (1954) derives the cephalochordates from archaic larval petromyzonts. From the cephalochords, two other chordate groups seem to be derived: the tunicates (Gregory, 1951, p. 86) and the enteropneusts (Knight-Jones, 1952, p. 351). From the enteropneusts the pterobranchs seem to be derived (Burdon-Jones, 1952, p. 587), and from the pterobranchs, the echinoderms (Grobben, 1923, cited in Hyman, 1959, p. 198). It is possible also to suggest probable ancestors of the hoplonemertines and thus to extend still further the line of probable ancestors of man. These probable ancestors include primitive nemertines (Böhmig, 1929), turbellarians (Wijnhoff, 1914), and a series of protistan groups, the most primitive of which is ancestral to both animals and plants (Hanson, 1958).

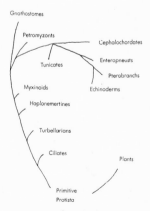

FIGURE 9-11. Revised chordate phylogeny, showing probable early origins.

The hoplonemertine hypothesis and the phylogeny that has been outlined offer innumerable opportunities for research. Each of the homologies suggested may be, and should be, directly investigated. The biochemistry, serology, and ultrastructure as well as the morphology, embryology, and behavior of the related groups can be studied to test and hopefully to improve the hoplonemertine hypothesis of vertebrate origins.

REFERENCES

Adelmann, H. B.
    1922   The significance of the pre-chordal plate: an interpretive study. Amer. J. Anat. 31:55–101.

Berrill, N. J.
    1955   The Origin of Vertebrates. Clarendon, Oxord.

Böhmig, L.
    1929   Vierte und letzte Klasse der Plathelminthes. Nemertini. Handb. Zool. 2, 2d half, no. 3:1–110.

Brinkmann, A.
    1917   Die pelagischen Nemertinen (monographisch dargestellt). Bergens Mus. Skr. (n.s.) 3, no. 1: 1–194.

Burdon-Jones, C.
    1952   Development and biology of the larva of *Saccoglossus horsti* (Enteropneusta). Phil. Trans. 236B:553–589.

Bürger, O.
    1897–
    1907   Nemertini (Schnurwürmer). Bronn's Klassen 4, Suppl.:I–VIII, 1–542.

Coe, W. R.
    1926   The pelagic nemerteans. Mem. Mus. comp. Zool. Harv. 49:1–246.
    1943   Biology of the nemerteans of the Atlantic Coast of North America. Trans. Conn. Acad. Arts Sci. 35:129–328.

Cole, F. J.
    1905   A monograph on the general morphology of the myxinoid fishes, based on a study of *Myxine*. I. The anatomy of the skeleton. Trans. roy. Soc. Edinb. 41:749–788.
    1907   *Idem.* II. The anatomy of the muscles. *Ibid.* 45:683–757.
    1909   *Idem.* III. Further observations on the skeleton. *Ibid.* 46:669–681.
    1913   *Idem.* IV. On some peculiarities of the afferent branchial arteries of *Myxine*. *Ibid.* 48:215–230.
    1914   *Idem.* V. The anatomy of the gut and its appendages. *Ibid.* 49:293–344.
    1926   *Idem.* VI. The morphology of the vascular system. *Ibid.* 5:309–342.

Conel, J. L.
    1929   The development of the brain of *Bdellostoma stouti*. I. J. comp. Neurol. 47:343–379.
    1931   *Idem.* II. *Ibid.* 52:365–438.

Conklin, E. G.
    1932   The embryology of *Amphioxus*. J. Morph. 54:69–118.

Cravens, M. R., and H. Heath
    1907   The anatomy of a new species of *Nectonemertes*. Zool. Jb. (Anat.) 23: 337–356.

Dahlgren, U., and W. A. Kepner
  1908   A Textbook of the Principles of Animal Histology. Macmillan, New
          York.

Dean, B.
  1899   On the embryology of *Bdellostoma stouti*. A general account of myxinoid
          development from the egg and segmentation to hatching. Pp. 221–276
          in: Festschrift C. von Kupffer. Fischer, Jena.

Garstang, W.
  1954   Appendix (pp. 140–142) to Hardy, A. C., Escape from specialization.
          In: Evolution as a Process, Huxley, J. *et al.*, Eds. Allen and Unwin,
          London.

Goodrich, E. S.
  1917   Proboscis pores in vertebrates. Quart. J. micr. Sci. 62:539–553.

Gregory, W. K.
  1951   Evolution Emerging. Macmillan, New York.

Grobben, K.
  1908   Die systematische Einteilung des Tierreiches. Verh. zool.-bot. Ges. Wien
          58:491–511.

Hanson, E. D.
  1958   On the origin of the Eumetazoa. Syst. Zool. 7:16–47.

Hörstadius, S.
  1937   Experiments on determinism in the early development of *Cerebratulus
          lacteus*. Biol. Bull. 73:317-342.

Hubrecht, A. A. W.
  1883   On the ancestral forms of the Chordata. Quart. J. micr. Sci. 23:349–368.
  1887   The relation of the Nemertea to the Vertebrata. *Ibid.* 27:605–644.

Hyman, L.
  1951   The Invertebrates. Vol. II: Platyhelminthes and Rhynchocoela—the
          Acoelomate Bilateria. McGraw-Hill, New York, Toronto, London.
  1959   *Idem.* Vol. V: Smaller Coelomate Groups. McGraw-Hill, New York,
          Toronto, London.

Jansen, J.
  1930   The brain of *Myxine glutinosa*. J. comp. Neurol. 49:359–507.

Jarvik, E.
  1960   Théories de l'Évolution des Vertébrés. Masson, Paris.

Jensen, D. D.
  1960   Hoplonemertines, myxinoids, and deuterostome origins. Nature 187:
          649–650.

Johansen, K.
  1960   Circulation in the hagfish, *Myxine glutinosa* L. Biol. Bull. 118:289–295.

Kleerekoper, H., and G. A. van Erkel
  1960   The olfactory apparatus of *Petromyzon marinus* L. Can. J. Zool. 38:209–
          223.

Knight-Jones, E. W.
  1952   On the nervous system of *Saccoglossus cambrensis* (Enteropneusta). Phil.
          Trans. 236B:315–354.

Kupffer, C. von
  1899   Zur Kopfentwicklung von *Bdellostoma*. S. B. Ges. Morph. Physiol.
          Münch. 15:21–35.

Macfarlane, J. M.
  1918   The Causes and Course of Organic Evolution. Macmillan, New York.

Olson, R.
    1958   Studies on the subcommissural organ. Acta zool., Stockh. 39:71–102.
Pietschmann, V.
    1933–
    1955   Einzige Klasse der Marsipobranchia Cyclostomata. Handb. Zool. 6, 1st
            half:127–547. [1933, sect. 2:127–208, sect. 3:209–336; 1934, sect.
            4:337–448; 1935, sect. 5:449–554; 1955, sect. 6:545–547.]
Romer, A. S.
    1959   The Vertebrate Story. Univ. Chicago, Chicago.
Southgate, A. J.
    1959   Personal communication.
Stensiö, S.
    1958   Les Cyclostomes fossiles ou Ostracodermes. Traité Zool. 8, fasc. 1:173–
            425.
Stockard, C. R.
    1906   The development of the mouth and gills in *Bdellostoma stouti*. Amer. J.
            Anat. 5:486.
Wedin, B.
    1955   The origin and development of the extrinsic ocular muscles in *Torpedo
            ocellata*. J. Morph. 97:473–495.
Wijnhoff, G.
    1914   The proboscidian system in nemertines. Quart. J. micr. Sci. 60:307.
Wilson, C. B.
    1900   The habits and early development of *Cerebratulus lacteus* (Verrill).
            Quart. J. micr. Sci. 43:97–198.
Worthington, J.
    1905   Contributions to our knowledge of the myxinoids. Amer. Nat. 34:625–
            663.

B. PORIFERA

10 ◆ The Phylogeny of Sponges According to Embryological, Histological, and Serological Data, and Their Affinities with the Protozoa and the Cnidaria

ODETTE TUZET

LABORATOIRE DE ZOOLOGIE ET BIOLOGIE ANIMALE,
FACULTÉ DES SCIENCES DE MONTPELLIER, MONTPELLIER

The Porifera, or sponges, constitute a distinctive group of aquatic animals distributed widely in the sea at all depths from the equator to the poles. Only the Spongillidae live in fresh water. Because sponges are simple in structure, they were formerly considered to be colonial protozoa (Dujardin, 1838, and Carter, 1859, for example). James-Clark (1868), who discovered the collar cells, regarded the sponges as choanoflagellates and was followed in this by Carter (1871) and Saville Kent (1880, 1899).

Other authors, while recognizing that the sponges are organisms provided with germ layers, have refused to consider them as true metazoa. These authors believe that the sponges are descended from choanoflagellates, which are not related to the Metazoa proper. This was the opinion of Bütschli (1884) and of W. J. Sollas (1884) who proposed the term "Parazoa" for the sponges. This course was followed later by Minchin (1900), I. Sollas (1906), and Hentschel (1924).

At the present time the sponges are regarded as metazoa with differentiated cell layers, but Delage (1892, 1898), stressing their development, isolated them as the group Enantiozoa. In his view the ectoderm of sponges invaginates into the endoderm and forms the digestive cavity made up of flagellated cells. He argued that the flagellated cells of the larva are necessarily ectodermal, and took sponges with a profound metamorphosis as the type for his studies.

The point of view of Delage, which won the approval of Minchin (1900) and Maas (1894), was not accepted by embryologists such as Korschelt and Heider (1936). Since then the work of Brien (1932, 1936, 1943), Brien and Meewis (1938), Meewis (1939a, 1939b, 1941), and Lévi (1956) on the Demospongiae and of Duboscq and Tuzet (1937, 1938, 1942) and Tuzet (1948) on the cal-

---

This paper was translated from the French by W. D. Hartman.

careous sponges has shown that there is no inversion of the germ layers in the course of sponge development. In *Oscarella lobularis,* for example, Meewis (1939a) has shown that the egg develops into a large morula and then into a blastula with externally oriented flagella. The blastula becomes fixed to the substrate by its anterior pole and spreads out; the fixed surface then invaginates. The blastoderm condenses, a certain number of cells undergoing histolysis (a widespread phenomenon in the development of sponges); the blastopore closes and the endoderm is constricted to form the flagellated chambers.

Léger and Duboscq (1910) upheld the origin of sponges—and of the Metazoa generally—from flagellates. They supported their theory on the basis of the constancy of the structure of the spermatozoön in the animal kingdom. The morphology of the microgamete reproduces that of the undifferentiated or ancestral state.

Chatton (1911), in his study of *Pleodorina californica,* after having established certain similarities between that organism and the sponges, did not maintain, however, that the calcareous sponges arose from the Volvocales. He believed that, if the sponges descended directly from protozoa, they could have done so only by way of the choanoflagellates. This opinion was also held by de Saedeleer (1930) and Duboscq and Tuzet (1937), for example.

Saville Kent (1880) described a new genus of choanoflagellates, *Proterospongia*[1] (with a single species, *haeckeli*), which he considered as transitional between the choanoflagellates and the sponges (regarded by him as nothing more than protozoa close to the choanoflagellates). Following him, Mechnikov (1886), Minchin (1897), Caullery and Mesnil (1901), and Lameere (1901, 1908, 1916, 1923) regarded protozoa analogous to *Proterospongia* as the ancestors of sponges.

Duboscq and Tuzet (1937) and Tuzet (1945) have not accepted this notion, since no larval stage of sponges shows a resemblance to *Proterospongia.* We suggested that *Proterospongia,* which, up to 1945, had not, to our knowledge, been described again since Saville Kent, was perhaps a restitution body of a sponge.

But Braarud (1935) and Schiller (1953) have described new forms of the genus (*Proterospongia nana* and *P. haeckeli* var. *clarkii,* respectively), and, more recently, Lackey (1959) has observed this genus again, and has considered its species to be typical choanoflagellates. *Proterospongia,* therefore, cannot be considered as a stage in the phylogeny of sponges.

Haeckel (1870), Lameere (1901 and later), Léger and Duboscq (1910), Chatton (1911), Duboscq and Tuzet (1937), Tuzet (1949), and Jägersten (1955, 1959) have all regarded the sponges as metazoa, belonging to the same series as the celenterates. According to this view the Metazoa are held to be monophyletic. The theory of Hadži (1929), according to which the sponges have developed, independently of other metazoa, from a stock in common with the rhizopods, is rejected.

Our studies of the calcareous and siliceous sponges have demonstrated to us

---

[1] Editors' note: In describing this organism, Saville Kent referred to it as *Protospongia* in the text (vol. I, p. 363) and as *Proterospongia* in the explanation of the plate (vol. III, pl. X). The name *Protospongia* is unavailable since it was applied to a fossil sponge by J. W. Salter (1864, Quart. J. geol. Soc. Lond. 20:233–241). The name *Proterospongia* must be used for Kent's choanoflagellate.

that these animals must be placed at the base of the Metazoa and are intermediate between protozoa and cnidarians. They manifest some characters of protozoa mingled with numerous characters of metazoa.

The choanocytes (fig. 10-1), endodermal or digestive cells, remain in a single layer like any metazoan endoderm, but they resemble the choanoflagellates in the presence of a collar and a flagellum arising from a blepharoplast to which is attached a parabasal body.

According to de Saedeleer (1930), in *Sycon* the flagellum is doubly bent and functions as a pulsatory organelle as in the case of the Craspedomonadina. The collar of the choanocytes of fresh-water sponges has an aspect similar to that of choanoflagellates according to the electron microscope studies of Kilian (1954), Rasmont *et al.* (1957), and Rasmont (1959). In each case the collar is formed of a circlet of contiguous tentacles.

W. J. Sollas (1884), on the basis of the presence of choanocytes, placed the sponges in a sub-kingdom, the Parazoa, separated from the sub-kingdom Metozoa, the species of which, he maintained, never have similar cells. But collar cells have been found for the Echinodermata in the pluteus of the echinoid, *Echinocyamus pusillus,* and in the epithelium of the oviduct of *Caudina arenata* (Gerould, 1896). The blastula of sponges has flagellated cells without collars, but with a parabasal body attached to the blepharoplast. Identical cells have been described by Cowdry (1921) in the thyroid of *Mustelus canis,* by Hovasse (1934) in the larva of *Paracentrotus lividus* (fig. 10-2), and by Tuzet and Sanchez (1954) on the surface of the brachia of *Terebartulina caputserpentis* (fig. 10-3). Finally, cells with a single flagellum are found in all Cnidaria, in the larva as well as the adult.

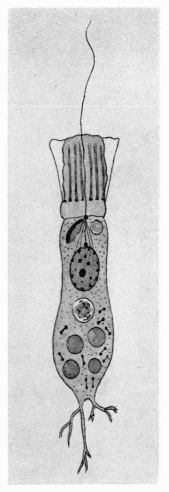

FIGURE 10-1. Schematic diagram of a choanocyte.

As protozoan characteristics can be considered the loose cohesion of the choanocuytes, which can wander into the mesenchyme, and the ameboid nature of certain cells, especially the oöcytes, which, in *Sycon raphanus,* for example, traverse the mesenchyme to go to the atrium in search of their nutritive cells (fig. 10-4).

When the spermiocyst, contained in the choanocyte transformed to a carrier cell, penetrates the oöcyte, the last-mentioned cell forms, in order to pick up the spermiocyst, a cytostome (fig. 10-5) similar to that described by Ivanić (1933, 1936) in several fresh-water amebae at the moment of the capture of prey.

Finally, during the embryogenesis of calcareous sponges, the larva turns inside out and the surfaces are inverted, thus recalling what is seen in *Volvox* (Zimmermann, 1925; fig. 10-6). The young blastulae with large ectodermal cells, the

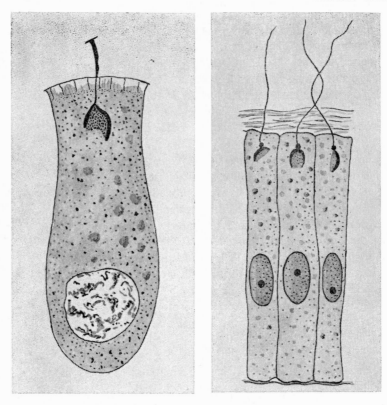

FIGURE 10-2. Flagellated cell of larva of *Paracentrotus lividus* (Lemarck). (After Hovasse, 1934.)
FIGURE 10-3. Flagellated cells of the brachial ectoderm in *Terebratulina caputserpentis* (Linn.).

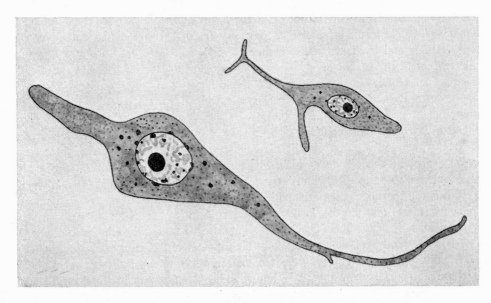

FIGURE 10-4. Ameboid eggs of *Sycon raphanus* Schmidt.

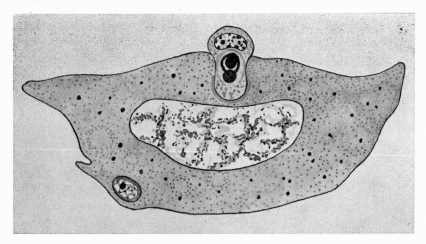

FIGURE 10-5. *Grantia compressa pennigera* Haeckel. Carrier cell transmitting a spermiocyst to a large oöcyte that has formed a cytostome.

stomoblastulae, show an opening limited by eight ectoblastic cells functioning as a mouth to draw in the choanocytes or their posterior prolongations (fig. 10-7).

The ectodermal cells multiply, the mouth closes, and the endodermal cells acquire internal flagella; at this stage the embryo is a blastula with flagella directed

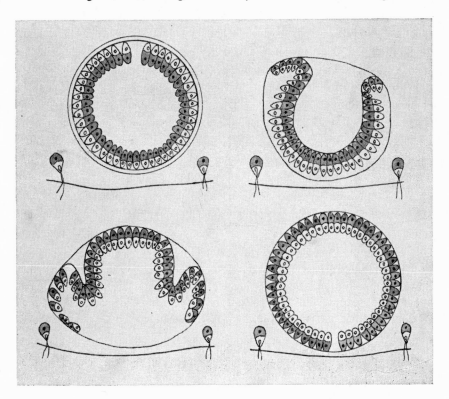

FIGURE 10-6. Stages in the process of turning inside out in the blastula of *Volvox aureus* Ehrenb. (After Zimmerman, 1925.)

into its cavity. A new blastular mouth forms and enlarges, unmasking the flagellated cells. The flagellated region of the larva bulges out, generally assuming a dome-shaped configuration, while the edges, limited by the dermal cells, curve inward more and more. There exists at this time a sort of cellular plate that, at first in-curved in one direction, later curves outward in the other direction, like a *Volvox* blastula. There results finally an amphiblastula with flagella directed outward (fig. 10-8).

This inversion of the surfaces is unknown in the Metazoa; several examples of it occur, on the other hand, among the Protista. It cannot be concluded from this

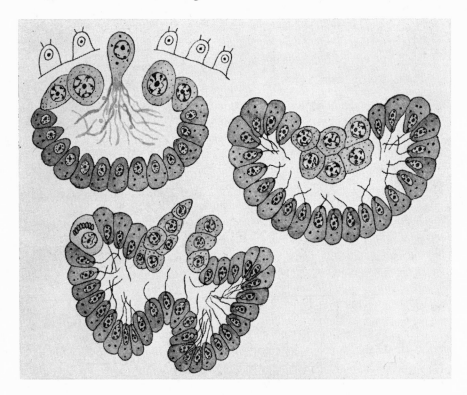

FIGURE 10-7. *Sycon raphanus* Schmidt. Upper left, stomoblastula; upper right, blastula with flagella directed internally; lower left, onset of the process of inversion of the blastula surfaces.

that the sponges are derived from the volvocines, but it can be suggested that the sponges might have arisen from colonies of choanoflagellates recalling the vol-vocines.

Sponges can reconstitute themselves from previously dissociated cells. Many authors have studied this reconstitution (Wilson, Müller, Huxley, Galtsoff, Fauré-Fremiet, Penney, Brien, Child, Hargitt, and Tuzet, for example), but this property is not peculiar to the sponges. It is found also in the Cnidaria (Wilson, 1911; Okada, 1927; Föyn, 1927). Therefore it cannot be invoked to separate the Porifera from other metazoa.

In addition to protozoön-like characters, the sponges present numerous metazoan characters. The cells of the mesenchyme are similar to certain elements observed

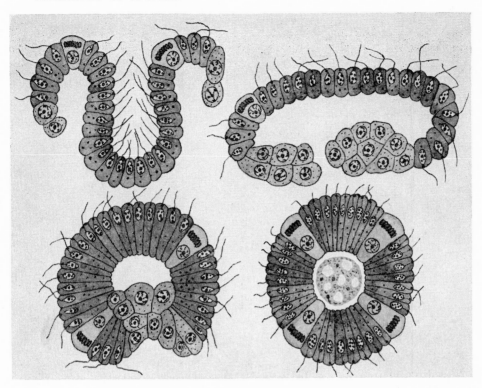

FIGURE 10-8. *Sycon raphanus* Schmidt. Upper figures, two stages in the inversion of the surfaces of the blastula; lower left, amphiblastula with flagella directed externally; lower right, section of amphiblastula showing the four cross cells.

in the Metazoa: stellate cells forming the network of the tissues; hyaline and eosinophilic amebocytes (fig. 10-9); nerve cells (fig. 10-10) with their fibers and Nissl bodies (Tuzet and Pavans de Ceccatty, 1952, 1953a; Pavans de Ceccatty, 1955).

Among the Demospongiae (*Hippospongia, Pachymatisma*) highly differentiated cells can be observed: cells of a neuromuscular type and the curious lophocytes (fig. 10-11), which can, according to the species, play a role in excretion or in the

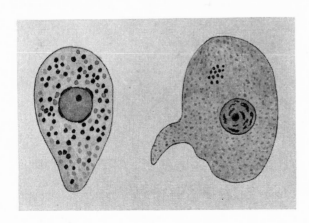

FIGURE 10-9. Eosinophilic (left) and hyaline (right) amebocytes of *Sycon raphanus* Schmidt.

secretion of spongin fibers (Tuzet and Pavans de Ceccatty, 1953b; Tuzet and Paris, 1957).

I believe that in the sponges as in other invertebrates the various sensitive cells, nervous or neuromuscular, must have an ectodermal origin, while the free cells of the mesenchyme are generally of endodermal origin. I have been able to observe

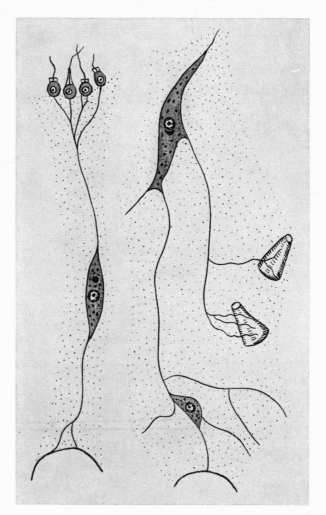

FIGURE 10-10. Nerve-like cells of *Cliona celata* Grant.

pinacocytes detach themselves from the epidermis, sink into the mesenchyme, and there transform into nerve cells.

The processes of spermatogenesis and oögenesis of sponges are similar to those of metazoa.

In *Hippospongia communis* spermatogenesis is identical to that of an echinoid or a mollusc (figs. 10-12, 10-13). The spermatozoön is the same as that of a celenterate, of an echinoid, or of a tunicate (fig. 10-14).

There is no ovary in the sponges; the eggs develop in isolation. In certain cnidarians, such as *Sympodium coralloides* (Tuzet, 1941), the eggs also develop separately (fig. 10-15). Oögenesis is like that of a metazoön (fig. 10-16).

Following the oögonial divisions the young oöcyte passes through a period of little growth during which one can observe in the nucleus the prophase stages of the primary meiotic division. The nucleus returns later to a resting stage and remains so during the period of increase in size of the cell. At the end of this period of growth one sees double chromosomes reappear in the form of tetrads. During its growth the egg absorbs the nutritive cells or is nourished at their expense.

The fertilization of sponges is peculiar. The spermatozoön is always transported

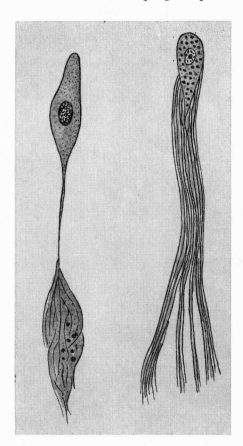

FIGURE 10-11. Lophocytes of (left) *Pachymatisma johnstonia* Bowerbank and (right) *Tethya aurantia* (Pallas).

to the egg by a carrier cell, generally derived from a choanocyte (Gatenby, 1920a, 1920b, 1927; Duboscq and Tuzet, 1937; Tuzet and Pavans de Ceccatty, 1958). It is then transferred to the egg in the form of an encysted sperm, the spermiocyst (figs. 10-17, 10-18). But one cannot obtain from this process of fertilization any argument to separate the sponges from other metazoa. In *Spadella cephaloptera* (Elpatevskiĭ, 1910a, 1910b; Vasil'ev, 1925) two special cells, the synergids, lead the spermatozoön to the egg, and one does not consider isolating the Chaetognatha from the Metazoa on this basis.

All the phenomena of polar body formation and of the union of the pronuclei in the sponges are similar to what one observes in the higher animals.

If one excepts the inversion of the surfaces of the blastula of calcareous sponges (a phenomenon, moreover, that does not appear in the siliceous sponges, in which the blastula is formed at the onset with externally oriented flagella as in the primitive Metazoa), development from the egg presents nothing that removes the sponges from other metazoa.

There are among the calcareous sponges, however, three possible pseudogastrulations. The first is passed in the stomoblastula with internally directed flagella, when the mouth closes following the multiplication of the eight dermal cells, which may sink down into the segmentation cavity. The second, discovered by Barrois

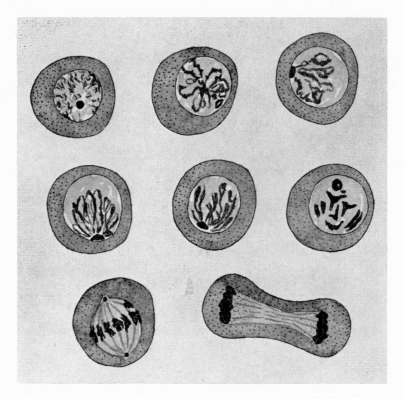

FIGURE 10-12. Spermatogenesis of *Hippospongia communis* (Lamarck):
spermatocytes I and primary meiotic division.

(1876), occurs in the amphiblastula located beneath the choanocytes of the parent sponge. The third takes place in the free larva and is the true gastrulation—the only one having phyletic importance. Jägersten (1955, 1959), in his works on the "bilaterogastrea theory," also thinks that the developmental features of sponges do not separate them from other metazoa. From the standpoint of ontogeny the Calcarea are the most primitive sponges. The pores should not be considered as a new formation phylogenetically (although this opinion is often expressed because the blastula closes after fixation). The fixation of the larva of sponges, although differing from that of the Cnidaria, is not, for Jägersten, an obstacle to a phylogenetic relationship between the larvae of the Porifera and Cnidaria. In fact, important changes take place in numerous animals in the orientation of the body and

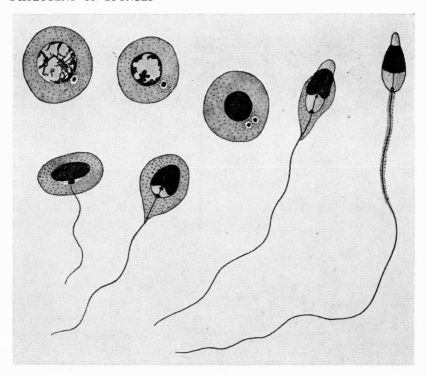

FIGURE 10-13. Spermatogenesis of *Hippospongia communis* (Lamarck):
spermatocytes II, spermatids, and spermatozoa.

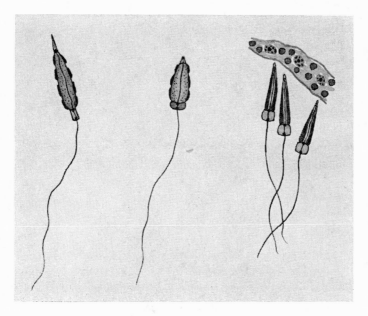

FIGURE 10-14. Spermatozoa of (left to right) *Styela partita*
(Stimpson), *Paracentrotus lividus* (Lamarck), and *Sympodium*
coralloides (Stimpson), *Paracentrotus lividus* (Lamarck), and
Sympodium corralloides (Pallas).

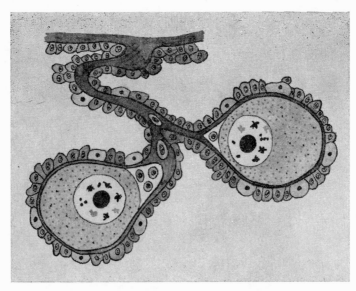

FIGURE 10-15. *Eggs of Sympodium coralloides* (Pallas).

in the position of the mouth and other openings during phylogeny and therefore in ontogeny.

Another character by which the sponges may be compared to the Metazoa is the presence in the former of a tetraradial symmetry so characteristic of the Cnidaria and many of the Metazoa. The four cross cells of the amphiblastulae of

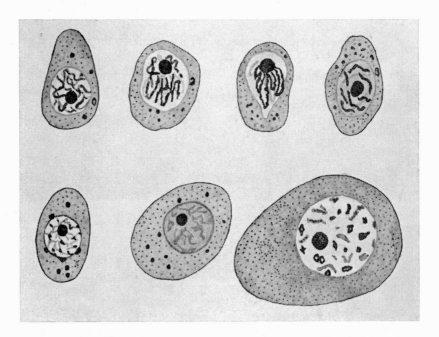

FIGURE 10-16. Oögenesis of *Grantia compressa pennigera* Haeckel. Prophase stages of primary meiotic division and period of growth of secondary oöcyte.

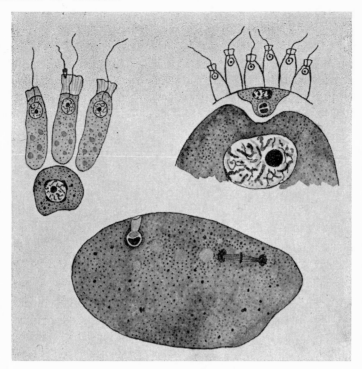

FIGURE 10-17. Stages in fertilization of *Sycon raphanus*
Schmidt.

calcareous sponges (fig. 10-8) demonstrate the existence of this symmetry and
show it, as in the hydroids, to be established as two planes perpendicular one to
another, one of perfect symmetry and one of approximate symmetry. This tetra-
radiality is found, for example, in the larvae of polychetes, gastropods, and sipunculids.

Serological reactions have been carried out by the method of "complement fixation" (Diacono, 1933) between two species of the class Demospongiae, *Tethya*

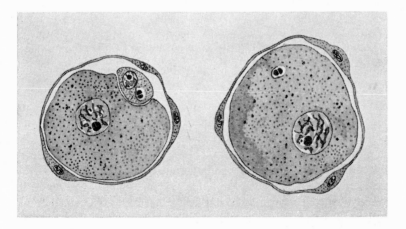

FIGURE 10-18. Fertilization in *Hippospongia communis* (Lamarck).

aurantia (syn. *lyncurium*) and *Suberites domunculus,* and the octocoral, *Veretillum cynomorium.* Examination of the curves (figs. 10-19, 10-20, 10-21) shows a close relationship between the two sponges, *Tethya aurantia* and *Suberites domunculus.* The curve in figure 10-21 indicates that a serological relationship does not seem to exist between the two sponges studied and *Veretillum cynomorium.* The curve relating to this cnidarian shows, in fact, a high complement fixation in the combination of the *Veretillum* antigen with its homologous antibody, whereas the

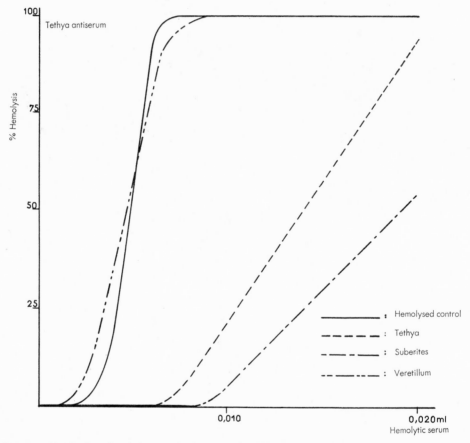

FIGURE 10-19. Graph of the serological reaction of anti-*Tethya aurantia* (Pallas) serum with sera of *Tethya aurantia* (homolog), *Suberites domunculus* (Olivi), and *Veretillum cynomorium* (Pallas).

antigens of the sponges give rise to no fixation with respect to the same antiserum.

The sponges constitute, therefore, a limited offshoot of the Metazoa, but the protozoan characters presented by them indicate that the sponges must be placed at the base of the metazoan line.

The ancestral stock of the sponges is generally sought among the choanoflagellates, the structure of the choanocyte being the evidence of this descent. De Saedeleer (1930) conceives of the sponge as having come from an organism that was at the same time the ancestor of the Craspedomonadina. I also believe that the sponges are not derived directly from the choanoflagellates, for one can recognize none of the latter organisms as being transitional to the Porifera. Recent observations made on *Proterospongia* by Lackey (1959) show that this genus is a typical choanoflagellate.

During development, the larva of calcareous sponges undergoes an inversion similar to that of the *Volvox* blastula. This phenomenon is not without significance, but it does not imply that the sponges have descended from volvocines. (This stage does not exist in the siliceous sponges.) One can speculate, however, that protozoa

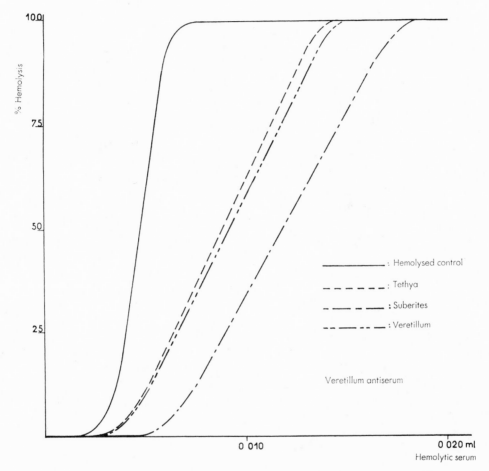

FIGURE 10-20. Graph of the serological reaction of anti-*Suberites* serum with sera of *Suberites* (homolog), *Tethya,* and *Veretillum.*

ancestral to the sponges may have consisted of colonies comparable to those of the higher volvocines.

Nothing is opposed, it seems to me, to the derivation of the Hydrozoa from the sponges. Jägersten (1955) thinks that the Porifera can be derived from the same line as the Cnidaria and the Ctenophora, but, in his view, the organization of the sponges has been modified by the sedentary life that they have led for vast epochs.

The sponges have, indeed, numerous characters in common with the Cnidaria: the same spermatogenesis and spermatozoön, the same oögenesis, and larval stages with the same appearance. The tetraradial symmetry observed in the sponges is characteristic of the majority of species of the Cnidaria and Ctenophora. Furthermore, the mouth of a polyp is also an anus, and attention has been called, in a certain number of sponges, to the possible functioning of the oscule as a mouth when the water current is reversed. The physiology of sponges cannot be invoked in opposition to their morphology.

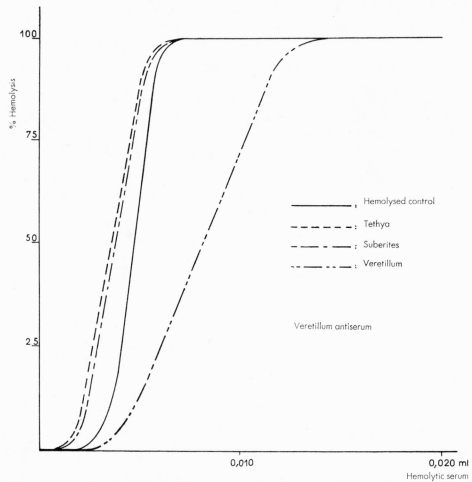

FIGURE 10-21. Graph of the serological reaction of anti-*Veretillum* serum with sera of *Veretillum* (homolog), *Tethya,* and *Suberites.*

REFERENCES

Barrois, C.
    1876   Mémoire sur l'embryologie de quelques Éponges de la Manche. Ann. Sci. nat. (sér. 6) 3:1–84.
Braarud, T.
    1935   The "Øst" Expedition to the Denmark Strait, 1929. II. The phytoplankton and its condition of growth (including some qualitative data from the Arctic in 1930). Hvalråd. Skr. norskeVidenskAkad. 10:1–173.

Brien, P.
    1932   Contribution à l'étude de la régeneration naturelle chez les Spongillidae: *Spongilla lacustris* (L.) et *Ephydatia fluviatilis* (L.). Arch. Zool. exp. gén. 74:461–506.

    1936   La réorganisation de l'Éponge après dissociation par filtration et phénomènes d'involution chez *Ephydatia fluviatilis*. Arch. Biol., Paris 48: 185–268.

    1943   L'embryologie des Éponges. Bull. Mus. Hist. nat. Belg. 19, no. 16:1–20.
Brien, P., and H. Meewis.
    1938   Contribution à l'étude de l'embryogénèse des Spongillidae. Arch. Biol., Paris 49:177–250.

Bütschli, O.
    1884   Bemerkungen zur Gastraeatheorie. Morph. Jb. 9:415–427.
Carter, H. J.
    1859   On fecundation in the two Volvoces, and their specific differences; on *Eudorina, Spongilla, Astasia, Englena, and Cryptoglena*. Ann. Mag. nat. Hist. (ser. 3) 3:1–20.

    1871   A description of two new Calcispongiae, to which is added confirmation of Prof. James-Clark's discovery of the true form of the sponge-cell (animal), and an account of the polype-like pre-area of *Cliona corallinoides* contrasted with Prof. E. Häckel's view on the relationship of the sponges to the corals. *Ibid*. (ser. 4) 8:1–27.

Caullery, M., and F. Mesnil.
    1901   Recherches sur les Orthonectides. Arch. Anat. micr. 4:381–470.
Chatton, É.
    1911   *Pleodorina californica* à Banyuls-sur-mer. Son cycle évolutif et sa signification phylogénétique. Bull. sci. Fr. Belg. (ser. 7) 44:309–331.

Cowdry, E. V.
    1921   Flagellated thyroid cells in the dogfish (*Mustelus canis*). Anat. Rec. 22: 289–297.

Delage, Y.
    1892   Embryogénie des Éponges. Développement postlarvaire des Éponges siliceuses et fibreuses marines et d'eau douce. Arch. Zool. exp. gén. (sér. 2) 10:345–498.

    1898   Sur la place des Spongiaires dans la classification. C. R. Acad. Sci., Paris 126:545–548.

Diacono, H.
    1933   Le phénomène hémolytique. Thèse, Doct. Pharmacie, Montpellier.
Duboscq, O., and O. Tuzet
    1937   L'ovogénèse, la fécondation et les premiers stades du développement des Éponges calcaires. Arch. Zool. exp. gén. 79:157–316.

    1938   La collerette des choanocytes chez les Éponges calcaires hétérocœles. C. R. Soc. Biol., Paris 129:296–298.

    1942   Recherches complémentaires sur l'ovogenèse, la fécondation et les premiers stades du développement des Éponges calcaires. Arch. Zool. exp. gén. 81:395–466.

Dujardin, F.
    1838   Observations sur les Éponges et en particulier sur la Spongille ou Éponge d'eau douce. Ann. Sci. nat. (Zool.) (sér. 2) 10:5–13.
Elpatevskiĭ, V. [Elpatiewsky, W.]
    1910a   Die Urgeschlechtszellenbildung bei *Sagitta*. Anat. Anz. 35:226–239.

1910b   Die Entwicklungsgeschichte der Genitalprodukte bei *Sagitta*. I. Die Entwicklung der Eier. Biol. Zh. 1:333–367.

Föyn, B.
1927   Studien über Geschlecht und Geschlechtszellen bei Hydroiden. II. Aus pressungsversuche an *Clava squamata* (Müller), mit Mischung von Zellen aus Polypen desselben oder verschiedenen Geschlechts. Arch. Entw-Mech. Org. 110:89–148.

Gatenby, J. B.
1920a   The germ-cells, fertilization, and early development of *Grantia* (*Sycon*) *compressa*. J. Linn. Soc. (Zool.) 34:261–297.
1920b   Further notes on the oögenesis and fertilization of *Grantia compressa*. J. R. micr. Soc. (1920):277–282.
1927   Further notes on the gametogenesis and fertilization of sponges. Quart. J. micr. Sci. 71:173–188.

Gerould, J. H.
1896   The anatomy and histology of *Caudina arenata* Gould. Proc. Boston Soc. nat. Hist. 27:7–74.

Hadži, J.
1929   Einige allgemein wichtige Resultate meiner Untersuchungen über Coelenterata (s. ampl.) C. R. Xe Congr. int. Zool., Budapest, 1927:924–932.

Haeckel, E.
1870   Über den Organismus der Schwämme und ihre Verwandtschaft mit den Corallen. Jena. Z. Naturw. 5:207–235.

Hentschel, E.
1924   Erste Unterabteilung der Metazoa: Parazoa. Handb. Zool., Berl. 1:307–418.

Hovasse, R.
1934   Sur l'existence d'un appareil parabasal dans les cellules flagellées des larves nageantes chez l'Oursin, *Paracentrotus lividus*. C. R. Acad. Sci., Paris 199:1664–1667.

Ivanić, M.
1933   Über die bei Nahrungsaufnahme einige Süsswasseramöben vorkommende Bildung cytostomähnlicher Gebilde. Arch. Protistenk. 79:200–233.
1936   Recherches nouvelles sur l'ingestion des aliments au moyen de cytostomes chez quelques Amibes d'eau douce (*Amoeba vespertilio* Penard et *Hartmannella maasi* Ivanić). La Cellule 45:177–206.

Jägersten, G.
1955   On the early phylogeny of the Metazoa. The bilaterogastraea theory. Zool. Bidr. Uppsala 30:321–354.
1959   Further remarks on the early phylogeny of the Metazoa. *Ibid*. 33:79–108.

James-Clark, H.
1868   On the Spongiae ciliatae as Infusoria flagellata; or observations on the structure, animality, and relationship of *Leucosolenia botryoides* Bowerbank. Ann. Mag. nat. Hist. (ser. 4) 1:250–264.

Kilian, E. F.
1954   Die Feinstruktur des Kragens bei den Choanocyten der Spongilliden. Ber. oberhess. Ges. Nat.-u. Heilk. 27:85–89.

Korschelt, E., and K. Heider
1936   Vergleichende Entwicklungsgeschichte der Tiere. Rev. E. Korschelt. Fischer, Jena.

Lackey, J. B.
  1959   Morphology and biology of a species of *Protospongia*. Trans. Amer. micr. Soc. 78: 202–206.

Lameere, A.
  1901   De l'origine des Éponges. Ann. Soc. zool. Belg. 36:vii–viii (Bull. Séances.)
  1908   Éponge et polype. Ibid. 43:107–124.
  1916   Une théorie zoologique. Bull. sci. Fr. Belg. 49:378–431.
  1923   Note de zoogénie. V. L'évolution des Spongiaires. Ann. Soc. zool. Belg. 53:33–39.

Léger, L., and O. Duboscq.
  1910   *Selenococcidium intermedium* Lég. et Dub. et la systématique des Sporozoaires. Arch. Zool. exp. gén. (ser. 5) 5:187–238.

Lévi, C.
  1956   Étude des *Halisarca* de Roscoff. Embryologie et systématique des Démosponges. *Ibid.* 93:1–184.

Maas, O.
  1894   Über die erste Differenzierung von Generations- und Somazellen bei den Spongien. Verh. dtsch. zool. Ges. (1893): 27–35.

Meewis, H.
  1939a   Contribution à l'étude de l'embryogénèse des Myxospongidae: *Halisarca lobularis* (Schmidt). Arch. Biol., Paris 50:3–66.
  1939b   Contribution à l'étude de l'embryogénèse des Chalinidae: *Haliclona limbata* (Mont.). Ann. Soc. zool. Belg. 70:201–225.
  1941   Contribution à l'étude de l'embryogénèse des Éponges siliceuses. Développement de l'oeuf chez *Adocia cinera* (Grant) et *Halichondria coalita* (Bowerbank). *Ibid.* 72:126–149.

Mechnikov [Metschnikoff], E.
  1886   Embryologische Studien an Medusen. Ein Beitrag zur Genealogie der primitiven Organe. Holder, Wien.

Minchin, E. A.
  1897   The position of sponges in the animal kingdom. Sci. Progr. (ser. 2) 1: 426–460.
  1900   Sponges. A Treatise on Zoology. 2, chap. 3: 1–178.

Okada, Y. K.
  1927   Étude sur la régenération chez les Coelenterés. Arch. Zool. exp. gén. 66: 497–551.

Pavans de Ceccatty, M.
  1955   Le système nerveux des Éponges calcaires et siliceuses. Ann. Sci. nat., Zool. (sér. 11) 17:203–288.

Rasmont, R.
  1959   Ultra-structure des choanocytes d'Éponges. Proc. 15th int. Congr. Zool., London (1958):707–708.

Rasmont, R., J. Bouillon, P. Castiaux, and G. Vandermeersche.
  1957   Structure submicroscopique de la collerette des choanocytes d'Éponges. C. R. Acad. Sci., Paris 245:1571–1574.

Saedeleer, H. de
  1930   Recherches sur les choanocytes; l'origine des Spongiaires. Ann. Soc. zool. Belg. (1929) 60:16–21.

Saville Kent, W.
  1880–
  1882   Manual of the Infusoria, Including a Description of All Known Flagel-

late, Ciliated, and Tentaculiferous Protozoa, British and Foreign, and an Account of the Organization and Affinities of the Sponges. Bogue, London. 3 vols.

1899   Discussion on the position of sponges in the animal kingdom. Proc. 4th int. Congr. Zool., Cambridge (1898):65–67.

Schiller, J.
1953   Über neue Craspedomonaden (Choanoflagellaten). Arch. Hydrobiol. 48:248–259.

Sollas, I. B. J.
1906   Porifera (Sponges). Cambridge Nat. Hist., London 1:163–282.

Sollas, W. J.
1884   On the development of *Halisarca lobularis* (O. Schmidt). Quart. J. micr. Sci. 24:603–621.

Tuzet, O.
1941   Sur l'ovogenèse, la spermatogenèse et la fécondation de *Sympodium coralloides* Pallas. Arch. Zool. exp. gén. 82:287–299.

1945
        Sur les agrégats de choanocytes et la question de la *Proterospongia*. *Ibid.* 84:225–238.

1948   Les premiers stades du développement de *Leucosolenia botryoides* Ellis et Solander et de *Clathrina* (*Leucosolenia*) *coriacea* Mont. Ann. Sci. nat., Zool. (sér. 11) 10:103–114.

1949   La place des Spongiaires dans la classification. C. R. XIIIᵉ Congr. int. Zool., Paris (1948): 429–432.

Tuzet, O., and J. Paris
1957   Les lophocytes de l'Éponge siliceuse *Tethya lyncurium* Lamarck et leur évolution. C. R. Acad. Sci., Paris 244:3088–3090.

Tuzet, O., and M. Pavans de Ceccatty
1952   Les cellules nerveuses de *Grantia compressa pennigera* Haeckel (Éponge calcaire hétérocoele). *Ibid.* 235:1541–1543.

1953a   Les cellules nerveuses et neuro-musculaires de l'Éponge: *Cliona celata* Grant. *Ibid.* 236:2342–2344.

1953b   Les lophocytes de l'Éponge *Pachymatisma johnstonni* Bow. *Ibid.* 237: 1447–1449.

1958   Le spermatogenèse, l'ovogenèse, la fécondation et les premiers stades du développement chez *Hippospongia communis* Lmk. (= *H. equina* O. S.) Bull. biol. 92:331–348.

Tuzet, O. and S. Sanchez
1954   Sur la présence d'un appareil parabasal dans les cellules flagellées des bras du Brachiopode *Terebratulina caputserpentis* L. C. R. Acad. Sci., Paris 238:1839–1841.

Vasil'ev [Vasiljev], A.
1925   La fécondation chez *Spadella cephaloptera* Lgrhs. et l'origine du corps déterminant la voie germinative. Biol. gén. 1:249–278.

Wilson, H. V.
1911   On the behavior of the dissociated cells in hydroids, Alcyonaria and *Asterias*. J. exp. Zool. 11:281–338.

Zimmermann, W.
1925   Die ungeschlechtliche Entwicklung von *Volvox*. Naturwissenschaften 13: 397–402.

C. MESOZOA

11 ◆ The Mesozoa

BAYARD H. McCONNAUGHEY

DEPARTMENT OF BIOLOGY,
UNIVERSITY OF OREGON, EUGENE

In 1876, van Beneden, having made the first careful study of dicyemids (parasites of cephalopods) using histological methods, felt that he had evidence for a true "missing link." Here was a group of animals that seemed to bridge the gap between protozoa and metazoa. The body consisted of only a few large ciliated cells inclosing an axial reproductive cell in which the young were generated. There was no sign of differentiated digestive, excretory, reproductive, respiratory, circulatory, nervous, muscular, glandular, or skeletal systems such as are found in unequivocal metazoa, in either the adult or embryonic stages. The functions were carried out at the cellular level as in protozoa, yet these animals were clearly not just colonial protozoa.

To express his views on their phylogenetic significance van Beneden coined the term "Mesozoa" for the group. The name and the concept were appealing and have stuck to the group despite different phylogenetic interpretations and alternative names offered by subsequent zoölogists. The discovery shortly thereafter of the orthonectids, and the studies of Giard (1877, 1879), Julin (1882), Caullery (1912; Caullery and Lavallée, 1905, 1908, 1912; Caullery and Mesnil, 1899), and others on this group gave a firmer and broader base for van Beneden's concept.

Other zoölogists, intrigued by the concept of "Mesozoa," were tempted to assign to this assemblage any minute enigmatic animals whose relationships they were unable to ascertain. Thus for a time the group became a hodgepodge with little internal consistency and no clear bounds. In time, however, the extraneous organisms have largely been assigned to their proper phyla, and the Mesozoa have again emerged as a rather homogeneous group.

Because the life cycle of the Orthonectida is more fully known and more familiar in pattern, I begin with a brief review of that group.

The Orthonectida

Orthonectids parasitize a variety of marine invertebrates, including nemerteans, polychetes, bivalve molluscs, brittle stars, and others. The adults are minute free-swimming, ciliated, short-lived, worm-like animals. In most species the sexes are separate. The body consists of several rings of cells, quite constant in number and arrangement in any given species. On the anterior rings long cilia are directed forward; those on the rest of the body, posteriorly. In most species the males are

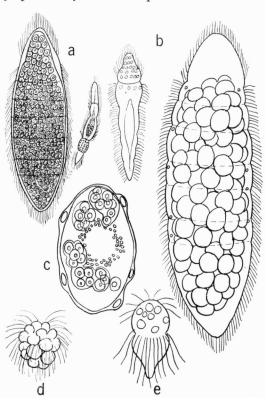

FIGURE 11-1. Orthonectida. (*a*) *Rhopalura ophiocomae,* male discharging sperm near the genital pore of the female. (After Lameere, 1929, from Caullery and Lavallée, 1908.) (*b*) *Rhopalura granosa,* male and female sketched from living specimens. (After Atkins, 1933.) (*c*) *R. ophiocomae,* plasmodium surrounded by a cellular sheath derived from the host. Masses of parthenogenetic germ cells and a circle of many small vegetative nuclei are shown. (After Lameere, 1929.) (*d*) *R. ophiocomae,* ciliated larva, from life. (After Lameere, 1929, from Caullery and Lavallée, 1908.) (*e*) *R. granosa,* ciliated larva squeezed from body of a mature female. (After Atkins, 1933.)

smaller than the females and have a neck-like region comprised of a few rings of non-ciliated cells containing large refractile bodies.

The adults are shed in large numbers from infected host animals, often late in the afternoon. The males discharge sperm near the genital opening of the female. These penetrate among, and fertilize, the egg cells, which fill the body of the female. The fertilized eggs give off polar bodies on long cytoplasmic processes and soon begin cleavage. The first division is unequal, resulting in a small cell and a larger quiescent cell, which soon becomes enveloped by the division products of the smaller cell. During the early cleavages some small bits of chromatin are eliminated from the embryos. Soon a characteristic ciliated larva is formed (fig. 11-1, *d, e*), composed of outer ciliated cells and a group of internal germ cells.[1]

---

[1] Unless otherwise indicated, the drawings for the figures were made with the aid of a camera lucida from the author's preparations. Several have been published earlier; figures 11-4, 11-11, and 11-12 are new.

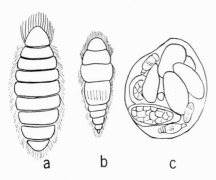

FIGURE 11-2. Orthonectida, *Rhopalura intoshii*. (*a*) Female, (*b*) male, and (*c*) plasmodium giving rise to both males and females. (After Mechnikov, 1881.)

When the larva infects a host animal, it loses its ciliated cells. The germ cells develop into a large, irregular syncytium occupying tissue spaces in the host and containing agametes (figs. 11-1, *c*; 11-2, *c*). The syncytia may multiply by growth and fragmentation and in some instances are quite destructive to their host. In mature syncytia the agametes develop into sexual males or females, which, when fully developed, are ready to leave the host. The plasmodia are said to give rise to only one sex in most cases, although hermaphroditic ones have been described.

In some orthonectids the females are more elongate and the egg cells arranged biserially (fig. 11-3, *a*). Finally in *Stoecharthrum* (fig. 11-3, *b, c*) we have a long, slender annulated form containing in each annulation either a single egg cell or, in fewer annuli, a testis—the animals being hermaphroditic.

The orthonectids, though morphologically simple, present a general pattern of life not unlike that of numerous other parasites. Sexual adults form zygotes, which develop into dispersal larvae and infect new hosts. In the host a period of asexual reproduction intervenes before the production of a new crop of adults.

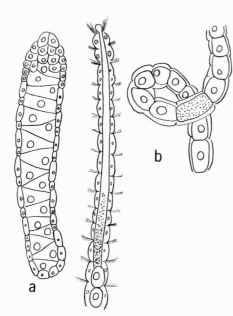

FIGURE 11-3. Orthonectida. (*a*) *Rhopalura metschnikovi,* female, germ cells arranged in a double row. Stained preparation. (After Hartmann, 1906, from Caullery and Mesnil, 1899.) (*b*) *Stoecharthrum giardi,* anterior end and portion of trunk. Egg cells in linear series, one to each apparent segment. One of the segments has developed as a testis. (After Caullery and Mesnil, 1899.)

The Dicyemida

The dicyemids, by contrast, present a more complex life cycle and certain morphological peculiarities that set them apart sharply from other animals. Since van Beneden's pioneering study they have been restudied by a number of zoölogists, including Whitman (1883), Hartmann (1906), Lameere (1916, 1918, 1919),

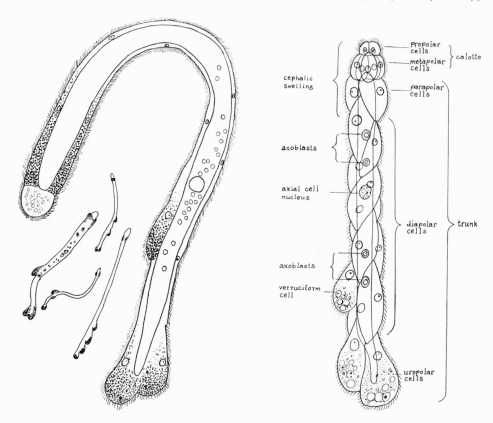

FIGURE 11-4. Dicyemida. Group of living dicyemids to show general appearance. *Dicyemennea granularis,* calotte, trunk, and verruciform and uropolar cells are evident. Under greater magnification the axial cell, its nucleus and contents, and some of the nuclei of somatic cells can be made out.

FIGURE 11-5. Dicyemida. Young dicyemid to show terms that have been applied to various parts. (Stained preparation, *Dicyemennea abelis.*) (After McConnaughey, 1951.)

Nouvel (1933, 1947, 1948), Gersch (1938), Stunkard (1954), and others, including me (McConnaughey, 1949, 1951; McConnaughey and McConnaughey, 1954). There are almost as many different interpretations of their morphology, life cycle, and phylogeny as there are zoölogists that have studied them.

Dicyemids (figs. 11-4, 11-5) are found only in the renal organs of cephalopod molluscs, where they often occur in great numbers. The body consists of a solitary long axial cell enveloped by a single layer of large ciliated cells, those at the anterior end being modified into a sort of head, the calotte, by which the dicyemid clings to the renal organ of its host. The rest of the body floats freely in the host's urine.

Germ cells and embryos in all stages of development are found inside the axial cell. The name "dicyemid" was suggested by the fact that two very different sorts of embryos are found. In young cephalopods all or most of the parasites give rise to vermiform larvae, similar to themselves, while in mature hosts most of them give rise instead to peculiar short, rounded larvae that look more like some sort of ciliated protozoön. Individuals of the first sort are termed *nematogens;* and their larvae, *vermiform larvae.* Those of the second sort are called *rhombogens;* and their larvae, *infusoriform larvae* or simply *infusoriforms.*

The vermiform larvae, when fully developed, escape from the parent nematogen

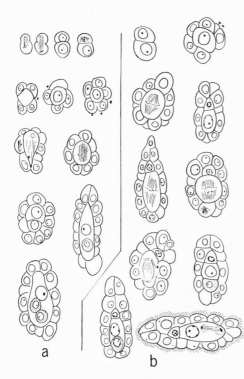

FIGURE 11-6. Dicyemida. Embryology of the vermiform larva: (*a*) genus *Dicyema,* (*b*) genus *Dicyemennea.* (After McConnaughey, 1951.)

and cling to the kidney tissue in the same cephalopod, thus increasing the population of dicyemids in a given host. The infusoriforms, on the other hand, after escaping from the parent rhombogen, are discharged into the sea with the urine of their host. Their fate is unknown.

A number of questions immediately present themselves. What is the origin of the germ cells, and how do they get inside the axial cell? Are any of the known stages sexual, or is the entire known portion of the life cycle asexual? What is the nature of the axial cell? These and other puzzling questions can be partly answered through a close study of the development of the larval stages.

In nematogens, a germ cell about to produce a vermiform larva undergoes an unequal mitosis, producing a large cell and a small cell, which do not separate as in the case of ordinary mitoses producing more germ cells. The large cell remains quiescent for a time while the smaller one undergoes several rapid divisions. During the first few divisions of the small cell a few deep-staining chromatin granules are eliminated and can be seen at the periphery of the developing embryo. Soon the large cell is wholly enveloped by smaller cells and differentiation into calotte and trunk is discernible. At about this time the large central cell resumes activity. There is at this point a difference between the two major genera.

In the genus *Dicyema* the central cell undergoes one unequal division, giving rise to the large, definitive axial cell anteriorly, and to a smaller posterior cell, the mother cell of all future germ cells. Though separate at first, the small cell soon invades or

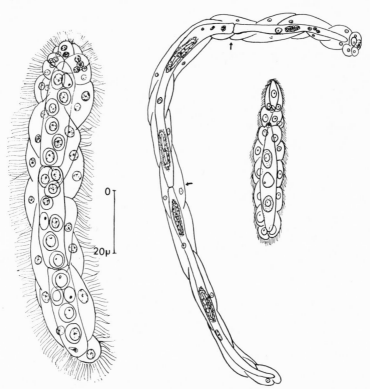

FIGURE 11-7. Young stem nematogen of *Dicyema schulzianum,* showing the axial cells. (After Nouvel, 1948.)

FIGURE 11-8. Stem nematogen of *Dicyema balamuthi* with fully developed larvel primary nematogens in its axial cells, one of which is shown more highly magnified. (After McConnaughey, 1949.)

is engulfed by the larger cell, becoming the first internal germ cell or axoblast. By mitotic divisions it gives rise to further similar cells, while the nucleus of the larger cell, in which this is going on, simply enlarges as the cell grows in size and is the so-called *axial nucleus* or *axial cell nucleus*. By the time the larva escapes from the parent nematogen there are usually from two to four or more axoblasts in its axial cell. A given nematogen may give rise to many larvae over a period of time, as the axoblasts continue to multiply, only part of them giving rise to embryos at any time (fig. 11-6, *a*).

In the genus *Dicyemennea* the embryonic development is slightly more complex in that the large central cell of the embryo divides twice instead of once. The first division cuts off a small anterior cell; the second, a small posterior cell. The posterior cell becomes the first axoblast, as in *Dicyema,* but the anterior cell remains in place in the developing larva in front of the axial cell and is eventually absorbed by one of the cells in the calotte, no trace being left in the mature individual (fig. 11-6, *b*).

In 1916 Lameere announced the surprising discovery that in exceedingly young cephalopods weighing only a few grams, the first nematogens of *Dicyema* and of *Microcyema* to be found contained three axial cells in linear series rather than one (fig. 11-7). The larvae engendered by such triple nematogens were, however, normal in all ways and had only one axial cell (fig. 11-8). Although the validity of this finding has been questioned by Gersch (1938), it has been confirmed by Nouvel (1933) and by me (McConnaughey, 1951). Both Nouvel and I have also found, in the youngest cephalopods examined, stem nematogens that are themselves larval in character and in which are present not only the three axial cells described by Lameere, but also a number of small, aborted additional axial cells

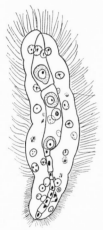

FIGURE 11-9. Larval stem nematogen of *Dicyemennea eledones,* a species in which the stem nematogen has only two functional axial cells. A cordon of aborted additional axial cells in the course of degeneration and absorption is present anterior to the first functional axial cell. (After Nouvel, 1948.)

anterior to the functional ones. These additional cells resemble the small anterior cell found in larval *Dicyemennea* and, like it, are absorbed by adjacent cells, leaving no trace in the adult stem nematogen (fig. 11-9).

In summary, then, the following points emerge in connection with the development of nematogens. The earliest forms found in very young cephalopods, in some species, are larval stem nematogens that have a row of internal axial cells, of which the posterior two or three become functional and produce and envelop germ cells, while the more anterior remain vestigial, being ultimately absorbed and leaving no trace in the adult. In the genus *Dicyemennea* all vermiform larvae develop one such vestigial axial cell, while in *Dicyema* ordinary nematogens develop no vestigial axial cells during their embryonic development. The stem nematogens produce ordinary nematogens by which the former are soon replaced in the population of dicyemids in a given cephalopod. Stem nematogens are almost never found in older cephalopods.

The cleavages are determinate, leading to a larva with a definite number and arrangement of somatic cells. Chromatin elimination occurs from the cells of the somatic line during the early cleavages. Growth, once the larva is formed, is by enlargement of cells already present, with the result that the adult consists of a relatively small number of giant cells.

The cells from which vermiform larvae develop are agametes. The axial cell and the first agamete are coördinate cells derived from a division of a single large internal cell of the embryo. The axial cell is, then, essentially a reproductive cell that has lost the capacity for reproduction and acts as a follicular cell for the protection and nourishment of the germ cells and embryos. The fact that the development of germ cells and embryos occurs intracellularly makes the pattern here different from that in other animals.

The change of phase from the nematogen to the rhombogen condition sweeps over the population of dicyemids as their cephalopod host nears maturity and the population of dicyemids in its kidneys becomes dense. It is manifested by cytological changes in the dicyemids as well as by the change in the type of embryos to which they give rise. The mature nematogens transform into rhombogens, while young vermiform individuals develop directly into rhombogens without having functioned as nematogens.

Most of the axoblasts present become pycnotic and degenerate. Some are digested in adjacent somatic cells; others are absorbed in place or even engulfed by sister axoblasts. Cytological irregularities such as enlarged binucleate axoblasts are common during the period of transition, and many of them become fusiform in shape and larger than normal. A few of these enlarged cells escape the fate of the majority and give rise to embryos of the next stage—the infusorigen (fig. 11-10).

The first step in the formation of an infusorigen is an unequal division of an enlarged axoblast, forming a small cell that has practically no cytoplasm and is freed in the axial cell of the rhombogen, where it persists as a nucleus, the *paranucleus,* which gradually increases in size, eventually becoming indistinguishable cytologically from the axial nucleus of the rhombogen. The enlarged axoblast, having given off the paranucleus, undergoes two more unequal divisions, forming a three-celled embryo consisting of one large cell, one medium-sized cell (product of the second division), and one small cell (from the first division). The small cell invades the large cell in the same manner that the first germ cell of a vermiform larva invades the axial cell. The medium-sized cell continues to proliferate on the surface of the young infusorigen, enveloping the large cell in a manner analogous to that of the somatic cells in the vermiform larva. Here, however, the similarity to the development of a vermiform larva ends. The small cell, now inside the axial cell of the developing infusorigen, multiplies for a time by mitosis. The cells so formed eventually undergo spermatogenesis and form small tailless sperm. Meanwhile the larger cells on the periphery of the infusorigen develop into enlarged egg cells. We have, then, in the infusorigen a very reduced hermaphroditic individual consisting only of an axial cell with developing sperm on the inside and developing egg cells on the periphery. It remains in the axial cell of the parent rhombogen, producing eggs and sperm until exhausted. There is no chromatin elimination during the early cleavages resulting in its formation, as in the case of the vermiform larva. The elimination of the paranucleus is regarded as an event comparable to the formation of abortive axial cells in embryonic stem nematogens and larval *Dicyemennea.* In figures 11-11 and 11-12 the development of the vermiform larva and that of the infusorigen are depicted side-by-side for comparison and contrast.

The sperm attach to the ripe egg cells while the latter are still attached to the infusorigen. The egg then detaches, the sperm penetrates into its cytoplasm, and the egg gives off polar bodies on long cytoplasmic protrusions. Following reconstitution of the female pronucleus, both pronuclei break down and the first cleavage of the zygote occurs with the two groups of chromosomes, in some cases at least, still distinguishable from each other.

Nouvel (1948) has described for *Dicyemennea schulzianum* a process of pseudogamy in which the sperm, after entering the egg and initiating the process of

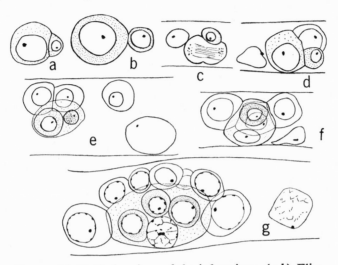

FIGURE 11-10. Embryology of the infusorigen. (*a,b*) Elimination of the paranucleus. (*c*) Second division of the mother cell of the infusorigen after having eliminated the paranucleus. (*d*) Young infusorigen after completion of the second division of the mother (axial) cell by the first daughter cell. (*e,f*) Young infusorigen following entrance of the first daughter cell into the mother cell, and first division of the second daughter cell in progress. The first daughter cell, now inside the mother cell, is the forerunner of all the internal (spermatogonial) cells of the infusorigen. The second one, which remains on the periphery, gives rise to all the oögonial cells. (*g*) Young infusorigen just before onset of maturation divisions of some of the germ cells. (After McConnaughey, 1951.)

maturation, is subsequently cast out of the cell, seemingly contributing no genetic material to the embryo, which develops by a process of diploid parthenogenesis after retention of one of the polar bodies. This is not unlike the instances reported for several nematodes by various workers, or those recorded by Benazzi for certain fresh-water triclads (chap. 30). Other cases have also been reported.

As more fertilized eggs are freed from the infusorigen, the older ones and developing embryos are moved further from it in the axial cell of the rhombogen, resulting, in species with large prolific infusorigens, in a string of embryos extending from each end of the infusorigens, the older ones at the ends.

During the early cleavages of the embryonic infusoriform, chromatin elimination analogous to that found in the vermiform larvae occurs (fig. 11-13).

The infusoriform (fig. 11-14) that develops from these embryos is a small, almost spherical larva with long, strong cilia directed posteriorly. In most species the two dorsal-anterior cells are much enlarged and are filled with a hardened refractile material forming very conspicuous refractile bodies that, during life, look almost like bubbles. Behind these, internally, there is a cavity termed the *urn,* which contains four germinal cells, each of which ordinarily contains two free nuclear cells and one axoblast-like germ cell. The urn is enveloped by two large capsular cells, while above these are two large, non-staining, glycogen-storing cells. The cavity of the urn communicates with the outside by a ventral pore.

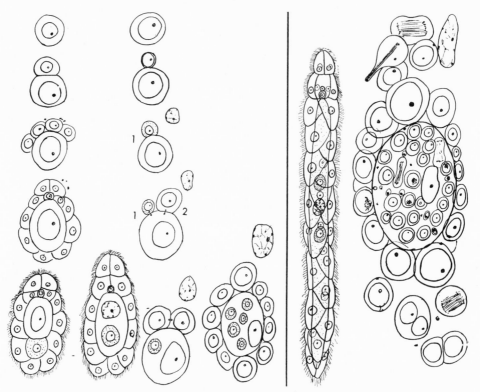

FIGURE 11-11. Comparison of the development of a vermiform larva and an infusorigen, to illustrate similarities and differences.
FIGURE 11-12. Fully developed vermiform larva and mature infusorigen. Fertilization, polar body formation, and first cleavages of zygotes are also shown.

When fully developed, the infusoriform liberates a secretion from around its refractile bodies, which causes the formation of a large vacuole in the axial cell of the parent rhombogen. Finally, the vacuole ruptures the body wall, and its contents, including the infusoriform, are squeezed out. The point of exit closes at once, leaving no scar.

The infusoriform larva escapes from the cephalopod in the host's urine. It goes at once to the bottom of the vessel containing it, and swims about in a seemingly undirected manner over the bottom. Attempts to infect young cephalopods or possible intermediate hosts with these larvae, or to demonstrate attraction to extracts of possible hosts in capillary tubes, have failed. It seems probable that the infusoriform is engulfed by some bottom-living animal, possibly a ciliary-mucus plankton feeder, and that the intervening stages develop in this host from the germinal cells in the urn, resulting eventually in the liberation of larval stem nematogens to infect young cephalopods (fig. 11-15).

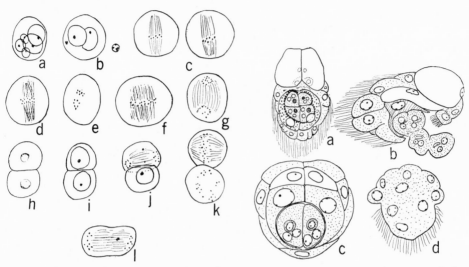

FIGURE 11-13. First cleavages of the zygote. (*a*) Nuclear vesicles sometimes seen during early stages of reconstitution of female pronucleus following second polar body elimination. (*b*) Zygote with both pronuclei, before first cleavage. The two polar bodies can be seen, one lying beneath zygote near the left side, one to the right of it. (*c*) Two views at different focal planes at about metaphase of first cleavage showing the two chromosome groups derived from the two pronuclei, still distinguishable on separate spindles. (*d*) Same zygote, drawn as a whole to show crossed appearance of spindle fibres at such a stage. (*e*) Polar view of a zygote in the same stage, showing the two groups of chromosomes. (*f*) Another zygote, similar to *d*. (*g*) Early telophase of first cleavage. (*h*) Two-celled embryo just after first cleavage. (*i*) Two-celled embryo just before second cleavage. (*j,k*) Second cleavage, showing earlier onset in one of the two blastomeres and the fact that the spindles in the two blastomeres are oriented at approximately right angles to each other in the second cleavage. (*l*) Isolated blastomere from a second cleavage embryo, showing a piece of chromatin lagging behind on the spindle. This is eventually eliminated from the embryo. (After McConnaughey, 1951.)

FIGURE 11-14. The infusoriform. (*a*) Optical frontal section of a mature infusoriform. (*b*) Optical parasagittal section of an infusoriform in the act of discharging the four cells comprising the contents of the urn. The germ cell in each of these seems to be undergoing a division. (*c*) Slightly oblique transverse optical section of an infusoriform to show the relation of the urn to the capsule and glycogen-storing cells. Section about two thirds of the way back from anterior end of the infusoriform. (*d*) An abortive infusoriform larva presumably formed from an unfertilized egg. (After McConnaughey, 1951.)

If the foregoing interpretation of the life cycle is correct, we have a rather peculiar condition in that the sexual stage (the infusorigen), usually considered the adult in most animals, is here reduced to a mere vestige consisting of only an axial cell and germ cells and existing solely inside the axial cell of one of the larval stages. This is somewhat reminiscent of the condition in higher plants where the reduced gametophyte generation is harbored by the large sporophyte.

The rhombogen, which gives rise to infusorigens, then nurtures the eggs produced by them, and finally gives birth to the infusoriform larva, is, we might say, giving birth to its grandchildren.

The cells-within-cells pattern is also noteworthy. All known stages develop intracellularly. If we think, for instance, of the axoblast-like germ cells inside the germinal cells in the urn of the infusoriform, which is itself inside the axial cell of its grandparent rhombogen, we have a condition of cells-within-cells to the fourth generation.

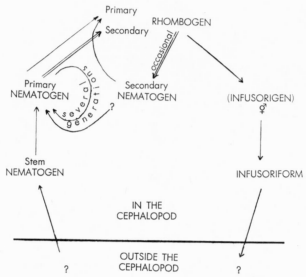

FIGURE 11-15. Diagram of known part of life cycle of dicyemids.

→ = Origin of a new individual from germ germ cells
⇒ = Transformation of an individual from one phase to another
( ) = Never leaves axial cell of parent stage

Phylogenetic Considerations

The position of the enigmatic *Salinella salve* Frenzel, 1892 (fig. 11-16) is an open question. It does not, however, seem to be closely related to either the dicyemids or the orthonectids. Other supposed mesozoa formerly assigned to the group have been shown to belong to other groups.

The structural peculiarities, simplicity, and host limitations, together with the complexity of the life cycle, at least in the case of the dicyemids, suggests that the Mesozoa, *sensu stricto,* have enjoyed a long history of parasitism. To what extent their characters are primitive and to what the result of long parasitism, we cannot say. It is difficult to trace their derivation from, or to relate them to, any other phyla, although several attempts have been made. Among the most plausible seems to be the idea that they represent an offshoot from a primitive stock of planuloid, acelous, ciliated worms with enclosed reproductive cells, possibly related to very early progenitors of the flatworms or certain of the earliest aschelminths. Their general mode of life and life cycle are strongly reminiscent of those of parasitic flat-

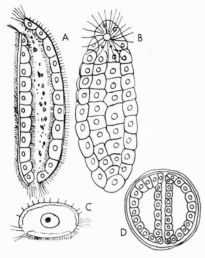

FIGURE 11-16. *Salinella salve* Frenzel. A peculiar organism consisting of a single layer of cells surrounding a gastric cavity and possessing a mouth at one end and anus at the other. Found in water from a salt works in Argentina. This organism is a taxonomic puzzle, often treated as a doubtful mesozoön for lack of a better place to which to refer it. It has not been reported again since Frenzel's original description. A. Longitudinal section; mouth opening above and anus below. B. Entire animal from ventral surface; mouth opening above. C. Probable unicellular juvenile form; nucleus in center. D. Section of cyst which forms after conjugation of two individuals. (After Frenzel, 1892.)

worms, while their cell constancy, chromatin elimination, and tendency to form syncytia in which cell boundaries are lost or become obscure are reminiscent of aschelminths. In either case their structure and embryological development are in line with speculations by Hyman (1940) that early metazoa may have had a solid rather than a hollow construction, one of the earliest steps being the relegation of reproductive cells to the interior.

REFERENCES

Only a few of the more important papers or general reviews are listed here. Complete bibliographies can be found in some of them.

GENERAL

Czihak, G.
 1958   Morphologie und Entwicklungsgeschichte der Wirbellosen (1945–1956): Mesozoa. Fortschr. Zool. 11:1–15.

Delage, Y., and H. Hérouard
 1899   Mésozoaires-Spongiaires. Pp. i–x, 1–244 in: Traité de Zoologie concrète. Vol. 2, pt. 1. Schleicher, Paris.

Frenzel, J.
 1892   Untersuchungen über die mikroskopische Fauna Argentiniens. Arch. Naturgesch. 58:66–96.

Hyman, L. H.
 1940   The Invertebrates. Vol. I: Protozoa through Ctenophora. McGraw-Hill, New York, Toronto, London.

Lameere, A.
 1929   Précis de Zoologie. Vol. 2. Suppl. to: Rec. Inst. zool. Torley-Rousseau 2, fasc. 2 (figures on pp. 86–88).

Stunkard, H. W.
 1954   The life-history and systematic relations of the Mesozoa. Quart. Rev. Biol. 29:230–244.

ORTHONECTIDA

Atkins, D.
1933   *Rhopalura granosa* sp. nov. an orthonectid parasite of a lamellibranch *Heteranomia squamula* L. with a note on its swimming behavior. J. Mar. biol. Ass. U.K. (n.s.) 19:233–252.

Braun, M.
1887   Die Orthonectiden. Zbl. Bakt. 2:255–261.

Caullery, M.
1912   Le cycle évolutif des Orthonectides. Proc. 8th Int. Congr. Zool, Graz (1910): 765–774.

Caullery, M. and A. Lavallée
1905   Sur les larves ciliées produites par la femelle d'un Orthonectide (*Rh. ophiocomae* Giard). C. R. Soc. Biol. Paris 59:265–266.
1908   La fécondation et le développement de l'œuf des Orthonectides. I. *Rhopalura ophiocomae*. Arch. Zool. exp. gén. (sér. 4) 8:421–469.
1912   Recherches sur le cycle évolutif des Orthonectides. Les phases initiales dans l'infection expérimentale de l'Ophiure, *Amphiura squamata,* par *Rhopalura ophiocomae* Giard. Bull. sci. Fr. Belg. 46:139–171.

Caullery, M. and F. Mesnil
1899   Sur l'embryogénie des Orthonectides et en particulier du *Stoecharthrum giardi,* Caull. et Mesn. C. R. Acad. Sci., Paris 128:516–519.
1901   Recherches sur les Orthonectides. Arch. Anat. micr. 4:381–470.

Giard, A.
1877   Sur les Orthonectida, classe nouvelle parasites des Échinodermes et des Turbellaires. C. R. Acad. Sci., Paris. 85:812–814.
1879   Les Orthonectides, nouvelle classe du phylum des Vermes. Anat. Paris 15:449–464. (Also in translation: 1880. The Orthonectida, a new class of the phylum of worms. Quart. J. micr. Sci. [n.s.] 20:225–240.)

Julin, C.
1882   Contribution à l'histoire des Mésozoaires: recherches sur l'organisation et le développement embryonnaire des Orthonectides. Arch. Biol. 3:1–54.

Lang, K.
1954   On a new orthonectid, *Rhopalura philinae* n. sp. found as a parasite of the opisthobranch *Philina scabra* Müller. Ark. Zool. (n.s.) 6:603–610.

Mechnikov [Metschnikoff], E.
1881   Untersuchungen über Orthonectiden. Z. wiss. Zool. 35:282–303.

Nouvel, H.
1939   Nouvelles observations sur la morphologie des Orthonectides. Bull. Soc. zool. Fr. 64:262–270.

Spengel, J. W.
1881   Die Orthonectiden. Biol. Zbl. 1:175–181.

Westblad, E.
1942   Studien über skandinavische Turbellaria Acoela. II. Ark. Zool. 33A, no. 14:1–48.

DICYEMIDA

Beneden, É. van
1876   Recherches sur les Dicyémides. Bull. Acad. Belg. Cl. Sci. (sér. 2) 41: 1160–1205; 42:35–97.
1882   Contribution a l'histoire des Dicyémides. Arch. Biol. Paris 3:195–228.

Gersch, M.
  1938   Der Entwicklungszyklus der Dicyemiden. Z. wiss. Zool. 151:515–605.
Hartmann, M.
  1906   Untersuchungen über den Generationswechsel der Dicyemiden. Mém.
          Acad. R. Belg. (sér. 2) 1, no. 3:1–128.
Lameere, A.
  1916   Contributions à la connaissance des Dicyémides. Première partie. Bull.
          sci. Fr. Belg. 50:1–35.
  1918   *Idem*. Deuxième partie. Bull. biol. 51:347–390.
  1919   *Idem*. Troisième partie. *Ibid*. 53:234–275.
McConnaughey, B. H.
  1949   Mesozoa of the family Dicyemidae from California. Univ. Calif. Publ.
          Zool. 55:1–33.
  1951   The life cycle of the dicyemid Mesozoa. *Ibid*. 55:295–336.
McConnaughey, B. H., and E. I. McConnaughey
  1954   Strange life of the dicyemid Mesozoa. Sci. Mon. 79:277–284.
Nouvel, H.
  1933   Recherches sur la cytologie, la physiologie et la biologie des Dicyémides.
          Ann. Inst. océanogr. Monaco (n. sér.) 13:162–255.
  1947   Les Dicyémides. 1° partie: systématique, générations vermiformes, in-
          fusorigène et sexualité. Arch. Biol. Paris 58:59–220.
  1948   *Idem*. 2° partie: infusoriforme, tératologie, spécificité du parasitisme,
          affinités. *Ibid*. 59:147–223.
Whitman, C. O.
  1883   A contribution to the embryology, life-history, and classification of the
          dicyemids. Mitt. zool. Sta. Neapel 4:1–89.

D. COELENTERATA, OR CNIDARIA

12 ◆ On the Interrelationships of the Coelenterata, with Remarks on Their Symmetry

TOHRU UCHIDA

ZOÖLOGICAL INSTITUTE, FACULTY OF SCIENCE,
HOKKAIDO UNIVERSITY, SAPPORO

There is dispute at present over the phylogeny of celenterates. For instance, recent zoölogists such as Hyman (1940), Jägersten (1955), and Hand (1959) are of the opinion that the modern forms have developed from a planuloid ancestor, whereas Hadži (1944) believes that certain rhabdocele turbellarians adopted sessile life and gradually differentiated to become the Anthozoa. Also, it has been affirmed by some and denied by others that the Hydrozoa are the most primitive of the Coelenterata and that the Scyphozoa and Anthozoa have developed from the Hydrozoa. Hand (1959) has explained the positive point of view on the basis of current knowledge. By contrast, Marcus (1958) and Jägersten (1955, 1959) have maintained that the Anthozoa are the most primitive group in the Coelenterata; Hadži is, of course, of the same opinion. Remane (1954) has held that there may be two possibilities: evolution from the Hydrozoa to the Anthozoa through the Scyphozoa, or *vice versa;* but he seems to favor the latter hypothesis. In any event, there remains, in bridging the gap between the Anthozoa and the Hydrozoa plus Scyphozoa, the problem of explaining the diversity of symmetry.

Hadži was the first to point out definitely that the Anthozoa are bilateral animals. His explanation was that the Anthozoa, having developed from the Turbellaria, have retained bilateral symmetry, but, because of their sessile life, have become radially symmetrical in external appearance. The Scyphozoa and Hydrozoa, subsequently derived from the Anthozoa, are forms that have become radially symmetrical even in internal structure. Jägersten (1955) has proposed a new theory that all multicellular animals trace their ancestry back to the *bilaterogastrea;* therefore, bilateral symmetry in the Anthozoa is primitive according to him also.

Recently I published a paper on the phylogeny of the Hydrozoa (Uchida, 1963). I pointed out that the Hydrozoa are the primitive, cardinal group in the Coelenterata from paleontological, embryological, and morphological evidence and also from the diversity of their life histories and wide distribution. I remarked, further, that, the three classes of the Coelenterata being so diversely differentiated from each other, no one of them could be ancestral to the others. While studying the morphology and life history of the Coelenterata, I came to the conclusion that, if symmetry alone were considered, there would be two phylogenetic lines: that is, one leading to a radially symmetrical group, containing the Hydrozoa and Scyphozoa, and the other leading to a bilaterally symmetrical group, represented by the Anthozoa.

Symmetry in the Hydrozoa

The polyps of the Hydrozoa are radially symmetrical over-all. In general they have a round mouth and one or two whorls of tentacles, which are arranged radially. Gigantic hydropolyps of the genus *Branchiocerianthus* and peculiar epizoic polyps of the genus *Proboscidactyla* (=*Lar*), show bilateral symmetry, it is true. But these are merely exceptional and secondarily "deformed" organisms. In young polyps we can usually see four tentacles, which arise at the same time and thus exhibit tetramery. But there also can be seen instances in which these tentacles do not appear synchronously; often one opposing pair precedes the other pair.

The medusae of the Hydrozoa are of typical tetramerous form, with four radial canals (or eight), a four-sided manubrium, four groups of gonads, and four clusters of tentacles, one in each tetrant (or, with eight groups of tentacles, one in each octant), and sometimes with four oral tentacles. Of course, there are some modifications of the typical form. For instance, the leptomedusan genus *Irenopsis* is characterized by six radial canals, and the members of the anthomedusan genus *Cladonema* often have nine radial canals. Hexamery can be derived from tetramery by bifurcation of an opposing pair of canals; and the situation in *Cladonema* can be produced from the hexamerous type by bifurcation of radial canals, alternating in position, as has been clearly indicated by me (Uchida, 1924, fig. 7). Some hydromedusae liberated from the gigantic hydroids, such as *Hybocodon* and *Euphysa*, are bilaterally symmetrical, because they sometimes have radial canals of different length and marginal tentacles of different size. But in their having a round mouth and four radial canals, they are tetramerous on morphological grounds.

It is generally admitted that the anthomedusan genus *Sarsia* represents the most primitive form of hydromedusae. Its representatives have four radial canals, four hollow marginal tentacles, and a manubrium with a round mouth encircled by a gonad. In hydromedusan genera of more advanced type, the manubrium becomes four-sided; radial canals and tentacles increase fourfold; and the gonad becomes divided into four (sometimes eight) masses. The increase of tentacles occurs successively at definite points in each tetrant or in each octant, radial symmetry generally being retained.

The sequences of appearance of tentacles have been reported by me in a previous paper (Uchida, 1927) and are summarized here as follows.

1. Medusae belonging to the Pandeidae and most of the Limnomedusae and Leptomedusae are subject to the following sequence in appearance of the marginal tentacles (fig. 12-1). The youngest medusa has a four-sided manubrium, generally four radial canals, and four marginal primary tentacles, one in each perradius. The second series of tentacles arises in

each interradius, the third series in each adradius, and the fourth in each eradius, and so on. The medusa *Polyorchis* shows the same sequence. Therefore, the tentacles are counted 4, 8, 16, 32, and so on. Because of the arrangement of the tentacles, the medusae are always radially symmetrical.

2. Some medusae belonging to the Bougainvilleidae, such as *Bougain-*

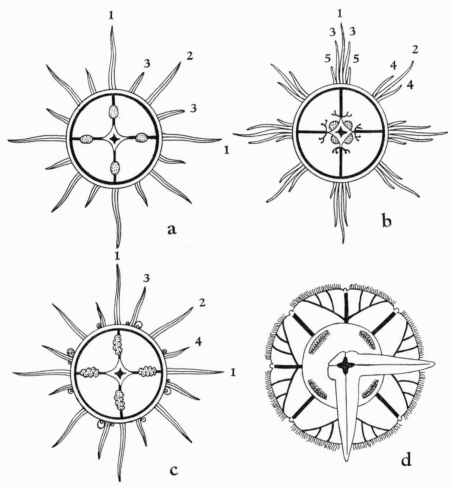

FIGURE 12-1. Several types of radial symmetry in the Hydrozoa and Scyphozoa: *a*, most of the Hydromedusae; *b*, Anthomedusae belonging to the Bougainvilleidae; *c*, radial asymmetry (= spiral symmetry) in the Olindiidae; *d*, Scyphozoa.

villea and *Nemopsis*, have four oral tentacles and four clusters of solid marginal tentacles, one in each perradius. There are one or two primary tentacles; and the secondary and tertiary tentacles appear one by one on both sides. Other medusae belonging to the Bougainvilleidae, such as *Rathkea* and *Koellikeria*, have four oral tentacles and eight clusters of solid marginal tentacles, one in each perradius and interradius. The mode of increase of tentacles is similar to the case just mentioned, though the interradii are growing points for tentacles as well as the perradii. The medusa *Spirocodon* with solid tentacles follows this mode. In these medusae, the interradial tentacles appear after the perradial ones, so that the former are always less in number than the latter. These medusae are also radially symmetrical, with four or eight planes of symmetry.

3. Some medusae of the Limnomedusae (*Gonionema, Scolionema,* and *Eperetmus*) and of the Trachomedusae (*Petasiella*) are eligible for a group, which was at one time designated the medusae of spiral symmetry by Kinoshita (1916), and afterward the group of radial asymmetry by me (Uchida, 1927). In these medusae the secondary tentacles appear close to the statocyst in the interradius at first, but gradually shift away from it with the enlargement of the margin. Tentacles of the third and fourth series also follow the same pattern. The medusa *Proboscidactyla* with four lips and, at first, four radial canals, also becomes radially asymmetrical by branching of radial canals and the appearance of new marginal tentacles at the bases of radial branches.

Symmetry in the Scyphozoa

The Scyphozoa are tetramerously symmetrical as polyps and medusae. In the scyphopolyp the mouth is four-sided; the enteric cavity is divided into four chambers by four septa; and the tentacles are at first four in number and increase gradually by multiples of four. In most polyps there are four primary tentacles, one in each perradius; the secondary tentacles arise interradially; and a third series appears in the adradial and a fourth in the eradial portions; thus a 16-tentacled polyp is formed. Sometimes young polyps occur with two opposite tentacles as in *Mastigias,* but they become four-tentacled very soon.

In the scyphomedusae there are generally a four-sided mouth (Cubomedusae and Stauromedusae), four oral arms (Semaeostomeae) or eight oral arms (Rhizostomeae), and four gonads, each with a cluster of gastral filaments. Moreover, the sensory organs are generally eight (four in Cubomedusae), and the marginal lappets and tentacles may be counted in multiples of eight.

Symmetry in the Anthozoa

It is well known that all members of the Anthozoa are morphologically of biradial symmetry. There are serial grades of bilaterality in anthozoan orders. The Octocorallia have a special dorsal pair of mesenteries besides three ventral pairs. The Actiniaria, Madreporaria, Zoantharia, and Antipatharia are all bilaterally symmetrical, viewed from the arrangement of their mesenteries (see fig. 12-2). Moreover, their larval stages, so far as is known, have all three pairs of mesenteries arranged bilaterally. The presence of one or two siphonoglyphs in them is also a bilateral feature. The paleozoic Tetracorallia were always bilateral in the arrangement of the mesenteries at first, but gradually tended to be tetramerous. Among the Anthozoa the Cerianthria seem to be obviously bilateral because their young pelagic forms have three pairs of mesenteries at first and new mesenteries appear in pairs always at a growing point, resulting in a quadrimesentery. New tentacles always arise in pairs from the growing point corresponding to that of the mesenteries. In spite of an external appearance of radial symmetry, the Ceriantharia are typically bilateral animals. Besides the Ceriantharia, the whole Anthozoa show distinct bilaterality, but still are of more or less biradial nature. Among them the sessile Madreporaria have a remarkable tendency to be biradial. Though they are bilateral in form, the Anthozoa mostly express biradiality, because they generally have many bilaterally arranged growing points. In the possession of many growing points, they are similar to the Hydrozoa and Scyphozoa. The Ceriantharia alone among the Anthozoa are quite different.

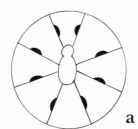 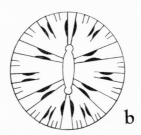

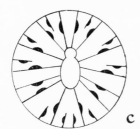 

FIGURE 12-2. Several types of biradial symmetry and bilateral symmetry in the Anthozoa: *a,* Octocorallia; *b,* Actiniaria; *c,* Zoantharia; *d,* Ceriantharia.

Other Animal Groups of So-Called Radial Symmetry

It is often stated that the Phoronidea, Bryozoa, and Entoprocta are radially symmetrical because of the arrangement of tentacles; but, notwithstanding their seemingly radial arrangement, these arise from both sides of a growth point just as in the Ceriantharia. In this feature the arrangement of tentacles is quite different from that in the Hydromedusae and Scyphozoa. Because of the sequence of tentacle appearance, the Ceriantharia and these Tentaculata are bilateral animals.

The Echinodermata have historically been considered a component of an animal group called the Radiata, together with the Coelenterata. Although the Echinodermata show pentamerous radial symmetry in the adult, their larvae are bilaterally symmetrical. Moreover, the radial symmetry of the adult is obviously secondarily derived; the left larval mesocele develops and forms the pentamerous circular canals, and subsequently pentaradiate animals are formed. From the embryological evidence, the Echinodermata are bilaterally symmetrical.

Discussion

As has already been stated, the Coelenterata can be divided on the basis of their symmetry into two groups, the Hydrozoa plus Scyphozoa and the Anthozoa. Because all the celenterates have the planula as the first larva just hatched from the egg, it seems to me highly probable that the Coelenterata developed from a planu-

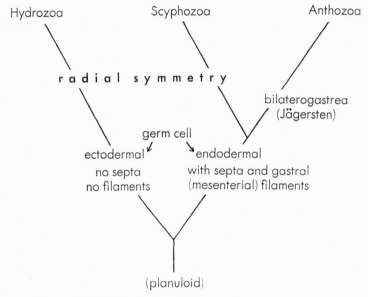

FIGURE 12-3. The phylogenetic tree of the Coelenterata.

loid ancestor, as Hyman (1940) and Hand (1959) have also conjectured. Planuloid ancestors would thus have given rise to two different groups; one with radial symmetry and the other with bilateral symmetry. The Hydrozoa and Scyphozoa belong to the former group and the Anthozoa to the latter. But these do not seem to represent natural phylogenetic groups. I believe that the Scyphozoa are rather more closely related to the Anthozoa than are the Hydrozoa (see fig. 12-3), because the Scyphozoa agree with the Anthozoa in having sexual cells of endodermal origin, septa, and gastral (in the former) or mesenterial (in the latter) filaments. Moreover, the asexual reproduction of anthozoöids of the genera *Fungia* and *Gonactinia* is more or less similar to the strobilation of the Scyphozoa. Therefore, the Hydrozoa seem definitely separate in phylogeny from these other two groups of celenterates. The pelagic larvae of the Anthozoa often present internally bilateral symmetry, as in the arachnactis and actinian larvae, etc.

It is possible that the Anthozoa developed from a bilaterogastrea and still retain the bilateral body. The most primitive form was naked, small, and probably equipped with only three pairs of septa, arranged bilaterally. It possibly dwelt in the sandy bottom, inserting its body perpendicularly, as seen in the habits of recent ceriantharians. Some of these burrowing forms became sessile, attached to littoral rocks, and secreted a calcareous skeleton like the recent Madreporaria; and some of them, attached to the substratum at a rather great depth, secreted a horny substance in their axis and calcareous material on their surface—as seen in the recent Gorgonaria and Antipatharia. The Actiniaria evolved rather well-developed muscles and are now able to move themselves slowly on the substratum to which they are attached. The Pennatulida were probably completely sessile animals at one time, but have reacquired a limited degree of locomotive ability.

The ancestor of the Scyphozoa was, I believe, closely related to that of the Anthozoa, but it was radially symmetrical. The polyps retain a form probably not very different from the ancestral one. The primitive polyp possibly had four (or eight) tentacles, four septa, and four clusters of gastral filaments. Some scyphopolyps evolved into chitinized colonial forms, as seen in the fossil Conulariida and recent *Stephanoscyphus,* but most have remained solitary and do not show much elaboration as sessile polyps. By contrast, the Scyphozoa have differentiated in a high degree as medusae, pelagic forms preserving the tetramerous shape of the polyps. The floating or slightly swimming habit of the medusa seems to coincide with the radially symmetrical body. Complicated pelagic forms have evolved within the Scyphozoa.

The primitive form of the Hydrozoa has been reconstructed as a pelagic actinula-like creature by Brooks (1886) and recently by Rees (1957) and Hand (1959). It was differentiated into sessile polyps as well as into pelagic medusae. The primitive form was naked and had probably four (or more) marginal tentacles and was devoid of septa. The forms mostly became sessile; many formed colonies and sometimes secreted a periderm. Although they have come to show polymorphism, they do not exhibit such complication of structure as some of the Scyphozoa and Anthozoa. Certain primitive polyps remained solitary and acquired the burrowing habit. They have become large and complicated in their hydranth and hydrocaulus, with a dozen longitudinal canals on the peripheral part as seen in *Corymorpha.*

It is generally known that several primitive animals are found in the sandy bottom of the sea. One can enumerate them as follows: cephalocarid *Hutchinsoniella* in the Crustacea, monoplacophoran *Neopilina* and ammonites in the Mollusca, *Lingula* in the Tentaculata, *Amphioxus* in the Protochordata, synaptids in the Holothuroidea, etc. The sand-burrowing celenterates (see fig. 12-4) *Corymorpha*-allies and *Cerianthus,* seem to be primitive, though well-developed forms in the Hydrozoa and Anthozoa respectively. They agree with each other in having pelagic larval forms (actinula or arachnactis) and in afterwards sinking to the bottom, where they exhibit burrowing habits in sandy flats. But they are in contrast as to symmetry: *Corymorpha*-allies have a radially symmetrical stalk, with a dozen longitudinal canals arranged radially on the periphery, whereas *Crianthus* has a bilaterally symmetrical column with many septa that increase pair-wise from a limited ventral region. Habits of adhering to seaweeds or rocks seem to have developed after burrowing patterns had evolved in the Coelenterata.

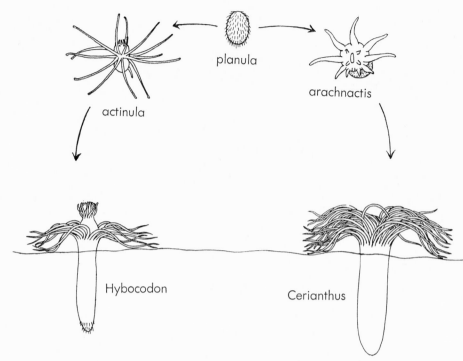

FIGURE 12-4. The life cycle of the sand-burrowing Hydrozoa and Ceriantharia.

REFERENCES

Brooks, W. K.
1886   The life-history of the Hydromedusae: a discussion of the origin of the medusae and the significance of metagenesis. Mem. Boston Soc. nat. Hist. 3:359–430, pl. 37–44.

Hadži, J.
1944   Turbelarijska Teorija Knidarijev. (Turbellarien-Theorie der Knidarier.) Slov. Akad. Znan. Um., Ljubljana. [In Slovenian, with German summary.]

Hand, C.
1959   On the origin and phylogeny of the Coelenterata. Syst. Zool. 8:192–202.

Hyman, L. H.
1940   The Invertebrates. Vol. I: Protozoa through Ctenophora. McGraw-Hill, New York, Toronto, London.

Jägersten, G.
1955   On the early phylogeny of the Metazoa. This bilaterogastraea theory. Zool. Bidr. Uppsala 30:321–354.

1959   Further remarks on the early phylogeny of the Metazoa. *Ibid.* 33:79–108.

Kinoshita, K.
1916   [On the arrangement and development of tentacles and statocysts in two craspedote medusae.] Zool. Mag., Tokyo 28:425–451. [In Japanese.]

Marcus, E.
1958   On the evolution of the animal phyla. Quart. Rev. Biol. 33:24–58.

Rees, W. J.
 1957   Evolutionary trends in the classification of capitate hydroids and medusae.
         Bull. Brit. Mus. (nat. Hist.) 4:453–534.
Remane, A.
 1954   Die Geschichte der Tiere. Pp. 340–422 in: Die Evolution der Organismen.
         Heberer, G., Ed. Vol. 2. 2d ed. Fischer, Stuttgart.
Uchida, T.
 1924   Some Hydromedusae from northern Japan. Jap. J. Zool. 1:81.
 1927   Studies on Japanese Hydromedusae. 1. Anthomedusae. J. Fac. Sci. Tokyo
         Univ. (Sect. 4, Zool.) 1:164–173.
 1929   *Idem*. 3. Olindiadae. Annot. zool. jap. 12:351–371, pl. 1.
 1963   The systematic position of the Hydrozoa. Jap. J. Zool. 13:1–14.

E. CTENOPHORA

13 ◆ A Note on the Phylogeny of the Ctenophora

TAKU KOMAI

ZÖOLOGICAL INSTITUTE,
UNIVERSITY OF KYOTO, KYOTO

Some recent authorities on animal classification, including Hyman (1940) and De Beer (1954), treat the Ctenophora as a phylum distinct from the phylum Cnidaria. This is mainly because the Ctenophora have no nematocysts, but are provided with colloblasts, and because the chief organ of locomotion consists of the so-called comb-plates. In addition, complete absence of the polypoid stage, distinctly biradial cleavage, and invariable hermaphroditism may be mentioned as distinctive features of the Ctenophora. On the other hand, the Ctenophora share with the Cnidaria radial (non-bilateral) symmetry in body shape and organ arrangement, absence of a celom, a branching gastro-vascular system, a diffuse nervous system, and absence of an excretory system and accessory genital apparatus (copulatory organs, etc.). Whether the points of difference merit recognition as a phylum, subphylum, class, or order depends on one's judgment. Weighing these differences and similarities, I incline to the subphylum rather than phylum rank for the Ctenophora. The phylum Coelenterata is thus divided in two subphyla, the Cnidaria and Ctenophora.

AFFINITY OF THE CTENOPHORA WITH CNIDARIAN CLASSES

Of the Cnidaria, the forms apparently most directly related to the Ctenophora may be found among the Hydrozoa. This is because the class Hydrozoa, as a whole, includes more generalized forms than does any other cnidarian class. It is, however, difficult to specify any particular existing species of the Hydrozoa as representing a possible ancestral ctenophore. The much discussed medusa *Hydroctena* (Davydov, 1904; Mayer, 1910; Mortensen, 1912) was considered by some workers to possess characteristics of both a hydromedusa and a ctenophore. Other workers take a different view and hold that the apparent similarity of the medusa to a ctenophore

The author is indebted to Drs. R. Dorn, T. Uchida, and F. Utinoumi for making literature available. He appreciates Dr. Uchida's kindness in reading this paper at the original Symposium.

is only superficial and has no phylogenetic significance. I favor this view. Here may be mentioned in passing Hadži's opinion (1958) that *Hydroctena* might be a monstrous product resulting from some damage incurred in the cleavage stage of a ctenophore egg.

INTERRELATIONSHIP OF CTENOPHORAN ORDERS

Of the ctenophore orders, Sydippida, Lobatida, Cestida, Platyctenida, and Beroida, the Cydippida contain forms such as *Pleurobrachia* and *Hormiphora,* which probably represent the ancestral type of the Ctenophora. The Beroida are often isolated from other orders and called Nuda because of the entire absence of tentacles (*e.g.,* by Hyman, 1940). The tendency for tentacles to degenerate is not uncommon in other orders; it may be seen in *Euchlora* among the Cydippida, and *Tjalfiella* and *Gastrodes* among Platyctenida. Similarly, among the Lobatida, the primary tentacles are at various grades of degenerative change. This change is undoubtedly associated with direct ingestion of food organisms without prior entanglement in the tentacles. It seems to me that the isolation of the order Beroida, on this character alone, brings an unnecessary complication to the classification of the Ctenophora.

All embryologically studied species belonging to the Lobatida, Cestida, or Platyctenida have a cydippid larval stage. These orders are adapted to different modes of living; namely, the Lobatida to swimming by lobe flapping, the Cestida to swimming by undulatory movement of the ribbon-like body, and the Platyctenida to a sessile, creeping, or parasitic habit. The shape and structure of organisms in these orders are specialized in accordance with their modes of life.

Ctenoplana among the Platyctenida is almost a cydippid, except for a few unimportant peculiarities. *Coeloplana, Tjalfiella,* and *Lyrocteis* have a larval stage much like *Ctenoplana.* Thus, it is likely that the Playctenida diverged from cydippid ancestors in the not very remote past, contrary to what might be suggested by casual observation of these aberrant forms. Furthermore, the order perhaps has a polyphyletic origin, since most of the forms belonging to this group are relatively rare and known from widely separated localities.

AFFINITY OF THE CTENOPHORA TO THE TURBELLARIA

The question of the affinity of the Ctenophora to the Turbellaria is familiar to anyone interested in the phylogeny of the Invertebrata. A belief in a close phylogenetic affinity of these groups was strongly advocated by Lang (1884) on various grounds, and this view was supported by several subsequent authors, including Mortensen (1912). The outline of the theory is well known, and its details need not be repeated here. My study on the structure and development of *Coeloplana* (Komai, 1922) seems to have upset one of the bases of this theory. *Coeloplana* is a genuine ctenophore, and its resemblance to a polyclad worm is only superficial and coincidental, so that it cannot represent a form midway in evolution from the Polycladida to the Ctenophora, as assumed by some previous workers. The flattened body of *Coeloplana* develops by extension of the external portion of the pharynx, as well as by shortening of the main axis; whereas the flatness of the turbellarian body results mainly from the elongation of the main axis of the larva. Furthermore, the gonads of *Coeloplana* have some peculiarities unknown in ordinary ctenophores. The spermaries in this genus, as well as in *Ctenoplana* (Willey, 1896) and *Lyrocteis* (Komai, 1942a), form a series of compact and separate masses located in each quarter of the body, each mass provided with a duct opening to the dorsal side. The ovaries in *Coeloplana* have pouch-like invaginations from the dorsal body wall that seem to serve as seminal receptacles. These complications of the genital system in the platyctenides, however, show nothing to suggest a phylogenetic relationship to structures with similar functions in the Turbellaria. At any rate, if one recalls the bilaterally symmetrical arrangement of all organs, the presence of an excretory system, the highly complicated genital system, and the concentrated nervous system in the Polycladida, and compares these to the biradial symmetry, absence of an excretory system, much simpler genital system, and diffuse nervous system in the Ctenophora, the gap between these major groups is too wide to be bridged by the scanty evidence brought forward by Lang and his followers. I feel it is best, therefore, to postpone a final judgment on the question until more decisive evidence is presented. Lang's theory will be remembered as symbolic of the stage of biology in the latter part of the last century.

HADŽI'S THEORY

In this connection, brief comment will be made on Hadži's views of invertebrate phylogeny (Hadži, 1923, 1944, 1953b), which have been carefully reviewed and warmly approved by De Beer (1954). I am restricting my comments here to the proposed relationship of the Cnidaria and Ctenophora to the Turbellaria. Hadži postulates this relationship through two routes: one, Rhabdocoela to Cnidaria; and the other, Polycladida to Ctenophora. It is striking that he postulates the evolution in a reverse direction to that assumed by other authors. He seems to have arrived at this conclusion from the idea that, first, sessile or parasitic modes of life induce degeneration of organs and regression to a radially symmetrical configuration; and second, the polyp, owing to its sessile habit, represents a regressive type and is more probably ancestral than the free-swimming medusa. Thus, according to Hadži, radial symmetry and the generally undifferentiated state of cnidarian organization are owing to regressive change rather than to a primitive condition.

Against this view is the improbability that the polyp is generally more primitive than the medusa. It is more likely that the polyp and medusa are dual prototypes of the Cnidaria, and that evolutionary specialization has taken place within each prototype quite independently. It might be sufficient to recall *Branchiocerianthus, Fungia,* and *Metridium* among the polypoid forms and *Olindias, Rhizostoma,* and the Lucernariae among the medusoids.

Among the Cnidaria, the Anthozoa are regarded by Hadži as preceding in evolution either the Hydrozoa or the Scyphozoa. This is because, among other things, the anthopolyp shows bilateral symmetry in the arrangement and development of septa, as well as in the position of the siphonoglyph, and this bilaterality is taken by him as a remnant of the general bilaterality of the ancestral stage. It is, however, very difficult to conceive that the other features of the anthopolyp, namely, septa, spicules and skeleton, acontia, complicated muscular system, and various kinds of nematocysts, should altogether represent an ancestral state, in contrast to the much simpler state with respect to all these points manifested by the hydropolyp or scyphopolyp.

It is true that radial symmetry is common among sessile or sedentary animals such as many of the Echinodermata, Entoprocta, and Phoronida, as mentioned by Hadži. Yet, the original bilateral symmetry, which the ancestors of these groups seem to have possessed, is to be found in the shape and arrangement of some organs; for instance, in the madreporite of the Echinodermata and in the digestive tract and excretory organs in the Entoprocta and Phoronida. The larvae of these groups, especially, show a distinct bilaterality. Among the Cnidaria, except for the slight sign of bilaterality in the anthozoan structure just mentioned, radial symmetry is universal in both polypoid and medusoid stages. The larvae, including planulae and actinulae, are not exceptions to this rule. In short, none of the evidence presented in support of Hadži's provocative theory is strong enough to convert adherents of the classical theory.

As for the Ctenophora, Hadži postulates a phylogenetic relationship of the group to the Polycladida, as did many previous workers. Like the latter, he puts emphasis on the similarity of the Müllerian larva to the ctenophore. But, since he postulates evolution in the reverse direction, he has had to introduce the assumption that the larvae are capable of neotenous development. Needless to say, neoteny is an exceptional phenomenon associated with a very unusual mode of life. It is, therefore, hard to believe that so exceptional a phenomenon should have determined the course of evolution of such a large group as the Ctenophora. It might be remembered also that Hadži takes, it seems to me, a self-contradictory attitude in deriving the biradially symmetrical Ctenophora from the bilaterally symmetrical Polycladida, without assuming any sedentary stage in between.

I should like to emphasize that discussion based on the scanty, outdated information now available to us will contribute very little to the advancement of animal phylogeny. Rather one should endeavor to obtain new factual evidence by sound observation or experiment. For this purpose, I wish to call attention to a few ctenophore species that still remain relatively unknown; intensive studies on them would seem to offer reward.

EUCHLORA (HAECKELIA) RUBRA

The curious ctenophore *Euchlora* (*Haeckelia*) *rubra* has been reported to possess nematocysts instead of colloblasts—a peculiarity that attracted my attention. Fortunately, I had a chance to examine four specimens of this species through the kindness of Dr. T. Tokioka of the Seto Marine Biological Laboratory (Komai, 1942b, 1951; Komai and Tokioka, 1943). Sections of these specimens clearly showed the presence of nematocysts. I thought then that the nematocysts were an element proper to the ctenophore. Later, however, thanks to the kind suggestion of Dr. L. Hyman, I came to realize the inadequacy of this view, and to admit the foreign origin of these elements, probably from food material. This is because all the nematocysts appeared to be decaying, and were not located in the expected place in the epithelium, but were found imbedded in various tissues. They occurred in abundance especially in the endoderm of the tentacular canal, where, in all ctenophores, the digestion of food seems to take place more actively than elsewhere. They were found also in the mesoglea of the tentacle, along the lateral sides. The nematocysts were of two kinds—macro- and micronematocysts, according to the difference in size. This distinction exactly corresponded with that found among nematocysts in hydromedusae. My mistake was corrected in the *American Naturalist* (Komai, 1951). Recently, Hadži (1953) has published a note on the nematocysts in this ctenophore and has suggested the foreign origin of this element.

Thus, the question of the nematocysts occurring in this species seems to have been settled. But a question still remains as to the absence of colloblasts. Nobody has ever observed in this particular species these structures, which are highly characteristic of the tentaculate ctenophores. Such a peculiarity may be correlated with the extensive pharynx in this species, which swallows its prey much as *Beroe* does, while the tentacles serve merely as balancing organs in swimming. At any rate, further studies seem necessary to elucidate whether the colloblasts are missing in all stages of development, or whether they are formed once and disappear later. In other words, does the absence of colloblasts indicate a degenerative or a primitive and undifferentiated state? Such a study may contribute to the understanding of the phylogenetic position of this species as well as of the Ctenophora in general.

GASTRODES PARASTICUM (GASTRA PARASITICA)

Following my paper in 1922, Raja (1930) and Davydov (1937) published their observations of the ctenophore *Gastrodes parasiticum* (*Gastra parasitica*). This genus lives as a parasite in the mantle layer of *Salpa*. It is small, reaching 3 mm. in diameter, disc- or bowl-shaped, and has most of the characteristics of a ctenophore: eight rows of comb-plates, an aboral sense-organ, a pair of rudimentary tentacles, and the main part of the canal system divided in the manner typical of a ctenophore. The gonad, however, shows the peculiarity that egg cells develop in the ventral epidermis, which is morphologically the pharyngeal wall; moreover, no male cells have been observed.

I was able to follow all the developmental stages of this parasite in its host. The larva enters the body of *Salpa* by penetrating its test. Its shape and structure are planuloid, having a cylindrical body covered with a ciliated epidermis and filled with large endodermal cells. I observed such a specimen in the process of penetrating the test. After entering *Salpa*, the parasite remains in the mantle layer of the host and develops there. At first it is cylindrical, but soon it changes into a bowl shape by the partial invagination of the posterior half; then it flattens and becomes disc-shaped. The endoderm in this stage has a simple, circular outline in apical view, but becomes four-lobed and later eight-lobed. This eight-lobed stage had been observed and sketched by Korotnev (1888, 1891) and Heider (1893).

Further stages of development into an unmistakable ctenophore are described and illustrated in my paper (1922). Raja (1930) followed the development of this species, in the living state, from the youngest discoidal stage through liberation. Davydov (1937) mentioned that he was able to follow all the developmental stages except the planula. He also describes the change of the ctenophore after its liberation from the host. He artificially liberated an apparently very advanced stage of *Gastrodes komaii*, which he considers to represent another species of the same genus. The bowl-shaped body of the liberated parasite became flattened and attached to the substratum, grew in size, and divided into four radial pieces, each comprising two meridional canals. The comb-plates, tentacles, and egg-cells had completely disappeared in the meantime.

This observation was made under very unnatural conditions on a single specimen, and it is doubtful how well it represents the natural development of the ctenophore after liberation. At any rate, it seems worth while to follow up the natural life cycle of this genus. The presence of egg cells in the ectoderm seems to be a secondary adaptation to its parasitic life. The primordial egg cells initially found in the endoderm of the planula larva migrate into the pharyngeal ectoderm where they can get nourishment directly from the host.

The presence of a planula stage in a ctenophore may be looked upon as evidence for a phylogenetic relationship between the Ctenophora to the Cnidaria. Further intensive study of *Gastrodes* would be rewarding. It is not a very rare animal; it may be obtained when one comes across a large swarm of *Salpa,* especially the common *S. fusiformis.* Although the rate of parasitism varies considerably from swarm to swarm, it may be as high as 25 per cent, according to my experience. The presence of the parasite may be recognized without difficulty by simple observation under low magnification. The final decision whether this genus should be placed in the Platyctenida or in the Cydippida (Krumbach, 1925; Raja, 1930) should be deferred until its complete life cycle is disclosed.

Summary

1. The difference between the Ctenophora and the rest of the Coelenterata seems to be approximately at the subphylum level.

2. The Ctenophora seem to be related more directly to the Hydrozoa than to the Scyphozoa or Anthozoa.

3. There is no necessity to isolate the Beroida, as the subclass Nuda, from the other orders of the Ctenophora. The Platyctenida are perhaps of polyphyletic origin and have evolved from the Cydippida relatively recently.

4. The question of the phylogenetic relationship of the Ctenophora to the Turbellaria remains unsettled. In any event, the resemblance of *Coeloplana,* as well as of other platyctenides, to the Turbellaria seems only superficial and thus without phylogenetic significance.

5. Hadži's theory, as it concerns the phylogenetic relationship of the Cnidaria and Ctenophora to the Turbellaria, is discussed. His assumption of the derivation of the Cnidaria from the Rhabdocoela, and the Ctenophora from the Polycladida, involves many difficulties and improbabilities, some of which are pointed out.

6. The need for new data is stressed, and studies are suggested on two imperfectly known, remarkable ctenophores, *Euchlora* and *Gastrodes.*

REFERENCES

Davydov, K. N. [Dawydoff, C.]
    1904   *Hydroctena salenskii.* (Étude morphologique sur un nouveau Coelentéré pélagique.) Mém. Acad. Sci. St.-Pétersb. (8 sér.) 14, no. 9:1–17.

1937   Les Gastrodes des eaux indochinoises et quelques observations sur leur cycle évolutif. C. R. Acad. Sci., Paris 204:1088–1090.

De Beer, C. R.
1954   The evolution of Metazoa. Pp. 24–33 in: Evolution as a Process. Huxley, J., *et al.*, Eds. Allen and Unwin, London.

Hadži, J.
1923   O podrijetlu, srodstvenim odnosima i sistematskoj poziciji ktenoforâ. Rad jug. Akad. Znan. Umj. 228:53–62. [In Croatian.] [Also: Über den Ursprung, die Verwandtschaftsverhältnisse und die systematische Position der Ktenophoren. Bull. int. Acad. Yougoslav. 15–18:53–62.]

1944   Turbelarijska teorija knidarijev. (Turbellarien-Theorie der Knidarier.) Slov. Akad. Znan. Um., Ljubljana. [In Slovenian, with German Summary.]

1953a   Haben die Ktenophoren eigene Kniden? Bull. Sci. Yougoslav. 1:18.

1953b   An attempt to reconstruct the system of animal classification. Syst. Zool. 2:145–154.

1958   *Hydroctena salenskii* Dawydoff 1902—eine unvollkommen entwickelte Ctenophore. Bull. Sci. 4:51–52.

Heider, K.
1893   *Gastrodes,* eine parasitische Ctenophore. S. B. naturf. Ges. Berlin (1893): 114–119.

Hyman, L.
1940   The Invertebrates. Vol. I: Protozoa through Ctenophora. McGraw-Hill, New York, Toronto, London.

Komai, T.
1922   Studies on Two Aberrant Ctenophores, *Coeloplana* and *Gastrodes*. Author's publication, Kyoto.

1942a   The structure and development of the sessile ctenophore *Lyrocteis imperatoris* Komai. Mem. Coll. Sci. Kyoto (ser. B) 17:1–36.

1942b   The nematocysts in the ctenophore *Euchlora rubra*. Proc. Acad. Japan 18:255–256.

1951   The nematocysts in the ctenophore *Euchlora rubra*. Amer. Nat. 85:73–74.

Komai, T., and T. Tokioka
1943   Three remarkable ctenophores from the Japanese seas. Annot. zool. jap. 21:144–151.

Korotnev [Korotneff], A.
1888   *Cunoctantha* und *Gastrodes*. Z. wiss. Zool. 47:242–251.

1891   Zoologische Paradoxen (*Cunoctantha* & *Gastrodes*). Z. wiss. Zool. 51: 613–628.

Krumbach, T.
1925   Erste und einzige Klasse der Acnidaria. Vierte Klasse des Stammes der Coelenterata. Ctenophora. Rippenquallen-Kammquallen. Handb. Zool., Berl. 1:905–995.

Lang, A.
1884   Die Polycladen (Seeplanarien) des Golfes von Neapel. Fauna u. Flora Neapel. Monograph 11:I–IX, 1–688.

Mayer, A. G.
1910   Hydromedusae. Pp. 1–230, i–xv, in: Medusae of the World, Vol. 1. Carnegie Inst. Washington, Publ. no. 109.

Mortensen, T.
1912   Ctenophora. The Danish Ingolf-Expedition 5, no. 2:1–98.

Raja, M.
    1930   Notizie su *Gastrodes parasiticum* Korotn., Ctenofore parasita della Salpe.
            Boll. Zool. 1:105–111.
Willey, A.
    1896   On *Ctenoplana*. Quart. J. micr. Sci. 39:323–342.

F. PLATYHELMINTHES

14 ◆ Relationships and Phylogeny of the Turbellaria

PETER AX

II. ZOOLOGISCHES INSTITUT UND MUSEUM,
UNIVERSITÄT GÖTTINGEN, GÖTTINGEN

Historically—and even today—the Turbellaria dominate much of our phylogenetic thinking on the lower Metazoa; hardly any other group of invertebrates has been accorded a position of comparable importance or been subjected to so many different interpretations.

By one school of thought, which really includes rather divergent viewpoints, the Turbellaria are considered the most primitive of the Bilateria (for example, in the sense of the Coelomata), and their derivation is traced back directly to the level of the Coelenterata. Approximately eighty years ago, Lang (1881, 1884) derived the Turbellaria, with the order Polycladida, from the Ctenophora. Another view is that of von Graff (1891, 1904), who postulated a phylogenetic connection between the Cnidaria and the order Acoela by way of the planula larva. Many authors have subscribed to the latter opinion (Bresslau, 1928–1933; Reisinger, 1928–1933; Meixner, 1938; Hyman, 1951; Beklemishev, 1958).

According to Hadži (1944, 1958) and Steinböck (1952, 1958), the Turbellaria have even a greater implication for the phylogeny of the Metazoa. On their view, the Turbellaria, with the order Acoela, descend directly from the Ciliata or ciliate-like multinucleate protozoa and must therefore represent the stem group not only of the Bilateria, but even of all the Metazoa. Such concepts—without critical discussion, however—have already been incorporated into certain English-language textbooks. For example, Moment (*General Zoology,* 1958) enumerates "the basic resemblances between multinucleate ciliates and acoelous flatworms" (p. 224), and in the second edition of *Practical Invertebrate Zoology,* by Bullough (1958), Hadži's theory is called "by far the most satisfactory explanation of the facts as they are known at present" (p. vii).

Others have reconstructed a metameric stem type of the Coelomata, with

This article is a condensation of the author's work "Phylogenie und Verwandtschaftsbeziehungen der Turbellarien," in *Ergebnisse der Biologie* 24, 1961.

initially three sets of celomic outpocketings. According to this reconstruction, the Turbellaria form a side-line of the Protostomia, without meaning for the evolution of the most primitive Bilateria—or even for the origin of the Metazoa from the Protozoa (Remane, 1950–1958; Ulrich, 1950, 1951; Jägersten, 1955, 1959; Marcus, 1958).

Not only is there much discussion of the position of the Turbellaria as a whole, but there are also differing views on the relationships between the various orders within the class. Many authors—from von Graff to Hyman, Riedl, Steinböck, and Hadži—consider the Acoela to be the most primitive group in all essential characters. Opposing that position, Lang (*loc. cit.*) and Wilhelmi (1913) have interpreted the Polycladida as the most primitive order; Karling (1940) has related the Catenulida closely to the supposed stem form; and Westblad (1949a) has placed the lately discovered Xenoturbellida at the foot of the turbellarian lineage.

In numerous phylogenetic speculations is to be found the erroneous suggestion that one recent great systematic group is derived directly from another. But the undeniable fact is that contemporaneous orders, classes, and phyla have a long evolutionary history extending far back in geological time. Thus it is quite impossible to derive the Turbellaria directly from such recent groups as the Ciliata, Cnidaria, Ctenophora, or Annelida. We have no greater justification in assuming that, within the Turbellaria, any order has retained its ancestral organization for all characters.

In attempting to settle these questions, we can only work with the criteria that have been proposed for the determination of homologies (Remane, 1956). First we must analyse the morphological importance of significant organs and structures within different systematic units of the Turbellaria. By attempting to assess permutations of primitive and derived characters, we may get an idea of the position of individual orders and suborders in a natural system. Hence a careful synthesis of primitive characters makes it possible to reconstruct a theoretical archetype ("systematischer Typus") as the stem form of the Turbellaria. These conclusions about relationships within the class form the basis for judgment as to the place of the Turbellaria in the Metazoa.

Recognition of Two Levels of Turbellarian Organization ("Stadiengruppen"): Archoophora and Neoophora

In order to establish an initial separation of the Turbellaria, let us examine two characters by which phylogenetic levels may be recognized and which clearly can be distinguished as either "primitive" or "derived."

If we consider the *female gonads,* we find that a uniform ovary with entolecithal egg-production characterizes the primitive level; the secondary level is distinguished by a structural and functional division of the ovary into germarium and vitellarium with the formation of ectolecithal eggs. All turbellarians with entolecithal eggs are further characterized by *spiral cleavage,* a primitive developmental pattern. By contrast, development in all groups with ectolecithal eggs is derived by reason of the modification of cleavage imposed by copious amounts of yolk.

A new classification of the Turbellaria in two great orders, mainly based on the first of the foregoing characters, has been proposed by Karling (1940) and Westblad (1948): all groups with undifferentiated ovaries and entolecithal eggs comprise the order Archoophora; all groups with germovitellaria, or germaria and vitellaria, and ectolecithal eggs make up the order Neoophora.[1]

In my opinion there are two points where this classification in two natural orders must be examined critically:

1. Entolecithal egg production and spiral cleavage are typical primitive characters, which alone do not suffice for establishing a natural grouping. By many other criteria there are evident differences among the Acoela, Macrostomida, Catenulida, and especially Polycladida.

2. Even among the Archoophora we can see several instances of a parallel tendency for the ovary to separate into ovum-producing and yolk-producing regions (for example, in the Macrostomida—Meixner, 1915; or in some of the Acoela such as *Polychoerus caudatus, Hofstenia atroviridis, Hallangia proporoides,* and *Myostomella pulchellum*— Löhner, 1919; Bock, 1923; Riedl, 1954; Westblad, 1946, 1948). Hence, in theory, the possibility exists that the level of the Neoophora has arisen from the Archoophora more than once.

As I see it, the Archoophora and Neoophora are not natural orders. Yet the confrontation of the Archoophora and the Neoophora is not at all "unqualifiedly bad" (Hyman, 1959, p. 734). It is, in fact, of great importance for a phylogenetic division of the Turbellaria into two levels of organization. I offer the following comprehensive classification:

a) *Primitive level of organization* ("*Stadiengruppe*"): *Archoophora*

Uniform ovary. Entolecithal egg production. Spiral cleavage as primary mode of development.

Orders: Acoela (including Hofsteniidae), Nemertodermatida,[2] Macrostomida, Proplicastomata, and Polycladida.

I have eliminated two lately described new orders, the Xenoturbellida (Westblad, 1949a) and Gnathostomulida (Ax, 1956c). These are discussed near the end of this article.

b) *Advanced level of organization* ("*Stadiengruppe*"): *Neoophora*

Female gonads separated into germovitellaria, or germaria and vitellaria. Ectolecithal eggs. Secondarily modified embryonic development.

Orders: Prolecithophora (Holocoela), Seriata (including Tricladida), Lecithoepitheliata, and Neorhabdocoela.

The orders of the Archoophora are more primitive than those of the Neoophora not only in ovary, egg production, and embryonic development, but also in several other characters. Thus in the following sections they are the main object of consideration.

---

[1] Karling defined only the order Archoophora. Later Westblad established the order Neoophora for all turbellarians with ectolecithal egg production. Furthermore, Karling did not place the Polycladida in the Archoophora. But on account of entolecithal egg production and the mode of spiral-quartet cleavage the polyclads definitely belong to the Archoophora as it is characterized in this report.

[2] By the time this manuscript was finished, Riedl (1960, Zool. Anz. 165) had published some new observations on the genus *Nemertoderma* Steinböck, which suggest its probable inclusion in the order Acoela (family Nemertodermatidae).

Primary Histological Structure of the Body

Most turbellarians are of typical cellular construction with an epithelial epidermis and digestive tract.[3] By contrast the Acoela, as is well known, are extensively characterized by a syncytial organization. In most aceles an intestinal lumen is lacking, they have a digestive parenchyma (endocytium—Westblad) central to more peripheral parenchyma (ectocytium), the latter in turn being covered by a syncytial epidermis (epicytium).

An important question that has been vehemently discussed is: what is the primary histological condition of the Turbellaria—the syncytial organization of the Acoela or the cellular structure of other orders?

Among modern authors, Westblad (1948) interprets at least the digestive tissue of the Acoela as primitive. But Steinböck (1955, 1958b) takes by far the most extreme view. By his formulation, the "primary plasmodium of the Acoela" is not only the original tissue of the Turbellaria, but also the "Urgewebe-Archihiston" of all metazoa.

Opposing this theoretical postulate stand the following ontogenetic, histological, and experimental facts:

1. The development of all the Turbellaria—including the Acoela—takes a clearly cellular course. All acellular tissues in the adult animal arise during ontogeny by fusion of initially separated blastomeres. Hence they are to be defined as syncytia and not as plasmodia.

2. Contrary to an often-advocated view, even the adult aceles do not have syncytial tissues only (fig. 14-1). In numerous forms, cell boundaries in the outer part of the epidermis have been found (Luther, 1912; Bock, 1923; Westblad, 1948; Papi, 1957; Marcus, 1949–1952). Some species, such as *Mecynostomum bathycola, Baltalimania (Mecynostomum) agile,* and *Mecynostomum pellitum,* even possess an ordinary epidermis with distinct cell boundaries and regularly arranged nuclei.

But it is not only the outer covering that shows cellular structures. Numerous glands and sense cells are individualized. There are, furthermore, typical spindle-like muscle cells with myofibrils; and, even the parenchyma of the Acoela—the classic example of a syncytial tissue—may have free, marked-off cells. Von Graff (1904, 1908), Böhmig (1908), and Beklemishev (1915) have observed ameboid digestive cells in the endocytium and undifferentiated connective tissue cells in the ectocytium. More recently Westblad (1948) has misinterpreted the phagocytes, dismissing them as incorrect observations. But now, especially since the excellent histological studies of Ivanov (1952), the existence and function of phagocytes is well established. Ivanov was able to show (for example, in the species *Oxyposthia praedator*) two different types of phagocytes

---

[3] This section is based without exception on the results of research with the light microscope. Yet the methods of light microscopy do not permit a definite decision as to cellular *vs.* "syncytial" organization. Evidence from electron-microscopic observations has rendered the existence of syncytia in the vertebrates as highly questionable (Bargmann and Knoop, 1959). Therefore a study of presumptive syncytial tissues of the lower celomates by electron microscopy is indicated.

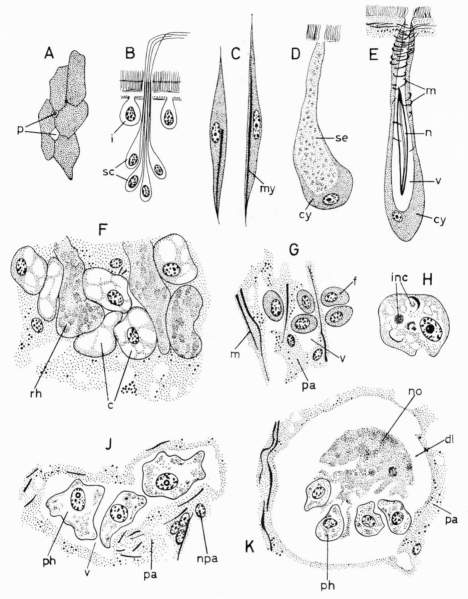

FIGURE 14-1. Examples of cellular structures in the Acoela. A, *Hofsteniola pardii,* cell boundaries in the outer part of the epidermis; B, in-sunk tangoreceptors of *Childia groenlandica;* C, muscle cells of *Oxyposthia praedator;* D, poison gland of *Convoluta sagittifera;* E, needle-producing gland of *Convoluta sagittifera;* F-K, *Oxyposthia praedator;* F, bubble-shaped connective tissue cells of the peripheral parenchyma; G, young connective tissue cells; H, phagocytic cell with engulfed food; J, ameboid phagocytes in the central digestive parenchyma; K, digestive cells following phagocytosis of food. c = connective tissue cells, cy = cytoplasm, dl = digestive lumen, f = free young connective tissue cells, i = in-sunk parts of the epidermis, inc = inclusion, m = muscle fibers, my = myofibrils, n = needle, no = nourishment, npa = nucleus of syncytial parenchyma, p = pores of glands, pa = parenchyma, ph = phagocytic cells, rh = rhabdite-forming gland, sc = sense cells, se = secretion, v = vacuole. (A after Papi, 1957; B after Luther, 1912; C-K after Ivanov, 1952.)

and several types of free connective tissue cells. Undifferentiated cells form characteristic elements in the peripheral parenchyma of the Acoela.

3. We know several evident transformations, in which a primary cellular structure directly turns into a syncytium. In the Tricladida, intracellular digestion, in conjunction with phagocytosis, leads to a total cell fusion (Westblad, 1923). Lately Reisinger (1959) has observed an analogous phenomenon in *Otomesostoma auditivum* (suborder Proseriata) after infection with sporozoa. Both processes are reversible. The cell structure remains, although too subtle to be seen with the light microscope;[4] it is restored to visibility at the end of digestion or after the delivery of the parasites, respectively. Finally, Reisinger (*loc. cit.*) has been able to produce syncytia experimentally in the Tricladida; reversing this, he could—by shaking—break down the seemingly syncytial epidermis of the neorhabdoceles *Gyratrix hermaphroditus* and *Koinocystis neocomensis* into individual cells.

Consequently there are, in principle, no differences between normal, experimental, or parasite-produced syncytia (Reisinger). In all instances they can be traced directly to the cellularity of the germ line.

The high regenerative capacity of some aceles (*Amphiscolops*)—which is one of Steinböck's main arguments for the postulated primordial character of acele tissue—does not contradict these facts in any way. Nowadays there is general acceptance of the high importance, in the Tricladida, of the free totipotent parenchymal cells (neoblasts) for the formation of the regenerative blastema (Dubois, 1949; Brøndsted, 1955; Pedersen, 1959). There seems to be no doubt that, in an analogous way, the so-called free cells in the parenchyma of the Acoela form the basis of regenerative capacity of some species. Hence, in my opinion, this phenomenon has no phylogenetic significance in the Acoela.

So we come to the following certain conclusion: cellular organization is phylogenetically primary for all the Turbellaria. The diverse types of syncytial tissues—with the extreme seen in the Acoela—are without exception the result of secondary cell fusions. All theoretical interpretations, from that of von Graff to those of Hadži and Steinböck, in which the syncytial organization of the Acoela is postulated as primary, are incompatible with the ontogenetic, structural, and experimental facts. The derivation of the Metazoa from multinucleate plasmodial ciliates—as hypothesized by Hadži and Steinböck—must be rejected.

Morphological Analysis of Some Important Organs

Intestine and Epidermis

Taking the foregoing considerations into account, I reconstruct a cellular entoderm and ectoderm as primitive for the Turbellaria.

At the organizational level of the Archoophora, the *digestive epithelium* is

---

[4] New electron-microscopic investigations by Pedersen (1961, Z. Zellforsch. 53:569–608 and 609–628) have indicated that the gastrodermal cells obviously do not form syncytia. Also the planarian connective tissue with free neoblasts and fixed parenchymal cells is primarily cellular and not syncytial.

formed by ciliated cells and so-called granular clubs in the Macrostomida and Polycladida and in a part of the Catenulida. Bresslau (1928, p. 33) traced these three orders separately to a supposed aceloid stem form ("acoeloide Urturbellarien"). But that these identical conditions have arisen in a parallel way is quite improbable. The turbellarian archetype must rather have had an intestine with ciliated cells and granular clubs. In the main, all deviating structures have arisen by reduction of cilia and secondary syncytiation of the digestive epithelium.

We can still follow these transformations within the Catenulida and the Acoela, step by step, in anatomical lineages ("anatomische Reihen").

In the order Catenulida, *Rhynchoscolex evelinae* (Marcus, 1945a) has a cellular ciliated intestine. *Rhynchoscolex remanei* (Rixen, 1961) has no cilia, but still has cell boundaries. Finally *Rhynchoscolex simplex* (Reisinger, 1924) reveals a typical syncytial intestine.

In such genera of the Nemertodermatida and Acoela as *Meara, Nemertoderma, Hofstenia,* and *Hofsteniola,* reduction of the cellular structure and disappearance of the digestive lumen may be demonstrated. *Meara stichopi* has a typical cellular intestine with ameboid cells and granular clubs, in addition to a constant digestive lumen (Westblad, 1946). In *Nemertoderma,* cell boundaries and granular clubs are to be observed in the ventral part of the intestine (Westblad, 1937) only. But in the family Hofsteniidae the intestine is absolutely syncytial, and the limit between the endocytium and the ectocytium is no longer clear-cut. Nevertheless *Hofstenia atroviridis* (Bock, 1923) shows a constant digestive lumen, which may also be present in *Hofsteniola pardii* (Papi, 1957). Finally *Hofstenia tinga* (Marcus, E. du B.-R., 1957) and *Hofstenia miamia* (Corrêa, 1960) have only vacuoles in the solid endocytium. Here the typical endocytium of the Acoela is reached.

As the primitive state of the *epidermis,* I reconstruct a cellular ciliated epithelium with intraepithelial nuclei and a basement membrane. In the Catenulida (*Rhynchoscolex simplex* and *R. diplolithicus,* Reisinger) and the Macrostomida (*Acanthomacrostomum spiculiferum,* Papi and Swedmark) there are a few forms without basement membranes and with intraepithelial muscle fibers; the logical interpretation of these organisms is to regard them as exceptional forms (Ax, 1961). By extension of this argument we can also interpret the lack of a basement membrane in the Acoela as a secondary loss. This seems a more likely interpretation than Beklemishev's (1960) derivation of a distinct epidermis and cellular, ciliated intestine from the aceloid parenchyma by "epithelialization."

PHARYNX

In the structure of the pharynx we distinguish three main levels of organization, corresponding to phylogenetic advance: the pharynx simplex, the pharynx plicatus, and the pharynx bulbosus.

In the stem type I reconstruct the *pharynx simplex,* a cellular ciliated tube, with circular and longitudinal muscle layers, that leads directly from the epidermis to the primary ciliated intestine (fig. 14-2, A). There is general agreement that the pharynx plicatus developed from the pharynx simplex by the formation of a fold. The pharynx plicatus is initially ciliated on both sides of this fold; it has extrapharyngeal glands and an open connection to the parenchyma of the body (fig.

14-2, B). By contrast, the pharynx bulbosus is fastened tightly to the parenchyma by a septum. Ciliation is much reduced; the glands are transferred into the interior of the pharyngeal bulb; and the pharyngeal fold is shortened at the mouth (fig. 14-2, C).

Figure 14-3 presents a phylogenetic reconstruction for these three types.

At the level of the Archoophora the pharynx simplex is present as a stem character in all the Macrostomida and in most of the Catenulida. By contrast, only in a

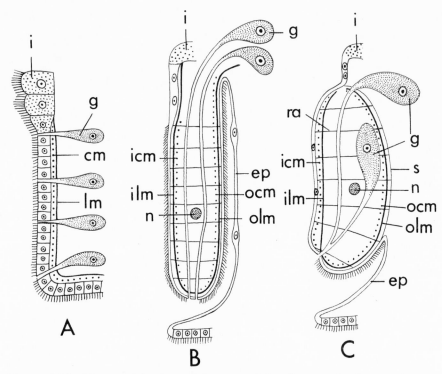

FIGURE 14-2. Scheme of the three main types of the pharynx. A, pharynx simplex; B, pharynx plicatus; C, pharynx bulbosus (subtype rosulatus). cm = circular muscle layer, ep = epithelium of the pharyngeal cavity, g = glands of the pharynx, i = intestine, icm = inner circular muscle layer, ilm = inner longitudinal muscle layer, lm = longitudinal muscle layer, n = circular nerve, ocm = outer circular muscle layer, olm = outer longitudinal muscle layer, ra = radial muscle, s = septum. (Original.)

few of the Acoela is the pharynx developed in accordance with the foregoing concepts of primitiveness (*e.g.,* in *Diopisthoporus, Proporus, Hallangia*—Westblad; *Hofsteniola pardii*—Papi; or *Hofstenia tinga*—du Bois-Reymond Marcus). The structure is complicated by different degrees of muscularity in *Hofstenia atroviridis* (Bock) and *Myostomella pulchellum* (Riedl). I consider the rudimentary form of the pharynx in most of the Acoela a consequence of reduction, probably in connection with the transformation of the cellular intestine into a syncytial parenchyma.

The *pharynx plicatus* is already realized not only in the Archoophora with the orders Polycladida and Proplicastomata, but also within the Neoophora in most of the Prolecithophora and in the Seriata. There are no difficulties in postulating a common origin for the last two orders. On the other hand, the possibility exists, because of specializations in shape and arrangement of the musculature, that the pharynx plicatus of the Polycladida and the Proplicastomata originated inde-

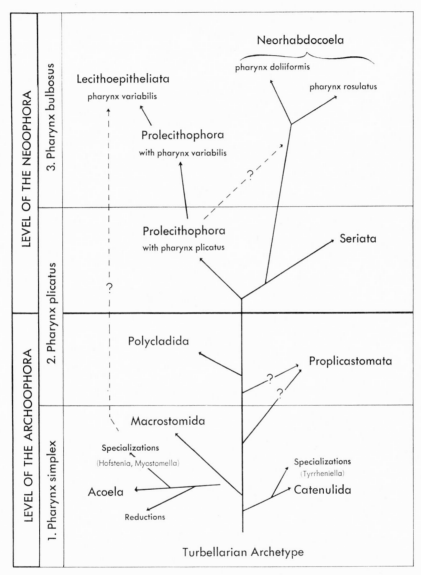

FIGURE 14-3. Scheme of the phylogenetic development of the pharynx from the simplex type through the plicatus type to the bulbosus type. (Original.)

pendently from the line leading to the Neoophora. But at present the question of monophyletic *vs.* polyphyletic origin of the pharynx plicatus cannot be decided definitely.

The *pharynx bulbosus* of the Neoophora most certainly developed in a parallel way several times from the pharynx plicatus. We distinguish three subtypes: the pharynx variabilis of the Prolecithophora (some genera of the suborder Separata) and the Lecithoepitheliata; and the pharynx rosulatus and pharynx doliiformis in the order Neorhabdocoela.

One line leads from the pharynx plicatus to the pharynx variabilis of the Prolecithophora (fig. 14-4, A-C). The transition can be followed step by step in the family Plagiostomidae (Karling, 1940). Probably also the pharynx of the Lecithoepitheliata (fig. 14-4, D) originated from the pharynx variabilis of the Prolecithophora by a total reduction of ciliation and pharyngeal fold (Karling).

In another line the subtypes pharynx rosulatus and doliiformis, as seen in the Neorhabdocoela (fig. 14-4, E-G), must be derived from the pharynx plicatus. Karling placed the origin of this line in the family Solenopharyngidae. But the recently described family Ciliopharyngiellidae (Ax, 1952) assumes an ideal intermediary position between the Proseriata and the Neorhabdocoela. With total ciliation and extrapharyngeal glands, the pharynx of *Ciliopharyngiella intermedia* (fig. 14-4, F) shows typical characters of the pharynx plicatus, but, in the development of a septum and in the arrangement of the musculature, it presents unequivocal marks of the rosulate pharyngeal type. From my point of view, therefore, the pharynx of the Neorhabdocoela is to be derived from that of the Proseriata. The bulbosus-like pharynx of the genus *Bulbotoplana* of the family Otoplanidae (fig. 14-4, J) unquestionably originated independently (Ax, 1956c). In the same way I attribute the bulbosus-like pharynx of the Solenopharyngidae (fig. 14-4, E) to convergence.

NERVOUS SYSTEM

Most of the Turbellaria have an internal nervous system. In the main it consists of a brain and a varying number of longitudinal cords and transverse commissures (orthogon—Reisinger).

In the Archoophora, however, there are several cases with an epithelial nervous system at the base of the epidermis (for example, in the Nemertodermatida, the genera *Nemertoderma* and *Meara*—Steinböck, 1931; Westblad, 1937, 1949b; and, in the Acoela, the genera *Tetraposthia*—Steinböck, 1931, and An der Lan, 1936; *Myostomella*—Riedl, 1954; *Hofsteniola*—Papi, 1957; and the species *Hofstenia atroviridis, Haploposthia brunea, H. albiventer, Mecynostomum evelinae, M. pellitum, Otocelis gullmarensis, Convoluta stylifera, C. viridipunctata,* and *C. karlingi* —Bock, 1923; Westblad, 1948; Marcus, 1948, 1951, 1952). I stress that in these genera other species with an internal nervous system are present.

Such an epidermal nervous system can be interpreted in two ways. On the one hand, there is no doubt that, in the primitive "archicelomate phyla" (such as the Phoronidea and Brachiopoda—Protostomia; Hemichordata and Pogonophora— Deuterostomia), the epidermal location represents a primary position. On the other hand, in the Archiannelida, which are considered to be reduced forms of the Polychaeta, the ventral nerves lie in the epidermis—a location that is most certainly secondarily acquired. Probably it arose by persistence of juvenile characters. In an analogous way the epithelial nervous system of the family Aeolosomatidae (Oligochaeta) is interpreted as a neotenic feature (Avel, 1959).

Hence, we must put this question: is the epidermal nervous system of some aceles primitive or derived? Nearly all authors agree upon the first alternative. But

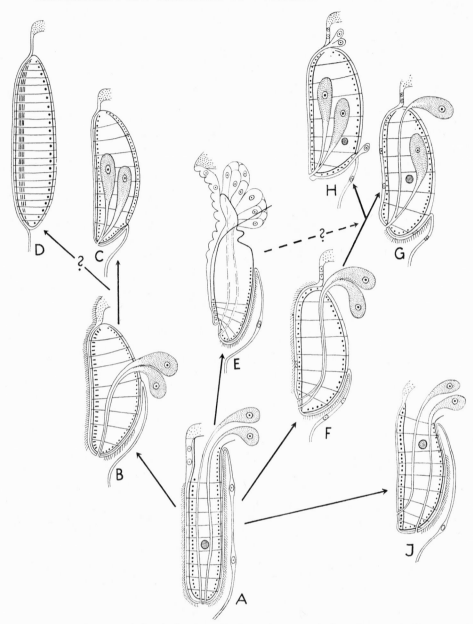

FIGURE 14-4. Phylogenetic derivation of the subtypes of the pharynx bulbosus and bulbosus-like types from the pharynx plicatus stage. A, scheme of the pharynx plicatus; B, primitive pharynx variabilis of the Prolecithophora (*Plagiostomum ponticum*) with outer and inner ciliation and extrapharyngeal glands; C, developed pharynx variabilis of the Prolecithophora (*Plagiostomum lemani*–type), fold of the pharynx shortened, glands in the interior with ciliation reduced; D, pharynx variabilis of the Lecithoepitheliata (*Prorhynchus*); E, bulbosus-like pharynx of the Solenopharyngidae (*Anthopharynx vaginatus*); F, *Ciliopharyngiella intermedia* (? Proseriata) with combination of plicatus —and rosulatus—characters; G, scheme of the pharynx rosulatus (Typhloplanoida); H, scheme of the pharynx doliiformis (Dalyellioida); J, bulbosus-like pharynx plicatus of *Bulbotoplana acephala* (Proseriata, Otoplanidae). (B after Ax, 1956a; C,E,H,G after Karling, 1940; D after Steinböck, 1927; F after Ax, 1952; J after Ax, 1956b.

the fact is of great importance that organisms with an epidermal nervous layer are scattered irregularly over several families and genera of the Acoela. In genera such as *Hofstenia, Haploposthia, Mecynostomum, Otocelis,* and *Convoluta,* species with an epidermal system and species with a highly differentiated internal nervous system coexist (fig. 14-5). Therefore I absolutely agree with the statement of Ivanov (1952) that the construction of the nervous system cannot be used for a taxonomic classification of the Acoela. But, this fact granted, just as little can the epidermal nervous system be considered primitive in these instances. Such an interpretation is not possible, for it would require that the irregularly distributed species all represent direct descendants of a common stem type with an epidermal system and that they all belong together systematically (=phylogenetically). We can avoid these methodological difficulties only if we interpret the existence of the epidermal nervous system within different groups of the Acoela as a parallel persistence of juvenile characters.

Consequently, in my opinion, the reconstruction of an internal nervous system with a brain, several pairs of longitudinal cords, and transverse commissures is more probable for the turbellarian archetype than that of a superficial nerve plexus.

Sense Organs

Among the sense organs the existence of a *statocyst* is certainly a primitive feature. It is to be found in the Acoela, Nemertodermatida, and Catenulida; but it is also retained in the Proseriata of the Neoophora. A repeated parallel origin of this character is quite improbable in view of the clear structural conformity of the statocyst in all these groups. Rather we must suppose that in the other orders the statocyst has been reduced.

I consider the possession of one statolith to be primitive. In the few instances with two or three statoliths, I believe a secondary multiplication has taken place (*Nemertoderma, Meara stichopi, Rhynchoscolex diplolithicus,* and *R. remanei*).

For the turbellarian archetype I also include the so-called *frontal organ,* an aggregation of glands and nerve cells in the front end of the animal.

Protonephridia

The general structure of the protonephridia in the Platyhelminthes, Rhynchocoela (Nemertinea), and Aschelminthes harmonizes quite well, so that a homology for all these phyla is very probable (Reisinger, 1928–1933). But, within the Turbellaria, the protonephridia are completely lacking in the Acoela and the related Nemertodermatida. Their absence is generally judged to be a primitive character; but this interpretation has the consequences that (*a*) phylogenetically the protonephridia must have originated within the Turbellaria and "above" the Acoela, and (*b*) all the other "Scolecida" must have inherited the protonephridia from the Turbellaria, which would mean that they must be derived directly from the "higher turbellarians."

I cannot accept the foregoing interpretation; hence I am forced to interpret the lack of protonephridia in the Acoela and Nemertodermatida as secondary. This morphological derivation is also easy to understand from a functional point of view. Osmoregulation is the most important task of the protonephridia (Westblad, 1923;

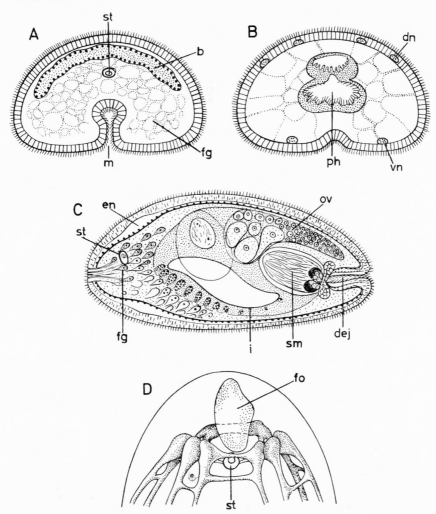

FIGURE 14-5. Different types of nervous system in the "Acoeloida." A, B, cross section through *Hofstenia tinga*—interior brain, four dorsal epidermal nerves and two ventral subepidermal nerves; C, sagittal section of *Nemertoderma bathycola* with epidermal nervous system; D, front of *Convoluta sagittifera* with internal nervous system (orthogon with four pairs of longitudinal cords and commissures). b = brain, dej = ductus ejaculatorius, dn = dorsal nerve, en = epidermal nerve layer, fg = frontal glands, fo = frontal organ, i = intestine, m = mouth, ph = pharynx simplex, ov = ovary, sm = seminal vesicle, st = statocyst, vn = ventral nerve. (A, B after Du Bois Reymond-Marcus, 1957; C after Westblad, 1937; D after Ivanov, 1952.)

Reisinger, 1922, 1923). Accordingly this organ is less developed in marine turbellarians than in their limnetic relatives, or it may even be completely missing in the former. In consequence of the compact nature of all tissues in the Acoela, the excretory function can be performed by the digestive parenchyma unaided by protonephridia.

Thus I reconstruct the existence of protonephridia as necessary for the turbellarian archetype and, with Bresslau and Karling, I consider as primitive the presence of paired lateral main stems with one nephridiopore each. The single median protonephridium of the Catenulida is most certainly a secondary condition, as is the development of several tubules and numerous nephridiopores in the Tricladida. In my opinion this multiplication is analogous to the ramification of the intestine in being a consequence of the increase in body size.

REPRODUCTIVE SYSTEM

The reproductive system of the Turbellaria is one of the most complicated in the animal kingdom. In this report I can only touch on some problems and must refer to the German original work (1961) for a more complete presentation of my opinion.

It is quite certain that the turbellarian archetype was a hermaphrodite with internal fertilization and, as already mentioned, with a simple ovary and entolecithal egg production. But there is a difference in opinion as to the original arrangement of the gonads. Some authors (Steinböck, 1931; Karling, 1940; Westblad, 1948; and Ivanov, 1952) consider a hermaphroditic gonad with mixed eggs and sperm cells to be primitive. This interpretation seems to me incorrect, for the following reasons:

1. Most of the Turbellaria have separated, bilaterally arranged gonads. Also, in the Acoela, ventral paired ovaries and numerous dorsal testes are the common condition.

2. A typical hermaphroditic gonad is known only in a few aceles (for example, *Diopisthoporus longitubus, Haploposthia brunea* and *H. rubra, Convoluta viridipunctata*—An der Lan, 1936; Westblad, 1940–1948), in one species of the Catenulida (*Thyrreniella sigillata*—Riedl, 1959), and in one species of the Prolecithophora (*Archimonotresis limophila*—Karling, 1940). If these isolated, randomly distributed examples are to be considered primitive, we have quite the same difficulty as encountered with "epidermal" *vs.* internal nervous systems.

3. A hermaphroditic gonad may also be secondary. As a classic example I mention the Pulmonata within the Gastropoda.

So, with Marcus (1949), I consider the paired arrangement of separated gonads to be the original condition in the Turbellaria.

Another important problem in phylogenetic reconstruction is posed by the primary gonoducts and the copulatory apparatus.

There is no doubt that the archetype had a simple copulatory organ ("primäre Kornsekretblase"—Karling, 1940) in the male sex. Further, it is certain that the separation of the male and female gonopores in the Macrostomida, Acoela, and Polycladida is primitive.

It is the opinion of Reisinger (1933) and many other investigators that the atrium femininum and the vagina of the Macrostomida are respectively homologous with the bursa and the vagina of the Acoela (Proandropora-Bursalia) (Fig. 14-6). But, contrary to the general view, I interpret this homology as indicating a derivation of the Acoela from the phylogenetic line of the Macrostomida. As Marcus has said, "Mouthpiece and bursa (Acoela) may be as well remainders of the 'passage apparatus' and atrium (Macrostomidae) as precursors of the latter" (1946, p. 159).

I think it probable, moreover, that the bursa (Lang's vesicle) and the vagina of the Polycladida also have the same origin as these structures.

Hence I reconstruct for the ancestral type a simple bursa with a vagina opening separately in front of the male gonopore. Probably the primitive form also had oviducts leading from the ovaries to the vagina. In the Archoophora we find this situation at present in the Macrostomida and particularly well developed in the Polycladida, which possess large ciliated oviducts.

In the phylogeny of the Acoela the oviducts have been reduced; egg laying takes place secondarily out of the mouth or through the body wall. But the cement

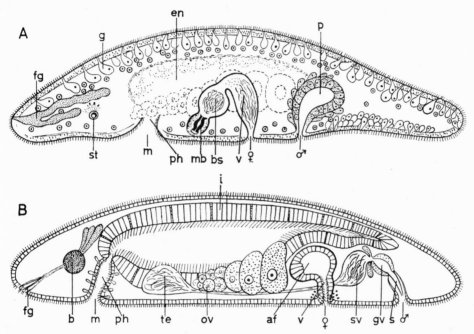

FIGURE 14-6. Sagittal scheme of the Acoela (Proandropora-Bursalia) and the Macrostomida with homologous bursa (bs = af) and vagina (v). A, *Convoluta convoluta;* B. *Macrostomum.* af = atrium femininum, b = brain, bs = bursa, en = endocytium, fg = frontal glands, g = gland in epicytium, gv = granular vesicle, m = mouth, mb = mouth piece in of the bursa, ov = ovary, ph = pharynx simplex, p = penis, s = stylet, st = statocyst, sv = seminal vesicle, te = testis, v = vagina. (A after Westblad, 1946; B original.)

glands, which enter the vagina in many digonoporous aceles (Meixner, 1926; Marcus, 1946), are remaining indications of primitive egg laying through the female gonopore.

In my opinion this interpretation is much more probable than the derivation of the gonoducts from the aceloid condition by progressive evolution. For, in the Neoophora, we also know several remarkable examples in which the eggs or embryos are transported secondarily through the intestine (for example, *Bresslauilla relicta*—Reisinger, 1929; *Baicalellia evelinae*—Marcus, 1946; and *Ethmorhynchus anophthalmus*—Meixner, 1938; Karling, 1956). Above all, *Bresslauilla relicta* shows unequivocally that the female gonoducts are reduced in connection with the secondary development of eggs in the intestine.

Embryology

In this report I want to present only one embryological problem, which is of great importance for a discussion about the turbellarian archetype.

All orders of the Archoophora that have been studied up to now (Polycladida, Acoela, Macrostomida, and Catenulida) have a typical spiral cleavage. The embryonic development of the Polycladida is even characterized by the so-called spiral-quartet 4d cleavage. In all details of cell lineage through formation of the 4d (mesentoblast) blastomere, its division into $4d_1$ and $4d_2$, and the further development of mesoderm and entoderm, this mode harmonizes with cleavage in the Annelida, Mollusca, Rhynchocoela (Nemertinea), and Sipunculoida. It is quite impossible to interpret this identical, very complex phenomenon as occurring by reason of a manifold parallelism. As has been pointed out by Wilson, Surface, Heider, Hyman, Remane, and Marcus, spiral-quartet 4d cleavage must represent a highly specific state of homology; this forces the acceptance of a natural relationship between the Turbellaria and the other "Spiralia."

In view of these facts, our approach in principle allows the following two possibilities of phylogenetic derivation: (*a*) spiral-quartet 4d cleavage has arisen within the Turbellaria, and all the other Spiralia must be derived directly from the Turbellaria; or (*b*) spiral-quartet 4d cleavage is not a new formation within the Turbellaria, but rather, the Turbellaria together with the other Spiralia derive from a common ancestral type with spiral-quartet 4d cleavage.

The first alternative is surely to be rejected in view of certain arguments (see Ax, 1961, and, further on here, the section "Position of the Turbellaria in the System of the Metazoa"). By consequence, the second alternative, spiral-quartet 4d cleavage, must represent the primary mode of development of the Turbellaria. To avoid misunderstanding, I stress that the Polycladida by no means can represent the base of the Turbellaria in all other characters. Spiral-quartet 4d cleavage is merely demanded for the archetype, and I state that this mode has been kept unchanged in the phylogenetic line to the polyclads.

Bresslau (1909) has already pointed out the extensive correlation between development in the Polycladida and in the Acoela. The main difference is the formation of only two macromeres in the Acoela, in contrast to four macromeres in the Polycladida. Accordingly in the further course of cleavage in the Acoela only duets are given off. Bresslau has discussed, as a central problem, the question as to whether the course of phylogeny passes from the Acoela to the Polycladida or *vice versa*. But this question is formulated incorrectly. It is impossible to derive one recent order directly from another: we can only trace both to a common ancestor. From this methodologically correct standpoint, derivation of spiral-duet cleavage from spiral-quartet 4d cleavage is the only possible interpretation. In the Polycladida, blastomeres A and C are in general somewhat smaller than B and D. As in the Acoela, they are given off in a sinistral direction and then lie at a higher level than blastomeres B and D. If the lateral blastomeres A and C do not move downwards, but remain above the other cells, one has duet cleavage such as occurs in the Acoela. Hence the secondary cleavage pattern of the Acoela can be derived with certainty from primary spiral-quartet 4d cleavage.

In my report in German (Ax, 1961), I presented a phylogenetic interpretation of the different types of development in the Neoophora. Here I only want to mention that, even in the much modified development of ectolecithal eggs, reminiscences of the primary spiral cleavage may be detected, as has been pointed out by Steinböck and Ausserhofer (1950) for *Prorhynchus stagnalis* (Lecithoepitheliata); by Bogomolov (1949) for *Phaenocora* and *Bresslauilla relicta* (Neorhabdocoela); and by Reisinger (1955) for *Otomesostoma auditivum* (Proseriata).

Phylogeny of the Orders

The results of morphological analysis and the establishment of the primary mode of development provide the basis for a phylogenetic interpretation of the Turbellaria. My conclusions about the relationships of the different orders and suborders are presented in a genealogical tree (fig. 14-7).

I begin with the *Macrostomida*. They have numerous primitive characters, such as a strictly cellular structure, a pharynx simplex, a straight ciliated intestine, and paired protonephridia. The formation of the reproductive system, with primary paired gonads and the simple bursa-vagina (*Macrostomum*), most probably is also primitive. But there are also some derived characters in the Macrostomida (for example, lack of a statocyst and great simplification of the nervous system to two longitudinal cords).

On the whole the Macrostomida represent a very primitive order, but because of a few reductions and specializations they cannot be placed directly at the base of the genealogical tree.

The controversial *Acoela* are more primitive than the Macrostomida in the following characters: existence of a statocyst, the well-developed frontal organ, and the orthogonal nervous system of most species. But the Acoela are exceedingly derived in view of syncytiation of the body to varying degrees—from as little as the transformation of a cellular intestine into a syncytial parenchyma without digestive lumen to the extreme of cell fusions in the epidermis. The reduction of protonephridia and the frequently limited development of the pharynx simplex are consequences of this syncytial tendency. Doubtless the mode of spiral-duet cleavage is also secondarily derived. The existence of a bursa and vagina in the group Proandropora-Bursalia is primitive.

Altogether I interpret the Acoela as an early but extremely specialized line of the Archoophora, for which I postulate a common root with the Macrostomida. In my opinion the Acoela are without any importance in the progressive evolution of the Turbellaria.

The *Nemertodermatida* (*Meara, Nemertoderma*) are, of course, most nearly related to the Acoela. They have most of the reduced aceloid characters, but are doubtless more primitive in the structure of the intestine, with its cell boundaries and granular clubs. A specialization is the doubling of the statolith.

The *Catenulida* form another highly derivative branch of the Archoophora. The single protonephridium is a secondary development, as are the unpaired ovary and testis and, in particular, the dorsal position of the male gonopore. On the whole the reproductive system of this order demonstrates a striking reductive tendency. In *Rhynchoscolex* this trend leads, by a total loss of the male organs, to a parthenogenetic mode of reproduction (Reisinger, Marcus). Another specialization is the widely distributed asexual propagation by paratomy. In a parallel way this mode is to be found in the Microstomidae (order Macrostomida), but it also has arisen independently in a few members of the Acoela and Tricladida (Ax and Schulz, 1959).

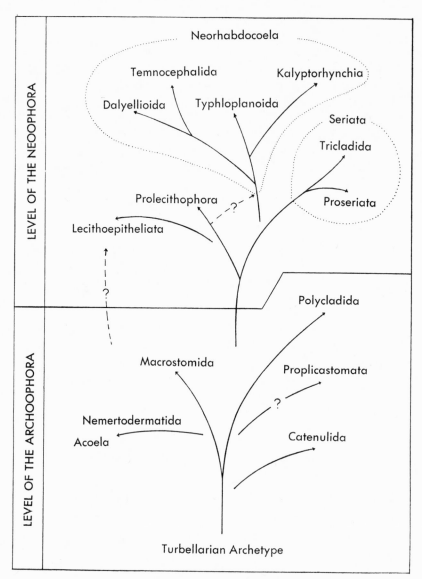

FIGURE 14-7. Genealogical tree of the Turbellaria. (Original.)

Although the *Polycladida*—like the Acoela—assume an important place in phylogenetic speculations, they just as little represent the base of the genealogical tree. They are doubtless highly differentiated with respect to the pharynx plicatus and the complicated brain with a brain capsule. Certain other characters, such as the thick basement membrane, the strong subepidermal musculatures, and the branching of the intestine, are surely the consequence of the considerable increase in body size realized by the polyclads in the course of evolution.

But, in spite of these complications, the Polycladida have kept some important primitive characters (for example, the ciliated intestine, the uniform ovary, and, in my opinion, also the bursa-vagina). And, above all, the typical spiral-quartet 4d cleavage is a primitive attribute. The polyclads have retained this mode unchanged from the turbellarian archetype.

Finally, the lack of a statocyst and absence of the frontal organ in the adult polyclads are degenerate characters.

At present the position of the *Proplicastomata,* which consist of but one species, *Proporoplana jenseni* (Reisinger), is quite uncertain. Having a typical pharynx plicatus, the Proplicastomata doubtless stand above the level of the Macrostomida, Catenulida, and Acoela. But there is a question as to whether the pharynx plicatus of this group has a common origin with the pharynx of the Polycladida, Prolecithophora, and Seriata, or whether it represents an independently evolved condition.

On the derived group, the *Neoophora,* I can add only a few remarks. The *Prolecithophora* and the *Proseriata* are primitive groups within the Neoophora, but it is not possible to connect them directly to a particular order of the Archoophora. In their morphology and ontogeny, the Proseriata form the phylogenetic precursors of the *Tricladida.* It is the opinion of Karling (1940) that the great order of the *Neorhabdocoela* arose from the Prolecithophora. But, taking into consideration the discovery of *Ciliopharyngiella intermedia* (Ax, 1952), I think it more probable that this most highly differentiated order of the Turbellaria is phylogenetically connected with the Proseriata at the base. Within the Neorhabdocoela, the Typhloplanoida assume a central position. One early lateral line leads to the suborder Dalyellioida and further to the Temnocephalida. In a second line, the suborder Kalyptorhynchia with the characteristic proboscis arose.

It is Steinböck's opinion that the *Lecithoepitheliata* may be derived directly from the aceloid type of organization found in *Hofstenia* (Acoela). But in view of Karling's findings (1940), this order is highly specialized and can be traced to a common origin with the Prolecithophora.

Reconstruction of the Turbellarian Archetype ("Systematischer Typus")

In the discussion of the natural system of the Turbellaria, we have demonstrated that no recent order lies in all respects at the base of the genealogical tree. Already in the Archoophora, all known orders have different combinations of primitive and derived characters. I reconstruct the turbellarian archetype, based on primitive characters analyzed (fig. 14-8), as follows:

1. Primary cellular structure of body with an epithelial entoderm and ectoderm; space between organs filled with parenchyma.

2. Ciliated epidermis with basement membrane and subepidermal musculature.

3. Pharynx simplex; straight intestine with ciliated cells and granular clubs.

4. Internal nervous system with a brain, several pairs of longitudinal cords, and transverse commissures (orthogon).

A   B

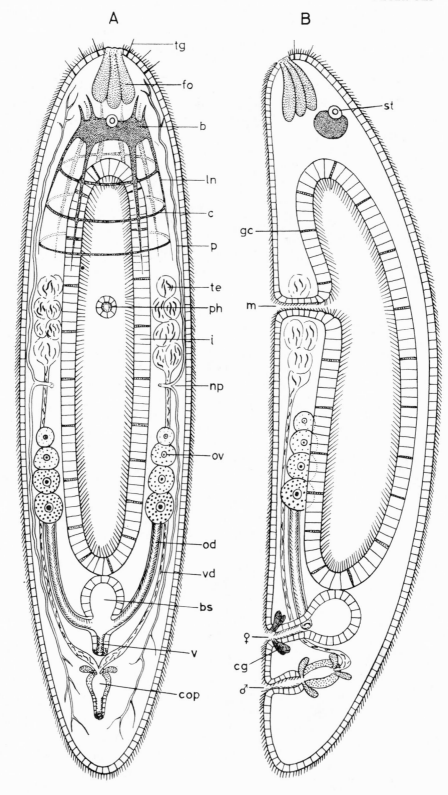

5. Single statocyst with one statolith; frontal organ opening on the anterior tip.

6. A pair of protonephridia in the sides of the body; two nephridiopores.

7. Hermaphroditic with internal fertilization.

8. Separated testes and ovaries.

9. Separated male and female gonopores.

10. In the male sex, paired testes, vasta deferentia (or "Pseudosamenleiter"), and a simple copulatory organ.

11. In the female sex, paired ovaries with entolecithal egg production, oviducts, a simple bursa, and a vagina.

12. Embryonic development with spiral-quartet 4d cleavage.

Of course we must reckon with emendations consequent upon an increase in our knowledge. Yet the possible modification of single characters would hardly result in any essential change in the general concept.

Position of the Turbellaria in the System of the Metazoa

My conception of the position of the Turbellaria within the Metazoa has a natural basis in the reconstruction of the turbellarian archetype.

At present we have four main theories to consider: (1) ciliate-acele theory (Hadži, Steinböck, Hanson); (2) planula-acele theory (von Graff, Hyman, Beklemishev); (3) ctenophore-polyclad theory (Lang); (4) spiralian theory (Heider, Remane, Marcus).

In a critical confrontation there are two problems to be considered for all theories, the consequences of which must be weighed carefully: (a) the derivation of the Turbellaria from a lower phylogenetic level, and (b) the derivation of "higher taxa" from the turbellarians, depending upon the postulated position of the Turbellaria.

In the ciliate theory as well as in the planula theory, the Acoela are interpreted as the most primitive group, in all characters, of the Turbellaria. Yet we have shown that this supposition is incompatible with the reconstruction of the turbellarian archetype.

The foundation of the ciliate theory is destroyed if one takes full account of the fact that neither the Acoela nor the other Turbellaria have a primary plasmodium. There is no genealogical connection between the secondary syncytium of the Acoela and the multinucleate plasmodial protozoa. Steinböck's "archihiston" is a pure fiction (Reisinger, 1959). Hadži's interpretations are also incorrect (for example, the supposed homology between trichocysts and rhabdites, the derivation of the endocytium from food vacuoles, or the protonephridia from contractile vacuoles—the Acoela do not possess protonephridia!). If the criteria of homology are used

FIGURE 14-8. Theoretical reconstruction of the turbellarian archetype. A, horizontal view; B, sagittal section, b = brain, bs = bursa, c = commissure, cg = cement glands, cop = copulatory organ, fo = frontal organ, gc = granular club, i = intestine, ln = longitudinal nerve, m = mouth, np = nephridiopore, od = oviduct, ov = ovary, p = protonephridia, ph = pharynx simplex, st = statocyst, te = testes, tg = tangoreceptor, v = vagina, vd = vas deferens. (Original.)

exactly, these apparent conformities—as well as the confrontation of certain specialized holotrichous ciliates (*Dileptus, Remanella*) with the Acoela (Hanson, 1958)—prove to be mere superficial similarities (Remane, 1958). "By such a method a group can be derived from almost any other group" (Jägersten, 1959, p. 102). Beyond that we have several complex structures in the Acoela, which are not present in the ciliates. These are, in the Acoela, hermaphroditic reproductive system with a copulatory organ, orthogonal nervous system with brain, typical statocyst, complicated glandular organs, cellular embryonic development, and partly cellular structures in the adults.

But there are also no specific homologies between the Turbellaria and a planula larva without a mouth—quite aside from the question as to whether the ancestral planula ("Planaea") had a solid entoderm or, as Hyman (1959) recently believes, an epithelial entoderm.

Finally, the striking correspondence of body shape between the Polycladida and creeping ctenophores (*Coeloplana* and *Ctenoplana*) are convergent characters consequent upon a similar mode of living. They are "Lebensformmerkmale" just as are the surprising similarities between the turbellarian family Otoplanidae and the marine (macrodasyoid) gastrotrichs, or between many "rhabdoceles" and some molluscs (*Pseudovermis, Rhodope*). Furthermore, in view of this formulation of the turbellarian archetype, the Polycladida represent the base group of the Turbellaria no better than do the Acoela.

We now turn to the second problem: the derivation of "higher groups" from the Turbellaria. In the three theories discussed, the Turbellaria assume a central position: all the Bilateria must have arisen from the Turbellaria—also, by the ciliate theory, the Cnidaria and Ctenophora. In the latter case even the Porifera can hardly be excluded, because the facts of embryology, the identical type of sperm and perhaps the "nerve cells,"[5] are evidence for a monophyletic origin with the other Metazoa (Tuzet, 1950, 1956; Pavans de Ceccatty, 1955).

Among the numerous consequences of this postulated position of the Turbellaria are the following:

1. The celom of the Protostomia and Deuterostomia, as well as the circulatory system and the proctodeum-anus, must have arisen by progressive modification of the turbellarian condition.

2. The primitive mode of external fertilization must have been acquired repeatedly in the Bilateria and—according to the ciliate theory, at least, also in the Coelenterata—from the turbellarian condition of internal fertilization. But we have no model for such a step, whereas the reverse transformation—from external to internal fertilization—is known within numerous groups of invertebrates (Remane, Jägersten).

3. It has been stated by Franzén (1956) that the different phyla of the invertebrate Metazoa from the Porifera to the Acrania possess a specific, uniform type of sperm in correlation with external fertilization. This sperm is characterized by a rounded or oval head with acrosome, a middle piece containing four to five mitochondrial spheres, and a tail formed by a thin filament (fig. 14-9). "It is probably seldom that a character

---

[5] But according to the recent work of Jones (1962, Biol. Rev. 37:1–50) the existence of a nervous system in the Porifera is very doubtful.

can be designated as primitive with greater certainty than in this case" (Jägersten, 1959, p. 94). In contrast, the sperms of the Turbellaria are without exception highly specialized (fig. 14-10). According to the ciliate, planula, and ctenophore theories, the primitive type of sperm, which correlates with external fertilization, must have arisen independently several times from the highly modified sperm of the Turbellaria. This is most improbable.

4. The derivation of other groups of invertebrates, from the neoo-

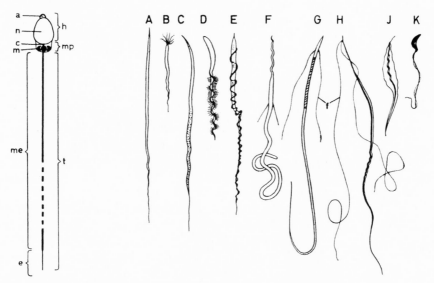

FIGURE 14-9. Diagram of the primitive sperm in the Metazoa. a = acrosome, c = centriole, e = end piece, h = head, m = mitochondrial spheres, me = main piece, mp = middle piece, n = nucleus, t = tail. (After Franzén, 1956.) FIGURE 14-10. Highly specialized sperm in different orders of the Turbellaria. A, common type in the Acoela; B-D, various aceles; B, *Paraphanostoma submaculatum* with bundle of flagella; C, *Convoluta convoluta;* D, *Convoluta fulvomaculata,* sperm with undulating ciliated seam; E, *Haploposthia viridis;* F, *Macrostomum,* with two flagella (Macrostomida); G, *Prostheceraeus vittatus,* with two flagella (Polycladida); H, *Dendrocoelum lacteum,* with two flagella (Tricladida); J, *Plagiostomum* (Prolecithophora); K, *Paravortex cardii* (Dalyellioida). f = flagella ("Nebengeiseln"). (A,B,C,E after Westblad, 1948; D after Ax, 1959; F after Hyman, 1943; G after Franzén, 1956; H after Hammerschmidt, 1908; J after von Graff, 1911; K after Hallez, 1909.)

phoran level of the Turbellaria has the following further consequence. Primitive entolecithal eggs and typical radial cleavage must have been derived from ancestors with separated gonads (germaria and vitellaria) and a highly specialized ectolecithal type of embryology that is unique in the animal kingdom. Of course, this derivation is exceedingly unlikely.

These examples demonstrate that the postulated primary position of the turbellarians, which is demanded by the ciliate, planula, and ctenophore theories, cannot be accepted.[6]

---

[6] Beklemishev (1958, 1960) is of the opinion that several lines of the Bilateria have arisen independently from the level of the Coelenterata—such as the Scolecida (Platyhelminthes,

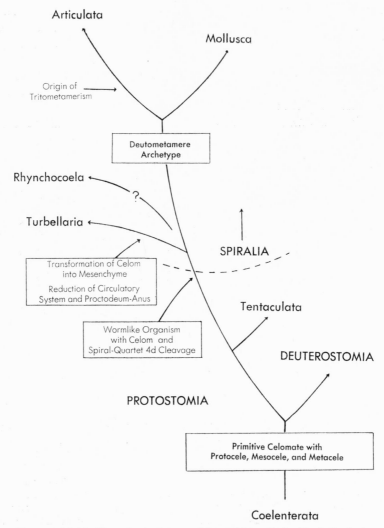

FIGURE 14-11. Genealogical tree with position of the Turbellaria in the system of the Metazoa according to the spiralian theory. (Original.)

The spiralian theory—which was discussed as early as 1914 by Heider—takes the spiral-quartet 4d cleavage of the polyclads as the primary mode of development of the Turbellaria. By this theory the turbellarians are not derived directly from any other recent group, but it is postulated that they, as well as the Rhyncho-

Rhynchocoela, Aschelminthes), the Trochozoa (Articulata, Mollusca, Entoprocta, Sipunculoida), the Podaxonia (Phoronidea, Bryozoa), and also the Deuterostomia. But I cannot follow this view of a polyphyletic origin of the Bilateria. The acceptance of such origins would presume a very improbable parallel development of many organs, and also of some complex modes of development (spiral-quartet 4d cleavage in the Scolecida and Trochozoa!). Furthermore, we should have to ignore the homology of the essential components of the Bilateria (celom, circulatory system, nervous system with brain, nephridial organs, and intestine with proctodeum-anus). In my opinion the monophyletic origin of the Bilateria is the only possible interpretation.

coela, Annelida, Mollusca, and other Spiralia, have arisen in the line of the Proto-stomia from a common primitive celomate ancestor with spiral-quartet 4d cleavage (fig. 14-11). The unacceptable consequences resulting from the theory of a direct connection between the Turbellaria and Protozoa or Coelenterata are thereby avoided. Apart from the Trematoda and the Cestoda, this theory also traces no other groups back to the Turbellaria.

In the spiralian theory we obviously must accept some morphological alterations in the line from a primitive celomate up to the origin of the turbellarian archetype; for example, the transformation of celomic cavities into parenchyma—or more ex-actly the change in function of blastomere 4d from the formation of epithelial cavities between ectoderm and entoderm, to the formation of a diffuse parenchyma —and, dependent on this transformation, probably the loss of a circulatory system. Similar reasoning applies to the reduction of the proctodeum-anus and the change from external to internal fertilization. But we have many comparable examples in the invertebrates for these alterations: a reduction of the celom or a partial trans-formation into parenchyma in the Mollusca (*Neopilina galatheae* Lemche of the class Monoplacophora still possesses a paired, well-developed celom!), Hirudinea, Myzostomida, and Enteropneusta; a reduction of the circulatory system in the Hirudinea and several lines of the Arthropoda (Copepoda, Ostracoda, Acarina); the loss of the anus in some of the Echinodermata, Brachiopoda, Rotifera, etc. (Marcus, 1934; Remane, 1951).

Hence from my point of view the spiralian theory, at present, represents by far the most probable interpretation of the position of the Turbellaria within the Metazoa.

Systematic Position of the Xenoturbellida and Gnathostomulida

In the reconstruction of the turbellarian archetype, the Xenoturbellida (Westblad, 1949a) and the Gnathostomulida (Ax, 1956b) are not considered, although in the original description both were placed in the Turbellaria. But I do not accept West-blad's conception of the relationships between the Xenoturbellida and the Turbel-laria; also, the initially proposed position of the Gnathostomulida is not certain. I should like here only to mention some facts from a new study by Reisinger (1960) and my own surveys (1960, 1961).

Xenoturbella bocki Westblad, 1949, has been described from the Scandinavian west coast. The animal reaches a length of 2–3 cm.; it has two ciliated furrows at the sides of the body and one furrow in the middle (fig. 14-12, A, B). The internal structure is astonishingly simple (fig. 14-12, E). The intestine has only one ventral opening. A strong subepidermal musculature is developed; a loose parenchyma lies between ectoderm and entoderm. In these characters there are, of course, some for-mal similarities with the turbellarians, but no specific homologies are evident. The structure of the reproductive system reveals that resemblances to the Turbellaria are superficial. *Xenoturbella* has no localized gonads or copulatory organ; it lacks both gonoduct and gonopore. Egg cells and sperm cells are produced all over the paren-chyma. Furthermore, *Xenoturbella* possesses the primitive type of sperm described for the Metazoa (fig. 14-12, C, D), from which we may with certainty infer external fertilization.

Finally, *Xenoturbella* has two specific complex structures that are also incompatible with placement in the Turbellaria and show a clear relation to the Deuterostomia. Reisinger has stated (1960) that the complicated epidermis of *Xenoturbella* is essentially identical with the epidermis of the Enteropneusta (Fig. 14-13). Further, *Xenoturbella* possesses a statocyst with about 20 (!) statoliths, in astonishing agreement with the structures to be found in certain holothurians (*Elpidia, Kolga;* larvae

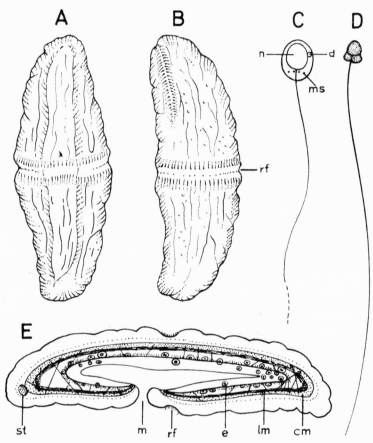

FIGURE 14-12. *Xenoturbella bocki.* A, living specimen from the ventral side; B, from the dorsal side; C, late spermatid; D, sperm; E, sagittal section through the body. cm = circular muscle layer, d = dictyosome, e = egg cells, lm = longitudinal muscle layer, m = mouth, ms =mitochondrial sphere, n = nucleus, rf = circular fold, st = statocyst.
(A,B,D,E after Westblad, 1949a; C after Franzén, 1956.)

of the Synaptida) (fig. 14-14). Doubtless the problem of the exact position of the Xenoturbellida within the Deuterostomia is not yet solved, but I agree with Reisinger that they definitely do not belong in the Turbellaria.

The Gnathostomulida (figs. 14-15 and 14-16) were found first in the bay at Kiel, later on the French coast of the Mediterranean Sea (Ax, 1956a), and even in the archipelago of the Maldive Islands (Gerlach, 1958) and in the Barents Sea (Mamkaev, 1961). At present we know four species—*Gnathostomula paradoxa* Ax, *Gnathostomula maldivarum* Gerlach, *Gnathostomula murmanica* Mamkaev,

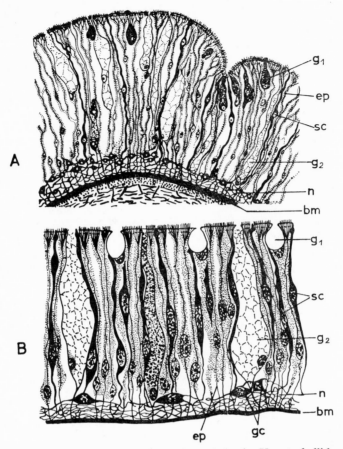

FIGURE 14-13. Scheme of the epidermis in the Xenoturbellida and the Enteropneusta. A, *Xenoturbella bocki;* B, *Balanoglossus.* bm = basement membrane, ep = epidermal cells, g_1 and g_2 = different types of gland cells, gc = ganglion cells, n = nerve plexus, sc = sense cells. (After Reisinger, 1960; B from Bullock, 1945.)

and *Gnathostomaria lutheri* Ax—which are all very small animals of the mesopsammon.

In the lack of a celom, circulatory system, and anus, the Gnathostomulida show general agreement with the Turbellaria. Because, beyond this, they possess a typical

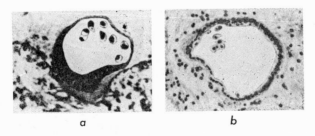

a   b

FIGURE 14-14. Statocysts. A, *Xenoturbella bocki;* B, *Synapta* sp. (After Reisinger, 1960.)

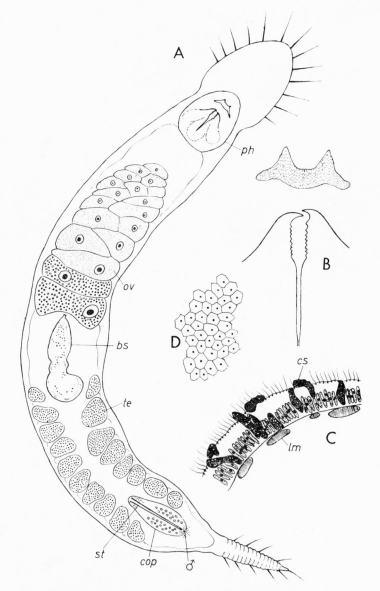

FIGURE 14-15. *Gnathostomula paradoxa.* A, shape and internal organization; B. jaws and base plate of the pharynx; C, cross section through the epidermis (flagellated epithelium); D, superficial section through the epidermis. One basal body in each cell. bs = bursa, cop = copulatory organ, cs = cyanophilous secretion, lm = longitudinal muscle, ov = ovary, ph = pharynx, st = stylet, te = testes. (After Ax, 1956c.)

hermaphroditic reproductive system, I originally placed them in the Turbellaria. But I did so with great reservation, because the Gnathostomulida also have two strange special characters.

First, they possess only one flagellum per cell in the epidermis (fig. 14-15, C, D). Such a flagellated epithelium is distributed throughout the Porifera and Cnidaria, but is unknown in the Turbellaria and on the whole is found very seldom in the Bilateria (Brachiopoda, larvae of Echinodermata and Acrania). Of course with none of these groups is there a close relationship.

Second, the Gnathostomulida have a pharynx armed with two circular jaws and,

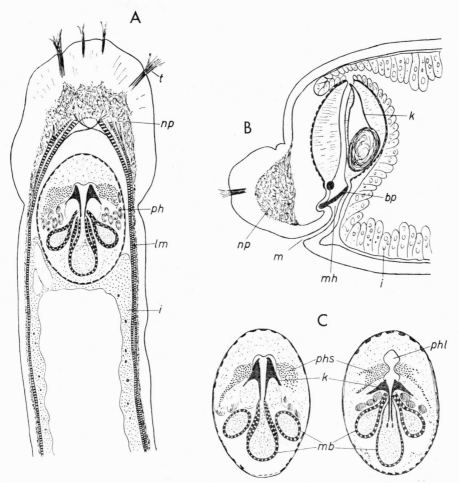

FIGURE 14-16. *Gnathostomula paradoxa.* A, horizontal section through the front; B, sagittal reconstruction of the front with the pharyngeal aperture; C, horizontal sections through the middle part of the pharynx. bp = base plate, i = intestine, k = jaw, lm = longitudinal muscle, m = mouth, mb = muscle bag, mh = mouth cavity, np = nerve plexus (neuropileme), ph = pharynx, phl = lumen of the pharynx, phs = secretion of the pharynx, t = tangoreceptor. (After Ax, 1956c.)

in addition, a very complicated musculature of the pharynx (fig. 14-16). The latter consist, in the genus *Gnathostomula,* of three great muscle-sacs in the interior, which probably have an ectodermal origin. In this character also there is no correspondence with the Turbellaria. I do not see any possibility of deriving the pharynx of the Gnathostomulida from the turbellarian condition.

In my view the Gnathostomulida also do not have any specific connection by homology with the Archiannelida, Rotifera, and Gastrotricha (Ax, 1956c, 1961).

The opinion has been stated by Delamare Deboutteville (1960) and in several discussions with other workers that the Gnathostomulida should be separated from the Turbellaria. At present I too believe that they must be placed in their own taxon (class) in the lineage of the Protostomia. We can hope that study of the still unknown embryonic development will contribute to a better understanding of this enigmatic group.

REFERENCES

NOTE: in the main, only a number of newer works are quoted. Detailed reference to the earlier literature is to be found in my report of 1961 (Ax, 1961).

An de Lan, H.
 1936   Ergebnisse einer von E. Reisinger und O. Steinböck mit Hilfe des Rask-Ørsted Fonds durchgeführten zoologischen Reise in Grönland 1926. 7. Acoela. I. Vidensk. Medd. dansk naturh. Foren. Kbn. 99:289–330.

Avel, M.
 1959   Classe des Annélides oligochètes. Traité Zool. 5, fasc. 1:225–470.

Ax, P.
 1952   *Ciliopharyngiella intermedia* nov. gen. nov. spec., Repräsentant einer neuen Turbellarien-Familie des marinen Mesopsammon. Zool. Jb. (Syst.) 81:286–312.

 1956a   Les Turbellariés des Étangs côtiers du littoral méditerranéen de la France méridionale. Vie et Milieu (Suppl.) 5:1–215.

 1956b   Monographie der Otoplanidae (Turbellaria). Morphologie und Systematik. Abh. math.-nat. Kl. Akad. Wiss. Mainz (1955) Nr. 13:1–298.

 1956c   Die Gnathostomulida, eine rätselhafte Wurmgruppe aus dem Meeressand. *Ibid.* (1956):531–562.

 1960   Die Entdeckung neuer Organisationstypen im Tierreich. Ziemsen, Wittenberg-Lutherstadt.

 1961   Phylogenie und Verwandtschaftsbeziehungen der Turbellarien. Ergebn. Biol. 24:1–68.

Ax, P., and E. Schulz.
 1959   Ungeschlechtliche Vermehrung durch Paratomie bei acoelen Turbellarien. Biol. Zbl. 78:615–622.

Bargmann, W., and A. Knoop
 1959   Elektronenmikroskopische Untersuchungen an Plazentarzotten des Menschen (Bemerkungen zum Synzytium-Problem). Z. Zellforsch. 50: 472–493.

Beklemishev, V. N. [Beklemischev, W. N.]
 1958   Die Grundlagen der vergleichenden Anatomie der Wirbellosen. Vol. I. Dtsch. Verl. Wissensch. Berlin.

 1960   *Idem.* Vol. II. Dtsch. Verl. Wissensch. Berlin.

Bogomolov, S.
 1949   [On the cleavage type of the Rhabdocoela.] Ann. Leningr. Univ. Nr. 113 (Biol.) 20: 128–142. [In Russian.]

Bresslau, E.
 1928–
 1933   Turbellaria. Handb. Zool., Berl. 2. Sect. 1: 52–304. [1928:52–112; 1930: 113–192; 1933:193–304.]

Brøndsted, H. V.
  1955   Planarian regeneration. Biol. Rev. 30:65–126.
Bullough, W. S.
  1958   Practical Invertebrate Anatomy. Macmillan, London.
Corrêa, D. D.
  1960   Two new marine Turbellaria from Florida. Bull. mar. Sci. Gulf Carib-
          bean 10:208–216.
Delamare Deboutteville, C.
  1960   Biologie des Eaux souterraines littorales et continentales. Hermann, Paris.
Dubois, F.
  1949   Contribution à l'étude de la migration des cellules de régénération chez
          les planaires dulcicoles. Bull. biol. 83:213–283.
Franzén, Å.
  1956   On spermiogenesis, morphology of the spermatozoon and biology of
          fertilization among invertebrates. Zool. Bidr. Uppsala 31:355–480.
Gerlach, S. A.
  1958   Ein neuer Vertreter der Gnathostomulida (Turbellaria?) aus dem Meeres-
          sand der Malediven. Kieler Meeresforsch. 14: 175–176.
Hadži, J.
  1944   Turbelarijska Teorija Knidarijev. (Turbellarien-Theorie der Knidarier.)
          Slov. Akad. Znan. Um., Ljubljana, pp. 1–238. [In Slovenian, with German
          summary.]
  1951   Izvajanje knidarijev iz turbelarijev in nekatere posledice tega izvajanja.
          (Die Ableitung der Knidarien von den Turbellarien und einige Fol-
          gerungen dieser Ableitung.) Razred. (Dissertationes) prir. med. Vede
          Slov. Akad. Znan. Um. 1:107–126. [In Slovenian, with German sum-
          mary.]
  1953   An attempt to reconstruct the system of animal classification. Syst. Zool.
          2:145–154.
  1958   Zur Diskussion über die Abstammung der Eumetazoen. Verh. dtsch.
          zool. Ges., Graz (1957) (Zool. Anz., Suppl. 21):169–179.
Hanson,E. D.
  1958   On the origin of the Eumetazoa. Syst. Zool. 7:16–47.
Heider, K.
  1914   Phylogenie der Wirbellosen. Pp. 453–529 in: Die Kultur der Gegenwart.
          Hinneberg, P., Ed. 3, sect. 4, pt. 4. Teubner, Berlin, Leipzig.
Hyman, L. H.
  1951   The Invertebrates. Vol. II: Platyhelminthes and Rhynchocoela—the
          Acoelomate Bilateria. McGraw-Hill, New York, Toronto, London.
  1959   *Idem*. Vol. V: Smaller Coelomate Groups. McGraw-Hill, New York,
          Toronto, London.
Ivanov, A. V.
  1952   [Turbellaria Acoela from the southern coast of Sakhalin.] Trav. Inst. zool.
          Acad. Sci. URSS 12:40–132. [In Russian.]
Jägersten, G.
  1955   On the early phylogeny of the Metazoa. Zool. Bidr. Uppsala 30:321–354.
  1959   Further remarks on the early phylogeny of the Metazoa. *Ibid*. 33:79–
          108.
Karling, T. G.
  1940   Zur Morphologie und Systematik der Alloeocoela cumulata und Rhab-
          docoela lecithophora (Turbellaria). Acta zool. fenn. 26:1–260.

Kato, K.
1940   On the development of some Japanese Polyclads. Jap. J. Zool. 8:537–573.

Mamkaev, IU. V.
1961   [A new representative of the gnathostomulids: *Gnathostomula murmanica* sp. n.] Doklady Akad. Nauk SSSR 141(6):1501–1504. [In Russian.] [1962. Doklady Akad. Nauk SSSR (Biol. Sci. Sect. Transl.) 141(1/6): 1115–1117.]

Marcus, E.
1934   Über *Lophopus crystallinus* (Pall.). Zool. Jb. (Anat.) 58:501–606.
1945a   Sôbre Catenulida brasileiros. Bol. Fac. Filos. Ciênc. S. Paulo (Zool.) 10:3–133.
1945b   Sôbre Microturbelarios do Brasil. Comun. zool. Mus. Montevideo 1:1–74.
1946   Sôbre Turbellaria brasileiros. Bol. Fac. Filos. Ciênc. S. Paulo (Zool.) 11: 5–254.
1948   Turbellaria do Brasil. *Ibid.* 13:111–243.
1949   Turbellaria brasileiros (7). *Ibid.* 14:7–155.
1950   *Idem.* (8). *Ibid.* 15:5–191.
1951   *Idem.* (9). *Ibid.* 16:5–215.
1952   *Idem.* (10). *Ibid.* 17:5–187.
1958   On the evolution of the animal phyla. Quart. Rev. Biol. 33:24–58.

Marcus, E. du B.-R.
1957   On Turbellaria. Ann. Acad. bras. Sci. 29:153–191.

Meixner, J.
1938   Turbellaria (Strudelwürmer). I. Tierwelt N.-u. Ostsee 4b:1–146.

Moment, G. B.
1958   General Zoology. Riverside, Cambridge, Massachusetts.

Papi, F.
1957   Sopra un nuovo Turbellario arcoofora di particolare significato filetico e sulla posizione della fam. Hofsteniidae nel sistema Turbellari. Pubbl. Staz. zool. Napoli 30:132–148.

Papi, F., and B. Swedmark.
1959   Un Turbellario con lo scheletro: *Acanthomacrostomum spiculiferum* n. gen. n. sp. Monit. zool. ital. 60:229–250.

Pavans de Ceccatty, M.
1955   Le système nerveux des Éponges calcaires et siliceuses. Ann. Sci. nat., Zool. (sér. 11) 17:203–288.

Pedersen, K. J.
1959   Cytological studies on the planarian neoblast. Z. Zellforsch. 50:799–817.

Reisinger, E.
1928-
1933   Vermes amera (allgemeine Einleitung). Handb. Zool., Berl. 2, Sect. 1: 19–33.
1935   Ergebnisse einer von E. Reisinger u. O. Steinböck mit Hilfe des Rask-Ørsted Fonds durchgeführten Reise in Grönland 1926. 6. *Proporoplana jenseni* n. gen. n. sp., ein morphologisch bedeutsamer Turbellarientyp. Vidensk. Medd. dansk naturh. Foren. Kbn. 98:243–259.
1955   Kärntens Hochgebirgsturbellarien. Carinthia II 65: 112–150.
1959   Anormogenetische und parasitogene Syncytienbildung bei Turbellarien. Protoplasma 50:627–643.
1960   Was ist *Xenoturbella*? Z. wiss. Zool. 164:188–198.

Remane, A.
1950   Die Entstehung der Metamerie der Wirbellosen. Verh. dtsch. zool. Ges., Mainz (1949) (Zool. Anz., Suppl. 14):16–32.

1951   Die Bursa-Darmverbindung und das Problem des Enddarmes der Turbellarien. Zool. Anz. 146:276–291.

1954   Die Geschichte der Tiere. Pp. 340–422 in: Die Evolution der Organismen, Vol. 2. G. Heberer, Ed., 2d ed. Fischer, Stuttgart.

1956   Die Grundlagen des natürlichen Systems, der vergleichenden Anatomie und der Phylogenetik. 2d ed. Geest und Portig, Leipzig.

1958   Zur Verwandtschaft und Ableitung der niederen Metazoen. Verh. dtsch. zool. Ges., Graz (1957) (Zool. Anz., Suppl. 21):179–196.

Riedl, R.
1954   Neue Turbellarien aus dem mediterranen Felslitoral. Zool. Jb. (Syst.) 82:157–244.

1959   Turbellarien aus submarinen Höhlen. 1. Archoophora. Pubbl. Staz. zool. Napoli 30 (Suppl.):178–208.

Steinböck, O.
1927   Monographie der Prorhynchidae (Turbellaria). Z. Morph. Ökol. Tiere 8:538–662.

1931   Ergebnisse einer von E. Reisinger und O. Steinböck mit Hilfe des Rask-Ørsted Fonds durchgeführten Reise in Grönland. 2. *Nemertoderma bathycola*. Vidensk. Medd. dansk naturh. Foren. Kbn. 90:47–84.

1938   Über die Stellung der Gattung *Nemertoderma* Steinböck im System der Turbellarien. Acta Soc. Fauna Flora fenn. 62:1–28.

1952   Keimblätterlehre und Gastraea-Theorie. Pyramide 2:13–15, 26–31.

1955   Regeneration acoeler Turbellarien. Verh. dtsch. zool. Ges., Tübingen (1954) (Zool. Anz., Suppl. 18):86–94.

1958a   Zur Phylogenie der Gastrotrichen. *Ibid.*, Graz (1957) (Zool. Anz., Suppl. 21):128–169.

1958b   Schlusswort zur Diskussion Remane-Steinböck. *Ibid.*:196–218.

Steinböck, O., and B. Ausserhofer.
1950   Zwei grundverschiedene Entwicklungsabläufe bei einer Art (*Prorhynchus stagnalis* M. Sch., Turbellaria). Arch. EntwMech. Org. 144:155–177.

Tuzet, O.
1950   Le spermatozoïde dans la série animale. Rev. suisse Zool. 57:433–451.

Tuzet, O., and M. Pavans de Ceccatty
1956   Les cellules nerveuses des Éponges. Proc. 14th Int. Congr. Zool., Copenhagen (1953):188–190.

Ulrich, W.
1950   Über die systematische Stellung einer neuen Tierklasse (Pogonofora K. E. Johansson), den Begriff der Archicoelomaten und die Einteilung der Bilateria. S. B. dtsch. Akad. Wiss. (1949) no. 2:1–25.

1951   Vorschläge zu einer Revision der Grosseinteilung des Tierreiches. Verh. dtsch. zool. Ges., Marburg (1950) (Zool. Anz., Suppl. 15):244–271.

Westblad, E.
1937   Die Turbellariengattung *Nemertoderma* Steinböck. Acta Soc. Fauna Flora fenn. 60:45–89.

1940   Studien über skandinavische Acoela. I. Ark. Zool. 32A(20):1–28.

1942   *Idem.* II. *Ibid.* 33A, no. 14:1–48.

1945   *Idem.* III. *Ibid.* 36A, no. 1:1–56.

1946   *Idem.* IV. *Ibid.* 38A, *no.* 1:1–56.

1948   *Idem.* V. *Ibid.* 41A, no. 7:1–82.

1949a   *Xenoturbella bocki* n. gen. n. sp., a peculiar, primitive turbellarian type. *Ibid.* (ser. 2) 1:11–29.

1949b   On *Meara stichopi* (Bock) Westblad, a new representative of Turbellaria Archoophora. *Ibid.* (ser. 2) 1:43–56.

15 ◆ Some Evolutionary Trends in Turbellarian Morphology

TOR G. KARLING

EVERTEBRATAVDELNINGEN, NATURHISTORISKA RIKSMUSEET, STOCKHOLM

The interstitial animals of sandy beaches have structures that, as a whole, characterize the forms of organisms in this habitat ("Lebensformtypus," Remane, 1952). Here we find evolutionary trends, restricted by "environmental factors favoring development in certain directions" (Rensch, 1959, p. 70). Remane gives such trends the name "Spezialisationsanalogien" (1961, p. 458). Trends of this type are well known in turbellarians of different taxa (Meixner, 1929, 1938; Remane, 1952; and others). Adaptive responses of another kind are demonstrated in other habitats. Some evolutionary trends in turbellarian morphology, obviously less dependent on the habitat, are discussed here. Final answers regarding taxonomic and morphological problems are not realized in this discussion, and matters of controversy are avoided as much as possible.

Description

An ectodermal opening surrounded by glands is the theoretical first stage in the evolution of the distal male genital apparatus (fig. 15-1, a). The primary male genital canal (fig. 15-1, b) represents a further step in the evolution of this organ. In the next stage the secretory wall cells differentiate, forming a prostatic vesicle, opening generally into the atrium at the tip of a penis papilla (fig. 15-1, c). This vesicle may be either interposed, symmetrically enclosing the sperm duct, or else freely situated by the side of the sperm duct. Prostatoid organs may also appear distally, but in their construction they resemble in principle the more proximal reservoirs. Another trend is the transformation of some secretory wall cells to matrix cells producing cuticular structures such as thorns, hooks, stylets, etc. (fig. 15-1, e, f).

The copulatory organ is often provided with double walls. The outer wall arises in different evolutionary lines from muscles extending from the wall of the prostatic vesicle to a fold of the male genital canal (fig. 15-1, c, d). The enclosed duct may show trends similar to those of the simple male genital canal, its proximal part being, as a rule, transformed to a prostatic vesicle. The distal part, the ejaculatory duct, is often an armored eversible cirrus, so that the outer sac may be spoken of as a cirrus sac. No borderline can be drawn, however, between organs with and without an outer septum, the interspace being more or less filled out by mesenchyme or muscles. (For more detailed information about the copulatory organ see Karling, 1940, 1956.)

In the evolution of the pharynx, trends can be demonstrated similar to those in the evolution of the copulatory organ. A mouth aperture without a differentiated pharynx (fig. 15-2, a) is known in several of the Acoela. Ax regards this structure as a secondary simplification (1961, p. 19). The tubiform pharynx simplex (fig. 15-2, b) is realized in most of the Archoophora (excluding the Polycladida). The pharynx plicatus (fig. 15-2, c), comparable to a penis papilla, is found in the Polycladida, the Seriata (including the Tricladida), and many of the Prolecithophora. It arises by the formation of folds in the wall of the tubiform pharynx. The pharynx bulbosus (fig. 15-2, d) of the Neorhabdocoela and many of the Prolecithophora is characterized by a muscular septum in the same way as in the double-walled copulatory organ. There are also transitional stages between the pharynx simplex and the pharynx plicatus, as well as between the pharynx plicatus and the pharynx bulbosus. The differentiation of the pharyngeal glands corresponds to that of the prostatic glands, and a pharynx bulbosus may often be regarded as a secretory vesicle with muscular walls and internal muscular septa. Structures corresponding to the armored cirrus and the cuticular hooks, etc., of the copulatory organ (fig. 15-2, e, f) are rare in the turbellarian pharynx. (For more detailed information about the pharynx of the Turbellaria see Karling, 1940, and Ax, 1961.)

Hyman speaks about three different types of adhesive organs in the Turbellaria: namely, glandulo-epidermal and glandulo-muscular adhesive organs and true suckers (1951, pp. 80–82). Apart from the lack of an aperture, these organs evolve in a way resembling that of the copulatory organ and the pharynx. Simple glandulo-epidermal organs (fig. 15-3, a) are common attributes of haptic (=thigmotactic) species, for instance those representing a mesopsammic life form (Karling, 1950, fig. 7B). They readily evolve adhesive pits (fig. 15-3, b) comparable with the primary male genital canal and the pharynx simplex (*Trigonostomum*—Meixner, 1924; *Acmostomum*—Marcus, 1947). Then extensible structures arise resembling a penis papilla or a pharynx plicatus (fig. 15-3, c; *e.g.*, *Rhynchomesostoma* and *Astrotorhynchus,* von Graff, 1904, pp. 2081–2082). The true sucker parallels the duplex copulatory organ and the pharynx bulbosus separated from the surrounding parenchyma by a septum. The "conorhynch" of the Eukalyptorhynchia is a modified sucker (fig. 15-3, d). Armored proboscides (fig. 15-3, e, f) arise in the Eukalyptorhynchia as well as in the Schizorhynchia. (For more detailed information about the proboscis see Karling, 1961.) In the Trematoda, as well as in the Cestoda, there are adhesive organs showing trends similar to those in the Turbellaria.

The female accessory organs are often difficult to interpret; and specialists are not fully agreed about their origin (*cf.,* Ax, 1961). In my opinion, however, it seems possible to regard the bursal organs as derivatives either of the parenchymatous stroma (stromatogenous bursa, also bursa parenchymalis—see Karling, 1940) or of the body wall (ectodermal bursa).

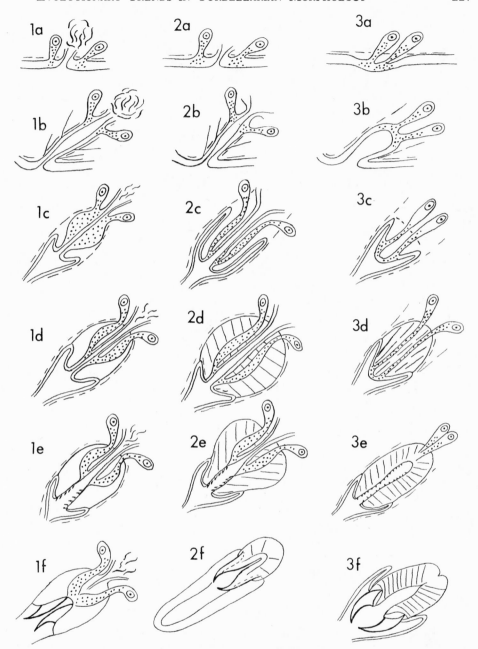

Figure 15-1–15-3. Diagrams demonstrating different evolutionary stages (a-f) in the morphology of the copulatory organ (1), the pharynx (2), and the adhesive organ-proboscis (3). 1e is based on *Paracicerina maristoi* Karling, 1f on *Karkinorhynchus primitivus* Meixner, 2e on *Carcharodopharynx arcanus* Reisinger, 2f on *Gnathostomula paradoxa* Ax, 3e on *Carcharodorhynchus subterraneus* Meixner, 3f on *Baltoplana magna* Karling; for other figures see the text (Fig. 15-2f after Ax, 1956a).

Internal fertilization is primarily brought about through seminal impregnation or injection, and the first female genitalium is the stroma or the follicle in which the oöcytes are imbedded (figs. 15-7, 15-8). To quote Hyman (1951, p. 125), "the impetus for the evolution of a female system appears to have been the desirability of safeguarding the sperm received in copulation." A subsequent trend is the derivation of a more or less closed solid bursa from a part of the stroma; then we generally speak of a seminal receptacle (figs. 15-4, 15-9). This bursa appears sometimes only as a more or less temporary enlargement of the oviduct (fig. 15-5), the latter duct being evidently also a derivative of the stroma. It is difficult, however, to draw a border line between the oviduct and the more distal ectodermal part of the female canal.

Another impetus for the derivation of a bursa is the need for a structure receiving the male organ in copulation (*viz.*, a copulatory bursa). Such a bursa arises as an ectodermal pocket either in the body wall or in the atrial wall (figs. 15-4, 15-5, 15-8). It may further evolve into a vaginal pore, a copulation canal, and a bursal vesicle (fig. 15-6). Eventually insemination canals may appear by coalescence of adjacent tissues leading sperm to the ovary, the oviducts, or one or several stomatogenous bursal organs. These canals often consist of two parts produced by the different bursal tissues (Karling, 1940, p. 54; 1952, p. 23; 1956, p. 272). In many species we may find two or several bursae of different origin (figs. 15-4, 5, 8, 9, 10). Particular complexity as regards the bursal structures is demonstrated by Ax in the family Octoplanidae (1956b, 1961).

The development of bursal (vaginal) canals from the body wall (the atrium) to the ovary involves a fusion of two contiguous structures. Similar fusions are especially frequent in the intestine. Intestinal branches may grow together; the intestinal cavity may be more or less displaced by coalescence of the gastrodermis; one or several accessory intestinal apertures may arise by coalescence of the gastrodermis and the body wall; but also different parts of the genital apparatus tend to join with the intestine. Bursal structures of different origin release half-digested sperm to the intestine, and even sperm produced by the animal itself may sometimes be discharged into the intestine from the sperm duct (Marcus, 1949, 1950, 1954; Ax, 1956b). Most genito-intestinal communications have been described in highly specialized forms, but they occur also in rather primitive forms such as the peculiar macrostomid genus *Myozona* (Marcus, 1949; Papi, 1953; Ax, 1956c). Observations that female cells too may sometimes be discharged into the intestine cannot in my opinion, alter the fact that here we are dealing with secondarily evolved structures.

Discussion

The evolutionary lines as regards the male copulatory organ, the pharynx, and the adhesive organs demonstrate a peculiar parallelism between quite different organs in a restricted taxonomic group. This parallelism is quite independent of taxonomic relations and consequently more convincing than a parallelism in the evolution of a single organ—for example, the pharynx—in different more or less related groups.

These three organs, to a certain extent, have similar functions. The pharynx is an organ functioning by ciliary movement, adhesive secretion, and muscular contrac-

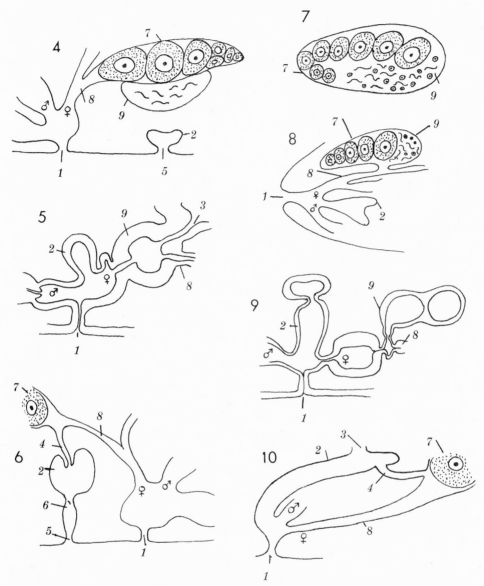

FIGURES 15-4–15-10. Different kinds of bursae with adjacent organs: 15-4, *Cheliplana stylifera* (after Karling, 1949); 15-5, *Pseudograffilla arenicola* (after Luther, 1948); 15-6, *Thylacorhynchus conglobatus* (after Karling, 1950); 15-7, *Nemertoderma* (after Westblad, 1937); 15-8, *Annulorhynchus adriaticus* (after Karling, 1956); 15-9. *Halammovortex nigrifrons* (after Karling, 1943); 15-10. *Lurus evelinae* (after Marcus, 1950). *1*, common genital pore; *2*, copulatory bursa; *3*, genito-intestinal duct; *4*, insemination canal; *5*, vaginal pore; *6*, copulation canal; *7*, ovary; *8*, oviduct; *9*, seminal receptacle (stroma).

tion. Apart from the ciliary movement, the same is true for the adhesive organs, especially those of the proboscis type. Seminal impregnation or injection demands male organs capable of piercing the body wall by means of secretion, stylets, or muscular power. The stylets are shown to be produced by cells homologous with the penis gland (*cf.* Karling, 1956). Besides this there is an adhesive or grasping function, especially pronounced by evolution of thorns and hooks.

In animals with a simple mouth (pharynx simplex) the entire body is involved in sucking in or ingesting large objects. The evolution of a pharynx plicatus or pharynx bulbosus implies a specialization making the pharynx functionally more or less independent of the rest of the body. The evolution of a septum separating the pharynx from adjacent tissues can be regarded as the last step in this process. It renders possible a reinforcement and specialization of the pharyngeal muscles themselves and makes the pharynx a secretory vesicle capable of violent extrusion and withdrawal. The corresponding stages in the adhesive organs and the copulatory organ can be functionally explained in the same way. The selective factor seems to be indisputable.

The properties of the constituent involved tissues constitute the second factor determining the evolutionary trends of the three types of organs here dealt with. General properties of the epithelial cells are their ability to evolve depressed glands and to produce cuticular muscle fibers, giving rise to pits and annular folds such as the pharynx plicatus, etc. The fibers then evolve to protractors, retractors, etc., crossing the parenchyma. The membranous septa are further derivatives of these muscular systems (Karling, 1956).

There are, of course, some differences in the adaptive responses of the organs in question. The pharyngeal types were described as early as the end of the nineteenth century, and our opinion about them has altered very little since then. The pharynx shows great structural stability, because of small differences in its mode of function. In the kalyptorhynchid proboscis the relationship between function and structure is very distinct; there are different methods of catching prey, and hence the morphological diversification is considerable (Karling, 1961). The wide structural variations in the organ of copulation must be regarded in the context of maintaining reproductive barriers between the species. Nevertheless, the evolutionary process is not easy to understand in this case (Stammer, 1959, pp. 201–204). The corresponding female organs show a rather restricted variability in several groups characterized by pronounced variability as regards the male organs (e.g., the genera *Dalyellia* and *Rogneda*). A certain parallelism between the cuticular organs in these two genera has obviously a functional basis (Karling, 1956, p. 209, fig. 16). Random mutations, however, may persist as regards details—number, shape, and size—with restricted functional value.

Even the evolution of the bursal organs seems to be governed by the two factors —functional and structural properties. Copulation without bursal organs implies a topographically random injection or impregnation, alien sperm being found in almost all parts of the body (Marcus and Marcus, 1951, p. 15). Even in cases of copulation through the common atrium the sperm can "make their way through the parenchyma to the ovarian follicles" (Hyman, 1938, pp. 16–17). The stroma, embedding the oöcytes, seems to be predisposed (Remane, 1961, pp. 460–461) by their nutritive ability to preserve sperm and to evolve into sperm receptacles. In a species lacking bursal organs sperm are accumulated in the yolk glands, rich in nourishment (*Danorhynchus duplostylis*—Karling, 1955, p. 33). Primitive ectodermal bursae with external vaginae resemble adhesive pits, a fact evidently based on similar functional and structural factors. Insemination canals are improvements, obviously predisposed functionally (ovarian induction; *cf.* Karling, 1955, pp. 33–

34) as well as structurally (fusion of tissues, see below). Most cases of genito-intestinal communication are functionally based on the necessity for digesting excess sexual products. Such communication sometimes makes a bursa unnecessary (Meixner, 1938, p. 68).

The functional advantage of coalescing neighboring parts of the gastrodermis, or of the gastrodermis and the body wall, seems to be indisputable. A more detailed discussion of this matter, however, is omitted here.

The structural basis for the several trends, discussed above, is the tendency to fusion between adjacent tissues. The insemination canal, the genito-intestinal communications, the intestinal network in triclads and polyclads, the endocytium of the Acoela, and the accessory intestinal apertures exemplify such trends. No one has stressed more emphatically than Bock (1927) the importance of such fusions for our understanding of turbellarian structure.

The effect of function seems to be indisputable in these trends. The adaptive responses are restricted, however, by the "specific structure and organization of the living substance" (Rensch, 1959, p. 73). The spontaneous variability, affording the basis for selection, is restricted by the rather simple turbellarian organization, only a few ways existing to solve the problems in construction.

The number of evolutionary trends in turbellarian morphology can be easily multiplied. It may be mentioned that follicular gonads arise in different turbellarian groups as well as in the Trematoda and Cestoda. This improves the nourishment of the genital products and seems to have a functional basis. In my opinion such a phenomenon does not support the idea of an autogenetic trend "bei deren Ausbildung die Selektion keine Rolle gespielt haben kann" (Stammer, 1959, pp. 192–199). The theory of the "Eigengesetzlichkeit der Organismen" (*ibid.*, p. 206) in evolution is not supported by the trends in turbellarian morphology. These trends are satisfactorily explained by the "Struktur und Verhalten der Ausgangsform" (Remane, 1961, p. 460).

Summary

Trends in the evolution of the following structures in the turbellarian body are described and discussed as regards their functional and structural bases: male copulatory organ, pharynx, adhesive organs, female accessory organs, coalescence between neighboring parts of the gastrodermis, between the gastrodermis and the genital organs, and between the gastrodermis and the ectoderm.

It is shown, in all these cases, that spontaneous variability, affording the basis for selection, is restricted by the structural properties of the turbellarian tissues. The results do not support the theories of an autogenetic evolution independent of selection.

REFERENCES

Ax, P.
    1956a   Die Gnathostomulida, eine rätselhafte Wurmgruppe aus dem Meeressand. Abh. math.-nat. Kl. Akad. Wiss. Lit., Kiel (1956):531–562.

1956b   Monographie der Otoplanidae (Turbellaria). *Ibid.* (1956):499–796.

1956c   Studien über psammobionte Turbellaria Macrostomida. IV. *Myozona stylifera* nov. spec. Zool. Anz. 157:251–260.

1961   Verwandtschaftsbeziehungen und Phylogenie der Turbellarien. Ergebn. Biol. 24:1–68.

Bock, S.

1927   Ductus genito-intestinalis in the polyclads. Ark. Zool. 19A, no. 14:1–15.

Graff, L. von

1904–
1908   Acoela und Rhabdocoelida. Bronn's Klassen 4, sect. Ic (Turbellaria, sect. 1): i + xxii, 1733–2599 [1904–05, pp. 1733–1984; 1907, pp. 1985–2192, 2193–2256; 1908, pp. 2157–2599].

Hyman, L. H.

1938   North American Rhabdocoela and Alloeocoela. II. Rediscovery of *Hydrolimax grisea* Haldeman. Amer. Mus. Novit. 1004:1–19.

1951   The Invertebrates. Vol. II: Platyhelminthes and Rhynchocoela—The Acoelomate Bilateria. McGraw-Hill, New York, Toronto, London.

Karling, T.G.

1940   Zur Morphologie und Systematik der Alloeocoela Cumulata und Rhabdocoela Lecithophora (Turbellaria). Acta zool. fenn. 26:1–260.

1943   Studien an *Halammovortex nigrifrons* (Karling) (Turbellaria Neorhabdocoela). *Ibid.* 37:1–23.

1949   Studien über Kalyptorhynchien (Turbellaria). II. Die Familien Karkinorhynchidae und Diascorhynchidae. *Ibid.* 58:1–42.

1950   *Idem.* III. Die Familie Schizorhynchidae. *Ibid.* 59:1–33.

1952   *Idem.* IV. Einige Eukalyptorhynchia. *Ibid.* 69:1–49.

1955   *Idem.* V. Der Verwandtschaftskreis von *Gyratrix* Ehrenberg. *Ibid.* 88:1–39.

1956   Morphologisch-histologische Untersuchungen an den männlichen Atrialorganen der Kalyptorhynchia (Turbellaria). Ark. Zool. (ser. 2) 9:187–279.

1961   Zur Morphologie, Entstehungsweise und Funktion des Spaltrüssels der Turbellaria Schizorhynchia. *Ibid.* 13:253–286.

Luther, A.

1948   Untersuchungen an Rhabdocoelen Turbellarien. 7. Über einige marine Dalyellioda. Acta zool. fenn. 55:1–34.

Marcus, E.

1947   Turbelarios marinhos do Brasil. Bol. Fac. Filos. Ciênc. S. Paulo., Zool., 12:99–216.

1949   Turbellaria brasileiros (7). *Ibid.* 14:7–156.

1950   *Idem.* (8). *Ibid.* 15:5–192.

1954   *Idem.* (11). Pap. Dep. Zool. Sec. Agric. S. Paulo 11:419–489.

Marcus, E. du B.-R., and E. Marcus

1951   Contributions to the natural history of Brazilian Turbellaria. Comun. zool. Mus. Montevideo 3:1–25.

Meixner, J.

1924   Studien zu einer Monographie der Kalyptorhynchia und zum System der Turbellaria Rhabdocoela. Zool. Anz. 60:1–29.

1929   Morphologisch-ökologische Studien an neuen Turbellarien aus dem Meeressande der Kieler Bucht. Z. Morphol. Ökol. 14:765–791.

1938   Turbellaria (Strudelwürmer). I. Tierwelt N.-u. Ostsee. IVb:1–146.

Papi, F.
    1953   Beiträge zur Kenntnis der Macrostomiden (Turbellarien). Acta zool. fenn. 78:1–32.

Remane, A.
    1952   Die Besiedlung des Sandbodens im Meere und die Bedeutung der Lebensformen für die Ökologie. Verh. dtsch. zool. Ges., Wilhelmshaven (1951) (Zool. Anz., Suppl. 16):327–359.

    1961   Gedanken zum Problem Homologie und Analogie, Praeadaptation und Parallelität. Zool. Anz. 166:447–465.

Rensch, B.
    1959   Evolution Above the Species Level. Methuen, London.

Stammer, H. J.
    1959   "Trends" in der Phylogenie der Tiere; Ektogenese und Autogenese. Zool. Anz. 162:187–208.

Westblad, E.
    1937   Die Turbellariengattung *Nemertoderma* Steinböck. Acta Soc. Fauna Flora fenn. 60:45–89.

16 ◆ On the Relationship of the Turbellaria to Other Groups of the Animal Kingdom

V. N. BEKLEMISHEV

INSTITUT MEDITSINSKOĬ PARAZITOLOGII I TROPICHESKOĬ MEDITSINY,
MINISTERSTVO ZDRAVOOKHRANENIIA, MOSKVA (MOSCOW)

In "autobiology" one is concerned with the life cycle of a species "from ovum to ovum." [1] A genuine comparative morphology must be based on a comparison of life cycles, and an adequate phylogeny, on the phylogenesis of life cycles. A life cycle can be reckoned as a unit of the general life process. In most metazoa this covers the existence of an individual (one generation), but, in forms with an alternation of generations, the unit comprises two or more generations typical for the species in question. In the latter case one speaks of a complex life cycle.

For the study of the life cycle to be maximally useful, then all its phases (*i.e.,* anatomical peculiarities, order of their succession, etc.) must be treated as essential features in defining a species or any higher taxon.

Haeckel and his followers have considered the adult form as the only useful object of study, regarding phylogenesis as the history of adult phases and ontogenesis as a shortened and distorted repetition of the phylogenesis of the adult forms—a sort of manual for the study of phylogenesis of these same forms. Because of this limitation of approach, oriented, to such an extreme degree, about the adult phase, I feel that the Haeckelian point of view must be rejected.

Hadži, Steinböck, and some other modern adversaries of certain of Haeckel's theories share, in the main, his basic point of view, for they also consider that morphology means basically the comparative study of adult phases, and phylogeny, the phylogenesis of adult forms. They only differ from Haeckel in rejecting the biogenetic "law," for they consider that ontogenesis is of minor significance to phylogenesis. But they throw the baby out with the bath water: while rejecting the

---

Vladimir Nikolaevich Beklemishev died on Sept. 4, 1962.

[1] This contrasts with symbiology or biocenology, whose main object is the study of life on the earth as a whole, in all the complexity of its structure and activity (Beklemishev, 1931).

biogenetic "law," they quite deny that peculiarities of ontogenetic development can be used as meaningful criteria of homology in morphology and genetic relationship in phylogeny.

Therefore I am unable to follow in the steps of either Haeckel or Hadži. My approach is that of comparing life cycles as a whole, in all their phases and changes —with the aim both of establishing the degree of morphological similarity and of deducing phylogenetic hypotheses.

Karling (1940) and Westblad (1948) have suggested that the Turbellaria should be divided into two orders: The Archoophora and the Neoophora. But the archoophoran group is artificial, incorporating, as it does, a heterogeneity of primitive orders of the Turbellaria, among which there are some very basic differences. The Archoophora and the Neoophora are certainly not taxonomic orders (or subclasses), but *grades,* of which the Archoophora are evidently the lower. The latter include all the orders of the Turbellaria possessing simple ovaries, typical of metazoa in general, in contrast to female gonads differentiated into germaria and vitellaria as in the Neoophora. Because of this *last* feature, the early development of the Neoophora is quite aberrant. Therefore, in comparing the Turbellaria with other groups, especially where considered more primitive, only the Archoophora should be taken into consideration, the more so because in organ systems in addition to the female genital apparatus, we usually encounter the more primitive conditions among the Archoophora.

In its essence the life cycle of the Turbellaria is typical for the Metazoa: the diploid zygote is formed by a fusion of haploid gametes, the ovum and the spermatozoön. By cleavage reminiscent of the palintomic metagametic division of the Protozoa (Zakhvatkin, 1946, 1956), the zygote develops into a multicellular organism in which macro- and microgametes later differentiate. There are two pregametic divisions during which the chromosome number is reduced and the cycle starts all over again.

As has been known since the time of Mechnikov (1886), the most primitive types of cleavage and formation of germ layers are found in the development of the Hydromedusae (leaving the sponges out of consideration for the time being). The division of the zygote and of the first generation of the blastomeres is longitudinal and closely resembles that of flagellates. Cleavage is either anarchical (*Oceania*) or close to a spiral (*Rathkea, Tiara,* and others). A special peculiarity of cleavage in the Hydrozoa and other cnidarians is its unstable character. Considerable differences may be seen in the location of blastomeres when comparing relatively closely related forms. Even the cleavage of individual eggs in the same batch may assume quite different forms; as, for instance, a spiral cleavage according to a tetraradial or triradial type in *Funiculina* (Pennatularia) (Berg, 1941).

Among the Archoophora, cleavage has been studied in several representatives of the three orders: Acoela, Macrostomida, and Polycladida, where cleavage is of the comparatively primitive spiral type. Its primitive features are a complete cleavage with a homoquadrant orientation and the absence of pronounced differentiation in shape and size in individual blastomeres characteristic for polychetes and molluscs.

As to the symmetry of the cleaving egg, until lately one could suppose that the Polycladida and Macrostomida had a tetraradial type (quadrant cleavage). It has been recently established, however, that deviations from this pattern exist. Thus Seilern-Aspang (1957) has described two types of cleavage, quadrant and dual, in

Macrostomum appendiculatum.[2] The same has been reported by Bogomolov (1957) for *Convoluta borealis* (Acoela). In this connection Ivanova-Kasas (1959) emphasizes that, besides the usual quadrant type of cleavage, Lang has also observed individual cases of dual cleavage in *Discocelis tigrina* (Polycladida).

Thus the known cases of spiral cleavage in all the lower turbellarian orders (grade Archoophora) show a similarity to the situation in the Cnidaria in their unstable character and the variations in the type of symmetry. Hence, cleavage in the Archoophora is not only more primitive than the highly differentiated spiral cleavage of annelids and molluscs, but more so than the somewhat primitive cleavage of the Rhynchocoela (Nemertinea) and Phoronidea.

On the other hand the cleavage of all the Archoophora is less primitive than the spiral cleavage of the Hydromedusae (*e.g., Rathkea*). This manifests itself in the disappearance of such protozoan traits as the exclusively longitudinal fission of the first blastomeres and a closer correlation between the poles of the fertilized egg and embryonic axes (Zakhvatkin, 1946, 1956). Thus, in the character of their cleavage, the lower Turbellaria are more archaic and closer to the primitive Cnidaria than any other group of the Bilateria. At the same time the cleavage of the lower Turbellaria is less primitive than that of most cnidarians.[3]

In all hydrozoa that develop outside the parent, cleavage results in the formation of a flagellated blastula, the first larval stage. Its cells are strikingly similar to the free-living forms of some of the Protomonadina. The blastula becomes transformed into the parenchymula, because some of the blastoderm cells migrate into the blastocele. In the most primitive cases migration occurs from the blastular surface (multipolar immigration), and in others only at the oral pole of the larva (unipolar immigration). The immigrating cells give rise to the entoderm or phagocytoblast; those remaining on the surface develop into the ectoderm or kinoblast (Mechnikov, 1886).

Later a gastrovascular cavity is formed in the phagocytoblast of the parenchymula, because of the degeneration of the central cells, and the parenchymula turns into a planula. Still later the mouth is formed, and the tentacles protrude.

This type of formation of germ layers is the most primitive of those known in the animal kingdom (see also Hyman, 1940). Invagination, unknown in the Hydrozoa, but found in some other groups, is the result of extreme simplification and maximal efficiency in the formation of germ layers in blastula-like embryos.

A number of the Hydrozoa develop not free of the parent, but in gonophores; in such instances embryonization takes place. The celoblastula stage is omitted. Sometimes cleavage results in the formation of a morula and the germ layers are formed by parenchymal delamination (*Clava, Tubularia*). But in such instances, the final result is also a planula, which, when the mouth and the tentacles have been formed, becomes a fixed polyp or develops into a free-swimming actinula.

The early development of all known archoöphorans takes place not in direct contact with water, but under the protection of a firm, though thin, ovular mem-

---

[2] *M. appendiculatum* is a *nomen nudum* joining a number of species into one (Beklemishev, 1951; Ax, 1959). It is very important to discover which of the species of *Macrostomum*, as established by modern taxonomic criteria, Seilern-Aspang had to deal with.

[3] Among cnidarians specialized types of cleavage are found, including incomplete cleavage. It is obvious that in comparing the cleavage of the Cnidaria with that of Turbellaria these types can be disregarded.

brane, and a flagellated blastula is not formed. For these reasons the early stages are to be considered embryonized. As the result of cleavage in polyclads, a one-layer embryo, corresponding to the blastula, is formed, but with a rather poorly developed cavity. Then certain cells, namely, all the macromeres, all the cells of the fourth quartet, some of the descendants of the 2a-2d cells, and presumably some of the descendants of the cells of the third quartet, get inside it. These cells give rise to the phagocytoblast (*i.e.,* entoderm and mesoderm). Thus the phagocytoblast originates through multipolar immigration, with some tendency to be unipolar (Beklemishev, 1944, 1952). The latter tendency is expressed by the fact that the number of cells immigrating from the vegetative pole is much higher than cellular immigration at any other part of the body.

The Polycladida differ from the Hydrozoa by the determinative nature of polyclad cleavage and, in connection with that, by a comparatively stable and much lower number of immigrating cells. There are about 16 such cells in polyclads. Moreover, in hydrozoa, these cells have no definite lineage and their fate is not determined. In the Polycladida, however, they all have a strictly defined lineage and a definite prospective function.

The same apparently applies *mutatis mutandis* to the Acoela and the Macrostomida. The smaller cell number in the embryo at the time of germ layer formation and the differentiation of these cells, which enables us to establish the cell lineage and the prospective function of each cell, are specialized features that show cleavage and germ layer formation in the Archoophora to be less primitive than in the Cnidaria.

The planula and the parenchymula have a monaxial, heteropolar structure. At the aboral pole, the kinoblast is well provided with nerve cells, including sensory ones; the mouth is later formed at the other pole. The main axis of the body is the axis of a symmetry of an indefinitely high order. The phagocytoblast of the parenchymula forms an uninterrupted parenchymatous tissue; at the planula stage it acquires a gastral cavity and an epithelial organization. The most primitive Turbellaria are, in their structure, very close to the parenchymula or to the planula of the Cnidaria. Some aceles have a similar, in the main protaxial,[4] body, which is built of a ciliated epithelial kinoblast and an uninterrupted parenchymatous phagocytoblast. In many, the nervous apparatus consists of a diffuse subepithelial plexus and, as in cnidarian larvae, the sensory cells are also situated in the epithelium. Furthermore, the fore end of the body is especially rich in sensory nerve cells. During ontogenesis the mouth is shifted in most instances to one of the antimeres, which thus becomes ventral; but in some cases it remains at the oral pole (*Diopisthoporus,* Westblad, 1940). In the Acoela we find ingestatory structures at every stage of development; however, ectodermal pharynx is absent in many of the group, which resemble the Hydrozoa in that respect. In those cases where stems are differentiated in the nervous system, they are placed in radial symmetry around the main axis of the body. This indicates a protaxial structure of the animal and confirms that the shifting of the mouth to the ventral side is a relocation of the aperture and not a distortion of the body (von Graff, 1905). In the Acoela, the development of the nervous plexus (the orthogon of Reisinger, 1925), with its definitely ordered radial symmetry, proceeds as independently as that of the

---

[4] (The primitive axis of the embryo is also the major axis of the adult.—E.D.H.)

pharynx. The sexual apparatus of the Acoela, in its simplest form, is represented by diffusely distributed ova or groups of male sperm cells and a very simple male copulatory organ, the latter being even absent in *Xenoturbella* (Westblad, 1949). Thus, in their structure and the level of their organization, adult aceles are very close to the parenchymula of the Hydrozoa. The Xenoturbellida, having an intestinal cavity and a more or less epithelial intestine, reach the level of the planula in that respect. All the higher turbellarian orders show only a gradual improvement over the type of development and adult organization that we have seen in the lower orders.

The planula is the final migratory stage in cnidarian development.[5] During metamorphosis, as a rule, it attaches and becomes a sedentary polyp, devoid of the aboral thickening of the nervous plexus and equipped with entrapping tentacles. In the majority of the Hydrozoa and Scyphozoa, sexual maturity is only reached in the medusa stage, which, though free-swimming, is also devoid of an aboral thickening of the nervous plexus and possesses entrapping tentacles. The Turbellaria do not have stages homologous to the polyp and the medusa. A detailed comparison of the cycles of development in the Turbellaria and the Cnidaria tells us that turbellarian ontogenesis is shortened.

Adult turbellarians should not be compared with adult cnidarians, but with their larvae, parenchymulae, and planulae. Instead of the planula being transformed into a medusa, propelled by its umbrella, it undergoes histological and organ differentiation and reaches sexual maturity. The only change in the main features of its structure is the shifting of the mouth to the ventral side and new bilateral symmetry resulting from that shift—a symmetry quite foreign to the Cnidaria.

Thus we establish the following phases in the ontogenesis of both groups: cleavage to yield the blastula, formation of germ layers to produce the parenchymula, and finally organization of the planula. Cleavage in lower turbellarians is rather similar to that of cnidarians, but less primitive in some features. The blastula of the Turbellaria is embryonized, as in those hydrozoa that develop under the protection of the gonophores. The formation of germ layers in the Archoophora follows one of the primitive modes common among the Hydrozoa, but with specialization: the phase homologous to the parenchymula or the planula is terminal in the development of the Turbellaria, and further ontogenesis is in the main reduced to histological and organ differentiation with shifting of the mouth to the ventral side. The polyp and medusa stages are lacking. Hatschek (1881–1891) and later von Graff (1905) express the view that the Turbellaria are descended from parenchymula-like ancestors of the Cnidaria. At the time when the biogenetic law was predominant, this opinion was natural, since it was supposed that the parenchymula, like all the other larval stages of the Cnidaria, recapitulates the adult stage of the corresponding ancestor. At present this solution to the problem seems to be less certain, and it may be that neither the blastula, nor the parenchymula, nor the planula recapitulates the adult ancestors of the Cnidaria. It is quite possible, as suggested by Zakhvatkin, that the first metazoa, arising from sedentary colonies of flagellates, had always been sedentary animals, and that the blastula, the parenchymula, and the planula were the dispersive larval stages of their life cycle. In that case one should assume that the Turbellaria come from some ancient cnidarian or procni-

---

[5] Excepting those cases where an additional planktonic stage, that of the actinula, occurs.

darian by means of progressive neoteny—*i.e.,* by omitting the former adult (polyp or medusa) and reaching sexual maturity at the parenchymula or planula stage, with a progressive evolution of the neotenic forms. At present the origin of the Turbellaria described above seems to me to be the most probable.

The relationship of the Turbellaria to the Cnidaria is also confirmed by the similarity of the sagittocysts of some of the Acoela (*Convoluta viridis* and others) to the cnidocysts of the Cnidaria. This likeness is especially pronounced, according to the data obtained by me, in the early stage of cnidocyst and sagittocyst development; the adult cysts are less alike. This fact probably shows that the Turbellaria sprang from very ancient ancestors of the modern Cnidaria.

Besides the relationship of the Turbellaria to the Cnidaria, as outlined above, there have been attempts to trace their descent from the Ctenophora (Lang, 1884), the Annelida (Zalenskiĭ, 1912), or other primitive celomates (Remane, 1950) and, lately, directly from the Protozoa, particularly from the Ciliata (Hadži, 1944; Steinböck, 1958).

The first two theories were considered in my book in Russian, whose title may be translated as "Principles of the Comparative Anatomy of Invertebrates" (1944, 1952), and I shall only briefly dwell on the comparison of the Turbellaria with these various groups. (In the 1958 German edition the criticism of Lang's theory was considerably reduced.)

The early development (cleavage, formation of germ layers) of the Cydippoidea (Ctenophora) differ much more from the early stages of the Archoophora and the Hydrozoa than the two latter from each other. The most primitive of the Cydippoidea, however, preserve in their adult stage all the main features common to the planula of the Cnidaria and the adult of the Turbellaria, *i.e.,* free-swimming habit, ciliary locomotion, and sensory organs at the aboral pole. The main body axis of the Ctenophora is homologous to the longitudinal body axis of the Turbellaria and not to the dorso-ventral one, as was thought by Lang. As compared to the Cnidaria, the life cycle of the Ctenophora is also shortened, like that of the Turbellaria. An adult ctenophore, as well as a turbellarian, is a more evolved free-swimming larva of the planula type, but developed in a specific direction. One may suppose that the Ctenophora, as well as the Turbellaria, developed from the Procoelenterata or Procnidaria by neoteny followed by adaptational evolution of a progressive type. Thus, although the Ctenophora and the Turbellaria are to some extent parallel, they are in the main rather diverging stems. Their likeness is based on a similar origin from more or less close ancestors, and partly on a somewhat parallel direction of evolutionary development. The difference between them is partly caused by the fact that the Ctenophora largely remained planktonic, and only some of them later assumed a benthic mode of life. The Turbellaria, on the contrary, at the outset assumed a creeping pattern, which resulted in shifting of the mouth opening and consequent bilateral symmetry; and only some of them later returned to the planktonic mode of life. A greater similarity between the Turbellaria and the Ctenophora is in the formation of the aboral statocyst and, perhaps, in some peculiarities of their histological structure (*e.g.,* muscle cells). The most striking result of a parallel evolution of the two groups is the similarity in the symmetry of the nervous apparatus (see the explanation suggested in Beklemishev, 1958, pp. 72, 110, 328–329).

Comparing the Turbellaria with polychetes having the most primitive develop-

ment, we see in both cases a rather similar type of cleavage and germ layer formation, though both are more primitive in the Archoophora. Unstable symmetry of
cleavage (in many cases), homoquadrant development, and less differentiation of
individual blastomeres are signs of turbellarian primitiveness, not of simplification.
Germ layers are formed in both groups by multipolar immigration, with a tendency
toward the unipolar mode.

The first larva in many of the Polychaeta is a protochopore. In the most primitive examples, it is a protaxial larva with an aboral sense organ and a primary
mouth opening on the oral pole. In some forms the larva has a nervous system of
the orthogon type, situated radially around the main axis of the body (*Lopado-
rhynchus, Polygordius*). In all these respects the primitive larvae of the polychetes
are similar to the Turbellaria and, on purely promorphological grounds, to the
planula of the Coelenterata.

The most important peculiarity of the protochophore is the shape and size of
the primary mouth opening. Whereas the mouth in the Turbellaria is a small opening, like that of the hydroids, the primary mouth opening or blastopore of the protochophore forms a narrow slit, like the mouth of the Anthozoa. When the blastopore closes, the definitive mouth and anus are formed at its ends and the physiologically ventral side of the future animal is formed along the whole blastopore.
The circumblastoporal nervous plexus gives rise to the ventral nervous stems of the
Trochozoa (Articulata, Mollusca, etc.). The Turbellaria do not possess anything
homologous to the blastoporal side of the body or to the longitudinal nervous stems
of trochophoric animals. Thus, it may be quite probable that trochophoric animals,
independently of the Turbellaria, have developed from the larvae of the Coelenterata by means of "progressive" neoteny.

The origin and the transformation were, however, different in either case (Beklemishev, 1952, 1958). Trochophoric animals developed from a larva with a slit-
shaped mouth, an intestine with epithelial lining, and a pair of aboral tentacles and
not from a parenchymula-like larva. Trochophoric animals do not crawl on one of
their antimeres as the Turbellaria do, but on the oral (blastoporal) surface, as the
modern Platyctenida (Ctenophora) do. The latter illustrate the pattern of change to
crawling as in the ancestors of the trochophoric animals and are not ancestral to the
Turbellaria as Lang believed.

Thus, the trochophoric animals are not the descendants of turbellarian-like
ancestors, as believed by some, nor are the Turbellaria the descendants of annelid-
like ancestors. Both the Turbellaria and the Trochozoa arose directly and independently of each other from the Coelenterata.

The whole anatomy of the adult stage simply protests against attempts to derive
the Turbellaria from the annelids or any other form of celomic animals. It is often
said that simplicity is not a proof of primitiveness, which is true enough. But at
present we have learned sufficiently well how to distinguish between what is primitive and the kind of simplicity that comes from evolutionary simplification. Therefore, modern theories deriving the Turbellaria from celomic animals and the Hydrozoa from the Anthozoa become archaic as soon as they are put forward. Thus,
the nervous plexus of the lower Acoela and *Xenoturbella* is undoubtedly more
primitive than the differentiated, radially symmetrical orthogon of the higher Acoela
and most of the Neoophora, and the latter are phylogenetically simpler in their
nervous apparatus than the most primitive of the Annelida. It is impossible under

any circumstances to consider the orthogon of the Convolutidae, with its six, eight, or ten longitudinal stems, as a simplified ventral nervous chain; and it is still less possible to consider the diffuse nervous plexus of the lower Acoela the result of a simplification of some centralized nervous system. If we were to assume a neotenic origin of the Turbellaria from the larvae of the annelids, we would come to the fact that the polychete larva possesses a nervous apparatus, in the most primitive cases consisting of an orthogon and a circumblastoporal plexus, and that it is scarcely credible to derive the diffuse nervous plexus of the lower Acoela from such an apparatus by means of simplification. The same, *mutatis mutandis,* is true of other organs and tissues.

The Turbellaria and the trochophoric animals are two independent stems of the Bilateria, irreducible to each other, but it is the Turbellaria that have undoubtedly remained at a more primitive level of organization.

Hadži (1944) and Steinböck (1958) derive the Acoela directly from the Ciliata, considering the Acoela as original forms for all the Bilateria (Steinböck) or even for all the Enterozoa (Hadži). When comparing the life cycles of the Ciliata on the one hand, and those of the Metazoa on the other, we see that they have very little in common. There is nothing in the Metazoa like the dualism of the nuclear apparatus of the Ciliata. The conjugation of the Ciliata is a much more specialized type of fertilization than that of the Metazoa. If in the Ciliata we find progametic divisions of the micronucleus, they are very far from the gametogenesis and the cleavage of the Metazoa. The life cycle of the Metazoa is strikingly similar to that of the higher Volvocaceae. It is true that the Volvocaceae, being phytoflagellates, cannot be directly related to the Metazoa, but the similarity of their cycles shows that this type of transition of multicellular structure is quite possible (Zakhvatkin, 1956). Furthermore, cytological comparison confirms it. I have already referred to the similarity of the cells of the flagellated blastulae of the Coelenterata to the free-swimming, flagellated forms of the Protomonadina. The resemblance first of all refers to the structure of the nucleus and the mastigonts, and is on the whole striking. The same is true with respect to the cells of the blastoderm of sponges and echinoderms. In general, the cells of the Metazoa, which Steinböck considers to be the products of a secondary differentiation of the primary noncellular body, by their whole structure proclaim their relationship to the monoenergid protozoa, in particular to the Protomonadina.

Steinböck, who has done a great deal of work on the Turbellaria, affirms that all adult aceles possess a purely syncytial structure and in that respect have not progressed far from the original Ciliata. But his statement does not correspond to fact. Syncytial structures are widespread in the Acoela, as in many other metazoa. But it is impossible to speak of a syncytial structure of the whole body in the Acoela. The independence of the sexual and nervous cells is obvious in every case; the same is true of glandular cells. The external epithelium is cellular in some forms, as, for instance, in young *Oligochoerus erythrophthalmus* (Beklemishev, 1937), and syncytial in others (adult specimens of the same species). The same is true of dermal muscles. In some cases the muscle fibers pass through the syncytial epidermis (epicytium, in Westblad's terminology), as, for instance, in *Anaperus* (Luther, 1912) and *Pseudoconvoluta* (Beklemishev, 1937). In other cases all the dermal muscles are formed by independent muscular cells, as, for instance, in *Otocoelis chiridotae*—as I could see using methylene blue stain *in vivo*. Numerous independent cells can be observed in the peripheral parenchyma of many species of the Acoela, and in the cellular walls of the ovary and of the copulatory apparatus. Von Graff described alimentary phagocytes in some species. This discovery was questioned by Westblad, but fully confirmed by Ivanov (1952) for *Oxyposthia*. In general all that is required to discover cellular structures, in the Acoela, is an adequate histological technique and careful observation.

Even if the Acoela had a fully syncytial structure, however, it would be no proof of their descent from the ciliates and would only demonstrate a highly specialized histological structure.

The main point is that, in view of their life cycle, the cnidarians and sponges obviously derive from the flagellates, the whole cytology of the Metazoa confirming the homology of the metazoan cells to the monoenergid flagellates; and that the Turbellaria quite naturally and easily come by means of progressive neoteny from the parenchymula-like larvae of the Cnidaria or Procnidaria.

What groups derive from the Turbellaria? Hadži (1957) believes that the Ctenophora can be derived by means of neoteny from the Turbellaria. We have already seen that the Ctenophora and the Turbellaria are two independent groups, each arising from the lower Coelenterata. If the Ctenophora had been the neotenic descendants of the Turbellaria, it would be natural to expect that the early stages of their ontogenesis would coincide with those of the Turbellaria or could be derived from them. But neither is the case; the early stages of the Ctenophora and the Turbellaria originate from a more primitive type of ontogenesis, peculiar to the lower Cnidaria.

It is beyond doubt that the parasitic platyhelminths derive from the Turbellaria; moreover, all of them come from the Rhabdocoela, in particular from the Dalyellioidea. In the case of the Digenea it has been again confirmed by the remarkable similarity of the central nervous apparatus of *Opisthorchis* (Digenea) (Kolmogorova, 1959) to that of *Dalyellia* (Marcus, 1946; Luther, 1955).

It is also quite probable that all the classes of the Aschelminthes descend from some primitive archoöphoran turbellarian. I completely agree with Steinböck (1958) when he offers strong evidence that the Gastrotricha have descended from the Turbellaria.

The Rhynchocoela (Nemertinea) are in many respects very close to the Turbellaria, but in others, as, for instance, in the structure of the genital apparatus, they are so primitive that their relation to the Turbellaria must place their origin at the very base of the phylogenetic lineages.

Thus, though the lower Turbellaria are the most primitive of the Bilateria, they are in no way at the base of all their lineages. Only the rest of the Scolecida originate from turbellarian-like ancestors. The other big stems of the Metazoa, the trochophoric animals, the Podaxonia, the Deuterostomia, are each directly and independently connected with the Coelenterata. And, though these lineages have split from the Coelenterata at different stages of the latter's evolution by means of various adaptations and transformations, still the Bilateria form a consistent group and are a striking example of the fact that reasonable taxonomic treatment is far from always coinciding with the best phylogenetic reconstruction, and that not all seemingly homologous similarities have been inherited from common ancestors.

REFERENCES

Note: Titles in brackets are translated from the Russian.

Ax, P.
1959   Zur Systematik, Ökologie und Tiergeographie der Turbellarienfauna in den Ponto-Kaspischen Brackwassermeeren. Zool. Jb. (Syst.) 87:43–184.

Beklemishev, V. N.
1931   (Über die Anwendung einiger Grundbegriffe der Biocönologie auf tierische Komponente der Festlandbiocönosen.) Bull. Pl. Prot., (Sect. I, Entomol.) Leningr. 1:278–358. [In Russian, with German summary.]

1937   Turbellaria. Pp. 386–456 in: [Handbook of Zoology.] Vol. 1. Zenkevich, L. A., Ed. Biomedgiz., Moscow, Leningrad. [In Russian.]

1944   [Principles of the Comparative Anatomy of Invertebrates.] Sov. Nauka, Moscow. [In Russian.]

1951   [On the species of *Macrostomum* of the U.S.S.R.] Bull. Soc. Nat. Moscou (Biol.) 56:31–40. [In Russian.]

1952   [Principles of the Comparative Anatomy of Invertebrates.] Sov. Nauka, Moscow. 2d ed. [In Russian.]

1958   Die Grundlagen der vergleichenden Anatomie der Wirbellosen. Vol. I. Dtsch. Verl. Wissensch., Berlin.

1960   *Idem*. Vol. II. Dtsch. Verl. Wissensch., Berlin.

Berg, S. E.
1941   Die Entwicklung und Koloniebildung bei *Funiculina quadrangularis* (Pallas). Zool. Bidr. Uppsala 20:1–100.

Bogomolov, S. I.
1957   [New data on the cleavage of *Convoluta* eggs and the origin of spiral cleavage.] P. 16 in: [Abstracts of Proceedings, Second Meeting of the Embryologists of the U.S.S.R., Moscow.] [In Russian.]

Graff, L. von
1904–
1908   Acoela and Rhabdocoela. Bronn's Klassen 4, sect. Ic (Turbellaria, sect. 1): i–xxii, 1733–2599. [1904–1905, pp. 1733–1984; 1907, pp. 1985–2192, 2193–2256; 1908, pp. 2257–2599.]

Hadži, J.
1944   Turbelarijska Teorija Knidarijev (Turbellarien–Theorie der Knidarier). Slov. Akad. Znan. Um., Ljubljana, pp. 1–238. [In Slovenian, with German summary.]

1957   Die morphologische Bedeutung der Wimperrosetten der Ktenophoren. J. Fac. Sci. Hokkaido Univ. (Zool.) 13:32–36.

Hatschek, B.
1881–
1891   Lehrbuch der Zoologie. Vols. I–III. Fischer, Jena.

Hyman, L. H.
1940   The Invertebrates. Vol. I: Protozoa through Ctenophora. McGraw-Hill, New York, Toronto, London.

Ivanov, A. V.
1952   [Turbellaria Acoela from the southern coast of Sakhalin.] Trav. Inst. zool. Acad. Sci. U.R.S.S. 12:40–132. [In Russian.]

Ivanova-Kasas, O. M.

1959 [The origin and evolution of spiral cleavage.] Vestn. Leningr. Univ., no. 9 (Biol.):56–67. [In Russian, with English summary.]

Karling, T.
1940 Zur Morphologie und Systematik der Alloeocoela Cumulata und Rhabdocoela Lecithophora (Turbellaria). Acta zool. fenn. 26:1–260.

Kolmogorova, E. J.
1959 [Structure of the central parts of the nervous system in *Opisthorchis felineus*.] Zool. Zh. 38:1627–1633. [In Russian, with English summary.]

Lang, A.
1884 Die Polycladen des Golfes von Neapel und der angrenzenden Meeresabschnitte. Fauna u. Flora Neapel. 11:1–688.

Luther, A.
1912 Studien über acöle Turbellarien aus dem Finnischen Meerbusen. Acta Soc. Fauna Flora fenn. 36(5):1–60.
1955 Die Dalyelliiden (Turbellaria Neorhabdocoela). Eine Monographie. Acta zool. fenn. 87:1–337.

Marcus, E.
1946 Sobre Turbellaria Brasileiros. Bol. Fac. Filos. Ciênc. S. Paulo (Zool.) 11:5–254.

Mechnikov [Metschnikoff], E.
1886 Embryologische Studien an Medusen. Holder, Wien.

Reisinger, E.
1925 Über den Bau des Nervensystems von *Bothrioplana semperi*. Z. Morph. Ökol. Tiere 5:119–149.

Remane, A.
1950 Enstehung der Metamerie de Wirbellosen. Verh. dtsch. Zoologen, Mainz (1949) (Zool. Anz., Suppl. 14):16–23.

Seilern-Aspang, F.
1957 Die Entwicklung von *Macrostomum appendiculatum* (Fabr.). Zool. Jb. (Anat.) 76:311–330.

Steinböck, O.
1958 Zur Phylogenie der Gastrotrichen. Verh. dtsch. zool. Ges., Graz (1957) (Zool. Anz., Suppl. 21):128–169.

Westblad, E.
1940 Studien über skandinavische Turbellaria Acoela. I. Ark. Zool. 32A, no. 20:1–28.
1942 *Idem*. II. *Ibid*. 33A, no. 14:1–48.
1945 *Idem*. III. *Ibid*. 36A, no. 5:1–56.
1946 *Idem*. IV. *Ibid*. 38A, no. 1:1–56.
1948 *Idem*. V. *Ibid*. 41A, no. 7:1–82.
1949 *Xenoturbella bocki* n. gen., n. sp., a peculiar primitive turbellarian type. Ark. Zool. (ser. 2) 1:1–29.

Zakhvatkin, A. A.
1946 [On the nature of the blastula-like larvae in Metazoa.] Zool. Zh. 25:305–324. [In Russian.]
1956 Vergleichende Embryologie der niederen Wirbellosen. Dtsch. Verl. Wissensch., Berlin.

Zalenskiĭ, V. V. [Salensky, W. W.]
1912 Über die Morphogenese der Nemertinen. 1. Entwicklungsgeschichte der Nemertine im Inneren des Pilidiums. Mém. Acad. Sci. St. Pétersb. 30, no. 10:1–74.

G. ASCHELMINTHES

17 ◆ The Systematic Position and Phylogeny of the Pseudocelomates

ADOLF REMANE

ZOOLOGISCHES INSTITUT UND MUSEUM,
UNIVERSITÄT KIEL, KIEL

The relationships of the so-called Pseudocoelomata (or Pseudocoelia) is one of the most difficult problems in systematic zoölogy. Here I cannot give a solution, but only a few remarks on the problem (see also Remane, 1929–1933, 1936, 1954, 1957). Hyman (1951, 1959) includes in this group the "phyla" Acanthocephala, Aschelminthes (with classes Rotifera, Gastrotricha, Kinorhyncha, Priapulida, Nematoda, and Nematomorpha), and Entoprocta. Chitwood (1940) recognizes the aschelminth "classes" as phyla. The word pseudocelomate signifies the presumptive nature of the body cavity. But we know that, although body cavities are very important for clarifying phylogenetic relationships, they differ among the Bilateria and there are many controversies in basing theory on them. The difficulties are intrinsic to the problem of how to characterize a space, a negative thing. Moreover, definitions originated variously for expressing ontogenetic, descriptive, and phylogenetic views do not necessarily coincide. I shall give two examples. In the ontogeny of the grass frog (*Rana temporaria*) sometimes the blastocele disappears, sometimes it is fused with the enteric cavities (gastrocele), as Peter (1940) states. If we identify these spaces, the enteric outpocketing in several frogs is a complex of gastrocele and blastocele; in others it is a gastrocele only. In the ontogeny of *Phoronis* and several enteropneusts and echinoderms, mesenchyme cells swarm out from the entoderm into the blastocele. Later on they unite into an epithelium and cut off a new cavity from the blastocele. Is the new cavity, usually designated a celom, a part of the blastocele?

These examples make it clear that the body cavities can only be classified if we consider the tissues forming and lining these spaces.

The following definitions seem to me helpful in clarifying the discussion.

1. *Ontogenetic terms, characterizing the ontogenetic development of the body cavities:*

BLASTOCELE—Primary body cavity, in the blastula stage without a lining tissue proper. In most genera a blastocele is only a transitory space not giving rise directly to body cavities of the adult. Genera with a stereoblastula forming the entoderm *in situ* have no blastocele.

ENTEROCELE—Secondary body cavity, in part formed by enteric pockets of the gastrodermis. The lining epithelium is directly derived from the entodermal epithelium.

SCHIZOCELE—Body cavity formed by spaces within a compact tissue of an embryo.

NEOCELE—Body cavity formed by cells first isolated, which come together and form the lining cells of a new cavity within the older one.

2. *Descriptive terms, characterizing the histological structure of the body cavities:*

EPITHELIOCELE—Body cavity lined by a typical epithelial peritoneum.

ENDOTHELIOCELE—Body cavity lined by a reversed epithelium—that is, the cells are placed with their bases to the cavity as demonstrated by many blood systems.

MESENCHYMOCELE—Body cavity within a mesenchymal tissue.

GYMNOCELE—Body cavity without special lining cells; other tissues border the cavities, often only the epidermis and gastrodermis.

GONOCELE—Body cavity lined with the genital cells (*e.g.,* gonads of Nemertinea [Rhynchocoela]).

3. *Morphological terms:*

Morphology can be defined as the search for homologies. Many very different structures can be homologous and therefore represent a related morphological series. Examples are the celom, the hemocele, and others. Morphological series are difficult to define, because their transformation in phylogeny into different structures makes it often impossible to give a short definition for all the resulting structures. A typical celom is a body cavity with a lining epithelium—therefore, an epitheliocele—that receives the gametes; with a musculature formed by the epithelium; with mesenteries; and with the funnels of nephridia. But often, even if one or more of these criteria are not realized, we refer to such cavities as celoms when they are derived from a typical celom. The celomic epithelium is often reduced, but its musculature is present (*e.g.,* in the Chaetognatha, Enteropneusta, etc.); often there are no nephridial funnels (*e.g.,* in the Echinodermata); frequently the epithelium is more or less transformed into a mesenchyme, and strands of tissue traverse the celomic cavity (*e.g.,* in the Enteropneusta); or the celom is represented by the lacunar spaces within a mesenchyme with the function of a blood system (*e.g.,* in the Hirudinea). From the standpoint of ontogeny, the celom may be an enterocele, a schizocele, or a neocele; in histological terms it may be an epitheliocele, a gymnocele, or perhaps a gonocele.

These formidable definitions are necessary in discussing the so-called Pseudocoelia. The Pseudocoelomata or Aschelminthes are nearly always characterized as animals with a primary body cavity (= blastocele; pseudocele). Hyman gives the following definition (1951, p. 23): "Pseudocoelomatic phyla, with a persistent pseudocoel (= blastocoel) between digestive tube and body wall." But the explanation of the body cavity as blastocele or pseudocele seems to me not well founded by facts. Most of the embryos of Pseudocoelia are compact; they have no blastocele, or, if it is present, it is reduced in more advanced stages. The body cavity of the adult is therefore not the direct continuation of an embryonic blastocele; it is a schizocele.

From the histological standpoint the body cavity has mixed characters of an epitheliocele, a mesenchymocele, and a gymnocele. Often several but not all criteria of a celom are present. In nematodes the muscle cells of the body wall are arranged like an epithelium, especially in the platymyarian free-living forms. This outer lining of the body cavity is more similar to a typical celomic wall than that in many celomates. The muscle cells come from two mesodermal bands of entomesoderm, like the mesodermal bands of annelids or molluscs. Therefore it is not astonishing that R. Hertwig (in O. and R. Hertwig, 1881) attributed the Nematoda to the "Enterocoelia."

The order Macrodasyida (class Gastrotricha) have an interesting array of body spaces of a different kind (fig. 17-1). There are three cavities, two lateral and one central around the intestine. The lateral spaces contain the germ cells in a special area in the middle or posterior part of the body. The sperm and eggs lie at first in these cavities; later the eggs migrate into the central body cavity. The lateral body cavities are surrounded by longitudinal muscle bands and special cells, highly characteristic in the genus *Turbanella*. The central cavity is surrounded by a thin membrane containing circular muscle fibers. In the anterior part of the body these fibers lie so close to the pharynx that they seem to be a circular pharyngeal musculature. Thus it seems possible that the lateral cavities are celomic in nature, but reduced. In the second order of the Gastrotricha, the simple Chaetonotida, such cavities are not visible. The most primitive genus, *Neodasys* Remane, has no distinct cavities. The other genera have a gymnocele between the digestive tract and the epidermis; the eggs lie within this cavity.

But we find in the Nematomorpha a tripartition of the body cavity like the situation described in the Macrodasyida. The gonads lie in lateral spaces surrounded by mesenchyme; the digestive tract lies in a central cavity.

Very peculiar is the situation in the Rotifera and Acanthocephala. The body cavity of rotifers was thought to be a gymnocele between digestive tract and epidermis with no connection with the gonads, which have a distinct special membrane continuing in the oviduct. (Only in the bdelloid genus *Rotaria* does there seem to be no oviduct, and the embryos develop in the body cavity.) But new investigations on the morphology of the genus *Lacinularia* have demonstrated the existence of a very fine membrane limiting the body cavity; this membrane is not connected with the epidermis. Nuclei are not found in this membrane. This structure is reminiscent of the ligamentous sacs of the Acanthocephala, but the latter receive the oöcytes and eggs. A thin membrane without nuclei in the Priapulida is also described by Lang (1953); and in the dinophilids (commonly regarded as primitive annelids) the body cavity, which was first taken to be a hemocele, has a similar thin lining membrane, but with several nuclei. This space in the dinophilids is therefore regarded as a celom by Jägersten (1944). The Entoprocta have a mesenchymal tissue between their organs.

The body cavities of the "Pseudocoelia" are therefore different from class to class. There are many structures that contradict the explanation of all these cavities as blastoceles or pseudoceles. Several structures resemble celomic cavities, but it is best to consider the homology of these body cavities to be an open problem.

Regarding the possible affinities of the classes of the so-called Pseudocoelia, we have many similar structures in the Gastrotricha, Nematoda, and Nematomorpha. The digestive tract in the Gastrotricha and Nematoda is nearly identical. There is a terminal mouth provided with cuticular rings or hooks and a long pharynx; in

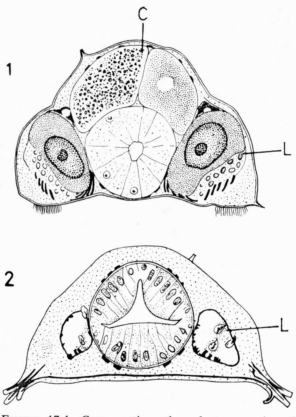

FIGURE 17-1. Cross sections through two species of Gastrotricha Macrodasyida. 1. *Turbanella cornuta* Remane, posterior part of the body. 2. *Pleurodasys helgolandicus* Remane, pharyngeal region. C = central cavity (in *1* with intestine and two ripe eggs on the dorsal side). L = lateral cavities (in *1* with an egg, the ovarian tissue, muscles, and y-cells on the dorsal side). (After Remane, 1926.)

the pharynx the musculature is formed within the epithelial cells, not by a surrounding mesenchyme as in the Platyhelminthes; the pharyngeal epithelium has cross-striated radial muscle fibers. The intestine is without annexed digestive glands; it is typically without cilia (only in the gastrotrich genus *Dactylopodalia,* has Wilke, in 1954, described cilia—a primitive character of this genus). The anus lies ventrally. The brain is ring-shaped and surrounds the pharynx well behind the mouth. In other organs, however (*e.g.,* the longitudinal nerves and the musculature), there are many differences between the Gastrotricha and Nematoda not bridged by known genera or ontogenetic stages.[1] The similarities in the body cavities of the Macrodasyida (class Gastrotricha) and the Nematomorpha have already been mentioned. All in all, though the affinity of the Gastrotricha, Nematoda, and Nematomorphia, already surmised by Bütschli (1876) and Ziegler (1898), is not definitely proved, it is the best connection that we can formulate today, unless, like Wilke, we assume the problem of affinities as insoluble.

The rotifers pose other problems in the reconstruction of relations. Since the last century their similarities with trochophore larvae have been discussed (Hatschek, 1891), not only with those of annelids, but also with those of molluscs (de Beauchamp, 1909). Such affinities, first based only on structural similarities of typical rotifers with typical trochophores, seemed to be strengthened by a connecting form, the genus *Trochosphaera* Semper. But this rotifer has only a superficial resemblance to several specialized trochophores; it is not a connecting form, but a specialized rotifer of the order Monogonontida, suborder Flosculariina. Nevertheless, there is no doubt that, even omitting *Trochosphaera,* there exist remarkable similarities between rotifers and typical trochophores. The apical plate with ciliated tufts, glands (*e.g.,* retrocerebral organs of rotifers), the formation of the brain from the apical plate, the ciliary ring with enlarged trochoblasts, the "foot," and other structures are comparable. It is true that these special similarities are not so specific as to permit us to assume definite homologies and affinities, but, as no other phylum has so many similarities, a connection of rotifers and trochophores seems a highly reasonable hypothesis. There is no need to derive the rotifers from a trochophore by typical neoteny. We have an example in the Dinophilidae in which many larval characters of the trochophore exist in forms without a typical pelagic trochophore larva (fig. 17-2). The investigations of Jägersten (1944) have revealed new similarities to rotifers (*e.g.,* the epithelial musculature of the pharynx), but it

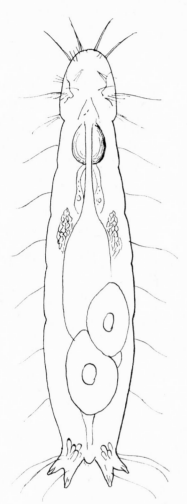

FIGURE 17-2. *Diurodrilus minimus* Remane, a little dinophilid living in the interstitial region of sandy bottoms. It is very similar to gastrotrichs and rotifers, but has probably no close affinity to these groups. Length 0.3 mm. (After Remane, 1926.)

seems to me that these similarities are better explained by parallelism. (The penis of the Dinophilidae is probably not homologous with that of rotifers. The most primi-

---

[1] Formerly I thought it possible that the subventral excretory glands of the Nematoda are reduced protonephridia, as are to be observed in the Gastrotricha. But, if descriptions of typical protonephridia in the Macrodasyida by Wilke (1954) are confirmed, such a derivation is without support.

tive order of rotifers, the Seisonida, has no penis. The dwarf males of several species of *Dinophilus* surely represent an evolution parallel to the dwarf males of the mono-gonont rotifers.) The rotifers are certainly not ancestors to any other group, but simplified forms with persistence of many larval characters. Nor does this mean a derivation of rotifers from annelids. Trochophore-like larvae exist in so many phyla that such a larva must have been present near the base of the Protostomia, but only as a juvenile stage. Several classes of the Pseudocoelomata have special similarities to the rotifers. We find such similarities especially in the parasitic Acanthocephala (von Haffner, 1950—*e.g.,* the existence of a cloaca into which lead the proctodeum, the genital ducts, and the protonephridia; invagination of the anterior part of the body by specific retractor muscles; the segmentation of the egg). A phyletic affinity between rotifers and acanthocephalans is therefore very probable.

Many of the characters discussed are also found in the Priapulida and Kino-rhyncha, and the affinities of the Acanthocephala, Priapulida, and Kinorhyncha are presented comprehensively by Lang (1953). All these groups are able to invaginate the anterior part of the body by retractor muscles; this anterior part is provided with many cuticular hooks. The Priapulida also have a cloaca that receives the digestive tract, the gonads, and the protonephridia. In the Kinorhyncha the openings of these organs are close together, but without formation of a cloaca. The body cavity of Priapulida is lined by a membrane without nuclei (Lang, 1953) and therefore is similar to the body cavity of rotifers and the ligamentous sac of acanthocephalans. But both groups have a set of special characters difficult to explain. The priapulids have the type of sperm that is primitive in the Metazoa, with external fecundation—a type not found in the other groups of Pseudocoelo-mata, which have internal fecundation wherever more or less typical sexual proc-esses are found (Franzén, 1956). Segmentation of the eggs is not similar to that in classes of definitive Pseudocoelomata, and the typical spiral-quartet 4d cleavage found fully developed in the Entoprocta and seen vestigially in rotifers and gastro-trichs is not found in the Priapulida. The Kinorhyncha have a segmentation not only in the cuticle, but even in the diagonal musculature and in the ganglia of the ventral nerve, which resemble very much the well-known ventral nerve chain of annelids. Yet it is possible that this segmentation of many organs, not known in other Pseudocoelomata, is independent in origin of segmentation in annelids; this is to be sure entirely hypothetical. The Priapulida and Kinorhyncha have a pharynx with a typical mesenchymal musculature around the pharyngeal epithelium, etc. The similarities of the gastrotrichs to reduced annelids (*e.g.,* the dinophilids— see Remane, 1926), and of the gastrotrichs to the turbellarians (Steinböck, 1957) are only of the type usual in convergence.

The union of the rotifers and gastrotrichs in a class or phylum (=Trochel-minthes), as proposed in the last century and frequently utilized thereafter, is not justified. The similarities in possession of protonephridia and adhesive tubules and of ciliation are superficial and widespread in the simple Protostomia. De Beau-champ (1907, 1909) has shown that the pharynx of the Rotifera can be derived from a triradiate pharynx with epithelial muscles like the pharynx of the Gastro-tricha and Nematoda. But the dorsal wall of the pharynx of the Rotifera is ciliated in the Flosculariina (order Monogonontida) and has tufts of cilia in other rotifers. This makes it probable that the dorsal wall of the rotiferan pharynx not provided with radial muscle fibers has not passed through a stage characterized by a fully developed triradiate pharynx like that of the gastrotrichs and nematodes, but comes from a ventral pharyngeal sac. Jägersten (1944) has shown that the muscles of the ventral pharyngeal sac in the Dinophilidae are of epithelial origin and are in this respect similar to those of rotifers and other pseudocelomates. On the other hand, the new order Gnathostomulida (Ax, 1956) has a pharynx like that of rotifers. I agree with Ax that these similarities are probably convergences.

The similarities of rotifers and gastrotrichs to the turbellarians (Wesenberg-Lund, 1923; Steinböck, 1957) are fewer than those to the dinophilids. In my opinion the similarities to the latter are probably parallelisms or convergences; the similarities to the turbellarians are of lesser importance and, in many characters upon which Steinböck bases his arguments, surely represent convergences.

The result of our investigations is not satisfying. No phyletic connection of the classes (or phyla) of Pseudocoelomata is so well founded as to be definitely established. The connection between gastrotrichs, nematodes, and nematomorphs is the most probable; the connection of rotifers and acanthocephalans, the next. It is possible that all the groups named came from a simplified ancestor of the "Spiralia" with a trochophore larva, but it is equally possible that, at several times, different groups within the "Spiralia" gave rise to the special classes of the Pseudocoelomata. The problem of monophyletic or polyphyletic origin in this assemblage must remain *sub judice* at this time. And, in no case is a sharp distinction of acelomate and pseudocelomate phyla justified. If we wish to place together in a comprehensive taxon all the groups without typical celom, with protonephridia (the Nematoda being exceptions here), often with ciliated epidermis, with internal fecundation, and without or with but feeble (Kinorhyncha) segmentation, it is best to choose the old term Scolecida or Amera. Treatment of rotifers, gastrotrichs, nematodes, etc., as separate phyla is no solution to the problem, but a failure to face it squarely.

We need (1) a more intensive study of the microscopic marine fauna. (I have

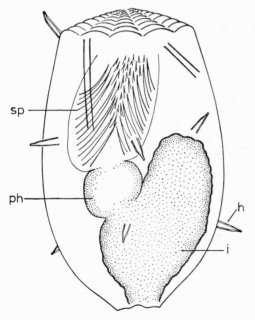

FIGURE 17-3. A curious, not yet described animal from the sandy bottom of the Red Sea. The anterior end provided with many hooks is retracted and invaginated. The body has a thin cuticle, but no typical lorica. h = adhesive tubules; i = intestine; p = pharynx; sp = spines or hooks of the invaginated anterior end.

seen in the Red Sea an animal with a head bearing hooks and resembling the larva of priapulids, but lacking a lorica and provided with a number of adhesive tubules and a digestive tract like the priapulids—fig. 17-3. This material is insufficient to give us a clear concept of the organism's affinities.) And we need further (2) an anatomical and embryological study of many genera hitherto only known as to external characters and a few internal ones.

From all present evidence I am convinced, in any event, that the Pseudocoelia have not been phylogenetically productive taxa, important for the evolution of higher animals, but are structurally simplified descendents of the Protostomia, or, more precisely, of the Spiralia.

REFERENCES

Ax, P.
 1956   Die Gnathostomulida, eine rätselhafte Wurmgruppe aus dem Meeressand.
          Abh. math.-nat. Kl. Akad. Wiss. Mainz. (1956):531–562.
Beauchamp, P. M. de
 1907   Morphologie et variations de l'appareil rotateur. Arch. Zool. exp. gén.
          (sér. 4) 6:1–29.
 1909   Recherches sur les Rotifères: les formations tégumentaires et l'appareil
          digestive. *Ibid.* (sér. 4) 10:1–410.
Bütschli, O.
 1876   Untersuchungen über freilebende Nematoden und die Gattung *Chaetonotus*. Z. wiss. Zool. 26:363–413.
Chitwood, B. G.
 1940   Nemic relationships. Pp. 190–204 in: Chitwood, B.G., *et al.* An Introduction to Nematology. Sect. I., Pt. 3. Monumental Press, Baltimore.
Franzén, Å.
 1956   On spermiogenesis, morphology of the spermatozoon and biology of
          fertilization among invertebrates. Zool. Bidr. Uppsala 31:355–482.
Haffner, K. von
 1950   Organisation und systematische Stellung der Acanthocephalen. Festschrift
          Klatt (Zool. Anz. Erg. Heft zu 145):243–274.
Hatschek, B.
 1891   Lehrbuch der Zoologie. Fischer, Jena.
Hertwig, O., and R. Hertwig
 1881   Die Coelomtheorie. Fischer, Jena.
Hyman, L.
 1951   The Invertebrates. Vol. II. Platyhelminthes and Rhynchocoela—the
          Acoelomate Bilateria. Vol. III. Acanthocephala, Aschelminthes and Entoprocta—the Pseudocoelomate Bilateria. McGraw-Hill, New York,
          Toronto, London.
 1959   The Invertebrates. Vol. V. Smaller Coelomate Groups. McGraw-Hill,
          New York, Toronto, London.
Jägersten, G.
 1944   Zur Kenntnis der Morphologie, Enzystierung und Taxonomie von *Dinophilus*. K. svenska VetenskAkad. Handl. (ser. 3.) 21, no. 2:1–90.
Lang, K.
 1953   Die Entwicklung des Eies von *Priapulus caudatus* und die systematische
          Stellung der Priapuliden. Ark. Zool. (ser. 2) 5:321–348.

Peter, K.
    1940   Untersuchungen über die Entwicklung des Dotterentoderms. Z. mikrosk. anat. Forsch. 47:322–350.

Remane, A.
    1926   Morphologie und Verwandtschaftsbeziehungen der aberranten Gastrotrichen. Z. Morph. Ökol Tiere 5:623–754.

    1929–
    1933   Rotatoria. Bronn's Klassen 4, sect. 2, book I [1929, Lieferung 1:1–160; 1932, Lieferung 3:289–448; 1933, Lieferung 4:449–576].

    1936   Gastrotricha und Kinorhyncha. Ibid. 4, sect. 2, book II, pt. 1:1–385 [1935, Lieferung 1:1–160; 1936, Lieferung 2:161–385.]

    1954   Die Geschichte der Tiere. Pp. 340–422 in: Die Evolution der Organismen. Heberer, G., Ed. 2d ed. Fischer, Stuttgart.

    1957   Zur Verwandtschaft und Ableitung der niederen Metazoen. Verh. dtsch. zool. Ges., Graz (1957) (Zool. Anz., Suppl. 21):179–195.

Steinböck, O.
    1957   Zur Phylogenie der Gastrotrichen. Ibid. 128–169.

Wesenberg-Lund, C.
    1923   Contributions to the biology of the Rotifera. I. The males of the Rotifera. Kgl. dansk. vidensk. Selsk. Skr., Naturv. Math. (ser. 8) 4:189–354.

Wilke, U.
    1954   Mediterrane Gastrotrichen. Zool. Jb. (Syst.) 82:495–550.

Ziegler, E.
    1898   Über den derzeitigen Stand der Cölomfrage. Verh. dtsch. zool. Ges., Heidelberg (1898) 8:14–78.

18 ◆ The Relation between the Kinorhyncha and Priapulida and Their Connection with the Aschelminthes

KARL LANG

EVERTEBRATAVDELNINGEN,
NATURHISTORISKA RIKSMUSEET, STOCKHOLM

Opinion as to the systematic position of the Priapulida has changed very considerably. Though it is not my intention to give an historical survey of this change, I should like to recall that Shepot'ev (1908) and Rauther (1909) had already assumed a near relation between the priapulids and the acanthocephalans and that Hammarsten (1915) looked upon the kinorhynchs as the nearest relatives to the priapulids.

I myself have in two papers, of 1949 and 1953 respectively, expressed agreement with Hammarsten's opinion.

Some authors, however, do not share this opinion. Fischer (1925) defends the old idea that the priapulids are most nearly related to the holothurians. This view, which goes back to Linnaeus, is convincingly rejected by Baltzer (1934) in the *Handbuch der Zoologie*. Fänge (1950) readopts the opinion of Quatrefages (1847) that the priapulids are most closely related to the sipunculids, and Fänge and Åkesson (1951) include the brachiopods in this relationship, their only argument being that the red cells of the body fluid contain hemerythrin. In my opinion, there cannot be a close relation between these animals, as they differ from each other in all anatomical respects. Here I only want to mention that the body cavity of the sipunculids and brachiopods is a secondary one, whereas that of the priapulids is most probably primary, and that the priapulids, unlike the other two classes, have protonephridia. The ontogeny of the sipunculids and brachiopods is also totally different from that of the priapulids: egg cleavage in the priapulids is of the radial type; that of the sipunculids, of the spiral type. The priapulids hatch as an unciliated stereogastrula; the sipunculids and brachiopods, as a trochophore-like larva; and so on.

Hammarsten founded his opinion upon a comparison of the *Halicryptus* larva with the adult kinorhynchs. No other course, however, was open to him, since the larvae of *Priapulus* as well as of the kinorhynchs were unknown at that time.

As has been pointed out by Remane (1936), the *Halicryptus* larva differs from the kinorhynchs in some important characters. The *Halicryptus* larva has glands in the esophagus, the kinorhynchs do not. The armor in the *Halicryptus* larva is sack-shaped, whereas it is divided into zonites in the kinorhynchs; and, unlike the kinorhynchs, the *Halicryptus* larva lacks dorso-ventral muscles.

Later on the larva of *Priapulus* (Lang, 1939 and 1949) and some early stages of the kinorhynchs (Nyholm, 1947) have been found. The *Priapulus* larva lacks glands in the esophagus (fig. 18-1) and its dorsal as well as ventral armor consists of two plates or zonites.

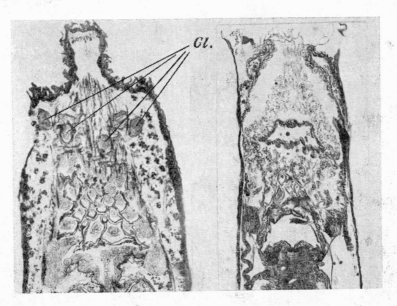

FIGURE 18-1. Horizontal section of the larva of *Halicryptus spinulosus* (to the left) and *Priapulus caudatus* (to the right). 170×. *Gl.* = esophageal glands.

As shown by Nyholm (*loc. cit.*), in the kinorhynchs the division of the armor into zonites takes place successively during their ontogeny. In the earliest larval stages found by him, the anterior body-part is equipped with a weakly bipartite armor. Most probably this stage is preceded by at least two other stages, the first of which is unarmed, the second provided with an undivided armor around its posterior part. If we make the simple assumption that the *Halicryptus* larva remains in this stage, the difference disappears.

To the fact that the priapulids, unlike the kinorhynchs, lack dorso-ventral muscles I can attach no phylogenetic importance. In my opinion the dorso-ventral muscles of the kinorhynchs are the remains of a circular musculature, partly reduced in consequence of the division of the ventral armor and thus homologous with the circular muscles found in the unarmed first zonite—or the head—of the kinorhynchs and also homologous with the circular musculature of the priapulids.

My main reason for regarding the priapulids as belonging to the Aschelminthes is that the lining of their extensive body cavity is devoid of nuclei (fig. 18-2). Consequently, the celom is, in all probability, a pseudocele as defined by Hyman (1959).

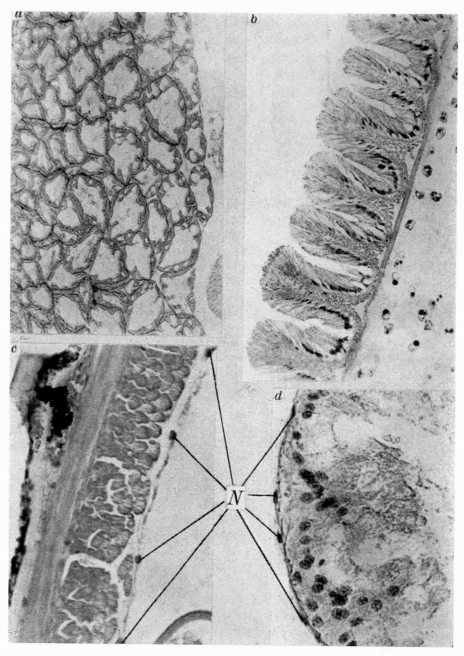

FIGURE 18-2. *a, b, Halicryptus spinulosus.* Cross section of (*a*) the longitudinal muscles of the body-wall and the body cavity, 470 ×, and (*b*) the intestine and the body cavity, 295 ×. *c, d, Cloesiphon* sp. (Sipunculoida). Cross section of (*c*) the body wall and (*d*) the intestine, 540 ×. N = nuclei.

In discussing the systematic position of the priapulids in this phylum, I exclude at first the Acanthocephala, the systematic position of which is discussed later on.

From a phylogenetic point of view, the body-wall musculature is of special interest in this connection. In the kinorhynchs and priapulids this musculature consists of a more or less well-developed layer of outer circular and inner longitudinal muscles. The longitudinal muscles are tubular (fig. 18-3) and consist of an outer fiber-mantle enclosing a granulated protoplasm. Each mantle consists of columns of nucleated, cross-striated primitive fibers. Topographically as well as histologically the body-wall musculature of these two classes shows a total agreement.

In the other aschelminths such a subepidermal muscle sheath seems to be lacking. This, however, may be owing to lack of sufficient investigations.

Other characters to be found only in the kinorhynchs and priapulids are as

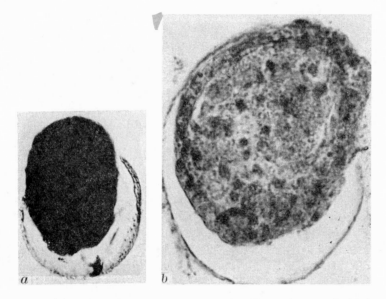

FIGURE 18-3. *Priapulus* larva: *a,* emerging from the egg; *b,* horizontal section of an emerging larva, 730 ×.

follows: (1) The presence of an eversible proboscis, provided with rings of spines or tubercles on the inside clothed with hypodermis. Each ring contains, in the priapulids, five spines; in the kinorhynchs, a multiple of five spines. This seems to indicate that in the kinorhynchs there originally was a greater number of quinary rings or else a smaller number of rings in which the number of spines was a multiple of five. The presence of a multiple of five spines would thus, according to the first alternative, be owing to a fusion of rings, whereas according to the second alternative the rings are split up. It is evident, however, that in both classes the spines can be arranged in the same way originally. (2) The pharynx is spinulous. (3) The nervous system is in close contact with the epidermis and consists of a pharyngeal ring and of a mid-ventral cord. (4) The priapulids are loricate during their larval stages, the kinorhynchs also as adults. (5) *Priapulus* hatches as an unciliated stereo gastrula consisting of an outer ectodermal layer and an inner syncytial mass (fig. 18-3). At this stage the larva lacks plates. As already mentioned, the young larva of the kinorhynchs also lacks plates and, according to Nyholm (*loc. cit.*), all inner organs as well as the anus are missing.

To this I can add that the priapulids molt throughout their life, whereas—as far as is hitherto known—the kinorhynchs, like the nematodes, molt only during their "larval" period. It is, however, not impossible that the adult kinorhynchs molt too. In the Baltic Sea, near Stockholm, the species *Pycnophyes flaveolatus* Zelinka is very abundant. Among my material of this species there are two integuments of adult specimens containing five and six eggs respectively in their hindmost part. This, as far as I can see, indicates that the kinorhynchs, after having laid their eggs, either die or molt.

From what has been said it is evident that the priapulids and kinorhynchs agree in so many significant characters that this cannot reasonably be interpreted in any other way than by assuming them to be related.

The priapulids agree with the other aschelminths in different respects. The juvenile nematodes as a rule undergo four molts, in which the entire cuticle, including the lining of the buccal capsule, pharynx, rectum, and vagina, is shed. The priapulids molt in exactly the same way (as is well known, there is no vagina in the priapulids; what is shed instead are the ectodermal parts of the urogenital system).

Like the gastrotrichs and kinorhynchs, the priapulids have no cell constancy and their protonephridia are solenocytes. As in all classes of the Aschelminthes, the alimentary canal is straight.

In possessing a urogenital system, the priapulids, however, hold an isolated position among the classes under consideration.

Among pseudocelomate animals, a urogenital system of the same appearance is to be found only in the acanthocephalans. The embryonic development of this system in the latter has been completely investigated by Meyer (1928). The propriety of his opinion that this urogenital system is homologous with that of the priapulids is denied by Lüling (1940). The earlier genesis of this system being unknown in the priapulids, it is impossible to decide which of them is right. Conformity of structure is, however, so striking that it is most plausible to assume that the systems are homologous.

Meyer shares the opinions of Shepot'ev and Rauther that the priapulids and acanthocephalans are closely related. He considers that the kinorhynchs also share in this general relationship, and he looks upon these three classes as belonging to the Aschelminthes.

Some of the arguments advanced by him for the affinity of the priapulids and the acanthocephalans I find of no phylogenetic value. Of these I take two examples only: his homologizing of the cuticular spines in the priapulids and the acanthocephalans, and his homologizing of the egg shells—or, more correctly, the embryonic shells—of the latter with the armor of the *Halicryptus* larva. The presence of cuticular spines is such a common thing among invertebrates that no phylogenetic conclusion can be drawn from it. The embryonic shells of the acanthocephalans are formed at a very early stage between the fertilization membrane and the original egg membrane. The armor of the larvae in priapulids is formed as an ectodermal secretory product after hatching. Consequently, they cannot be homologous.

Apart from the urogenital system, already discussed, the following facts seem to indicate that the priapulids and the acanthocephalans are related.

The body-wall musculature agrees fundamentally both topographically and histologically. Among the Aschelminthes such a musculature is, moreover, found only in the kinorhynchs. The body-cavity of the acanthocephalans agrees with that of the kinorhynchs. The formation of the celom in the priapulids and kinorhynchs being unknown, there may, however, be some doubts as to its comparability with that of the acanthocephalans. The fact that in all of them the new-born larva consists of an ectodermal layer enclosing an inner syncytial mass strongly indicates that their celom is of the same nature.

There are also some reasons for supposing that the proboscis is homologous in all three classes and that the proboscis receptacle of the acanthocephalans is homologous with the pharynx of the priapulids and the kinorhynchs. Moreover, there is nothing to contradict the view that some parts of the retractor musculature of the proboscis receptacle in the acanthocephalans is homologous with some of the retractor muscles of the pharynx in the priapulids.

On account of what has been said, I have (Lang, 1953) proposed a division of the Aschelminthes into one group comprising the rotifers, gastrotrichs, nematodes, and nematomorphs and another group comprising the kinorhynchs, priapulids, and acanthocephalans. Hyman (1959) makes the suggestion that each of these groups could reasonably constitute a phylum.

Concerning the division I will point out that the groups diverge from each other in such a degree that, in my opinion, no one of them can be the ancestor of the others.

REFERENCES

Baltzer, F.
    1934   Priapulida. Handb. Zool., Berlin 2:161–168.
Fischer, W.
    1925   Echiuridae, Sipunculidae, Priapulidae. Tierwelt N.- u. Ostsee. 6d:1–55.
Fänge, R.
    1950   Haemerythrin in *Priapulus caudatus* Lam. Nature 165:613–614.
Fänge, R., and B. Åkesson
    1951   The cells of the coelomic fluid of priapulides and their content of haemerythrin. Ark. Zool. (ser. 2.) 3:25–31.
Hammarsten, O.
    1915   Zur Entwicklungsgeschichte von *Halicryptus spinulosus* (von Siebold). Z. wiss. Zool. 112:527–571.
Hyman, L.
    1959   The Invertebrates. Vol. V: Smaller Coelomate Groups. McGraw-Hill, New York, Toronto, London.
Lang, K.
    1939   Über die Entwicklung von *Priapulus caudatus* Lam. (Vorläufige Mitteilung). K. fysiogr. Sällsk. Lund Förh. 9:80–87.
    1949   On the morphology of the larva of *Priapulus caudatus* (Lam.). Ark. Zool. 41A, no. 9:1–8.
    1953   Die Entwicklung des Eies von *Priapulus caudatus* Lam. und die systematische Stellung der Priapuliden. Ark. Zool. (n.s.) 5:321–348.

Lüling, K.
  1940   Über die Entwicklung des Urogenitalsystems der Priapuliden. (Ein
          Beitrag zur Anatomie und Histologie dieser Tiere.) Z. wiss. Zool.
          153:136–180.

Meyer, A.
  1928   Die Furchung nebst Eibildung, Reifung und Befruchtung des *Gigan-
          torhynchus gigas*. Ein Beitrag zur Morphologie der Acanthocephalen.
          Zool. Jb. (Anat.) 50:117–218.

Nyholm, K. G.
  1947   Studies in the Echinoderida. Ark. Zool. 39A, no. 14:1–36.

Quatrefages, A. de
  1847   Études sur les types inférieurs de l'embranchement des Annelés. Ann.
          Sci. nat., zool. (Sér. 3) 4:129–184.

Rauther, M.
  1909   Morphologie und Verwandtschaftsbeziehungen der Nematoden und
          einiger ihnen nahe gestellter Vermalien. Ergbn. Zool. 1:491–596.

Remane, A.
  1935–
  1936   Gastrotricha und Kinorhyncha. Bronn's Klassen 4, sect. 2, book 2, pt.
          1:1–385. [1935, Lieferung 1:1–160; 1936, Lieferung 2:161–385.]

Shepot'ev [Schepotieff], A.
  1908   Das Exkretionssystem der Echinorhynchen. Zool. Jb. (Anat.) 26:293–
          304.

19 ◆ The Interrelationships of the Rotatoria

AGNES RUTTNER-KOLISKO

BIOLOGISCHE STATION LUNZ,
ÖSTERREICHISCHE AKADEMIE DER WISSENSCHAFTEN,
LUNZ-AM-SEE, AUSTRIA

I

Within the Aschelminthes the Rotatoria—if one excludes the marine epizoic Seisonida with only one genus and two species—form a well-delineated class. They consist of two orders, the Bdelloidida and the Monogonontida, comprising about two hundred genera, which in general are well defined. Difficulties in the separation of genera arise only in a few instances, where, for generic diagnosis, criteria have been selected that later were revealed as inconstant (*e.g.,* tooth structure in *Lecane* and *Monostyla*—see Edmondson, 1935), but in general the generic distinctions are clear enough.

Whereas generic categories are well defined, variability *within* genera is very great, so that the establishment of clear species boundaries in many—one might almost say in all—cases is extremely difficult. Very frequently this has led to an excessive splitting of genera: for example, about one hundred and fifty species have been established for the genus *Lecane,* and the number of *Cephalodella* species has in recent years risen to almost two hundred. We have here in the zoölogical field conditions similar to those in the plant genera *Hieracium* and *Rubus,* "in which a clear separation of species is impossible (but in which, nevertheless, a tremendous number of 'species' have been described)" (Dobzhansky, 1951, p. 272).

There can be no doubt that in all these cases the splitting is tied up with non-sexual reproduction, a fact to which various authors besides Dobzhansky have referred: "Solche schwierige Gattungen, die eine 'crux et scandalum' darstellen, kommen hauptsächlich bei Formen vor, die sich ungeschlechtlich fortpflanzen" (Baur, quoted by Dobzhansky); "the species as a category which is more or less fixed and therefore less arbitrary than the rest, is lacking in asexual and obligatory self-fertilizing organisms. All the criteria of species distinction break down in such forms." (Dobzhansky, p. 274).

The types of reproduction in the Rotatoria can be summarized as follows: the Bdelloidida multiply by parthenogenesis only, and for them what was said above is valid without reservation. The far more diversified order of the Monogonontida, on the other hand, is characterized by a *heterogonous* mode of reproduction, *i.e.,* there is an alternation between parthenogenetic and sexual multiplication. (Although this is the rule, there are some forms of the Monogonontida in which parthenogenesis is obligatory.) In the amictic phase the individual genetic constitution of one animal is transmitted by diploid parthenogenesis to a whole clone, and not until the next mictic phase, *i.e.,* fertilization by dwarf males produced by haploid parthenogenesis, does an eventual recombination of genes occur, provided the fertilization is not effected by a male from the same clone; in the latter case sexual reproduction means not a recombination, but a gene loss of 50 per cent as in self-fertilization.

It seems particularly important to me to estimate the numeric relation between parthenogenetic and sexual reproduction. From experience with the rearing of different species (Luntz, 1926, 1929; Buchner, 1936; Ruttner-Kolisko, 1938, 1949) one can conclude that a heterogonic rotifer inhabiting a small body of water will live for about ten days, and during this time will, from the third day, produce one young rotifer daily. On this assumption, the number (a) of individuals in the clone on a given day (n) can be expressed by a mathematical series (known as "Gerhardtsche Reihe") as follows:

$$a_n = a_{(n-1)} + a_{(n-2)} - a_{(n-10)}$$

Consequently, in the course of 60 days about 10^{12} individuals can develop from one egg. (In this calculation the normal death rate is taken into consideration, but not death through predation or infection, a subject on which practically no information is available.) In these 60 days the first descendants will have gone through almost 30 generations, the last through only six. This intensive parthenogenetic multiplication is followed by a single sexual reproductive step in which, in a small body of water, the greater part of the population participates.

If one assumes the population density of the chosen species to be 1,000 individuals per liter—a high figure according to the evidence provided by various plankton counts, and one that occurs only at the stage of maximum development before the onset of the sexual period—then a clone arising from one individual (again disregarding premature destruction) would populate a water volume of 1,000,000 cubic meters. This would correspond to a water body about 1 kilometer long, 500 meters wide, and 2 meters deep—quite a respectable small lake.

It is thus possible that small bodies of water may be populated in each vegetative period by the descendants of one individual, or at any rate of no more than a few, and that therefore the likelihood of "self-fertilization" in the sense of a union of a female and a male from one and the same clone is greatly increased. The genetic importance of the fertilization process is correspondingly diminished.

For the inhabitants of the pelagic zones of large lakes the development of a clone must be calculated somewhat differently. These forms can only be reared with difficulty, and very few data on individual biology are available. In general the life cycle is somewhat slower, and the rate of multiplication can be estimated at one egg in 48 hours and the life span at two weeks. The population density for the nth day can accordingly be expressed by:

$$2^{\left(\frac{n}{2}-1\right)} - 2^{\left(\frac{n-14}{2}-1\right)}$$

In 60 days such a population would grow only to a size of about 10^6. The sexual period in most pelagic forms is less pronounced than with the dwellers in small bodies of water; mictic animals and dormant eggs often appear over a longer time, but only sporadically, so that the situation is difficult to evaluate numerically. In my opinion, no predominant genetic importance is to be attributed to sexual reproduction in these cases, where only a small proportion of the population participates in it. In fact, in many pelagic forms it is entirely lacking.

These numerical calculations suggest that the differences that occur within a pelagic population or between the populations of several small biotopes may often be based on nothing more than individual differences. Multiplied in millions of genetically identical animals, these differences may well produce the impression that one is dealing with genetically fixed races or even species; moreover, the selective influence of environment can manifest itself very quickly in the parthenogenetic phase: the smallest advantage that any genetic change brings to the members of one clone must, by reason of the great reproductive rate, quickly lead to a clear predominance of this clone, whereas the compensating process of gene recombination remains limited to a single sexual reproductive step and comes into play only in the next developmental cycle. (In the case of self-fertilization or obligatory parthenogenesis there is no recombination of genes at all.)

It may seem that these are self-evident things, to which no especial reference need be made and which have been made amply clear before (*e.g.*, by Lieder, 1952, for the Cladocera, which shows the same reproductive pattern). The fact is, however, that in papers dealing with rotifer taxonomy one continually finds descriptions of morphological variability in which the categories of race and species are used, while its genetic meaning remains entirely obscure. Moreover, attempts are sometimes made to explain this variability in terms of genetic concepts formulated and valid for the bisexual pattern of reproduction only. The fact that the reproduction of the Rotatoria is largely nonsexual must of necessity lead to a great increase in variability, corresponding to the diversity of environmental factors. The category of "species," based as it is on the fact of a fecund crossing, cannot aptly describe this variability: "a species remains a group of populations which are actually or potentially able to exchange genes" (Dobzhansky, 1951, p. 273).

For such groups of the animal and plant kingdoms, in which the term "species" in the strict sense of the word has no validity, there remain nevertheless the tasks of systematics: to describe diversity, to group, and to name. With these groups it is, however, merely a "question of expediency" (Dobzhansky, 1951) how far the process of systematic arrangement ought to be carried, and I must therefore try to illustrate my views on the limitations of this process in the case of heterogonic rotifer genera by a few examples. I am fully aware that these are the subjective views of an ecologist, for whom inevitably the relation between the conditions of the milieu and morphological characters carries more weight than other systematic criteria. To the ecologist variability as such does not mean a great deal, and the establishment of systematic units on the basis of minute morphological differences only makes ecological work more difficult; not until these differences are correlated with various conditions in the environment do they become meaningful in his eyes.

For the purpose of illustration I am not going to chose the genus *Cephalodella,* which contains the greatest number of "species." Here the situation is so chaotic that it is impossible to sort out from among the current "species" the synonyms, which undoubtedly exist. Often reliable identification is equally difficult. What we need in order to deal with this extremely variable genus is a careful monograph based on cultivation and variation statistics. It would then be possible to decide upon the selection of distinguishing characteristics and the extent of suitable systematic units.

The genus *Polyarthra* (reviewed by Nipkow, 1952), which is present in the plankton of most lakes and small bodies of water, is somewhat easier to evaluate. Until a few years ago this genus was differentiated into only two species, *P. platyptera* (*trigla*) and *P. euryptera,* with clear morphological differences. Intensive statistical work on a rich material and also the description of some deviations have since led to the creation of no fewer than eleven different "species," in some cases connected by intermediate forms, so that today identification has become difficult or even impossible.

For example, the species *P. bicerca* (Wulfert, 1956) was established on the basis of only two specimens found. The distinguishing features: displacement of the ventral bristles onto an abnormally shaped posterior end and an increase in the number of fins in the dorsal bundle (a feature contrasting sharply with the characteristic pattern of the whole genus) suggest, if not faulty observation, at any rate a malformation, which may have affected several members of a clone. (The "species" has, to my knowledge, not been found again.) Since in heterogonous rotifers one must always consider a whole clone to be the genetic equivalent of one individual, it seems to me here, even more than with other groups of animals, that to formulate new descriptions on the basis of a few individuals is a dubious—if not an indefensible—procedure.

For the species *P. proloba* (Wulfert, 1941) the hernial, sac-like ventral protrusion of the mastax is accorded diagnostic status. Observation of numerous *Polyarthra* populations during a whole vegetative cycle has made it apparent, however, that this characteristic is to be regarded as a temporary variation that can appear in different members of the "formenkreis" *dolichoptera-vulgaris* (Ruttner-Kolisko, 1959). A similar gullet-sac form of a *dolichoptera* population was recently described as *P. pseudoproloba* (Albertova, 1960). Both "species" must now be cancelled, since the gullet-sac formation lies within the "reaction norm" (Woltereck, 1920) of various morphologically different *Polyarthra* forms. The surest way to establish the extent of a reaction norm is doubtless the rearing in the laboratory of a genetically homogeneous material. It seems to me therefore essential as far as possible to incorporate cultivation into taxonomic work in order to avoid error and confusion as exemplified by *P. proloba.*

On the basis of extensive, statistically interpreted material Carlin (1943) divided the old species *P. platyptera* into two new species, *P. dolicoptera* and *P. vulgaris,* which in their typical forms are easily distinguished. They are also ecologically different: *P. dolicoptera* being cold-stenothermous with low O_2 requirement, and *P. vulgaris* eurythermous with high O_2 requirement. The two species can live separately without intermediate forms in the same biotope because their sexual period falls at a different time. Pejler (1956, 1957), however, in his thorough examination of waters in Lapland and central Sweden found that small ponds can contain a wide variety of intermediate forms between *P. dolichoptera* and *P. vulgaris*—findings that are fully confirmed by my own in Austrian lakes and pools.

The question now arises whether there is any point in retaining the two "species" despite the intermediate forms, which are difficult to classify. I should say yes, for there is a consistent correspondence between given conditions of the milieu and definite morphological characteristics, which makes it possible to deduce the milieu from the organism and conversely the latter from the milieu. Since the two types are, however, connected by intermediate forms, it seems to me more correct in this case to speak of physiological races (or ecotypes) within the polytypic species *P. platyptera*, or of a rassenkreis of *dolichoptera-vulgaris* (in the sense of Rensch, 1929) in which the extreme members have become completely isolated genetically and can thus inhabit the same biotope next to one another in different ecological niches. The genetic isolation is, moreover, easily explicable by the physiological situation: the sexual period comes about when living conditions have gone past the optimum, *i.e.*, for *vulgaris* in the declining temperature and decreasing O_2 content of the water, and for *dolichoptera* in the rising temperature and increasing O_2 content of the water, so that for the former it is shifted toward the fall, for the latter toward the spring.

There are probably transitions, too, between *P. major* and *P. vulgaris,* but research is still in progress, and it must first be ascertained whether possession of ventral bristle appendages is in fact a constant character. The types described as *longiremis* and *dissimulans* belong most probably to the formenkreis *dolicoptera-vulgaris*. If we adhere to the principle of formulating categories in a useful manner, there finally remain out of the aforementioned eleven "species" of the genus *Polyarthra* after careful scrutiny only the old species *P. euryptera, P. minor,* and the whole formenkreis of the old *P. platyptera* with the well-differentiated physiological races *dolichoptera, vulgaris,* and *major* (?), and any number of intermediate forms between these.

That there are limits to the division that is useful in the presence of great variability is further shown by the example of the genus *Keratella. Keratella quadrata* (formerly *Anuraea aculeata*) is a polytypic species characterized by great fluctuation in the length of the caudal spines. This variability was described by Krätzschmar (1908) from field investigation and cultivation of material from Upper Lunz Lake as a cyclomorphosis—an interpretation that has emerged in many textbooks of general biology. Again with the help of the method of variation statistics applied to a very large material, Carlin (1943) divided *Keratella quadrata* into a great number of subgroups and into several new species, taking into account not only, like Krätzschmar, the length of the caudal spines, but especially the armor pattern of the several forms. On rechecking the situation in Upper Lunz Lake by means of individual cultivation (Ruttner-Kolisko, 1949), I found that there three forms live next to one another in complete genetic isolation, corresponding to Carlin's species *K. hiemalis, K. testudo,* and *K. quadrata* (fig. 19-1). The armor pattern of the three forms is constant, the length of the caudal spines variable; the time of appearance and the type of reproduction are different, likewise their physiological needs.

K. hiemalis is a cold-stenothermous form of a characteristic, scarcely variable shape, which appears in Upper Lunz Lake before and during the breaking up of the ice, multiplies parthenogenetically at a fast rate, produces thick-shelled eggs without fertilization (so-called pseudosexual eggs) at the onset of summer conditions in the water, and subsequently disappears altogether from the plankton. At great depths in Lower Lunz Lake and in others of the larger Alpine lakes the form occurs in small numbers during the entire year, and in this habitat it seems to be obligatorily parthenogenetic and does not seem to form pseudosexual eggs.

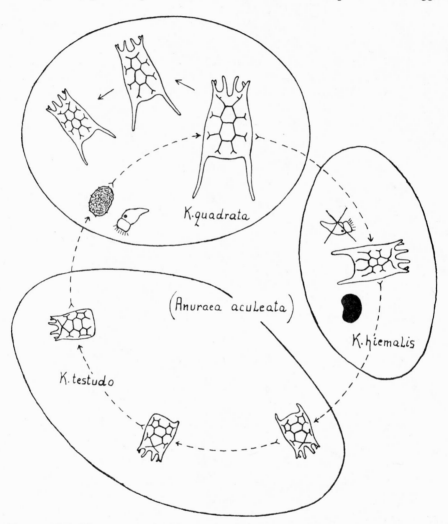

FIGURE 19-1. The pattern of cyclomorphorsis based on cultivation and on observations under natural conditions in Upper Lunz Lake. (After Krätschmar, 1908.)

K. testudo is eurythermous, occurs in Upper Lunz Lake during the whole year, and has no sexual period; size and armor pattern are constant, while the caudal spines vary from a short length to complete reduction.

K. quadrata (in the narrow sense), which is found alternating with *K. hiemalis,* shows—again with a constant armor pattern—the most marked variability in respect of body size and length of caudal spines; in the late fall it has a sexual period, not very marked, though males and dormant eggs are occasionally produced.

In these cases the spread of the reaction norm of a clone was found by individual rearing, and the extent of discontinuity in the variation of the natural populations by statistical analysis. If we compare the results with Carlin's statistics on his Swedish material, we get a picture similar to that of the genus *Polyarthra,* except that the fixation of forms in *Keratella* seems to be somewhat more advanced. No intermediate forms between *K. testudo, K. hiemalis,* and *K. quadrata* are known. For these reasons we may usefully and with justification accept these three forms as separate species.

By contrast, *K. valga* is linked by a number of intermediate forms with the typical *K. quadrata,* but seems to have achieved considerable stability in tropical lakes. The various "series," designated by different names, by means of which variability in the form and size of the caudal spines has been described, belong— as Carlin already has indicated—to the formenkreis *K. quadrata;* nothing is known of their ecological significance.

The rearing of individual clones of *K. quadrata* and the investigation of sexual patterns have thus confirmed Carlin's statistical data and shown that the old pattern of cyclomorphosis was incorrect, and that we have here three well-distinguishable units in complete genetic isolation, one of them polytypic and comprising several physiological races.

With these examples I hope to have shown that our knowledge of the genetic complexity and the relationships within the individual rotifer genera cannot be increased by more or less arbitrary description and naming of morphological peculiarities, and that, on the contrary, such description is apt to lead to confusion. If a genus is little subdivided, the only danger is that organisms may be inadequately defined and identification become imprecise. If, on the other hand, one attempts to cope with diversity by means of detailed subdivision, assertions will apparently be very precise, but in fact are more likely to be incorrect, which, to my mind, is worse than imprecision.

The examples mentioned also make it sufficiently clear, I hope, that there are only two ways of clarifying in each case the significance of certain variations and the relationship between different forms: first, statistical analysis of characteristics in a natural population; and, second, the laboratory cultivation of a genetically identical clone. Consequently, I would suggest the following rules for taxonomic work with heterogonous rotifers (and other predominantly or entirely apogamous groups of animals):

1. New descriptions should never be based on a few individuals, but always on fairly large, uniform populations from different biotopes.

2. These populations should be analysed by variation statistics, so that the constancy of characteristics or their continuous *vs.* discontinuous variation is established.

3. Several cultures derived from single individuals from these populations should, if possible, be reared in order to make clear the width of the "reaction norm" of the individual genetic constitution.

4. In diagnosis the same weight should be attributed to physiological and ecological criteria, and to sexual isolation, as to morphological features.

II

Concerning the relationship of the Rotatoria with other animal groups, and concerning their origin, many opinions have been expressed, and a number of divergent theories have been promulgated. The factual information on which these views are based is, however, relatively small. In simply constructed organisms the distinction between homologous organs, on the one hand, and convergent adaptation, on the other, is particularly difficult, since frequently the various criteria of homology (Remane, 1956) cannot be applied and judgments tend to be formed more or less intuitively. Of the ontogeny of the Rotatoria very little is known, apart from a thorough investigation of *Asplanchna* (Nachtwey, 1925). The evident lack of gastrulation and mesoderm formation points to a primitive type of development and makes a secondary reduction of more highly developed forms (Hyman, 1951) seem unlikely.

The Rotatoria as a class do not lend themselves to phylogenetic speculation, for in many respects they are very specialized. This is understandable in a group of animals whose development has gone—or is going—on in fresh water. Apart from some heterogonic genera, which have secondarily penetrated into sea water of low salinity, only the Seisonidea—a little-known and in every respect deviant order —live in a marine biotope. At present we cannot tell how the ancestors of the Rotatoria may have penetrated into fresh water. It is by no means impossible, however, that the investigation of little-known environments, such as the fresh-water psammon and the transitional biotopes from fresh to marine ground water, may reveal forms (Ruttner-Kolisko, 1955) that would enable us to link up the Rotatoria with marine fauna, a case in point being that of the Gastrotricha (Chaetonotida), which until the discovery of the Macrodasyida occupied a similarly isolated position.

An indication of the specialization of the rotifers is their cell-constancy (eutely). At a fairly early embryonic stage mitosis ceases, and further development is limited to the differentiation of organs without multiplication of cells. There is thus no true post-embryonic growth and no regeneration. One can hardly expect much further evolution from such organisms. Moreover, the predominantly parthenogenetic reproduction leads to fragmentation and further specialization within the lower taxonomic units rather than continued evolutionary development. On the genealogical tree of the animal kingdom the Rotatoria are apparently out on a limb, from which there is nowhere to go.

Among the Aschelminthes living today, the Rotatoria are the most closely connected with the Gastrotricha. Cuticle, syncytium, musculature, nervous system, protonephridia, adhesive glands, and the lack of a celomic covering, all point to a near relationship between the two groups. There is, however, no evidence for the assumption of some authors that the Rotatoria should be directly descended from the Gastrotricha.

That the ancestors of the Rotatoria were benthic creeping forms, worm-like in shape, is generally accepted today; in my opinion, the following features might be regarded as characteristic of this ancestral form: (1) a cuticular outer covering, as well as apical and ventral ciliation; (2) syncytial structure of the hypodermis as well as of most other organs; (3) possession of protonephridia with typical terminal cells and the lack of a true celom with epithelial covering and segmentation; (4) a muscular pharynx; (5) prehensile organs and adhesive glands at the posterior end.

There are two groups of animals with which such an ancestral form might be connected: in the first place the Turbellaria, whose structure is so plastic that most animal lineages might be derived from them; and, second, the simply constructed annelids, which used to be lumped together under the name of Archiannelida. Since, however, reduced forms occur among the latter, the order has been dissolved; its genera have been united with various polychete families. It does not seem to follow necessarily from this, judging from the evidence available, that all simply constructed former annelids must be secondarily simplified.

Of these simply constructed annelids the Dinophilidae bear a striking resemblance to the Rotatoria, and it is among primitive annelids constructed, *e.g.,* like *Diurodrilus*—forms that in their turn might, I think, be traced back to the Turbellaria—that one should look for the ancestral form of the Rotatoria. This to me is a more plausible assumption than to say that all the Aschelminthes are a branch of the animal kingdom derived by secondary reduction from the already segmented annelids (Remane, 1958).

REFERENCES

Albertova, O.
  1960   Eine neue Art der Gattung *Polyarthra*. Mém. Soc. zool. tchécosl. (Věst. česk. zool. Společ.) 24:16–18.

Buchner, H.
  1936   Experimentelle Untersuchungen über den Generationswechsel der Rädertiere. Z. indukt. Abstamm.-u. VererbLehre 72:1–49.

Carlin, B.
  1943   Die Planktonrotatorien des Motalaström. Medd. Lunds. Univ. limnol. Instn. 5:1–255.

Dobzhansky, T.
  1951   Genetics and the Origin of Species. 3rd ed. Columbia Univ., New York.

Edmondson, W.
  1935   Some Rotatoria from Arizona. Trans. Amer. micr. Soc. 54:301–306.

Hyman, L.
  1951   The Invertebrates. Vol. III: Acanthocephala, Aschelminthes and Entoprocta—the Pseudocoelomate Bilateria. McGraw-Hill, New York, Toronto, London.

Krätzschmar, H.
  1908   Über den Polymorphismus von *Anuraea aculeata* (Ehrbg.). Int. Rev. Hydrob. 1:623–675.

Lieder, U.
  1952   Über die kurzfristige Veränderung des Rassencharakters einer *Daphnia longispina* Population. Schweiz. Z. Hydrol. 14:358–365.

Luntz, A.
  1926   Untersuchungen über den Generationswechsel der Rotatorien. I. Die Bedingungen des Generationswechsels. Biolog. Zbl. 46:233–278.

1929   *Idem.* II. Der zyklische Generationswechsel von *Brachionus bakeri. Ibid.*
        49:193–211.

Nachtwey, R.

1925   Untersuchungen über die Keimbahn, Organogenese und Anatomie von
        Asplanchna priodonta Gosse. Z. wiss. Zool. 126:239–492.

Nipkow, F.

1952   Die Gattung *Polyarthra* Ehrenberg im Plankton des Zürichsees und
        einiger anderer Schweizer Seen. Schweiz. Z. Hydrol. 14:135–181.

Pejler, B.

1956   Introgression in planktonic Rotatoria with some points of view on its
        causes and conceivable results. Evolution 10:246–261.

1957   On variation and evolution in planktonic Rotatoria. Zool. Bidr. Uppsala
        32:1–66.

Remane, A.

1956   Die Grundlagen des natürlichen Systems, der Vergleichenden Anatomie
        und der Phylogenetik. Geest und Portig, Leipzig.

1958   Zur Verwandtschaft und Ableitung der niederen Metazoen. Verh. dtsch.
        zool. Ges. (1957) (Zool. Anz., Suppl. 21):179–196.

Rensch, B.

1929   Prinzip der geographischen Rassenkreise. Bornträger, Berlin.

Ruttner-Kolisko, A.

1938   Beiträge zur Lebensgeschichte der Rädertiere auf Grund von Individual-
        zuchten. Arch. Hydrobiol. 33:165–207.

1949   Zum Formwechsel- und Artproblem von *Anuraea aculeata* (*Keratella
        quadrata*). Hydrobiologia 1:425–468.

1955   *Rheomorpha neiswestnovae* und *Marinellina flagellata,* zwei phylogene-
        tisch interessante Wurmtypen aus dem Süsswasserpsammon. Öst. zool.
        Z. 6:55–69.

1959   Über die Populationen der *Polyarthra dolichoptera* Idelson (Rotatoria)
        in den Kapruner Stauseen. Anz. öst. Akad. Wiss. 96:1–6.

Woltereck, R.

1920   Variation und Artbildung. Intern. Rev. 9:1–145.

Wulfert, K.

1941   Einige seltsame Plankton-Rädertiere des Netzschkauer Schachtteiches.
        Z. Nat. Wiss. Sachsen u. Thüringen 95:167–173.

1956   Die Rädertiere des Teufelssees bei Friedrichshagen. Arch. Hydrob.
        51:457–495.

20 ◆ Comparative Morphology in Nemic Phylogeny

ARMAND R. MAGGENTI

DEPARTMENT OF NEMATOLOGY, COLLEGE OF AGRICULTURE,
UNIVERSITY OF CALIFORNIA, DAVIS

In 1945 Simpson wrote: "Phylogeny cannot be observed. It is necessarily an inference from observations that bear on it, sometimes rather distantly, and that can usually be interpreted in more than one way." Certainly this applies to a study of nemic phylogeny where our reasoning is based upon degree of resemblance and subject to confusion by convergence and reversal. Many feel that, because fossil records are lacking, it is of little purpose to indulge in speculation on nemic phylogeny. Nemic taxonomy, however, requires such speculation when it is based upon comparative morphology. Our attempts in taxonomy are really an effort to express phylogenetic relationships. These relationships have developed through time and cannot be understood without extrapolation into the past.

In presenting the modification proposed here, I have largely avoided use of zoöparasitic nemas for which a phylogeny was proposed by Dougherty in 1951. Although these are phylogenetically important, understanding the evolutionary sequence of the so-called "free-living" soil, freshwater, and marine nemas should be attempted first.

Changes in the current concepts are necessary if the classification of the Nemata is to be consistent with the available knowledge of their comparative morphology. The modifications suggested in this paper are based upon studies of the cephalic sensory structures (setae, papillae, and amphids), esophagus (its nuclear arrangement, glands and valves—fig. 20-2, A), esophago-intestinal valve, excretory system (fig. 20-2, B), reproductive system, and total number of intestinal cells. Some use is also made of the stoma, somatic sensory structures, and cuticular specializations.

Rudolphi (1808) proposed a class Helmintha that encompassed five orders, one of which was the Nematoidea. Cobb (1919) proposed that the latter group be recognized as a distinct phylum, Nemates. Chitwood and Chitwood (1950) utilized the concept that these animals represented a phylum, but used the name Nematoda for the phylum designation. Later B. G. Chitwood (1958) proposed a name change for the phylum to Nemata (Rudolphi, 1808) Cobb, 1919. In this same paper two classes were proposed and assigned names derived from ones originated by von Linstow (1905): Adenophorea (syn. Aphasmidia) and Secernentea (syn. Phasmidia). It is the phylogenetic relationships of the orders, families, and genera within this phylum that will be discussed here.

Chitwood and Chitwood (1933) proposed an animal combining features of the Rhabditidae and Plectidae as the hypothetical primitive nema. As a consequence modern representatives of the Rhabditidae and Plectidae were considered as basic to nemic taxonomy and phylogeny (fig. 20-1). It was as a result of my studies of the morphology and biology of the genus *Plectus* that the likelihood of their being basic in the phylogeny of the Monhysterida, let alone nemic phylogeny, was subjected to suspicion. On gross examination the Plectidae and Rhabditidae seem to exhibit a resemblance of morphologic structures. Close examination reveals, however, that their similarity of structure is the result not of homologous development, but of convergent development. The modified concept presented here is still ar-

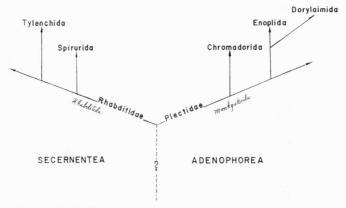

FIGURE 20-1. Current concept of the evolution of the major groups in the phylum Nemata.

ranged so that the orders Monhysterida and Rhabditida are rather closely related and represent the point of the split between the Secernentea and Adenophorea (fig. 20-2). It is not believed that either the Plectidae or Rhabditidae are basic to nemic phylogeny or to the evolution of each order. If these forms were basic, we should be led to the conclusion that the ancestral nemas not only were similar to one or both of these orders, but also resembled these two families. Yet none of the modern groups, on this basis, seem to qualify as a possible ancestor.

Other theories of nemic phylogeny, though less widely accepted, have been proposed: de Coninck and Schuurmans Stekhoven (1933) offered *Areolaimus* for consideration as the modern representative of the primitive nema; Filip'ev (1934) stated that the primitive nema probably was marine and of the group Enoplida; Hyman (1951) agreed that the primitive nema was most likely marine, but suggested that it was probably of the group Chromadorida. These conflicting hypotheses on nemic phylogeny stimulated the present study, which is based on an investigation of the comparative morphology, either in totomounts or serial sections, of all the nematodes included and of many others not specifically mentioned here.

Our concept of the primitive nema must be based on our knowledge of the

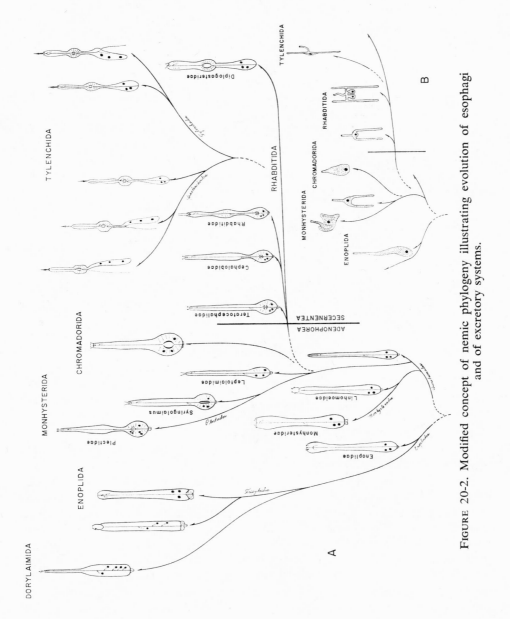

FIGURE 20-2. Modified concept of nemic phylogeny illustrating evolution of esophagi and of excretory systems.

morphology of the present forms. Such a form must include the characters common to all nematodes and to some extent those that are now limited to individual groups. Therefore, certain assumptions can be made. It had an integument, likely non-striated. The oral opening was probably surrounded by six simple lips, the cephalic sensory structures must have consisted of six circumoral setiform papillae and two post-labial whorls of six and four setiform papillae respectively and two post-labial amphids, non-spiral and not pore-like. The stoma was possibly open, cylindrical and unarmed, with the orifices of the esophageal glands opening into or near it. The esophagus was likely to have been of one part, non-valvated and muscular with esophageal glands enclosed posteriorly. The esophago-intestinal valve probably had a triradiate lumen. Little speculation can be made concerning the remainder of the alimentary canal except that it probably consisted of relatively many cells and possibly had a bacillary layer. The female gonads were didelphic and amphidelphic, and outstretched with the equatorial vulva opening separately from the alimentary canal. The male probably had two testes, opposed and uniting with the rectum to form a cloaca with two spicules and a gubernaculum. There was possibly a single ventral row of supplementary tubuli and also genital tactile papillae coincident with this system. The excretory system was almost certainly a single cell connected with a ventral excretory pore. Caudal glands and spinneret were present. The presence of two sublateral rows of hypodermal glands and possession of pigment spots and ocelli should be considered. These characters are commonly put forward for the primitive nema (Chitwood and Chitwood, 1933) with the exception of the one part, non-valved posterior bulb of the esophagus.

Some representatives of the Enoploidea (Leptosomatidae) come closest to resembling such an animal. The Enoplida are also for the most part marine, therefore consistent with the concept of the origin of life in the sea. The general opinion has been that nemas did arise in the shallow intertidal zones of an oceanic habitat. The concept that the primitive nema was of the Rhabditidae-Plectidae type does not conform well with this idea. This is because in both of these families marine forms are rare.

The first major division in the Nemata probably was the segregation of the order Enoplida. At present the Enoplida are divided into the Enoploidea and Tripyloidea and as a group maintain many characters considered to be primitive. Reviewing the primitive characters we note that they generally exhibit a non-striated integument that, as far as we know, lacks lateral longitudinal alae. The males commonly have a series of preanal supplements in a single ventral row. The esophagus is one part non-valvated and shows a random placement of both marginal and radial nuclei; that is, they are not congregated anteriorly and posteriorly. The esophageal glands open anteriorly in the region of the stoma—at least, in the Enoploidea. The Enoplida have, with few exceptions, a polycytic intestine (256 or more cells). The somatic musculature usually exhibits a polymyarian condition. Normally they possess caudal glands and a spinneret. The excretory system is a single cell opening through a ventral pore.

Some characters that are considered non-primitive are also represented. The amphids are post-labial but relatively anteriorly placed; usually they are found in the region where the lips join the body. The females usually have short didelphic amphidelphic gonads with few developing oöcytes, and they are reflexed.

The Dorylaimida may have had their origin from forms near the Ironidae of

Tripyloidea because the internal morphology of the esophagus shows the same type of cuticular thickenings for muscle attachments. This relationship of Dorylaimida is substantiated, at least in part, by what we know occurs in the production of stomatal teeth of the tripyloid *Ironus*. An adult *Ironus* has a well-armed stoma, and the ontogenetic development of these teeth is in the nearby tissue of the esophagus. As the larva progresses in age the developing teeth migrate forward until at the time of molting they are positioned in the stomatal wall. This same migration of the stomatal armature, though more pronounced, can be observed in the development of the spear of the Dorylaimidae. The Dorylaimoidea are rare in oceanic habitats; the great majority are found in a terrestrial habitat.

Within the Monhysterida there are forms reminiscent of the Enoplida. An example of such a form is the genus *Sphaerolaimus* (Monhysterida: Linhomoeidae). In this genus the lip region, stoma, esophagus, and cephalic sensory setae are very similar to those of some Enoplida. Cross sections of the esophagus show the same type of cuticular thickenings for muscle attachments as is found in some of the Tripyloidea of the Enoplida. The lumen of the esophago-intestinal valve is, however, dorso-ventrally flattened. The nuclear arrangement of the esophagus is unknown.

The Monhysterida are not a homogeneous group. This is mainly because the order contains forms representing the various stages in the development of the three-part esophagus from a one-part. The order Monhysterida has been separated into three superfamilies: Plectoidea, Axonolaimoidea, and Monhysteroidea. A change in the accepted concept of the superfamily arrangements is necessitated within the Monhysterida in order to bring those forms most closely resembling the concept of the primitive Monhysterida into a basic position. Thus, the superfamily Axonolaimoidea (subfamily Cylindrolaiminae) becomes closer to a likely basic form, and the superfamily Plectoidea, previously considered basic, assumes the position of the most advanced group in the Monhysterida.

It seems that segregation occurred early, and that the Monhysteroidea and Axonolaimoidea developed almost coincidentally. Both have characters considered basic or primitive, and at this time they should be considered of equal primitiveness. The Monhysteroidea are here treated as a separate line of development and the Axonolaimoidea as that part of the Monhysterida more likely to be basic to the remaining Nemata.

The significant primitive characters of the Monhysteroidea are the oligocytic nature of the intestine (26–128 cells) and the convergent ends of the esophageal radii. The form of the esophagus and the long outstretched ovary make it difficult to conceive of these forms as basic to Nemata. The Axonolaimoidea have numerous characters illustrating a relationship to the Plectoidea as well as to the order Chromadorida and the class Secernentea. The tuboid ending of the esophageal radii is a feature common to the Axonolaimoidea and Plectoidea and to the Rhabditida of the Secernentea. Some representatives of the Axonolaimidae also exhibit an almost one-part esophagus with the first set of nuclei in the esophagus being the marginals. In addition the radial nuclei tend to aggregate anteriorly and posteriorly. These are significant points and are important to the development of the two- and three-part esophagus. Such a feature prepares the way for the division of labor of parts of the esophagus. This pre-adaptation, through natural selection, could finally give rise to the three-part esophagus.

The female gonads of the Axonolaimidae differ somewhat from those of the remaining Nemata, but form a foundation consistent with the development noted in the remainder of the phylum. The gonads of the Axonolaimoidea are outstretched and have a very shortened area for oöcyte development, generally only 20–25 oöcytes in each ovary. The Plectoidea have a reflexed ovary, very short and club-shaped, very similar to the type found in the Chromadorida and Enoplida. In these there are generally less than 20 developing oöcytes. The Monhysteroidea have the long, outstretched ovary with a greatly lengthened area of oöcyte development containing many more than 25 oöcytes. Most of the Secernentea also have the elongated gonads, but these may or may not be reflexed. In this type of gonad there may be more than a hundred developing oöcytes.

The Plectidae probably represent the most advanced Monhysterida and exemplify the highest development of the three-part esophagus in this order. The groups mentioned above consist for the most part of marine forms, whereas the Plectidae with a well-developed three-part esophagus are mainly terrestrial. Therefore it seems possible that this development is correlated with the invasion of the terrestrial habitat.

The family Leptolaimidae can be placed somewhere between the Axonolaimidae (Cylindrolaiminae) and the Plectidae. The ontogeny of *Plectus parietinus* lends evidence to the development of the three-part esophagus from a two-part esophagus. The first larval stage of *P. parietinus* has a very weakly developed two-part esophagus (Maggenti, 1961). The posterior portion of the esophagus shows only a slight swelling, which contains a simple valve. The gross appearance of this larval esophagus is very similar to that found in the adults of *Leptolaimus*. The valve of the posterior bulb is entirely different from that which is found in the adult. In the first larval stage of *Plectus parietinus* the valve consists merely of three longitudinal plates. These plates amount to little more than a thickening of the cuticular lining of the posterior bulb and are constructed much the same as the valve of *Syringolaimus* and *Rhabdolaimus*.

In the later larval stages and adult, the valve differs from that found in the first stage larvae in having a complex triradiate valve. In later larvae and adults each radial arm of the valve is, in cross section, triangular; longitudinally, each arm is arched so that it is narrowest anteriorly and widest posteriorly (fig. 20-3,A). The whole structure can be considered a reservoir, and it functions as a bellows. The expansion of this reservoir, with the corresponding closure of the lumen in the posterior portion of the bulb, acts to draw in food (fig. 20-3,B). Contraction of the reservoir, with the coincident dilatation of the esophageal lumen in the posterior portion of the bulb, forces food out posteriorly and into the intestine (fig. 20-3,C). Dilatation of the valve (reservoir) is owing to muscular contraction; the collapsing of the reservoir is coincident with muscle relaxation.

The construction and operation of the valve in the Plectidae is different from that found in the Rhabditida (Secernentea). This is one of the evidences supporting the hypothesis that the similarity of these animals is due to convergent development. In the Rhabditida the lumen of the posterior bulb expands to a trilobed reservoir; into this reservoir project three muscular lobes (fig. 20-3,D,E). The face of each lobe is lined with cuticle. The action of this valve involves more than the dilatation and contraction of a reservoir. Muscular contraction rotates the three lobes posteriorly, thus drawing food into the reservoir formed in the lumen pos-

PLECTIDAE

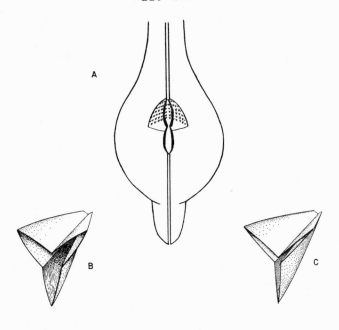

RHABDITIDAE

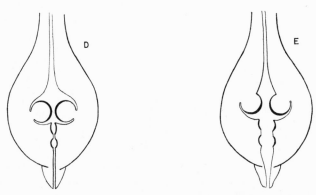

FIGURE 20-3. Diagrammatic illustrations, action of valve in the posterior bulbs of Plectidae (A-C) and Rhabditidae (D-E): A, posterior bulb and valve, adult Plectidae; B, contracted, valve reservoir open; C, at rest, valve reservoir collapsed; D, at rest; E, contracted. (D-E after Chitwood and Chitwood, 1950.)

terior to the lobes. Muscle relaxation permits the movement of the lobes to be reversed, and this collapses the reservoir and forces food posteriorly into the intestine.

Other evidences of convergent rather than homologous development are: the marginal nuclei are the most anterior in the esophagus of the Plectidae, and the esophago-intestinal valve is dorso-ventrally flattened. In the Rhabditidae the radial nuclei are the most anterior set, and the esophago-intestinal valve is triradiate.

It appears that the Chromadorida as well as the Secernentea have their origin in closely related forms of the Monhysterida. In both of these groups the radial nuclei of the esophagus are the most anterior set and both groups have the triradiate esophago-intestinal valve. The Secernentea seem to have undergone their main development terrestrially, whereas the majority of the Monhysterida and Chromadorida occupy a marine habitat. The tremendous array of niches that are available in terrestrial habitats can account for the Secernentea's diverse morphologic development.

Within the Chromadorida the line of development seems to be two-directional: the Chromadoroidea represent one line; the Desmodoroidea and Desmoscolecoidea, the other. It is within the Chromadoroidea that one finds forms most reminiscent of the Monhysterida. This is especially true of the family Microlaimidae.

The characters exhibited by the Monhysterida are important to our understanding the subsequent class and ordinal divisions. The Secernentea probably developed out of the Monhysterida; characters common to the two groups support a phylogenetic relationship. A significant character that is unknown except in the esophagus of the Axonolaimoidea, Plectoidea, and Secernentea is the radial tubuli on the arms of the lumen of the corpus. Other common features are the transverse annulation on the integument commonly interrupted by lateral longitudinal alae. Certain features of the divergence of these two groups are strikingly apparent: the loss of caudal glands and the coincident acquisition of phasmids. It is unfortunate that more is not known concerning the histology and function of these structures. The cephalization of the sensory structures onto the lips is significant. It is a rare exception in the Secernentea that does not have the full complement of 16 papillae (or their remnants) and the two amphids on the lips.

The triradiate esophago-intestinal valve is a common feature of the Secernentea. The dorso-ventrally flattened valve, however, does occur in the Spirurida and Camallanida. The triradiate valve is also common to the Chromadorida (Adenophorea) and is general in the Enoplida. The Spirurida have a two-part esophagus and both forms of the esophago-intestinal valve. In this order as well as the Camallanida, however, all known forms are parasitic, and therefore these features may be not primitive, but rather the result of a secondary development.

Within the Secernentea the pattern of esophageal development is more nearly complete than in the Adenophorea. A logical serial development can be reconstructed from the modern forms of the Rhabditida and Tylenchida. The same is also true of the excretory system (fig. 20-2,B). Such a scheme, however, does involve certain changes in the accepted concept of family positions. In the organization of the order Rhabditida the family Rhabditidae has been considered basic, and we should, if this were true, be able to link it with the Adenophorea. The Teratocephalidae should really assume this position, for they exhibit more characters in common with the Monhysterida than any other secernenteans. Members of the genus *Euteratocephalus* have post-labial, circular amphids, and cephalic setae, and the males have a ventromedian tubular supplement as in the Monhysterida. The esophagus is two-part with little or no evidence of an isthmus. At present nothing is known of the excretory system of this genus or family. In the family Cephalobidae, however, to which the Teratocephalidae are closely related, the excretory system is described (Chitwood, 1950) and seems to be the simplest of the secernentean types. The construction of this system is: from the ventral excretory pore there is an excretory tube leading to the ventral sinus cell, and from this cell extend two posteriorly directed lateral longitudinal collecting tubules (fig. 20-2,B). The gonads of the Teratocephalidae have the structure common to the Adenophorea. The gonads are short, contain less than 20 developing oöcytes, and are reflexed at the junction of the oviduct and ovary. This is in contrast to the majority of the Secernentea, wherein usually the ovaries are long, commonly with 100 or more developing oöcytes, outstretched, and "reflexures" occur anywhere along the area of oöcyte development.

The Rhabditidae should be considered more advanced than the Teratocephalidae and Cephalobidae because they not only have the well-developed three-part esophagus but they also show an advancement of the excretory system and in some forms evidence of the formation of the median bulb in the posterior region of the corpus. The rhabditid excretory system has two anteriorly directed lateral longitudinal collecting tubules in addition to the posterior pair (fig. 20-2,B). It seems that the diplogasterid group separated from the Rhabditida and possibly should be considered as a distinct line of development. Genera now being considered as likely transitional forms are: *Pseudodiplogasteroides, Diplogasteroides,* and *Pseudodiplogaster.*

In the diplogasterids the anterior portion of the esophagus (corpus) is very muscular with a rather well-developed median bulb that is valved, behind which is a glandular terminal bulb. An example of this esophagus is found in the genus *Diplogaster.* Also within this family are the genera *Tylopharynx* and *Neodiplogaster,* which seem to be a logical step toward the Tylenchida. *Tylopharynx* shows possible evidence of a primitive stomatal stylet as well as the tylenchid-like esophagus. The next step is the typical tylenchid esophagus with the corpus, valved median bulb, isthmus, and a glandular posterior bulb (fig. 20-2,A). Modifications of this occur in some tylenchoids, where the glands increase in size and overlap the anterior portion of the intestine. The excretory system of the Tylenchida is restricted to one side of the body, but still with the anterior and posterior collecting tubules; that is, a unilateral reduction of the rhabditid type (fig. 20-2,B). The excretory system of *Tylopharynx* and *Neodiplogaster* has not been described.

From the similarity of esophagi it seems that the Aphelenchoidea developed from very near the family Tylenchideae; but they also show affinities to the diplogasterids. They differ from the Tylenchoidea in that the orifices of all the esophageal glands open posteriorly. The dorsal gland opens just anterior to the valve in the median bulb and the subventral glands open posterior to it. A possible phylogenetic sequence of the aphelenchoid esophagus is illustrated (fig. 20-2,A) by three modern genera: *Paraphelenchus, Aphelenchus,* and *Aphelenchoides* respectively. *Paraphelenchus* is basic because the esophagus is without overlapping glands; one species retains the remnant of caudal alae, genital tactile papillae, and a gubernaculum associated with the spicules and is thus reminiscent of the Diplogasteridae. These are considered basic even though most of the species lack caudal alae and retain only genital tactile papillae and a gubernaculum. The loss of caudal alae probably represents a secondary modification. The species of the genus *Aphelenchus* have well-developed caudal alae containing genital papillae and a gubernaculum associated with the spicules. In my opinion, however, the overlapping esophageal glands and the retention of the isthmus place it in an intermediate position in this group. *Aphelenchoides* is considered the most advanced of these because it has genital papillae and no gubernaculum, and the esophagus has overlapping glands and has lost the isthmus.

The modifications that have been proposed here for nemic phylogeny certainly do not represent the final answers. Yet they open the door to many complex questions. At present we are attempting to clarify as many cases of convergence as possible through a study of the histologic morphology of the various groups within the Nemata.

The implications of the valvular apparatus in the posterior bulb of the Plectidae and Rhabditidae offer a striking example of how a common feature, when more fully understood, can change our concepts of classification. It is also obvious that we need more knowledge of the comparative morphology of the Monhysterida and Enoplida. If and when such information becomes available, we may be able to sort secondary developments from primitiveness. It is only when we can make these decisions with some authority that we shall be able to approach an even closer understanding of nemic phylogeny.

REFERENCES

Chitwood, B. G.
    1958   The designation of official names for higher taxa of invertebrates. Bull. zool. Nom. 15:860–895.
Chitwood, B. G., and M. B. Chitwood
    1933   The characters of a protonematode. J. Parasit. 20:130.
    1950   An Introduction to Nematology. Sec. 1, Anatomy. Rev. ed. Monumental Press, Baltimore.
Coninck, L. A. de, and J. H. Schuurmans Stekhoven, Jr.
    1933   The free-living marine nemas of the Belgian coast. II. With general remarks on the structure and the system of nemas. Mém. Mus. Hist. nat. Belg. 58:1–163.
Dougherty, E. C.
    1951   Evolution of zooparasitic groups in the phylum Nematoda, with special reference to host distribution. J. Parasit. 37:353–378.
Filip'ev [Filipjev], I. N.
    1934   The classification of the free-living nematodes and their relation to the parasitic nematodes. Smithson. misc. Coll. 89, no. 6:1–63.
Hyman, L. H.
    1951   The Invertebrates. Vol. III: Acanthocephala, Aschelminthes and Entoprocta—the Pseudocoelomate Bilateria. McGraw-Hill, New York, Toronto, London.
Maggenti, A. R.
    1961   Morphology and biology of the genus *Plectus*. Proc. helm. Soc. Wash. 28:118–130.
Simpson, G. G.
    1945   The principles of classification and a classification of mammals. Bull. Amer. Mus. nat. Hist. 85:1–350.

21 ◈ Morphological, Biological, and Ecological Considerations in the Phylogeny of Parasitic Nematodes

GÜNTHER OSCHE

ZOOLOGISCHES INSTITUT,
UNIVERSITÄT ERLANGEN-NÜRNBERG, ERLANGEN

Exact insights into the phylogeny of the lower Metazoa are exceedingly difficult to realize because, for many groups, fossil material is either completely lacking or occurs so rarely that it is of little use. This is especially true for parasites generally and, above all, for endoparasites. Phylogenetic studies must consequently be based on recent material in the hope that recognizably primitive conditions have been retained or are recapitulated in ontogeny. In addition to morphological criteria one may, especially with parasites, draw on biological (life-cycle) and ecological (host-parasite-relationship) data in order to reconstruct a picture of the evolution of a group. For example, ecological situations in the larval development of present-day forms may sometimes quite clearly recapitulate primitive conditions.

In the present text three complexes of questions concerning the evolution of parasitic nematodes are treated, each with several examples:

1. How have transitions from free-living forms to parasitic ones occurred, which have been the stem groups, and what biological-ecological situations have brought the transitions about (preadaptation to parasitism)?

2. What different adaptational steps (types of parasitism) can be recognized, and which ones seem to be owing to convergence?

3. Is a "parallel evolution" of certain parasitic groups and their hosts confirmable, and what ideas can be derived therefrom as to the age of monophyletic parasitic groups?

Finally, in a general way, the evolution of the Ascaridoidea is taken as representing that of a widespread group of parasitic nematodes.

The author wishes to express his deep gratitude to Dr. Ellsworth C. Dougherty for his painstaking and authoritative translation of the original German manuscript.

The Origin of Parasitism in the Nematoda

For the origin of parasitism the nematodes furnish a favorable material for study on two accounts:

1. In addition to a significant number of more or less highly specialized parasitic groups we find an enormous range of free-living forms in practically every imaginable biotope—a circumstance in which the Nematoda differ strikingly from other definitively parasitic helminths (Cestoda, Trematoda, Acanthocephala).

2. Parasitism in the Nematoda is of polyphyletic origin—that is, free-living groups have at different times in terrestrial history given rise to parasitic branches independently of one another so that varyingly old "waves of parasitism" can be distinguished. By consequence, contemporary adaptations to parasitism are represented by taxa ranging greatly in size and presumptive age. Phylogenetically rather recent parasitic groups can be used with reasonable caution as *models* aimed at the reconstruction of primitive conditions in modified parasites.

A glance at the natural classification of the Nematoda (see Chitwood, 1937, 1950—also, here, fig. 21-1) shows that parasitic groups are very unequally divided between two "classes" Phasmidea and Aphasmidea (more recently renamed Secernentea and Adenophorea). Whereas in the Phasmidea, whose free-living members live principally under terrestrial conditions or in fresh water (practically never marine), all rather large systematic categories have given rise to, or constitute, parasitic groups, which are disseminated over a wide host range, the Aphasmidea, in which most of the free-living species are marine or fresh-water-inhabiting, include comparatively few parasitic groups. It seems that the terrestrial nematodes (Phasmidea) have therefore had far greater chance to make transitions to parasitism, as Dougherty (1951) has already remarked.

Among terrestrial biochores the *saprobiotic substrate* is outstanding (whether carrion, decaying plant material, feces, etc.) and provides conditions under which free-living nematodes can live in masses (Völk, 1950; Sachs, 1950; Weingärtner, 1953). For these organisms such conditions have obviously proved preadaptive (Osche, 1956) to the parasitic way of life. Saprobiotic substrates manifest a series of peculiarities—such as variable oxygen tension, strong osmotic fluctuations (Osche, 1952), high temperatures brought about by bacterial activity, and other features to which the nematode must be tolerant and which in many ways (one thinks, for example, of anaërobiosis) provide important prerequisites for parasitism. Moreover, for the most part saprobiotic substrates represent ephemeral biochores only, which are threatened constantly with desiccation and, especially, with the exhaustion of the material undergoing decay. Since such environments are frequently far apart and for relatively small worms (1–3 mm. long) rather difficult to reach unaided, there is the ever recurring problem of transport to suitable new substrates. To meet this problem the saprobiotic nematodes have typically responded with certain adaptations. Thus they produce, relative to other (for example, aquatic) free-living forms, considerable numbers of eggs in order to compensate for the vicissitudes of distribution—a favorable condition again for parasitism. Moreover, they form, when the substrate is exhausted, an extraordinarily

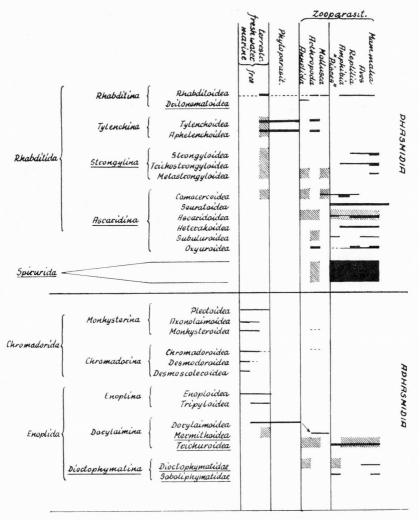

FIGURE 21-1. Distribution of the larger groups of nematodes (taxonomy according to Chitwood, 1950, with certain revisions).

SOLID BLACK = Typical distribution—for parasites, either definitive or exclusive host

DOTTED LINE = Rare occurrence

SHADED = Distribution of larval forms (free-living or in intermediate host) or of free-living stages of parasites otherwise

Exclusively parasitic groups are underlined

resistant larval stage, the "dauerlarva," which in the Rhabditoidea is always the third larval stage (third-stage larva) (Maupas, 1899). These larvae can live for months at a time without nourishment and develop only if favorable conditions resume, then passing through the further two molts required to reach the adult stage. Finally, with most saprobiotes these dauerlarvae, in order to be transported to fresh substrate, assume contact with other animals (mostly insects) whether attached to legs, under the wings, or in the genital segment—an occurrence that is also known for many mites and other animals and is designated *phoresis*. The third-stage larva of certain Rhabditoidea, free-living as adults, behaves in a special manner by which contact with the transport animal is facilitated. With the greater part of its body it waves over the substrate; significantly, such pendulous movements are characteristic of appropriate stages in the life history of certain unequivocal parasites (*viz., Strongyloides*—*cf*. Osche, 1952, 1954).

Assumption of contact with another animal is an important condition for the establishment of parasitism, in particular, by many *insect-parasitic nematodes*. Indeed, among certain of the latter, examples of all stages of transition from free life to parasitism are in clear evidence (Bovien, 1937; Stammer, 1955; Rühm, 1954; Wachek, 1955). Presumably as an early step there evolves a characteristic bond whereby certain insect species are preëmpted as transport-hosts (carriers)— a condition especially likely to arise if a potential transport-host or larval stage thereof has formed a specific association with a certain saprobiotic substrate. For example, there is a diplogasterid that develops only at a critical stage if it can associate itself with the egg cluster of the beetle *Geotrupes,* its transport-host (Sachs, 1950). Further striking examples are provided by a series of xylophagous beetles (Ipidae, Cerambycidae, Lucanidae) whose activities produce a decayed humus that is inhabited by sundry nematodes; the spread of the latter depends upon their having developed various kinds of intimate states with these insects (Fuchs, Rühm, Körner). The association of dauerlarva with transport-host can be so specific that the larva penetrates the hindgut, the tracheae, or even the body cavity and thus is particularly protected from desiccation. Under these circumstances larvae of most species take no nourishment from the transport-host. But in some instances the transition to larval parasitism must be reckoned as completed even in this respect. Thus Rühm has been able to demonstrate this degree of exploitation especially clearly with *Parasitorhabditis* species associated with Ipidae. The third-stage larvae of many of these species penetrate from the hindgut into the Malpighian tubules or into the body cavity, acquire nourishment there, developing further to the fourth stage, and only quit the beetle in order to complete development in the humus. Here is surely unequivocal parasitism, if only for a short stretch of larval development (Rühm speaks of "semi-parasites"). Finally, Körner (1954) has even been able to show *Rhabditis insectivora* behaving as an adult parasite in the larvae of *Dorcus parallelopipedus* (wood-dweller). This nematode species, which is *unable* to develop in the corroded frass produced by the beetle larvae, *can* become adult in the body cavity of the beetle larvae and can reproduce there. As the third-stage larva it can be carried by the beetle. Despite this specialization, I have had *Rhabditis insectivora,* which has hitherto been found in nature only with *Dorcus parallelopipedus,* in culture for years on animal excrement. Hence, this nematode can still live on a substrate that represents the normal environment for many related *Rhabditis* species.

Besides the Rhabditoidea there occur within the Phasmidea, in particular among the Tylenchina, numerous insect-parasites, which are to be further mentioned later on.

Next we can take up the *parasites of vertebrates* that stem on morphological grounds from rhabditoid-like saprobiotes—partly, in fact, belonging systematically within the Rhabditoidea (families Rhabdiasidae, Strongyloididae), but partly constituting independent taxa as currently classified. In the latter category falls the purely parasitic suborder Strongylina for which unequivocal relationships to free-living saprobiotes of rhabditoid type are still clear, both in the "strongyline-bursa" of the male and in the stoma and esophagus of the larva (developmental recapitulation). Moreover, the biology of many derived parasitic groups of the Rhabditida shows especially clear traces of a former saprobiotic life pattern, whether it be the regular occurrence of saprozoic generations (Rhabdiasidae, Strongyloididae) or saprozoic life of the first- to third-stage larvae (as with many Strongylina and such primitive Ascaridina as some Cosmocercoidea). Furthermore, it is a fact that both in the free-living Rhabditoidea and in the vertebrate-parasites of *all* Phasmidea the third-stage larva always assumes the stage of contact with the definitive host—a meaningful biological correlation that Maupas (1899) long ago recognized and Chabaud (1955) has illustrated in detail with a large quantity of material.

Therefore, it seems certain that these vertebrate parasites also sprang from saprobiotes; even so, "models" demonstrating this initial contact are extraordinarily rare. A close relation between nematode larva and vertebrate similar to phoresis in insects is known only for *Rhabditis strongyloides*. The latter, which up until recently had been found as a saprobiote only occasionally and relatively rarely in ulcers of domestic animals (dogs, cattle, horses, etc.—Chitwood, 1932, etc.), frequently lives its larval stages in Muridae (Rodentia) according to our investigations. We have been able to demonstrate it in *Mus musculus* (6.1 per cent of studied specimens), *Apodemus sylvaticus* and *flavicollis* (26 per cent), *Clethrionomys glareolus* (68 per cent), *Microtus arvalis* (73 per cent), and *Microtus agrestis* (83 per cent) (Stammer, 1956); thus it has been found far more frequently than many typical parasites. Invariably we have only been able to find larvae—for the Murinae in subcutaneous connective tissue and in the eye under the lids (the larvae usually very numerous), but for the Microtinae solely in the latter location. After the death of the mice the larvae for the most part bore actively out of the skin or quit the eyes, and, as soon as they are out of the host, develop on saprobiotic substrates (*e.g.*, animal feces) to adulthood. Thus I have had strains successfully in culture now for more than five years without the nematodes at any time being able to effect further contact with mice. Furthermore, *Rhabditis strongyloides* reveals itself as extraordinarily resistant to desiccation. Month-long dust-dry substrates yield blooming cultures again after the addition of suitable fresh substrate. *R. strongyloides* is thus a saprobiote that regularly (!), yet facultatively, assumes contact with mammals during the larval stage, penetrating at times actively through the skin ("percutaneous infection," as is typical for a number of fully evolved parasites such as *Rhabdias, Strongyloides,* and many of the Strongylina), but not developing further there. This species possesses a series of preadaptations to parasitism and can serve as a model for the first steps of the transition by free-living saprobiotes to vertebrate parasitism "in the range of tolerance within the realm of facultative forms" (Osche, 1956).

Outside the Rhabditoidea there are to be found in the Tylenchina a series of *insect-parasites* that similarly illustrate the transition of free-living forms to parasitism. Developmentally the Tylenchina also go back to a *Rhabditis*-like condition, but have evolved a phytoparasitism that has resulted in the transformation of the stoma into a stylet. As a "detour" in plant-predation and parasitism, many tylenchs have obviously come into contact with insects, phytophagous or otherwise associated with plants, and have exploited the insects as transport hosts (phoresis) initially in a manner reminiscent of rhabditoid use of the insects that frequent the saprobiotic environment. In both superfamilies of the Tylenchina—the Aphelenchoidea and Tylenchoidea—transition to parasitism in insects has taken place at different times and independently of one another, whereby all stages of phoresis—from parasitism by larva to that by adult (just as in the Rhabditoidea as already described)—are still to be observed today (Rühm, 1954, 1956; Wachek, 1955).

The Aphasmidea, with their relatively few parasitic groups, provide, as regards the question of interest here, no material for the first phases of the transition to parasitism since all transitional forms and models are lacking.

All aphasmidean groups (Trichuroidea, Dioctophymatina) parasitizing vertebrates are very highly specialized forms that provide no unambiguous connections with their free-living (now marine or fresh-water) relatives. Their parasitism seems to be phylogenetically old. The fact that younger parasitic transitions and thereby "models" are not to be found in the Aphasmidea is further an indication that it was, and presumably remains, much more difficult for aquatic free-living nematodes to proliferate parasitic lines. In fact, all the preadaptations already mentioned for terrestrial saprobiotes are fulfilled only to a trivial degree or not at all in open water. Thus for marine groups in particular there is lacking, among other things, a stage corresponding to that of the dauerlarva in saprobiotes, nor do they have associations comparable to phoresis. Although occasional marine and aquatic nematodes have been found in the gill chambers of crustaceans (summarized by Chitwood, 1935; also Osche, 1955), the relationships here are different, since these nematodes, to be reckoned as commensals (several of the Monhysteroidea and Chromadoroidea), are not transported as larvae, but pass their entire cycle in the confines of the gill chamber and, moreover, take no nourishment from the transport host. They seem to exploit only the sheltering space provided by the crustaceans and to draw on the steady supply of circulating water (respiration) and the nourishment sucked in along with the water.

Only the Mermithoidea, the sole parasitic aphasmideans that live exclusively in invertebrates, still permit recognition of certain relationships to free-living relatives —the dorylaims. To a conspicuous extent the latter are for the most part terrestrial forms that, like the Tylenchina, are phytoparasites (with a stylet-bearing stoma as a convergent development); perhaps by a "detour" through phytoparasitism, comparable to that of insect-parasitizing tylenchs, have arisen the Mermithoidea, which are limited to the insects and molluscs. Interestingly, in biology the mermithids (Aphasmidea) and tylenchs (Phasmidea) show surprising convergences, which deserve consideration in the following section.

Adaptational Steps to Parasitism ("Types" of Parasitism) in the Nematoda

In an animal group that, as the Nematoda, has repeatedly branched, even within rather small groups, into lineages parasitizing different host taxa with various life patterns, an especially interesting question is the elucidation of the various forms of adaptation to parasitism achieved by these organisms. Alongside a series of homologies resulting from the close relationship of the various parasites, convergences that are due to similar conditions of selection can also be found here— thereby affording further insights into various biological and ecological conditions.

In general, with free-living nematodes a basic organization already prevails that needs little morphological modification to make possible a parasitic existence. This explains the fact that the greater part of parasitic nematodes seem to be relatively little modified by parasitism, so that Chabaud and Campana have been able to write: "les Nématodes de Vertébrés conservent le plus souvent une anatomie qui ne diffère pas profondément de celle des Nématodes libres." This is equally true for a large part of the forms parasitizing invertebrates. It is otherwise with the *biology* of parasitic nematodes. Here one finds a series of adaptations, partly convergent, particularly arising out of the life cycle and the kind of infection of the definitive host. Several "adaptational types" can be summarized.

1. In particular, in the *Phasmidea parasitic in vertebrates* certain trends in the developmental cycle can be recognized for whose clear definition we are endebted to Baer (1952) and especially Chabaud (1955). There exists in these groups the tendency to diminish the free-living larval stages to an extent roughly proportionate to an increase in evolutionary level, whether by maintaining a part of the larval development within the protection of the eggshell (one or two larval molts in the egg) or by interposition of an intermediate host in which development likewise goes only as far as the third-stage larva. The manner of restriction of the free larval stages depends upon the ecology and biology of the host group in question. As a rule fresh-water or marine hosts must cope, as also must carnivorous, with an intermediate host; herbivorous host-groups by contrast more typically become infected by eggs. In this respect the different parasitic groups of the Phasmidea have taken identical paths many times quite independently, convergence repeatedly resulting. Thus we know within *one* group—for example, the Strongylina—not only forms whose first- to third-stage larvae live saprozoically, but others that pass a part of their larval development in the egg or use an intermediate host. Molts in the confines of the eggshell occur also in the Ascaridoidea (sometimes combined with a sojourn in an intermediate host) and Oxyuroidea. The Spirurida, by contrast, generally use invertebrates as intermediate hosts. If we are to see a convergence in these successive degenerations of the free-living stages in the different parasitic groups, the fact that, in the Phasmidea of vertebrates, the third-stage larva always infects the definitive host is to be reckoned a "reminiscence" of the dauerlarva so characteristic of free-living Rhabditoidea and thereby as a wholly general inheritance of all phasmideans belonging to this type. This regularity, demonstrated by Chabaud for the parasites of vertebrates, can be assigned to many of the Phasmidea that parasitize invertebrates. In summary, the developmental path of all parasites belonging to this type can be represented in the following scheme:

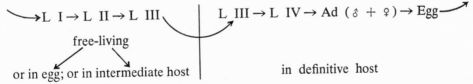

As this type of life-cycle is so well developed in the Strongylina, I propose that it be referred to as the "strongyline type."

2. Within the Phasmidea are to be found, however, a group of parasites with an importantly different development, which thereby represent a *Type 2*. These forms are the Tylenchina that parasitize insects. With their two superfamilies, the Aphelenchoidea and the Tylenchoidea, where members have gone over independ-

ently to parasitism, insofar as they are parasitic as adults (there is, especially in the Aphelenchoidea, also a series of larval parasites), one finds an identical developmental pattern (convergence), which is different in a fundamental way from that of other Phasmidea.

In the body cavity of the hosts (insects) the adult, fertilized females produce larvae that, subsequently remaining in the host, usually undergo two molts, then quit thereafter via the gut or through the female gonad as third-stage larvae. These larvae develop through two molts in a free-living state to males and females, without assimilating nourishment. While the female is still underdeveloped (subadult) and in the free-living state, it mates ("*koriogamy*," according to Wülker, 1923). It is this fecundated female alone that penetrates actively (mostly by way of the hindgut) back into a host, grows in the body cavity thereof, and produces the next generation (summarized by Rühm, 1956, and Wachek, 1955). Schematically, the following life cycle can be given:

$$\longrightarrow L\ III \to L\ IV \to Ad\ (\delta + \circ) \quad \llcorner \rightarrow Ad\ \circ \to L\ I \to L\ II \to L\ III \nearrow$$

$$\text{free-living} \qquad\qquad\qquad\qquad\qquad\qquad \text{in the host}$$

I propose to refer to this type of life cycle as the "tylenchine type." In the Tylenchina the distribution of the developmental stages, as regards the preparasitic and parasitic stages, is an importantly different one from that in Phasmidea of Type 1 (strongyline type). Here the third-stage larva does not infect, but rather leaves, the definitive host—adapting to the external milieu at that point. Thus in the Tylenchina important parts of the developmental cycle take place under free-living conditions, and the males are but larval parasites, since they live in the host only as first- to third-stage larvae.

Interestingly enough, it is not only in development that the insect-parasitic Tylenchina differ from the rest of the Phasmidea; a series of further conditions assigns their parasitism a special status in the Nematoda. Most striking is the fact that nourishment in the body cavity of the host is absorbed through the entire body surface: in fact, the digestive tract degenerates or serves as a storage organ. It follows that the body of these parasites often swells deformedly and in many forms (*e.g., Allantonema*) is no longer reminiscent of a nematode. In still other members the body of the female does not undergo this transformation; instead the uterus thereof begins to evaginate (*e.g.,* in *Atractonema* [syn. *Tripius*] incipiently) and to grow out massively, thus permitting the absorption of nutrients. This phenomenon was known for a long time only for *Sphaerularia*, but Wachek (1955) was able to demonstrate a similar occurrence for *Stictylus* (= *Sphaerulariopsis*). *Sphaerularia* belongs to the Aphelenchoidea; *Stictylus*, however, to the Tylenchoidea. Thus this highly aberrant phenomenon occurs convergently in the two superfamilies of the Tylenchina. Such modifications in fundamental organization are otherwise extraordinarily rare in the Nematoda. Reductions of the digestive tract occur in *Muspicea borelli* from Muridae and *Robertdollfusa paradoxa* from Corvidae (Aves), both forms being of uncertain systematic position (*cf.* Chabaud and Campana, 1950). Finally, there occurs in several tylenchoids a reduction of the four molts—a number characteristic, practically without exception, for the Nematoda (Maupas, 1889)—to three (as in *Allantonema*, according to Wülker, 1923) or even to only two or but one (in the "parthenogenetic intermediate generation" of

Heterotylenchus, Wachek, 1955, which lives parasitically through its entire cycle). Such instances, to be reckoned as neoteny, are likewise very rare in other groups of the Nematoda; as a further example, I know only the spiruride *Spirura rytipleurites* in which a reduction of a molt has been established (Chabaud and Mahon, 1958).

Both biological and morphological criteria therefore characterize the insect-parasitic tylenchs as belonging to a special category. What this unusual development rests upon is difficult to say. It seems that certain selective conditions have influenced these body-cavity parasites in such a way that both the Aphelenchoidea and the Tylenchoidea of insects have arrived at almost identical conditions independently of one another. And in the Mermithoidea (Aphasmidea), with similar life patterns in part, there exist corresponding relationships. There is no good evidence to assume, for parasitism in the Tylenchina of insects, that an especially great age is to be ascribed to this peculiar development. Actually the Oxyuroidea, parasitic in diplopods and orthopters (and certain other insects), seem to represent significantly older parasites—a point of view supported by their host-range and geographical distribution (Osche, 1960). They live, however, mostly on the hindgut content of their hosts, a manner of nourishment that does not depart very far from that of many free-living saprobiotes (on excrement). In fact, I have been able to maintain thelastomatids from diplopods alive on hindgut contents of their host, always kept moist in culture dishes, for more than three weeks. Correlated with this little-modified life pattern is the fact that these Oxyuroidea, in their inner organization (esophagus, gut, excretory system, etc.) and in many respects also in their external form, are unspecialized and have been regarded for some time as primitive parasites. But against these facts are others: their development (no longer any free larval stages—rather, molts in the egg), as well as many geographical and ecological oddities attesting to the position that in the Oxyuroidea one has highly evolved and phylogenetically old parasites (Dougherty, 1951; Osche, 1960).

For the *Aphasmidea* Chabaud (1955) has clearly established a special type of *vertebrate parasite.* Here the first-stage larva can itself infect the definitive host so that the complete larval development can take place therein, or intermediate hosts have been intercalated. The third-stage larva plays no special role (*i.e.,* in contrast to the conditions with Phasmidea), consequent upon the fact that, for the free-living Aphasmidea, a special dauerlarva is lacking. Most of the parasites belonging here show an organ specificity, on which Chabaud has already commented. Free-living larval stages are completely lacking in the vertebrate-parasitic Aphasmidea, and in the extreme case of "autoheteroxeny" *e.g., Trichinella*) the parasite develops from one definitive host to the next without having a period of host-free life. Therefore these parasites represent a characteristic, highly specialized type of parasitism (=Aphasmidean-type), to all appearances phylogenetically very old.

The single group of *invertebrate-parasites among the Aphasmidea,* the *Mermithoidea,* most of whose larvae parasitize insects, with some others living in molluscs, manifests a series of convergences with the Tylenchina. Thus they arise, seemingly like the latter, from plant parasites (dorylaims), live in the body cavity of their hosts, become adults in the free-living stage without acquiring nourishment, reduce the gut, and convert the gut partly into a storage organ (trophosome). The host can be infected either actively by the larva or passively by the egg *per os.*

The Phylogenetic Age of Parasitism in Specific Nematode Groups

With the lack of useful fossil materials the question, how old parasitism of nematodes may be, or, in other words, when in the course of terrestrial history this or that group may have adapted to parasitism, is to be estimated only indirectly. Therefore the absolute and the *relative* age of a group can be of interest. The latter can be estimated in certain cases from the degree of adaptation to parasitism and is based on the concept that phylogenetically older parasitic groups are modified to a greater extent than are those whose parasitism is more recent. Thus it can be said, for example, with reasonable certainty, that the Strongylina in comparison with the Spirurida represent the younger parasites. Such conclusions must, however, be drawn with great prudence, for evolutionary tempo is not the same in all groups. Respective ecological circumstances must be reckoned with, which under certain conditions result in considerable modifications (morphological, biological, etc.) that are unnecessary in other instances. The data already discussed for the Tylenchina *vs.* the Oxyuroidea are of particular significance in this connection.

An *absolute determination of age* is within certain limits possible by two methods:

> 1. Geographical distribution can provide certain conclusions on the age of a group of animals. This method is useful in rare cases for relatively low categories (genera, subfamilies) only, but scarcely permits conclusions as to the age of parasitism in a larger group.

> 2. For conclusions on the age of rather higher systematic categories one must turn to the "parasitophyletic method," which is based on correlations in the phylogeny of parasite and host. On the history and use of the so-called parasitophyletic rules worked out on this basis, Szidat (1956) and Stunkard (1957) have reported recently; for this reason only the points interesting in connection with our special questions are elaborated here.

The methods most generally useful for parasites derive from the following concepts: many parasites show a series of adaptations to their hosts, often of high degree (morphological, biological, physiological, etc.)—adaptations that can have been acquired only in a relatively long space of time and testify to a considerable phylogenetic age for the host-parasite relationship. Certain adaptations may include the binding of a parasitic group to *specific* host assemblages ("host-specificity"). If such parasitism corresponds to a rather considerable phylogenetic age, then the parasites must have participated in a part of the host-evolutionary process and have developed in "parallel" with the latter ("parallel evolution"). A phylogenetically old, but currently living, host group under such circumstances may "conserve" phylogenetically relict representatives of a parasitic group, whereas phylogenetically more advanced relatives of these hosts may shelter more evolved representatives of the general parasitic taxon. On this precept, knowledge of the age of the host group (derived from paleontology) can justify the indirect inference of the age of the parasites (Cameron, 1950, 1952; Dougherty, 1951; Szidat, 1956; Stunkard, 1957; Stammer, 1957; Osche, 1958, 1961). Fuhrmann and Baer have been able to establish corresponding correlations for cestodes and vertebrates and show that the cestodes, whose most primitive representatives live in fish and whose most highly evolved reside in the phylogenetically more recent birds and mammals, have seemingly undergone concomitant evolution as parasites of vertebrates and thus have developed in "parallel" with their hosts.

The phylogenetic age of parasitism of the Nematoda, however, has been, on this view, appraised many times as relatively brief, in part simply because host-correlations such as those for the cestodes cannot be recognized (Baer, 1933, 1947; Joyeux and Baer, 1951; Chabaud, 1957). To be sure, if one looks at the *totality* of parasitic nematodes from this standpoint, there emerges a very heterogeneous picture, and the parasitic nematodes, for example, of the selachians (Chondrichthyes), a host group that is relatively primitive within the vertebrates, have, it is true, "rien d'un Nématode primitif," as Baer (1933) remarks (nevertheless *primitive Ascaridoidea* are to be found in these hosts—see further on).

The basis for this situation and therefore for the difficulty in the use of the "parasitophyletic method" arises, for the Nematoda, from the unquestionable fact that parasitism of its groups is of polyphyletic origin and consequently a variable phylogenetic age is to be expected for different taxa. Thus, as we know, insect parasites have arisen independently of one another in the Rhabditoidea, Aphelenchoidea, Tylenchoidea, Oxyuroidea, and Mermithoidea—only the larger groups being named. By analogy, the fact that nearly all the superfamilies of the Ascaridina consist of exclusively parasitic species does not unconditionally establish that here one is dealing with monophyletic parasitism. It is quite conceivable that all these superfamilies (or certain of them) go back independently to free-living ancestors and that a part of the similarity of these groups rests on convergence, whereby they seem to be more nearly related than in truth they are. It is self-evident that correlations between the phylogeny of parasite and host can be expected only for such nematode groups whose parasitism is of monophyletic origin—that is, whose recent representatives stem exclusively from common, already parasitically living(!) antecedents. This condition, logical in itself, is excedingly difficult to fulfill with nematodes since, even within many small systematic units, free-living forms have made repeated transitions to parasitism (Rhabditoidea, Aphelenchoidea, Tylenchoidea)—a phenomenon that, in fact, continues in front of our eyes. It is very difficult, if not impossible, to identify and discriminate these different "waves" of parasite-transition from one another with certainty since they produce an abundance of common potentialities. The giant army of saprozoically living Rhabditoidea represents a stem-group of terrestrial nematodes (Chitwood, 1933, 1950) that for millions of years have varied little ("Dauertypen") in their relatively constant environment—saprobiotic substrates of this type having existed since there have been terrestrial and perhaps even estuarine organisms (plants and animals). Thanks to the rhabditoids' saprozoic life pattern, new parasitic lines have been elicited again and again in the course of terrestrial history. Accordingly, all parasitic groups within the Phasmidea can be traced back, more or less directly, to free-living Rhabditoidea; thus, they are descendants of quite homogeneous ancestors, who have altered only slightly to this day. That many homologies exist under these conditions, supplemented by a series of convergences, is understandable, thereby making the classification of closer relationships problematic (Osche, 1961).

Chabaud (1959) has correctly pointed out that the phylogenetic development of parasitic nematodes leads to an ever increasing accommodation to parasitism and that modern groups are "primitive parasites." This fact seems to be in gross contradiction to the concept established by the "parasitophyletic rules," whereby in the phylogenetically oldest hosts the most primitive parasites are always to be expected. Such a contradiction is only seeming and is but the consequence of our inability to differentiate definitively from one another different adaptational waves to parasitism. In practice the problem arises because, as Chabaud (1959) has written, "il est impossible de savoir si le parasite 'primitif' est archaique ou récent." But it is not reasonable on this account to draw the conclusion that the nematodes as a whole are in but a rather early period of parasitism. The facts that along with these parasites there are still free-living relatives and that parasitism is of polyphyletic origin do not necessarily permit any conclusions in this sense. On the other hand, since the saprobiotic-living groups have gone over to parasitism so often and successfully in more recent times, then it seems plausible that this also took place much earlier.

Regardless of whether or not a practical decision is to be made in each case, it is nevertheless necessary to make a theoretical distinction between two kinds of "primitive parasites":

1. Those that have been transformed to parasitism only a short time ago and therefore still show comparatively slight adaptation to parasitic life: these can serve as "models" for the inception of related, already transformed, parasite stem-groups, and such transitional forms can themselves serve as a basis for a monophyletic line of parasites that are to evolve in the future.

2. Those that cover a long stretch of terrestrial history, but stand closest to the basic group of an already richly subdivided parasitic monophyletic lineage: their "primitiveness" reflects their having survived in hosts themselves retaining primitive general characteristics, and only for such monophyletic lineages can one expect to make evolutionary correlations in host-parasite relationships.

If within rather small systematic units a polyphyletic parasitism already exists (as in the Rhabditoidea and Aphelenchoidea), then a different age of parasitism must be assumed for the different species. Within parasitic monophyletic lineages, however—even very extensive ones—the parasitism is of equal age for each group. How old the individual units (e.g., genera or families) of each monophyletic line are taxonomically is a second question—one that can also be answered by evaluating the "parallel evolution" of parasite and host.

In the face of the difficulties expounded, one should select, if one wishes to attempt reconstructing the age, as parasites, of a particular group, a lineage for which there is evidence of monophyletic parasitism and whose host circle supports the idea that its parasitism is old. Only in such groups can one hope to arrive at host-parasite "parallel evolution." The most primitive representatives of such taxa cannot therefore be "primitive parasites" in any absolute sense, but they are the "most primitive" of *their lineage*.

At least one other source of difficulty in the use of the "parasitophyletic method" should be pointed out. It must be reckoned that, in the course of the enormous gaps of time during which a parasitic group has evolved, some parts have broken out of rigid ties within a particular host-circle and have transferred to another circle, thereby falsifying, even destroying, the appearance of parallel-evolution.

In fact, such "host-range expansion" (Wirtskreiserweiterung) in some nematode groups has occurred repeatedly, but, in many instances, where such are reconstructable (Osche, 1957, 1958), there is no risk to parasitophyletic evaluation; on the contrary, one has ancillary help in tracing out the entangled path of evolution for a parasitic group.

The following section will demonstrate, on the basis of the Ascaridoidea, that by means of combining several approaches (morphological, biological, and ecological), insights into their evolutionary pattern can be obtained, thereby providing, over long periods of time, correlations with the host-phylogeny for nematodes too. The age of parasitism for the Ascaridoidea derived from these considerations is not ostensibly less than that reported by Baer for the Cestoda by use of similar methods.

The Phylogenetic Development of the Ascaridoidea and Its Correlation with the Evolution of the Vertebrates

The Ascaridoidea represent an apparently monophyletic superfamily of the Ascaridina comprised of exclusively parasitic groups; these are restricted to verte-

FIGURE 21-2. Dorsal lips of various ascaridoids: a, *Acanthocheilus;* b,c, *Contracaecum;* d, *Raphidascaris;* e, *Stomachus;* f, *Angusticaecum;* g, *Amplicaecum;* h, *Polydelphis;* i, *Ophidascaris;* k,l, *Porrocaecum;* m, *Ascaris.* (After Osche, 1958, simplified.)

brates as parasites and have representatives in all classes of this animal line above the jawless forms (lampreys and hagfishes). As criteria for systematic subdividing, the variously differentiated lips serve particularly well (fig. 21-2); with their help natural units can be delineated, which also can be proved by further homologies (Hartwich, 1957). Insights into the phylogenetic relations of these various groups to one another are facilitated by the fact that the morphogenesis of systematically important lips undergoes a recapitulation in the course of larval development of more highly evolved species. Thus the lips of a species of *Porrocaecum* (*P. ensicaudatum*) parasitic in birds undergo manifold transformations whereby the lip forms are represented as they occur in adults of other genera of the Ascaridoidea. *Porrocaecum ensicaudatum* thus recapitulates in its larval development a series corresponding in lip form to the Acanthocheilinae (fig. 21-2,a), Stomachinae (fig. 21-2,b,c,e), Raphidascaridinae (fig. 21-2,d), Angusticaecinae (fig. 21-2,f,g), and Ophidascaridinae fig. 21-2,h,i), until finally the lip form typical for *Porrocaecum* (fig. 21-2,k,l) is reached. This recapitulative development takes place in such a way that the recent groups of the Ascaridoidea are arranged in the foregoing series whereby it can be shown that a phylogenetic sequence is really represented here. The Ascarididae (fig. 21-2,m) are directly connected to the Porrocaecinae. Certain families, modified in special directions and unusually poor in species, such as the Goeziidae, Multicaecidae, and Crossophoridae, are not represented in the recapitulative series. They assume, for reasons of special characters, isolated positions, although quite generally within the Ascaridoidea (*cf.* fig. 21-3). With the exception of the Stomachinae, which are still to be gone into, all aforementioned groups of the Ascaridoidea with their representatives are parasitic only in hosts of a certain systematic unit of vertebrates, be it a class or an order. In the already represented series disclosed by recapitulative development the following picture is revealed in relation to the host groupings (*cf.* fig. 21-3):

	Host distribution
(Acanthocheilidae)	
Acanthocheilinae	Chondrichthyes
(Stomachidae)	
Raphidascaridinae	Osteichthyes
Stomachinae	piscivorous Aves, marine
	Mammalia, marine Reptilia
(Angusticaecidae)	
Angusticaecinae	Amphibia and Reptilia
Ophidascaridinae	Reptilia
(Toxocaridae)	
Porrocaecinae	Aves
Ascarididae	Mammalia

This series of host groups (again excepting the hosts of Stomachinae) corresponds to the temporal appearance—that is, to the radiation—of the vertebrate groups in the course of terrestrial history, whereby the fact of a correlating development of parasites and hosts is fulfilled. Thus, the phylogenetically old "Pisces" are parasitized by the most ancient Ascaridoidea (Acanthocheilidae, Raphidascaridinae), the Amphibia and Reptilia by the Angusticaecidae, and so on, up to the mammals, which have the most highly evolved Ascarididae as their parasites

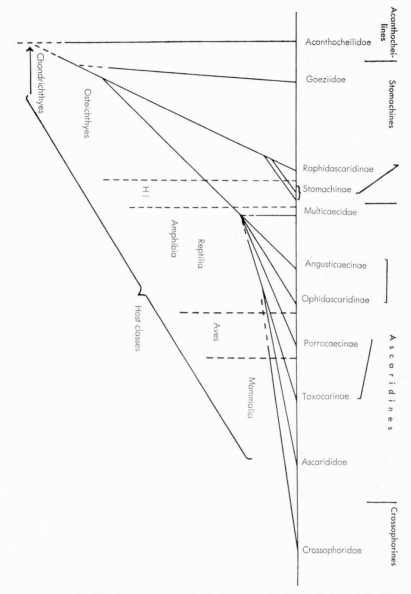

Figure 21-3. "Evolutionary tree" of the Ascaridoidea. Only subfamilies or family groups indicated; coördinated with host distribution. H! = host-range expansion. (Modified from Osche, 1958.)

(fig. 21-3). An exception in this series is posed, however, by the Stomachinae, which "abruptly" parasitize reptiles, birds, and mammals, although one would expect them, on the basis of their evolutionary position, only in fish wherein the nearly related Raphidascaridinae are exclusive inhabitants. A rather careful inspection of the host distribution of the Stomachinae shows, however, that essentially only marine-living vertebrates are parasitized: thus marine Chelonia, marine Aves (Lariformes, Sphenisciformes, Procellariiformes, etc.), and marine mammals (Pinnipedia, Cetacea)—all host groups that, primitively living on land, represent secondary sea-dwellers and have become fish-eating. Here is represented a typical instance of secondary "host-range expansion," whose ecological explanation is clearly recognizable. When these vertebrate groups each underwent its incisive biotopic transition from land to sea, most ("terrestrial") nematode parasites previously characteristic of them were not adapted naturally to the variously changed relationships of the new environment then encountered and thus became extinct. Following the loss of their old parasites acquisition of new ascaridoid parasites seems to have occurred readily; for one thing, these host groups (reptiles, birds, mammals) ate fish in the new environment and thereby came in contact with parasites of their prey. Phylogenetically the Stomachinae thus represent a relatively young branch arisen through host-parasite-extension from fish parasites, as a result of which a "parallel evolution" with the diverse host classes is not to be expected. In contrast, a parasite group that "survived" the transition of their hosts from land to sea—namely, the Pseudaliinae of the Cetacea—might be mentioned at this point. These Pseudaliinae represent a highly modified group of Metastrongylidae whose near relationship to the parasites of the Carnivora and Artiodactyla has been established (Dougherty, 1949, 1951). Since the Metastrongylidae occur only in mammals—in fact, the entire suborder Strongylina (to which the Metastrongylidae belong) reveals no representatives in fish—there can be no doubt that the Pseudaliinae could have been derived only from terrestrial relatives and consequently must have survived the radical change of biotope of their hosts.

To the picture, derived from morphology (lip recapitulation) and ecology (host-distribution and correlation), of the phylogeny of the Ascaridoidea (fig. 21-3) there may well be added other facts. If one compares, for example, the life cycles of different groups, it can be shown that, in the most primitive forms, intermediate hosts are always intercalated, whereas a direct development is found only in the highly evolved forms, presumably derivatively. Indeed, investigations of recent years have shown that the "detouring" direct development characterizing some species of *Ascaris, Parascaris,* and *Neoascaris,* with a curious wandering of larvae (passage through the lungs), can be understood best as "recapitulation" of a primitively heteroxenous (indirect) developmental pattern (Sprent, 1954; Chabaud, 1955) such as Fülleborn 1924) earlier suggested.

Finally, an *augmentation of body size,* characteristic for many parasitic nematodes (free-living forms are mostly only 1 to 5 mm. long) can be followed step by step in the course of evolution in the Ascaridoidea, as a function of the latter's increasingly advanced evolutionary status. The following maximal values are reached in the respective groups (*cf.* fig. 21-3):

Acanthocheilidae	35 mm.
Stomachidae	
Raphidascaridinae	80–120 mm.
Stomachinae	80–160 mm.
Angusticaecidae	140–190 mm.
Toxocaridae	160–260 mm.
Ascarididae	250–400 mm.

(For more comprehensive data, the remaining ascaridoid families being included, see Osche, 1958, p. 539). The body size reveals itself here as a measure of the evolutionary development of the parasites and is in a remarkable way independent of the size of the host animals. The relatively small Stomachinae are particularly illustrative as to their origin at the level of fish parasites (Raphidascaridinae), although they may inhabit giant whales. By contrast, there live in small terrestrial mammals (rodents) highly evolved Ascarididae of considerable body size.

If we turn, in closing, once more to the question of the *age of parasitism* in the Nematoda, we may conclude from the illustrated parallel-evolution of the Ascaridoidea and their hosts that this superfamily is apparently very old and has accompanied the greater part of the evolution of the vertebrates. With the general connection to certain host groups, the approximate age can be stated for the various systematic units. Thus the Ophidascaridinae, for example, must have developed with the radiation of the reptiles in the Permian (thus about 215 million years ago), the Porrocaecinae with the radiation of the Aves in the Jurassic and Cretaceous periods (thus about 120 to 130 million years ago), and the Ascarididae with the splitting off of the mammals in the Tertiary (100 million years or more ago). The fish-parasitic groups must be significantly older. Certainly, therefore, from all appearances the Ascaridoidea were already parasites in vertebrates when the latter began to invade the land. But for the Ascaridoidea themselves only the minimum age of their parasitism is established by this means, for all clues of the derivation of the primeval Ascaridoidea from some still free-living groups are now lacking. There exist no grounds, however, for assuming the Ascaridoidea to be the oldest parasites among the nematodes. It seems that many groups parasitic in invertebrates, such as the Drilonematoidea (in the Annelida) and many Oxyuroidea (in the Arthropoda), are still more ancient. The possibility of establishing parasitic lines certainly existed to an abundant degree for the Nematoda from the beginning of their saprobiotic way of life, and we must assume that these opportunities were exploited very early.

REFERENCES

NOTE: For a complete bibliography on this subject, see Osche, 1958 and 1960.

Baer, J. G.
    1933   L'adaptation des helminthes à leur hôtes. Bull. Soc. neuchâtel. Sci. nat. 58:57–76.
    1947   Les helminthes parasites des Vertébrés. Relations phylogéniques entre leur évolution et celle de leur hôtes. Ann. sci. de Franche-Comté, Besançon 2:99–113.
    1952   Ecology of Animal Parasites. Univ. Illinois, Urbana.

Bovien, P.
    1937   Some types of association between nematodes and insects. Vidensk. Medd. dansk naturh. Foren. Kbh. 101:2–114.

Cameron, T. W. M.
    1950   Parasitology and evolution. Trans. roy. Soc. Can. (Sect. 5, Ser. 3) 44:1–20.
    1952   Parasitentum, Evolution und Phylogenie. Endeavor 11:193–199.

Chabaud, A. G.
    1955   Essai d'interprétation des cycles évolutifs chez les Nématodes parasites de Vertébrés. Conclusion taxonomique. Ann. Parasit. hum. comp. 30:83–126.

1957   Specificité parasitaire chez les Nématodes parasites de Vertébrés. Un. int.
            Sci. biol. (Ser. B) 32:230–243.

1959   Remarque sur l'évolution et la taxonomie chez les Nématodes parasites
            de Vertébrés. Proc. 15th int. Cong. Zool., London (1958): 679–680.

Chabaud, A. G., and R. Campana

1950   Nouveau parasite remarquable par l'atrophie de ses organes: *Robert-
            dollfusa paradoxa*. Ann. Parasit. hum. comp. 25:325–334.

Chabaud, A. G., R. Campana, and E. R. Brygoo

1959   Les Nématodes Seuratoidea nov. sup. fam. et l'origine des Spirurida.
            C. R. Acad. Sci., Paris 248:1449–1451.

Chabaud, A. G., and J. Mahon

1958   Cycle évolutif du Nématode *Spirura talpae*. *Ibid*. 152:474–476.

Chitwood, B. G.

1932   The association of *Rhabditis strongyloides* with dermatitis in dogs. N.
            Amer. Vet. 13:35–40.

1935   Nematodes parasitic in and associated with Crustacea and descriptions
            of some new species and a new variety. Proc. helm. Soc. Wash.
            2:93–96.

Chitwood, B. G., and M. G. Chitwood

1933   The characters of a protonematode. J. Parasit. 20:130.

1950   An Introduction to Nematology. Sect. I. Monumental Press, Baltimore.

Dougherty, E. C.

1949   The phylogeny of the nematode family Metastrongylidae, a correlation
            of host and symbiote evolution. Parasitology 39:222–234.

1951   Evolution of zooparasitic groups in the phylum Nematoda, with special
            reference to host-distribution. J. Parasit. 37:353–378.

Fülleborn, F.

1924   The wandering of certain nematode larvae in the body of their hosts.
            J. Parasit. 11:98–99.

Fuhrmann, O.

1928–
1931   Trematoda und Cestoidea. Handb. Zool., Berlin 2:1–416.

Goodey, T.

1951   Soil and Freshwater Nematodes. Methuen, London, New York.

Hartwich, G.

1957   Zur Systematik der Nematoden Superfamilie Ascaridoidea. Zool. Jb.
            (Syst.) 85:211–252.

Ihering, H. von

1902   Die Helminthen als Hilfsmittel der zoogeographischen Forschung. Zool.
            Anz. 26:42–51.

Joyeux, C., and I. G. Baer

1951   Les rapportes des Helminthes et de leurs hôtes. Biol. méd., Paris 40:230–
            261.

Körner, H.

1954   Die Nematodenfauna des vergehenden Holzes. Zool. Jb. (Syst.) 82:245–
            353.

Leuckart, R.

1887   Neue Beiträge zur Kenntnis des Baues und der Lebensgeschichte der
            Nematoden. Abh. sächs. Ges. (Akad.) Wiss. 22:567–704.

Maupas, E.

1899   La mue et l'enkystement chez les Nématodes. Arch. Zool. exp. gén.
            7:563–632.

Osche, G.

1952   Die Bedeutung der Osmoregulation und des Winkverhaltens für freilebende Nematoden. Z. Morph. Ökol. Tiere 41:54–77.

1954   Über Verhalten und Morphologie der Dauerlarve freilebender Nematoden. Zool. Anz. 152:65–73.

1955   Über die Vergesellschaftung von Nematoden und Crustaceen, mit einer
Beschreibung von *Matthesonema tylosa* n. g. n. sp. aus dem Kiemenraum
einer Assel. *Ibid.* 155:253–262.

1956   Die Praeadaptation freilebender Nematoden an den Parasitismus. Verh.
dtsch. zool. Ges., Erlangen (1955) (Zool. Anz., Suppl. 19):391–396.

1957   Die "Wirtskreiserweiterung" bei parasitischen Nematoden und die sie
bedingenden biologisch-ökologischen Faktoren. Z. Parasitenk. 17:437–
489.

1958   Beiträge zur Morphologie, Ökologie und Phylogenie der Ascaridoidea.
Parallelen in der Evolution von Parasit und Wirt. *Ibid.* 18:479–572.

1959   Systematische, morphologische und parasitophyletische Studien an parasitischen Oxyuroidea exotischer Diplopoden. Zool. Jb. (Syst.) 87:395–
440.

1960   Aufgaben und Probleme der Systematik am Beispiel der Nematoden.
Verh. dtsch. zool. Ges., Bohn/Rhein (1960) (Zool. Anz., Suppl. 24):
329–384.

Rühm, W.

1954   Die Nematoden als Kommensalen, Halbparasiten und Parasiten der
Insekten. Deutscher Entomologentag Hamburg, 168–184.

1956   Die Nematoden der Ipiden. Parasitol. Schriftenreihe 6:1–437.

Sachs, H. G.

1950   Die Nematodenfauna der Rinderexkremente. Zool. Jb. (Syst.) 79:211–
271.

Sprent, I. F. A.

1954   The life cycles of nematodes in the family Ascarididae. J. Parasit.
40:608–617.

Stammer, H. J.

1955   Ökologische Wechselbeziehungen zwischen Insekten und anderen Tier-
gruppen. Ber. 7. WandVersamml. dtsch. Ent.:12–61.

1956   Die Parasiten deutscher Kleinsäuger. Verh. dtsch. zool. Ges., Erlangen
(1955). (Zool. Anz., Suppl. 19):362–390.

1957   Gedanken zu den parasitophyletischen Regeln und zur Evolution der
Parasiten. Zool. Anz. 159:255–267.

Stunkard, H. W.

1957   Host specificity and parallel evolution of parasitic flatworms. Z. Tropen-
med. u. Parasit. 8:254–263.

Szidat, L.

1956   Geschichte, Anwendung und einige Folgerungen aus den parasitogenetis-
chen Regeln. Z. Parasitenk. 17:237–268.

Völk, J.

1950   Die Nematodenfauna der Regenwürmer und aasbesuchenden Käfer.
Zool. Jb. (Syst.) 79:1–79.

Wachek, F.

1955   Die entoparasitischen Tylenchiden. Parasitol. Schriftenreihe 3:1–119.

Weingärtner, J.
    1953   Die Nematoden des Kompostes. S. B. phys.-med. Soz. Erlangen 76:86–
               107.
Wülker, G.
    1923   Über Fortpflanzung und Entwicklung von *Allantonema* und verwandten
               Nematoden. Zool. Anz. 56:160–164.

II. Comparative Physiology

A. GENERAL

22 ◆ Comparative Biochemistry and the Lower Metazoa

ERNEST BALDWIN

DEPARTMENT OF BIOCHEMISTRY,
UNIVERSITY COLLEGE, LONDON

The comparative biochemistry of the lower Metazoa is still practically a virgin field. Even so, more interest is being focused upon it now than formerly, and a good deal of new information has come to light during the last few years. Still, it would be very difficult to give a coherent account of the comparative biochemistry of these animals, for the bulk of the information available is very fragmentary indeed. Comparative biochemistry has not in the past been comparative enough.

There are many reasons why this has been so, but there are also reasons to think that progress will be much accelerated in the future. Financial support has always been generous for morphological and physiological studies of living things, but until fairly recently finance has been harder to come by for studying the biochemistry of such things as earthworms and starfishes. It is, however, being realized that earthworms are an important agricultural asset and that starfishes cause grievous losses to the oyster-farmers. In any case, one group of lower metazoa, the nematodes, are a most serious menace to plants and animals alike—to the farmer as well as to the things he farms. For the study of the biochemistry of these creatures alone vast sums of money could profitably be spent. But reasons such as these have attracted comparatively little support. Since the human species promises far to outgrow its food resources in the not very distant future, it is fast becoming imperative that the ocean and its inhabitants should be explored and investigated with every available means, including even comparative biochemistry. So in this direction at any rate, there seems to be considerable hope for the future.

Another reason for faith in the future is a matter of methodology. Among the earliest significant contributors to comparative biochemistry the names of Kutscher and Ackermann (1933b, 1936) are outstanding. Starting usually with several kilograms of raw material, they carried out laborious fractionation procedures, requiring

The author wishes gratefully to record his thanks to the Wellcome Trust for a generous travel grant.

much time and much chemical skill and leading to the isolation of a remarkable variety of nitrogenous substances from many vertebrate and invertebrate materials. For the most part these products were substances of unknown origin, fate, and function.

At that time there was no chromatography, no electrophoresis, and little in the way of spectrophotometry, but all these and many more are routine procedures in every biochemical laboratory today. The newer data of comparative biochemistry have largely been gathered together by precisely these methods, which call for far less starting material than was inevitably needed in the old days. Not uncommonly the most interesting material is the scarcest and the most difficult to come by.

As a familiar example of the way things are going one may recall the work which, up to about 1928, led to the belief that creatine is a characteristic constituent of vertebrate muscle, present only in traces, if at all, in invertebrate materials. On the other hand, arginine takes the place of creatine, equally characteristically, among the invertebrates (Hunter, 1928). These conclusions were reached through large-scale work, thanks mainly to Kutscher and Ackermann and their co-workers. A number of other more or less peculiar amidine derivatives were isolated at the same time, but the distribution of these seemed to be totally erratic and completely divorced from any orthodox scheme of taxonomy. They remained on the shelf as little more than biochemical oddities until rather recently.

Nothing was known about the functions of any of these compounds until about 1928, when it was discovered that creatine and arginine alike occur for the most part in muscle in the form of their phosphates, the so-called phosphagens (Eggleton and Eggleton, 1927, 1928; Fiske and Subbarow, 1927, 1929; Meyerhof and Lohmann, 1928); but a good many years passed before the functions even of these were discovered. This point is worth making because, even in the absence of any knowledge of function, distribution studies alone can be of considerable interest and importance. It soon became possible to extend the older distribution studies to many new species by taking advantage of certain of the special chemical properties of these very labile amidine phosphates (Needham, et al., 1932). This could now be done with a few grams, instead of a few kilograms, of starting material. Apart from a few cases, especially among the echinoderms, the old rule still seemed to hold: creatine in vertebrates and arginine in invertebrates; but not enough species had yet been studied.

Some later work was concentrated on the phosphagens of the annelid worms (Baldwin and Yudkin, 1949). These animals had hitherto been considered to be arginine-containing animals, but chemical methods of analysis failed to show the presence of any significant amount of arginine in polychetes (Arnold and Luck, 1933), although Kutscher and Ackermann (1931) had isolated it in small amounts from earthworms. It soon became apparent that arginine and arginine phosphate are absent from annelids as a whole and are replaced in polychetes by other amidines and the corresponding phosphagens, but, for a time, the nature and identity of their basic components remained unknown.

It was at this stage that Roche and his co-workers (Roche et al., 1952, and Thoai et al., 1953a,b,c; see also Thoai and Robin, 1954a,b; and Ennor and Morrison, 1958) brought paper chromatography to bear on the field. They showed that phosphagens derived from glycocyamine, taurocyamine, and even creatine are present in various polychetes in place of arginine. At the same time a rather fantastic new phosphagen, derived from a new amidine base, lombricin, was found in earthworms; still another, as yet unidentified, has recently been discovered in leeches.

In passing, it is worth-while to recall that creatine is formed from arginine by way of glycocyamine. Probably the ancestral annelids at first made use of arginine, abandoned it in favor of its product glycocyamine, and in some cases went even further by methylating the glycocyamine to produce creatine—quite a pretty case of chemical evolution. Taurocyamine, too, is worth a passing comment. Just as glycocyamine arises from glycine by trans-amidination at the expense of arginine, so, too, taurocyamine probably arises from taurine. This ties up with the widespread occurrence of taurine among invertebrates and especially with the presence of large amounts in some annelid worms (Kurtz and Luck, 1935). It may well be that taurocyamine and its phosphate will turn up elsewhere among invertebrates when more species are studied; free taurine, at any rate, is very widely distributed indeed (Kutscher and Ackermann, 1933b).

So methods have proceeded from kilograms to grams, from grams to milligrams, and potentially even to micrograms, with new discoveries and new thoughts for the future at every step of the way. But much that is recent or new in all this might well have been discovered a great deal earlier if only comparative biochemistry had been more comparative earlier on.

To take another case we may recall Hoppe-Seyler's (1933) discovery of a new substance, homarine, in lobster muscle. The same compound had already been obtained from a species of *Arbacia* (Holtz *et al.,* 1924) and from *Arca noae* (Kutscher and Ackermann, 1933a), but had been wrongly identified as the isomeric trigonelline at the time. Homarine itself is the N-methyl derivative of picolinic acid. Picolinic acid had not, however, been detected in biological materials, and homarine itself remained for many years a rare biochemical curiosity of unknown origin, unknown fate, and unknown function. Moreover, its distribution seemed to be highly erratic. In more recent times and with the use of more refined methods, homarine has turned up over and over again, even in celenterates (Mathias *et al.,* 1960). It is rather easily detectable by its highly characteristic absorption spectrum in the ultraviolet, and it now seems that homarine is very generally present in marine, though never in fresh-water, invertebrates (Gasteiger *et al.,* 1960). Its fate and function are as obscure as ever. As for its function, the suggestion has been made that, since it occurs in marine but not fresh-water animals, it may play some part in osmo-regulation. Perhaps it does, but this same suggestion has been made at some time or other for practically every soluble and physiologically inert substance that has been isolated from the tissues of aquatic animals. As for its origin, we have one clue. That clue is the fact that, in mammalian tissues at any rate, picolinic acid can arise from quinolinic acid as a side product in the conversion of tryptophan to nicotinic acid (Heidelberger, Abraham, and Lepovsky, 1949a,b; Heidelberger *et al.,* 1949), with which it is isomeric; and, of course, biological N-methylation is common enough. Finally, as far as evidence goes, there is reason to believe that tryptophan is essential for animals of every kind, so that the observed wide distribution of homarine is not difficult to account for. But, if one reasons along these lines, at once new problems arise. How is it possible to account for the seeming absence of homarine from fresh-water animals and the fact that it has not so far been detected in vertebrates if, in truth, tryptophan is an indispensable dietary factor for animals of every kind?

Taking a broad comparative view of biochemistry as a whole, it has become increasingly apparent that there exists a fundamental ground plan of metabolism to which all or nearly all living organisms conform. Of course, special features are present in particular cases, such as the photosynthetic machinery of the green plants and other phototrophic organisms. Even so, we find the cytochrome system, the reaction sequence of glycolysis, the so-called shunt pathway, the citric cycle, and many more metabolic pathways wherever one looks. Purists will claim that this is an overstatement, and so perhaps it is, but for purposes of argument it may be accepted as an approximation; science has, after all, been described by some sceptics as a successive series of approximations to an unattainable truth!

Many biochemists have been surprised, not so much by the fact that there are differences between groups of animals, and even sometimes between two species in a single genus, as by the fact that there are not *more* of these differences. Of course, on reflection this must obviously be a rather shortsighted view, for many more differences must undoubtedly exist than have yet been discovered. The reason once again is that comparative biochemistry has not in the past been comparative enough and has discovered only a mere handful of the innumerable differences that must certainly exist between one animal and the rest.

Most biochemists have accepted and grown so used to the notion of a common metabolic ground-plan that there is a tendency to assume that if such and such a substance discharges a particular function in one animal then it probably serves the same function in other animals. If one argues from a cat to a dog, one will, in general, be not too far wrong. But most workers are all too ready to carry the argument a step further, and assume that, if one animal does something and supports that particular activity by specific chemical processes, then, when some other organism does the same thing, it too will use precisely the same chemical manipulations. Again, if one argues from a cat to a dog, one will probably be fairly correct. When a muscle contracts, actomyosin, ATP, and a phosphagen come into action; the digestion of a protein calls for pepsin, trypsin, and the rest, or some analogous set of hydrolytic enzymes, which may be extracellular or intracellular. The list could obviously be extended a long way, but, even so, the range over which such parallels have a real existence is limited, and probably more limited than is usually realized.

An example of this sort is to be found in connection with the stinging powers of celenterates. Going back once more to the Kutscher and Ackermann period, it may be remembered that one classical achievement consisted in the isolation from *Actinia equina* of considerable quantities of tetramine (tetramethylammonium—Ackermann *et al.,* 1923). This, being a quaternary ammonium base, would be expected to have important pharmacological activity, and so indeed it does. It possesses a powerful paralyzant action. It was accordingly assumed for many years that this was the paralyzing agent used by celenterates generally—a typical jump from the particular to the general. But in more recent work, carried out this time largely by paper chromatography and electrophoresis on paper, a number of other toxic agents have been detected among celenterates. Many of them seem to possess polypeptide or protein-like toxins of high activity (Lane, 1960; Mathias *et al.,* 1960). In all probability these are species-specific, but none of them has yet been sufficiently purified for positive identification. (Parenthetically, it is interesting to notice that tetramine has also been found in the highly toxic saliva of a number of marine gastropods—Fänge, 1960; in octopus venom—Asano and Itoh, 1960; and elsewhere.)

Now, among others, Mathias *et al.* (1960) have carried out some biochemical and pharmacological studies on a few celenterates, and some of their results will bear mention. First of all, they found tetramine in *Actinia equina* and *Anemone sulcata.* It was also found in *Physalia,* about the most potent stinger of all, but could not be detected either in *Calliactis parasitica* or in *Metridium senile.* Histamine was also found in *A. equina* and *A. sulcata,* but not in the other two species, while another toxic substance, 5-hydroxytryptamine, rather closely related to histamine, was found in *C. parasitica,* but not in the other three species.

Here is, at any rate, one case in which comparative biochemistry has been ever so slightly more comparative than usual, though obviously enough there is still an immense range of work for the future. As far as the evidence goes, two species, *A. equina* and *A. sulcata,* do indeed resemble one another rather closely and differ very markedly from the other species studied. Moreover, it seems certain that all celenterates definitely do *not* use the same stinging agents. Nor, of course, do bees and wasps, or rattlesnakes and vipers. In fact, there is a large and wide-open field for comparative biochemistry in connection with animal toxicology—and a field, moreover, in which it should not be too difficult to be very comparative indeed. Very promising progress is now being made in this field.

To change the subject—without being competent to discuss morphological matters, I believe that there are important logical connections between biochemical and structural phenomena. Biological structures are composed of chemical materials, and, in the end, biological structure must depend on molecular architecture, just as physiological activity depends ultimately upon dynamic molecular events. This notion has considerable potentialities for comparative biology in general.

Few biologists can fail to be impressed by the fact that the further down one goes into the detailed structure, physiology, and biochemistry of living stuff, the more one kind of organism resembles every other kind. At the highest levels variety and diversity are most obvious, but at the lowest levels diversity becomes lost in community. Every organism consists of one or more cells, each cell contains a nucleus and particulate organelles (except in the bacteria and blue-green algae these organelles include mitochondria), and so on. All of these sub-cellular entities contain complex enzymatic machinery composed in its turn of proteins and other chemical materials of larger or smaller molecular size, the whole being suspended or bathed in water containing soluble protein and simple inorganic ions. This series of levels of complexity or organization corresponds to what Woodger (1930, 1931) many years ago described as "the spatial hierarchy."

Let it now be assumed that, at the lowest levels of organization, there indeed exists a fixed and fundamental metabolic ground-plan upon which life itself depends. There is plenty of biochemical evidence to support this assumption in a general way. Superimposed on this common ground-plan there are many special additional processes, compounds, and complexes that are secondary features of adaptational as opposed to communal and fundamental significance. One of the primary jobs of comparative biochemistry is to sort them all out and decide which is which.

The point to be made here is that, given a common chemical and metabolic ground-plan that is indispensable for survival, it follows that nothing can be added that is not wholly compatible with the maintenance of this fundamental set of conditions. It follows, too, that the number and variety of evolutionary and adaptational systems that can be built up on the common ground-plan are not unlimited, but very restricted indeed. The necessity for maintaining the common ground-plan constitutes a limitation for adaptive and evolutionary progress as well as an essential requirement for the survival of cells and tissues. So severe are these limitations that it is not to be wondered at that evolution is as slow a process as, in fact, it is.

And the matter does not end there. As each new set of compatible edifices is built up, new limitations will be imposed, for every new device incorporated must be compatible not only with the fundamental ground-plan, but also with what has already been laid down.

Biochemistry has developed so much in the last quarter of a century that already it has a very great deal to say about the constitution and functions of the cytoplasm, microsomes, and mitochondria and is well on the way with chromosomes and with the nucleus. Perhaps the time has come to start feeling our way toward even higher levels of organization and speculating to some extent about the emergent biochemical problems.

Some of these ideas are perhaps worth reviving (Baldwin, 1937), for they can provide at least partial if only provisional answers to a number of broad biological problems. The essential business of biochemistry is, after all, the study of biological problems by chemical and physico-chemical methods, and the broader the problems, the more comparative must be the biochemistry.

Now, biologists have often enough been impressed by the fact that the members of the animal kingdom fall into a relatively small number of major types (phyla), in spite of a large degree of variation within each type. The same sort of typification also occurs within groups of specialised tissues, such as plain and striated muscles, glandular tissues, and so on.

As a theorem it may be proposed that every new evolutionary and adaptational feature incorporated into an organism must be compatible with everything that has gone before. So severe are the limitations set upon evolutionary and adaptational progress, so limited is the choice of this feature or that, that of all the directions in which evolution and specialization might have proceeded, comparatively few have been possible, so rigid and insistent is the test of compatibility with what went before. Perhaps this is why the members of the animal kingdom fall into a rather small number of phyla in spite of a considerable range of variety within each major type. And it will be remembered how, as D'Arcy Thompson showed many years ago, varieties can commonly be reduced to a largely common form by plotting on appropriate coördinates.

Species-specific differences such as commonly exist between blood and tissue proteins could, perhaps, be produced by comparatively trivial alterations in the proteins themselves, though the altered proteins would, of course, have to stand the test of general compatibility. Successful alterations at the protein level might well form the basis of morphological changes at higher levels. Sickle-cell hemoglobin, as is now well known, differs from normal hemoglobin in only a single amino-acid among the hundreds that are present, but it alters the properties and behavior of the erythrocytes even to the extent of profoundly changing their shape when the hemoglobin is deoxygenated. There is no lack of evidence that morphological form can be profoundly influenced by chemical factors, as witness the numerous induction and organization phenomena encountered in embryology.

The response of a self-limited hierarchical arrangement such as is postulated here also ties up with a good deal of what is known about biochemical genetics. The majority of experimentally induced mutations are loss mutations, which may be lethal or may impose restrictions on the distribution of the species concerned. If, for example, mutation results in the blocking of some bio-synthetic pathway, the chances are that the whole system will die off because of the interference with chemical dynamics at one or another level of the whole organization. Mutants in which an enzyme involved in the conversion of substance A to substance B is lost can survive only in media in which B is preformed and available.

This may have ecological consequences of considerable importance, for it may lead to the establishment of commensalism or some form of symbiosis. Too many loss mutations of this sort, leading to very exacting nutritional requirements, could lead on to so intimate a dependence upon some second organism as to initiate an eventually wholly parasitic mode of survival. Still further mutations of the same kind could then lead on to the specificity that is such a marked and intriguing feature of parasitism as a whole.

Not all loss mutations are lethal, however, nor do all have ecological consequences of this kind, as we ourselves bear witness. Of the series of uricolytic enzymes—urico-oxidase, allantoinase, and allantoicase—that are present in most invertebrates and in some lower vertebrates, allantoicase is lost early on. Its loss is followed by that of allantoinase in mammals generally, in which only urico-oxidase survives. But in man and the higher apes even this last vestige of the original uricolytic system has disappeared. Probably all these must be mutational losses, and without doubt many more similar, non-lethal loss mutations have occurred in the course of evolution.

This suggests that, once a complex organizational pattern has been built up, parts of the whole can sometimes be dispensed with with impunity. They may even be replaced by others. This has happened, for example, in the replacement of ureotelism by uricotelism, with a regional overlap where both are used together at the same time. But the addition of new bits and pieces, depending as they do upon change or gain (as opposed to loss) mutations must be very rare. They are so rare precisely because of the manifold limitations imposed by everything that went before.

A good many other biological problems could be discussed against this same general background—the status of the theory of recapitulation and "the law of Dollo" of the paleontologists, for instance (Baldwin, 1937). There are challenges galore for the comparative biochemist in this large and very general field.

Progress within this field is bound to be difficult and slow at first and will call for many new techniques, experimental and conceptual alike, and much intellectual ingenuity. There will doubtless be many obstacles in the way, but, when one considers how biochemistry has progressed and how many technical and theoretical difficulties it has surmounted in its few short years of independence, there is no

312 ERNEST BALDWIN

need to despair. If the ideas propounded here could be developed and exploited, the outcome might well prove to be of the greatest importance to biological materials of many kinds and to reflect new light upon many broad biological problems, and not least upon those which surround the general biology of the lower Metazoa.

REFERENCES

Ackermann, D., F. Holtz, and H. Reinwein.
  1923   Reindarstellung und Konstitutionsermittelung des Tetramins, eines Giftes aus *Aktinia equina*. Z. Biol. 79:113–120.
Arnold, A., and J. M. Luck
  1933   Studies on arginine. II. The arginine content of vertebrate and invertebrate muscle. J. biol. Chem. 99:677–691.
Asano, M., and M. Itoh.
  1960   Salivary poison of a marine gastropod, *Neptunea arthritica* Bernardi, and the seasonal variation of its toxicity. In conference on: "Biochemistry and Pharmacology of Compounds Derived from Marine Organisms." Ann. N. Y. Acad. Sci. 90:674–688.
Baldwin, E.
  1937   Rigidification in Phylogeny. Pp. 99–107 in: Perspectives in Biochemistry. Needham, J., and D. E. Green, Eds. Cambridge Univ.
Baldwin, E., and W. H. Yudkin
  1949   The annelid phosphagen: with a note on phosphagen in Echinodermata and Protochordata. Proc. roy. Soc. B136:614–631.
Eggleton, P., and G. P. Eggleton.
  1927   The inorganic phosphate and a labile form of organic phosphate in the gastrocnemius of the frog. Biochem. J. 21:190–195.
  1928   Further observations on phosphagen. J. Physiol. 65:15–24.
Ennor, A. H., and J. F. Morrison.
  1958   Biochemistry of the phosphagens and related guanidines. Physiol. Rev. 38:631–674.
Fänge, R.
  1960   The salivary gland of *Neptunea antiqua*. In conference on: "Biochemistry and Pharmacology of Compounds Derived from Marine Organisms." Ann. N. Y. Acad. Sci. 90:689–694.
Fiske, C. H., and Y. SubbaRow.
  1927   The nature of the "inorganic phosphate" in voluntary muscle. Science 65:401–403.
  1929   Phosphocreatine. J. biol. Chem. 81:629–679.
Gasteiger, E. L., P. C. Haake, and J. A. Gergen.
  1960   An investigation of the distribution and function of homarine (N-methyl picolinic acid). In conference on: "Biochemistry and Pharmacology of Compounds Derived from Marine Organisms." Ann. N. Y. Acad. Sci. 90:622–636.
Heidelberger, C., E. P. Abraham, and S. Lepkovsky.
  1949a   Concerning the mechanism of the mammalian conversion of tryptophane into nicotinic acid. J. biol. Chem. 176:1461–1462.
  1949b   Tryptophan metabolism. II. Concerning the mechanism of the mammalian conversion of tryptophan into nicotinic acid. *Ibid.* 179:151–155.

Heidelberger, C., M. E. Gullberg, A. L. Morgan, and S. Lepkovsky.
  1949   *Idem*. I. Concerning the mechanism of the mammalian conversion of
          tryptophan into kynurenine, kynurenic acid, and nicotinic acid. *Ibid*.
          179:143–150.

Holtz, F., F. Kutscher, and F. Thielmann.
  1924   Über das Vorkommen des Pflanzenalkaloids Trigonellin in der Tierwelt.
          Z. Biol. 81:57–60.

Hoppe-Seyler, G. A.
  1933   Über das Homarin, einer bisher unbekannte tierische Base. Hoppe-Seyl.
          Z. 222:105–115.

Hunter, A.
  1928   Creatine and Creatinine. Longmans, Green, London.

Kurtz, A. C., and J. M. Luck.
  1935   Studies on annelid muscle. I. Taurine in *Audouinia spirabranchus*, Moore.
          J. biol. Chem. 111:577–584.

Kutscher, F., and D. Ackermann.
  1931   Über das alternative Vorkommen von Kreatin(in) und Arginin bei Verte-
          braten beziehungsweise Avertebraten. Hoppe-Seyl. Z. 199:266–272.
  1933a   Über das Vorkommen von Betainen in der Archenmuschel. *Ibid*. 221:
          33–39.
  1933b   The comparative biochemistry of the vertebrates and invertebrates. Ann.
          Rev. Biochem. 2:355–376.
  1936   Comparative biochemistry of the vertebrates and invertebrates. *Ibid*.
          5:453–462.

Lane, C. E.
  1960   The toxin of *Physalia* nematocysts. In conference on: "Biochemistry and
          Pharmacology of Compounds Derived from Marine Organisms." Ann.
          N. Y. Acad. Sci. 90:742–750.

Mathias, A. P., D. M. Ross, and M. Schachter.
  1960   The distribution of 5-hydroxytryptamine, tetramethylammonium, ho-
          marine, and other substances in sea anemones. J. Physiol. 151:296–311.

Meyerhof, O., and K. Lohmann.
  1928   Über die naturlichen Guanidinophosphorsäuren (Phosphagene) in der
          quergestreiften Muskulatur. Biochem. Z. 196:22–48.

Needham, D. M., J. Needham, E. Baldwin, and J. Yudkin.
  1932   A comparative study of the phosphagens, with some remarks on the
          origin of vertebrates. Proc. roy. Soc. B110:260–294.

Roche, J., N. V. Thoai, I. Garcia, and Y. Robin.
  1952   Sur la nature et la répartition des guanidines monosubstituées dans les
          tissus des Invertébrés. Présence des dérivés guanidiques nouveaux chez des
          Annélides. C. R. Soc. Biol., Paris 146:1902–1905.

Thoai, N. V., and Y. Robin.
  1954a   Métabolisme des dérivés guanidylés. II. Isolement de la guanidotaurine
          (taurocyamine) et de l'acide guanidoacétique (glycocyamine) des Vers
          marins. Biochim. Biophys. Acta 13:533–536.
  1954b   *Idem*. IV. Sur une nouvelle guanidine monosubstituée biologique, l'ester
          guanidoethylseryl phosphorique (lombricine) et le phosphagène cor-
          respondant. *Ibid*. 14:76–79.

Thoai, N. V., J. Roche, Y. Robin, and N. V. Thiem.
  1953a   Sur deux nouveaux phosphagènes: la phosphotaurocyamine et la phospho-
          glycocyamine. C. R. Soc. Biol., Paris 147:1241–1243.

1953b   Sur le phosphagène de *Lumbricus terrestris* sp. *Ibid.* 147:1670–1672.
1953c   Sur la présence de la glycocyamine (acide guanidylacétique), de la tauro-
         cyamine (guanidyltaurine) et des phosphagènes correspondantes dans les
         muscles des Vers marins. Biochim. biophys. Acta 11:593.

Woodger, J. H.
1930   The "concept of organism" and the relation between embryology and
         genetics. Part II. Quart. Rev. Biol. 5:438–463.
1931   *Idem.* Part III. *Ibid.* 6:178–207.

23 ◆ Nutrient Media for Axenic Organisms, with Special Reference to Micrometazoa

ELLSWORTH C. DOUGHERTY

DEPARTMENT OF NUTRITIONAL SCIENCES, COLLEGE OF AGRICULTURE,
UNIVERSITY OF CALIFORNIA, BERKELEY

Short of the context of a major treatise, which is yet to be realized for comparative nutrition, consideration of nutrient media for organisms grown or maintained axenically cannot be other than superficial. A general scanning, impressive in intellectual scope, has been realized by S. H. Hutner (1962) with an essay in a recent book, *This Is Life*. In the brief treatment here, I can hope to touch only on the highlights of my subject, with a few additional remarks, by way of example, in the area with which I am most familiar—namely, culture of micrometazoa (most of them falling in groups reasonably recognizable as "lower Metazoa").

Axenic organisms are individuals or populations of individuals of a given species isolated from members of all other species and from living cells thereof so that all the nutrition of the one or more *axenites* is provided, in an immediate sense, by non-living substances. Thus, the axenic state is to be distinguished from any in which more than one species are present. In the following discussion use is made of a nomenclature beyond "axenic," evolved to cope with the concepts of various associations of species (see table 23-1). If there is one or more accompanying forms, which are known or at least numerable, the culture is *synxenic*.

It is possible to make a further refinement of this aspect of the terminology according to the number of species present along with the one of interest—thus, *monoxenic* for one additional form; *dixenic* for two; etc. Axenic and synxenic assemblages are collectively *gnotobiotic*—that is, *known* as to *living* forms present. Such associations are to be contrasted with cultures in which there is a mixed population of subordinate forms, at least partly unknown in composition; then, with respect to the species of concern, the systems are *agnotobiotic,* or—designated by a less cumbersome word—*xenic*.

As organisms, I exclude viruses, which cannot be grown free of host cells, yet,

The preparation of this chapter has been aided by Grants G-18122 and G-23914 of the National Science Foundation.

TABLE 23-1

TERMINOLOGY FOR GROWTH OF ORGANISMS, MOSTLY UNDER KNOWN
(GNOTOBIOTIC) CONDITIONS

Term	Number of associated organisms	Reference
Gnotobiotic	None, or known species only	Reyniers *et al.* (1949)
Axenic	None	Baker and Ferguson (1942)
Synxenic	One or more known species	
Monoxenic	One known species	
Dixenic	Two known species	Dougherty (1953)
Trixenic	Three known species	
Polyxenic	Many known species	
Agnotobiotic, or xenic	Unknown	Dougherty (1953, 1959)

if present, should not—in my estimation—be considered of themselves as disqualifying the harboring species from being considered to be in a state of *axeny*.[1] The reasoning here is that I think of them in a manner contrary to that by which they are frequently conceptualized. I do not regard them as separate organisms; rather, I believe them to be semi-autonomous derivatives of more complex forms—and thus *without* an independent phylogeny from primitive, free-living ancestors of about the same level of organization. For the purpose of this discussion, I also exclude parts of multicellular forms grown as organ-, tissue-, or cell-aggregate-cultures, which do not constitute organisms in a strict sense, although, admittedly, the distinction may be without clear meaning if one considers such pleomorphic forms as sponges, multicellular fungi, and algae, and even higher plants, or metaphytes. In fact, insistence upon cultivation of the intact organism must be reckoned as very restrictive with respect to the many-celled land plants for which a relatively voluminous literature exists on "tissue culture" (see, especially, Gautheret, 1959) and a relatively modest one on cultivation of intact organisms (see, for example: Nilsson, 1957; Stotzky, Culbreth, and Mish, 1962). The same observation can be applied to the literature on the rearing of germ-free vertebrates *versus* vertebrate tissue elements.

I need also to discriminate terms with respect to the media themselves. Most broadly conceived, a nutrient medium (by which can be understood "nutrient diet" as well) is any environment or part thereof that nourishes. But I orient the consideration here primarily around media (or diets) that provide sustenance in the specific context of *indefinite cultivation* of a given species, generation after generation, with serial subculture at the will of the investigator. A second set of relatively new nomenclatural terms is used in the present discussion—in this instance reflecting state of chemical definition (see table 23-2). Thus, a medium

---

[1] In an earlier paper (Dougherty, 1953), for the state of being axenic I used "axenity"; this word must be reckoned as of hybrid Greek-Latin derivation. "Axeny" is better formed, being consistent with classic rules of word-derivation from Greek into English.

TABLE 23-2

TERMINOLOGY FOR MEDIA (USED FOR GROWING ORGANISMS)
IN TERMS OF DEGREE OF CHEMICAL DEFINITION

Term	Definition
Oligidic	Pertaining to a medium, consisting wholly or largely of crude materials, in which no compound (other, presumptively, than water and circumambient gases) has been clearly implicated as an absolute nutritional requirement.
Meridic	Pertaining to a medium in which the chemical identity of certain, but not all, of the essential component molecules has been established. (Media in which most of such requirements are known are *highly* meridic; those in which but one or a few are known are *slightly* meridic.)
Holidic	Pertaining to a medium whose intended constituents, other than purified inert materials, have exactly known chemical structure before the medium is compounded.

NOTE: Of these three terms, originating with Dougherty (1959), *meridic* and *oligidic* have been considerably recast, and the definitions of all three have been generalized, as compared with their earlier formulation, in order to extend their applicability to media consisting entirely of inorganic constituents.

for the axenic organism may be a crude mixture of substances—*i.e.,* may be *oligidic*—hence have no specific chemically defined component known with certainty to be essential. (Of course, there are always circumstantial points of evidence; for instance, either the medium is in aqueous solution or suspension, or both, implicating water and environmental gases as nutrients, or the diet may be dry in an atmospheric milieu, likewise suggesting a gaseous requirement.) Or chemical compounds may be more than presumptively demonstrated as essential; thus, when a medium consists partly of substances whose necessary role is known for the organism, such a mixture is *meridic*. Or, finally, it may be possible to provide an *holidic* medium—*i.e.,* consisting, at the time of compounding, entirely of substances whose exact chemical structure, including steric configuration, is known. Arguments for using this nomenclature instead of the ambiguous words "defined," "synthetic," or "artificial" and their derivatives are given by me elsewhere (Dougherty, 1959).

Although axenic conditions may not be necessary for the exact working out, within contemporary bounds of inevitable error, of most of the exogenous requirements for some organisms (especially the large-sized autotrophic plants and comparably big heterotrophic multicellular animals), it is at least theoretically true that the needs of any species can be known with least uncertainty if they have been determined with the organism isolated from other forms. Needs may be relatively very simple for autotrophs or near-autotrophs—such as many protists and higher green plants; for they may be very complex for extreme heterotrophs—such as some protists (bacteria and animalic protozoa) and as metazoa.

Nutrient Requirements in Terms of Chemical Elements

Before considering the media or diets of axenic organisms, it is useful to review, in passing, the least common denominator of constituents that living creatures require from the environment. If one excludes physical effects such as radiant energy and the like, the basic essentials are patently the chemical elements themselves. Thinking of nutrients in such minimal terms, one must view $_1H$, $_6C$, $_7N$, $_8O$, and $_{15}P$ as irreducible needs in protein and nucleic acid construction, with $_{16}S$ added for protein. But, just as clearly, these must be conceived of not as neutral atoms, but as chemical reactants; thus they are ionic in form or united as one or more atomic species, the degree of combination necessary being dependent upon the element and upon the organism concerned. Hence requirements in elemental terms are inevitably abstractions. Nevertheless, expressed as such, they constitute a usefully simple first approach to nutritional essentiality. In addition to the six elements specified, it is probable that absolute requirements for several others exist for all living forms—almost certainly for $_{26}Fe$ and probably for certain additional ones, even if, in some instances, at very low levels. Most organisms, in fact, seem to require, as essentials, $_{11}K$, $_{12}Mg$, $_{20}Ca$, $_{25}Mn$, $_{29}Cu$, and $_{30}Zn$. And more than half the members of the first four periods of elements, and a few of the fifth period, are implicated as irreplaceable participants in the metabolism of at least some organisms. (For a summary of nutritional requirements by element see Spector, 1956.)

Nutrient Requirements in Terms of Natural Chemical Configuration

Knowledge of the elements required in an organism's dietary is by no means an automatic key to the provision of a suitable medium—whether oligidic, meridic, or holidic. For this there must be an understanding of the ionic form or compounds in which the elements must be present and the quantities and relative levels of each component.

The completely photoautotrophic or chemautotrophic organism can subsist on a holidic medium of properly balanced mineral salts in solution and essential circumambient gases. The salts are hydrated ions of single elements or of compound ions, each typically comprised of an element combined with oxygen.

In an evolutionary sense, many lines of evidence, which are too elaborate to follow out here (see Dougherty and Allen, 1960), suggest that all living organisms today had, as a common ancestral group, photoautotrophic forms for which mineral salts and gases such as CO_2 and possibly N_2 provided all nutrient requirements. But a host of organisms are variously heterotrophic—that is, they must have sundry organic compounds in the nutrient environment: reduced carbon compounds, with hydrogen and oxygen, such as carbohydrates and fatty acids for energy and for building of many organic compounds; reduced carbon-nitrogen or carbon-nitrogen-sulfur compounds, also with hydrogen and oxygen, such as amino acids for protein or nucleic acid building; traces of special organic compounds—the vitamins and growth factors—as catalysts in numerous metabolic processes; and additional organic compounds for other purposes. By the evolutionary theory advocated here, these requirements progressively developed as various groups of organisms found it possible to exploit the biosynthetic competence of others coëxisting in the biosphere.

The essential components of a medium can be usefully thought of as macronutrient and micronutrient, the dividing line being essentially arbitrary. Whether autotrophic or heterotrophic, an organism needs at the macronutrient level the six elements collectively found in protein and nucleic acid. For all living entities certain mineral salts—although partly differing ones depending upon the group of organisms—must also be provided to yield hydrated ions at what is commonly regarded to be a macronutrient level. In the micronutrient category are mineral ions, simple or compound, of the so-called trace elements and, for many organisms, the organic compounds termed vitamins or growth factors.

At whatever level of nutritional complexity an organism's requirements may be, a vital feature that must be met in a satisfactory nutrient medium—in addition to what the needed components are—is how much, relative to one another, of each substance must be included. Some living groups have a wide range of tolerance by reason of an ability to absorb components selectively from media of relatively wide differences in composition; others have this ability to much more limited degrees. But in all instances there is a crucial interrelationship of nutrient substituents in the medium or diet, which can be expressed as a range of permissible ratios among the individual components. The problems of nutritional balance are exceedingly complex to study, for they rest on multiple variable factors that, by most present methodologies, call for changing levels of single components one at a time, or omitting them singly. New approaches to this problem of nutritional balance are needed in which simultaneous multiple changes can be more meaningfully studied.

The Major Groups of Living Organisms and Their Nutrient Needs

Let us now turn our attention from general requirements of all organisms to needs by major groups. For this purpose it is convenient to treat the living world in three great categories, which are implicit in the foregoing discussion: (1) the protists—bacteria, algae, fungi, and protozoa (*sensu restricto*); (2) the multicellular higher plants; and (3) the multicellular animals.

The protists.—In the context of the three groups enumerated, the most varied requirements are to be found, by present knowledge, among the protists, which embrace a great and diversified assemblage of primitive organisms. Here there are, at one extreme, many blue-green algae, which can subsist axenically on aqueous solutions of mineral salts, without initially added carbon or nitrogen, provided that sufficient gaseous CO_2 and N_2 are available in the surrounding atmosphere. At the other extreme are bacteria such as lactobacilli that require, *inter alia,* the 18 fundamental amino acids of protein; also there are the animalistic protozoa with many organic requirements—probably no less than twenty—in addition to mineral needs. The most thoroughly studied of the protozoa in this sense are certain of the ciliates and members of the zoöflagellate and ameboid groups. In between these extreme autotrophs and heterotrophs is a vast array of bacteria and fungi, with varying nutritional patterns.

The protists have been more extensively and intensively studied nutritionally under axenic conditions than either higher plants or higher animals. In fact, by common parlance the expression "pure culture" is then used for these organisms; and, in the context of such cultivation, the word "pure" has such time-honored usage that it is unambiguous despite its multiple meanings in many situations. But I adhere in this discussion to the word "axenic" out of preference for a term of unmistakable meaning whenever one speaks of a species of organism grown free of others (Dougherty, 1959).

The fact that there is such a large body of work on the axenic nutrition of protists rests on the easy "domesticability" of a great many forms to growth by themselves on media relatively easy to provide. A signal further advantage that has doubtless fostered such studies is the generally small protistan size, which lends these organisms to cultivation in receptacles of modest dimensions, especially test tubes.

For the bacteria there is no single comprehensive modern review of nutrient media for axenic culture, probably because the field is too old and vast. Bacterial nutrition is usually surveyed each year in the *Annual Review of Microbiology.* The same thing is true for fungi. For algae there is the excellent review of Provasoli (1958), which covers, *inter alia,* the unicellular flagellated phototrophs that are also often treated by the zoölogist as in his province. There is lacking a comprehensive recent review on the animalistic protists, or protozoa *sensu restricto;* but a great deal of information is to be found in the pages of the burgeoning *Journal of Protozoology,* which attests to the rapid growth of the field. The time draws nigh for a good synthesis that will review and tie this varied literature together. No doubt the most thoroughly studied protozoa are the ciliate *Tetrahymena pyriformis* and close relatives, which were the first organisms of essentially animal-type nutrition to be grown axenically on an holidic medium (see Kidder, 1953).

The higher plants.—The fact that many species of metaphytes studied hydroponically without axenic precautions show a simple mineral nutrition has made it possible to define their dietary needs so far as one can tell. There remain, nevertheless, tantalizing questions, in such xenic systems, as to possible contributions of trace nutrients by associated microflora and microfauna.

It is not appropriate to itemize here the literature on studies of intact axenic plants. Of particular interest, however, is work with such minute higher forms as the monocotyledonous duckweeds—family Lemnaceae—which float on the surface of water. Recently the subject of their biology, including cultivation, has been admirably reviewed by Hillman (1961). The Lemnaceae can be axenically reared and subcultured indefinitely on holidic media in which all requirements are met by inorganic salts. And it seems fair to assume that, to a wide extent, higher plants share this attribute of many phototrophic protists, bacterial and algal—namely, no need for organic substances in the diet. But it should be remarked by way of caution that the duckweeds are probably unique among metaphytes in meeting the criterion of long-term axenic growth with repeated subculture as set out at the beginning of this discussion.

A number of plants have been studied in such a way that, in each instance, the root system is kept axenically in sterile soil and the aërial part of the plant is exposed to a xenic environment with a barrier covering the soil and encircling the stalk tightly enough that the root system's axenic state is not invaded. Ingenious methods have been developed for feeding the roots and for sampling their exudates aseptically (Stotzky, Culbreth, and Mish, 1962).

The higher animals.—Like the metaphytes, the multicellular animals, or metazoa, have been irregularly studied axenically. Prolonged cultivation has been realized with members of a few, only, of the major taxa.

A striking fact about growing metazoa—whether vertebrate or invertebrate—is that the status of their most advanced cultivation or rearing contrasts markedly with that of many protists and certain higher plants: namely, unlike the latter groups, the multicellular animals count among their members *no form* that has been grown axenically for indefinite periods, generation after generation, *on an holidic medium.* The closest approach has been with the fruit fly *Drosophila melanogaster,* as is explained further on.

The tradition of growing vertebrates, the only large metazoa to be reared axenically, has, for the most part, been independent of work on invertebrates—to an important extent, no doubt, because the preoccupying and formidable problems of biological engineering that have had to be solved for the maintaining of the former in an axenic environment are of a higher order of magnitude than those besetting the student of invertebrate nutrition, particularly those concerned with minute forms or micrometazoa.

The status of vertebrate work was reviewed recently in a volume edited by Reyniers (1959). In certain respects, study of relatively large vertebrates has a parallel with that of higher plants. With animals much larger than their microbial associates, nutritional requirements have been determined with high precision without the imposition of axenic conditions. Thus it is known that the several vertebrate species exhaustively studied—practically all being laboratory mammals (mouse, rat, guinea pig, etc.) or economically important domesticated mammals and birds—have, with a few important exceptions, over-all requirements like those of the axenically studied ciliates already mentioned. From xenic investigations of these vertebrates one can recognize a group of ten amino acids (arginine, histidine, isoleucine, leucine, lysine, methionine, phenylalanine, threonine, tryptophane, and valine) and six vitamins of the B group (folic acid, niacin, pantothen, pyridoxine, riboflavin, and thiamine) as generally essential. But because the classical results with vertebrates derive from work with xenic systems we are inevitably left with the ambiguities of possible micronutrient contributions from microbial associates to their hosts. Some studies of axenic vertebrates have been made with variously meridic diets, but none as yet with holidic.

With invertebrates long-term axenic studies have been conducted on representatives of but three phyla out of the twenty-five or so into which a number of leading zoölogists compartmentalize the Metazoa—namely, the Arthropoda, Aschelminthes, and Annelida. Work with arthropods, mostly insects, has been relatively extensive (see reviews of Dougherty, 1959; House, 1961). Studies with aschelminths have mainly emphasized nematodes (especially *Caenorhabditis briggsae*—see Dougherty *et al.,* 1959; Dougherty, 1960), although there has been limited work with one species of rotifer (Dougherty, Solberg, and Ferral, 1961). The first axenic cultivation of an annelid (*Enchytraeus fragmentosus*—see fig. 23-1) has been only recently realized (Dougherty and Solberg, 1961). With the last species interesting discoveries (Ferral, Dougherty, and Brody, 1961a,b; Dougherty *et al.,* 1963) have been conditions whereunder tumor-like growths have been inducible and lysis has been elicitable, the latter with the apparent concomitant—possibly causative—production of an entity resembling some of the non-inclusion viruses of insects.

In work with micrometazoa synxenic cultivation of certain rotifers additional to the one grown axenically has also been obtained, and relatively controlled condi-

FIGURE 23-1.*Enchytraeus fragmentosus:* Seven "adult" microannelids of this gonadless species from axenic culture, killed and fixed with 5 per cent formalin. Present magnification: approximately 15 ×. (Photomicrograph by Victor G. Duran, Scientific Photographic Laboratory, University of California, Berkeley.)

tions have been established for xenically rearing a number of additional nematodes and rotifers (see Dougherty, 1960), as well as a species of gastrotrichs (*Lepidodermella squamata*), one of tardigrades (*Hypsibius arcticus*—see fig. 23-2) and some undetermined kinds of turbellarians and tyroglyphid mites. A major aim of this work has been the ultimate adaptation of such organisms to axenic culture and the development of them as tools in the search for possible new growth factors and in other basic nutritional studies. But such instances as the interesting growth phenomena of the aforementioned microannelid have served to draw attention to ways in which axenic culture techniques can be exploited in the study of other fundamental biological problems.

As already alluded to briefly, it has been axenic work with the fruitfly *Drosophila melanogaster* that has come closest to yielding long-term cultivation on a near-holidic medium for a metazoan species (particularly the work of Hinton—see Dougherty, 1959, table 3). A residual question as to holidicity remains because agar, the vehicle of Hinton's diet, is a complex polysaccharide from which a conceivable nutrient contribution cannot be precluded. In any event, growth has been for only a few generations—hence without prolonged subcultivation. Admirable work by Sang (1959) and Sang and King (1961) with the axenic cultivation of *Drosophila* on meridic diets has been of very high caliber; that these media must be regarded as meridic rather than holidic is a consequence of the fact that they have contained such relatively undefined chemicals as RNA (instead of nucleotides, or their bases) and as casein (instead of amino acids).

Work with rhabditid nematodes such as *Caenorhabditis briggsae* is somewhat less far along toward a controlled nutrient environment (Dougherty *et al.,* 1959). *C. briggsae* has been sustained axenically in an oligidic medium since 1954.

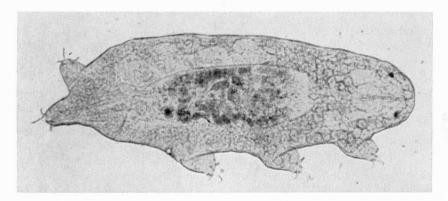

FIGURE 23-2. *Hypsibius arcticus,* a live tardigrade of antarctic provenance (despite specific name), maintained in xenic culture. It is here viewed from above and to the right so that only five of its eight legs are visible; the two eye-spots, pharynx with stylet, and gut are clearly evident in outline. Present magnification: 220 ×. (Photomicrograph by Victor G. Duran, Scientific Photographic Laboratory, University of California, Berkeley.)

Moderately meridic media, in which at least one liver fraction is the undefined component, have been worked out in more recent years, and both vitamin and amino acid requirements have been at least tentatively identified (Dougherty *et al.,* 1959; Nicholas, Hansen, and Dougherty, 1962).

The medium for the rotifer (*Lecane inermis*) referred to as having been grown axenically was crudely oligidic. What seems to have been the crucial component has not so far proved reproducible (Dougherty, Ferral, and Solberg, unpublished results) in a form active for the rotifer; this was a gently heated, Seitz-filtered liver extract that was a basic ingredient of the mixture on which some five months of cultivation of the organism with five subcultures were realized. The medium for the annelid (*Enchytraeus fragmentosus*) is also crudely oligidic, being ostensibly based upon a liver extract of the same recipe as that successful once with *L. inermis;* in contrast to experience with the rotifer, however, the annelid has grown on each of several preparations made.

As regards definition of the nutrient media or diets, the over-all picture of the axenic cultivation of multicellular animals is, in summary, still in a very primitive state as compared with work on protists and higher plants. This is an area of scientific inquiry that deserves much increased attention.

Conclusion

What contributions to general biology do or can nutrient media for axenic organisms make? The literal answering of this question would be impracticably complex for the present paper; the only reasonable alternative is to advance examples, actual or potential, of such contributions. In vital respects these are already strikingly evident for the bacterial and fungal protists. As a particularly good example one may point to the vast antibiotic industry, which is based upon the axenic culture, on suitable media, of such bacteria as actinomycetes and such molds as *Penicillium notatum*. Vitamin B_{12}, an important therapeutic agent in the treatment of pernicious anemia, is made commercially as a product of actinomycete metabolism.

Media for higher plants and for metazoa, including diets for germ-free vertebrates, have not yet shown widespread direct economic application. That such media may prove useful in rendering these forms suitable, for example, as assay organisms and test subjects for pharmaceutical products is largely a consideration for the future, but it seems a reasonable prediction that such application will evolve.

In particular, I would emphasize the promise of many micrometazoa—such as nematodes, rotifers, small annelids, etc. These are organisms small enough to be treated with the ease ordinarily associated with work based on protists. Not only are the micrometazoa minute, but they have very fast growth rates, nearer those of rapidly reproducing unicellular forms than those of higher animals—yet they stand much closer, on a number of lines of evidence, to the higher animals, including man, than do the bacteria and other conventional creatures in laboratory culture. The micrometazoa are, in effect, something in the nature of test-tube humanoids. It seems reasonable to predict that working out nutrient media for their axenic cultivation will provide many opportunities for asking questions—physiological, biochemical, nutritional, pharmacological, etc.—pertinent to the human organism and receiving the answers much more simply and swiftly than by putting the same problems to test with the costlier, larger, and more slowly responding laboratory mammals and birds now traditionally used as test objects. For example, putting a test tube of nematodes in a space capsule has indubitable advantages over placing a mouse cage therein if the questions and answers desired can be made comparable.

I think that in the coming decade the minute invertebrates will be finding roles by which they will become familiar to the experimental biologist, whether engaged in fundamental work or on economic problems of research, development, or standard laboratory procedures.

REFERENCES

Baker, J. A., and M. S. Ferguson
    1942   Growth of the platyfish (*Platypoecilus maculatus*) free from bacteria. Proc. Soc. exp. Biol., N. Y. 51:116–119.

Dougherty, E. C.
1953   Problems of nomenclature for the growth of organisms of one species with and without associated organisms of other species. J. Parasit. 42: 259–261.
1959   Introduction to axenic culture of invertebrate metazoa: a goal. Ann. N. Y. Acad. Sci. 77:27–54.
1960   Cultivation of aschelminths, especially rhabditid nematodes. Pp. 397–418 in: Nematology, Fundamentals and Recent Advances with Emphasis on Plant Parasitic and Soil Forms. Sasser, J. N., and W. R. Jenkins, Eds. Univ. N. Carolina, Chapel Hill.
Dougherty, E. C., and M. B. Allen
1960   Is pigmentation a clue to protistan phylogeny? Pp. 129–144 in: Comparative Biochemistry of Photoreactive Pigments. Allen, M. B., Ed. Academic Press, New York, London.
Dougherty, E. C., D. J. Ferral, B. Brody, and M. L. Gotthold
1963   A growth anomaly and lysis with production of virus-like particles in an axenically reared microannelid. Nature 198:973–975
Dougherty, E. C., E. L. Hansen, W. L. Nicholas, J. A. Mollett, and E. A. Yarwood
1959   Axenic cultivation of *Caenorhabditis briggsae* (Nematoda: Rhabditidae) with unsupplemented and supplemented chemically defined media. Ann. N. Y. Acad. Sci. 77:176–217.
Dougherty, E. C., and B. Solberg
1961   Axenic cultivation of an enchytraeid annelid. Nature 192:184–185.
Dougherty, E. C., B. Solberg, and D. J. Ferral
1961   The first axenic cultivation of a rotifer species. Experientia 17:131–132.
Ferral, D. J., E. C. Dougherty, and B. Brody
1961a   Conditions leading to lysis in axenically grown microannelids of the species *Enchytraeus fragmentosus* Bell, '59. Amer. Zoologist 1:447.
1961b   Conditions leading to tumor production in axenically grown microannelids of the species *Enchytraeus fragmentosus* Bell, '59. *Ibid*. 1:447–448.
Gautheret, R. J.
1959   La Culture des Tissus Végétaux. Techniques et Réalisations. Masson, Paris.
Hillman, W. S.
1961   The Lemnaceae, or duckweeds. A review of the descriptive and experimental literature. Bot. Rev. 27:221–287.
House, H. L.
1961   Insect nutrition. Ann. Rev. Entomol. 6:13–26.
Hutner, S. H.
1962   Nutrition of protists. Pp. 109–137 in: This Is Life: Essays in Modern Biology. Johnson, W. H., and W. C. Steere, Eds. Holt, Rinehart and Winston, New York.
Journal of Protozoology: Sundry articles on protistan nutrition.
Kidder G. W.
1953   The nutrition of invertebrate animals. Pp. 162–196 in: Biochemistry and Physiology of Nutrition. Vol. 2. Bourne, G. H., and G. W. Kidder, Eds. Academic Press, New York.
Nicholas, W. L., E. Hansen, and E. C. Dougherty
1962   The B-vitamins required by *Caenorhabditis briggsae* (Rhabditidae). Nematologica 8:129–135.

Nilsson, P. E.
    1957   Aseptic cultivation of higher plants. Arch. Mikrobiol. 26:285–301.
Provasoli, L.
    1958   Nutrition and ecology of protozoa and algae. Ann. Rev. Microbiol. 12: 279–308.
Reyniers, J. A. (Consulting Ed.)
    1959   Germfree vertebrates: present status. Ann. N. Y. Acad. Sci. 78:1–400.
Reyniers, J. A., P. C. Trexler, R. F. Ervin, M. Wagner, T. D. Luckey, and H. A. Gordon
    1949   The need for a unified terminology in germ-free life studies. LOBUND Reports 2:151–162.
Sang J. H.
    1959   Circumstances affecting the nutritional requirements of *Drosophila melanogaster*. Ann. N. Y. Acad. Sci. 77:352–365.
Sang, J. H., and R. C. King
    1961   Nutritional requirements of axenically cultured *Drosophila melanogaster* adults. J. exp. Biol. 38:793–809.
Spector, W. S.
    1956   Handbook of Biological Data. Saunders, Philadelphia, London.
Stotzky, G., W. Culbreth, and L. B. Mish
    1962   Apparatus for growing plants with aseptic roots for collection of root exudates and CO_2. Plant Physiol. 37:332–341.

B. COELENTERATA, OR CNIDARIA

24 ◆ Siphonophores, Bud Colonies, and Superorganisms

G. O. MACKIE

DEPARTMENT OF ZOÖLOGY, UNIVERSITY OF ALBERTA,
EDMONTON, ALBERTA

The problem of what constitutes an individual is an old one and was at one time much discussed by philosophers and naturalists. Attempts were made to classify animals and plants according to the level of individuality to which they had attained. Goethe, in suggesting that a plant could be viewed as an association of primary individuals (represented by leaves, stamens, petals, etc.), seems to have been largely responsible for a school of thought that, whatever truths it may have enshrined, produced some bizarre arguments. Perrier (1898) here serves us as a source of reference for the early writings on colonialism and individuality.

Individuality: Theories and Generalizations

From supposing that plants were colonies of organisms (phytons) the logical development was to treat animals similarly. It is true that authentic animal colonies exist: bryozoa, tunicates, corals, etc.; but zealous theorists extended the colony concept to the segmented worms and arthropods, viewing the annelid, say, as a sort of colony of segments (primary individuals, zoönites) united into a superorganism having its own, or secondary, individuality. This point of view necessitated granting to annelid worms an individuality of a different order from that of molluscs, a conclusion that would today find little favor. The vertebrates, a metamerically derived group, were also brought into line as "animaux zoonités," and there were outright statements by serious zoölogists that "the vertebrates are colonies" (*e.g.*, Perrier, 1898). It is possible, of course, to regard the metazoön as a colony of cells, so individuality can be made to ascend in steps from the cellular level up through tissues (which according to Virchow possessed their own order of individuality) to organs (where Bernard maintained the same), to the segment (in the case of zoönited forms), and to the individual organism itself. This by no means represents the ultimate degree of individuality, for the animal colonies *sensu stricto,* particularly the higher, polymorphic ones, require consideration as individuals on a super-organismic level. Above the individual level, too, we may find a social "organism" to which the primary individualities are subordinated. The insect society comes to be regarded as a superorganism. One can go further still, for colonial forms exist, such as certain calycophoran Siphonophora, in which the colony produces by strobilation groups of members ("colonies within the colony"—Beklemishev, 1958) that are eventually set free as eudoxids. For a time, while the eudoxid groups are attached and functional parts of the parent colony, the strobilating colony lays claim to status as a super-superorganism. If one is prepared to transfer the argument to the interspecific level the way is open, as Emerson (1939) points out, for classifying ecological associations by "ascending levels of super-superorganismic integration." The point arrives, however, when one comes to feel that the terms "organism" and "individual" are rapidly losing whatever meaning they originally had, and that it is time to stop classifying and return to an examination of basic principles. It immediately becomes clear that individuality is too elusive a thing to serve as a basis for classifications and schemes of a similar tendency.[1] Individuality is not simply a morphological concept nor an ecological one, but is equally genetical and physiological. Thus, separately born identical twins, though genetically one individual, are, in other respects, two; Siamese twins, on the other hand, though psychologically two individuals, are, in other respects and depending on the particular case, more or less one. We may exercise our minds with teasing questions all we wish. Is *Volvox* an individual metaphyte or a colonial protophyte? Is a tapeworm a "temporary bud-colony"? What is the status of the plasmodium? Is a multinucleate syncytial organism more or less colonial than a multicellular aggregate? Is the fusion aggregate (*Dictyostelium*) classifiable in the same terms as the fission aggregate (*Volvox*)? Are human societies "superorganisms" and, if so, how many humans and of what sorts are required to make one superorganismic unit? Questions such as these titillate the fancy and offer the same escape from actuality as "how many angels can dance on the point of a needle" offered participants in medieval disputations. But they in no way improve our understanding of organic relationships and may, indeed, if carried to excess, lead us out of touch with reality. Biology, as Stern (1962) has remarked, is like the giant Antaeus, becoming increasingly debilitated when lifted off the ground. Instead of attempting to classify end products of evolution, let us turn our attention to the processes by which they have arisen.

A conspicuous feature of organic evolution has been the achievement of increased complexity by means of replication of parts followed by their differentiation

---

[1] L. von Bertalanffy (*Problems of Life*, Watts & Co., London, 1952) provides a chapter on "Levels of Organization," which was overlooked when this paper was written. Bertalanffy suggests that the term "individual" is inapplicable to organisms produced by asexual fission or budding since, by definition, it applies to "something which cannot be divided." Even in higher animals the notion is difficult to apply when one considers cases such as the dizygotic individual newt produced by Spemann from fused half-blastulae, and the human monozygotic twin. Bertalanffy contrasts the "centralizing tendency" of the systems of integration (particularly the nervous system) wi h the "dis-integrative tendency" of the reproductive system and points out that a perfect individual would be one that did not reproduce, for reproduction "presupposes the construction of a new organism from parts of the old." Bertalanffy concludes that the concept of individuality "originates in a sphere quite different from that of science and objective observation. Only in the consciousness of ourselves as beings different from others are we immediately aware of individuality that we cannot define rigidly in the living organisms around us."

and specialization. Thus it appears that the Metazoa and Metaphyta arose from protistan ancestors (probably on several separate occasions—Nursall, 1962) by way of multicellular assemblages within which division of physiological labor and structural differentiation simultaneously and progressively became established. Among the Metazoa the same principle lies behind the process of metamery, the serial repetition of parts within the body. In the earliest metameric forms the serialized units are presumed to have been similar, but in the evolution of higher groups the original series has often become diversified and altered almost out of recognition. Evidently, whatever the initial advantages of metamery (and they may have been quite different in the chordate and annelid-arthropod stem groups), it predisposed its possessors to adaptive evolution on the grand scale. In the invertebrate bud colonies we have a third case where replication-differentiation has been at work. The simple bud colony consists of asexually budded units attached by direct tissue connections. The result is an interconnected assemblage of similar units, genetically all parts of one individual. One could think of the process as "external metamerism" or, alternately, one could think of metamerism as "internal budding," for the two phenomena are similar in principle. Originally bud colonies were monomorphic (and some still are), but in several existing groups, and most of all in the Siphonophora, evolution has led to considerable polymorphic specialization within the primitive series. A final example is that of the social insects. From the simpler communities, which are little more than persistent family groups, we pass to the higher societies with many sorts of individuals, so specialized and so interdependent, both metabolically and behaviorally, that they might as well be in direct physical connection. As Lüscher (1955) argues, the differentiation of castes in the termite society shows features analogous to cellular differentiation in a metazoan embryo.

It seems then that evolution, having produced an aggregate of similar units, next proceeds to develop them in different ways. In all four examples given, we start from simple aggregates. Differentiation ensues. The individual units lose certain functions and gain others. Corporately they become more interdependent as their individual potentialities become restricted. Carried to sufficient lengths, this process may lead to the submergence of the original individualities in the supervening and transcendent corporate individuality. The insect individual loses its individuality in the society, the cell in the body, the somite in the tagma, the zoöid in the colony. In each case a new individuality emerges on a higher plane.

It is doubtful if we can go much further than this in the way of meaningful generalization. The task now becomes one of examining in detail certain phases of the process as it applies in particular groups; we are here concerned with bud colonies in general and with siphonophores in particular.

Evolution of Simple Colonies

Asexually produced colonies are so common in the Invertebrata that one is bound to wonder what advantages the colonial arrangement offers and why it has so often been evolved. The bud colony is not far removed from the asexually reproducing organism in which the buds detach and in some groups both types of organism are found. Thus the majority of hydroids form bud colonies, but in *Hydra* itself the buds detach.

Asexual reproduction has clear advantages. It enables an organism to increase its tissue mass without increasing the size of the individuals. The proliferating tissues go to form numerous replicas of each genetic individual instead of toward making the individual larger. This avoids problems connected with large size and may be beneficial from the point of view of dispersion. The question then is—why were the first colonies, in which the budded individuals failed to separate, successful? One advantage of the colony would seem to be that the retention of the buds naturally leads to a branching, arborizing structure, "a very profitable mode of growth" (Thomson and Geddes, 1931), ensuring a high density of individual zoöids in a given space without overcrowding. As Knight-Jones and Moyse (1961) comment, "the colonial habit regulates competition between zoöids." Where a strong exoskeleton is produced, the colony may form a towering structure, permitting utilization of water layers some distance above the bottom.

A number of advantages of the colonial habit are really advantages associated with close aggregation of individuals and would apply whether or not the individuals were physically connected. It is probable, however, that the first colonies were developed among organisms in which the individuals tended to aggregate, and that the tendency to aggregation later became formalized in the retention of primary connections. We can therefore consider the benefits of aggregation as relevant to our topic. In the case of filter-feeders, close proximity, in addition to increasing turbulence in moving water, would permit the combination of the individual feeding currents and hence shifting of water masses from considerable distances into the vicinity of the colony. In the colonial ectoproct *Plumatella fungosa* the lophophores over wide regions become orientated by muscular action so that they point in the same direction (Mackie, unpublished). In tunicate colonies effluent currents often combine to carry wastes far away from the colony, and, in *Pyrosoma,* to serve for colonial locomotion. Although waste disposal would seem at first sight to be a wholly desirable function in an aggregated population, it is possible that a tendency to accumulate certain metabolites in the vicinity of the population might be important. Loomis (1961) has shown that densely aggregated hydras become sexual through feed-back effects of accumulated metabolites in the micro-environment surrounding them, and there are other possibilities for coördination of functions by what Lucas (1961) calls "ectocrine" mediation. In an established bud colony, however, chemical coördination could be achieved much more directly by means of the connecting tissues, and it is is doubtful that ectocrine influences continue to be important once the colonial stage has been reached. Knight-Jones and Moyse (1961) draw attention to a distinct advantage of the colonial organism over the non-colonial aggregate: if part of the colony is in an unfavorable location, the zoöids and connecting tissues in that region can be absorbed and the material derived from them used elsewhere. In crowded, non-colonial populations (*e.g.,* barnacles) many individuals die wastefully. Finally, the bud colony has a clear advantage over the non-colonial aggregate in those cases where coördinating nervous mechanisms are developed. Coördinated withdrawal responses occur in corals (Horridge, 1957) and hydroids (Josephson, 1961) and in the ectoproct *Cristatella* (Mackie, unpublished). Stimulation of one zoöid leads to a wave of contraction that spreads rapidly over part or all of the colony. Presumably the response makes the colony less vulnerable to predation. In a non-colonial aggregate a predator could work systematically through the group, without its presence being communicated to more than one individual at a time.

One need not suppose that all of these factors were equally important in the evolution of bud colonies, or that the different groups arose in response to the same needs, but it is clear that there are advantages in the colonial habit that enable one to explain the success of the first and simplest colonies without invoking the more dramatic benefits associated with polymorphism.

Integration in a Polymorphic Bud-Colony

In the first colonies evolved, polymorphism was presumably absent or developed only to a slight degree. Polymorphism has occurred to varying extents in the different major taxa, and it is possible to arrange colonies into categories according to the degree of polymorphism and the extent to which integration of functions has occurred. Thomson and Geddes (1931) offer such a series of categories (seven in number) culminating in the siphonophores. More recently Beklemishev (1958) has provided a valuable comparative account of animal colonies and has attempted to define the formative principles involved in colonialism. Theoretical treatment of this subject is, however, hampered by lack of exact knowledge concerning the functional organization of colonies. It is obvious, when one considers how the members of a siphonophore colony are morphologically specialized into six or more polymorphic types, that an equivalent degree of functional specialization must also exist and that, where the functions are spatially segregated in this way, integrative mechanisms are to be expected. Recent studies aimed at determining the extent and character of integration in the siphonophore colony can appropriately be reviewed, at this point, with *Nanomia cara* (suborder Physonectae) serving as an example.

While certain activities in this form are organized on a colonial level, others are carried on more or less locally. At the lowest level, that of cellular effectors, we find activities such as ciliary beating, discharge of nematocysts, and movement of pigment in chromatophores, which seem to be carried on without the direct involvement of the nervous system and are thus attributable, in Parker's sense (1919), to "independent effectors." (In other respects these cells are presumably no more independent than any other cells.) The chromatophore response is of recent discovery (Mackie, 1962) and requires further investigation, but the evidence now available indicates that the pigment movements are not endogenously controlled. The response is to light, the pigment dispersing in daylight, concentrating in the dark. The chromatophores in isolated members of the colony respond as do those in the intact colony. If part of the colony is placed in the dark and another part is illuminated, dispersion of the pigment occurs only in the region illuminated. Normal responses are exhibited by specimens subjected to prolonged deep magnesium anesthesia. From preliminary studies, acetylcholine and epinephrine seem to have no effect on the condition of dispersion or concentration. Here, then, we may have something approaching the ideal independent effector.

Moving from the cellular level up to that of the individual zoöid in the colony, we find certain activities that originate in and do not spread beyond individual zoöids. The latter behave, indeed, as if they were nervously isolated, though it is always necessary to bear in mind that, while the effector response is exhibited locally, the nervous excitation causing it may be more widespread; Fulton's (1961) observations on the hydroid *Cordylophora* show that peristaltic movements in the hydranths, which at first sight seem to originate locally, prove to be coördinated over the whole colony. Local effector action in *Namonia* (fig. 24-1,A) is shown by posterior nectophores, which pulsate when lightly touched; by nectophores and bracts in autotomy; by gastrozoöids ingesting and egesting food; by palpons eliminating wastes; and by tentacles performing spasmodic changes in length during fishing behavior (Mackie, in press; Mackie and Boag, unpublished). In some cases, however, instead of being expressed in pure isolation, activities spread to neighboring zoöids. The contraction of a tentacle following stimulation leads to elongation and writhing not only of the associated gastrozoöid, but of gastrozoöids further up or down the stem. The stem itself shows no muscular response in this behavior, and it is assumed that the excitation passes to the gastrozoöid by means of the nervous system. Such histological studies as exist indicate that nerves are present throughout most regions of the siphonophore colony—for instance, in *Physalia* (Mackie, 1960); but *Nanomia* itself has not yet been studied sufficiently from this point of view. The spreading of writhing behavior among the gastrozoöids occurs naturally when food is captured, and the movements doubtless increase the rapidity with which the gastrozoöids make contact with the food. After contact is made, the gastrozoöid proceeds to spread itself over the food, ingesting it in whole or in part. Food taken in is submitted to extracellular digestion in the basal region of the gastrozoöid, and the partially digested product passes into the stem canal through the basal valve. Both gastrozoöids and palpons are equipped with basal valves, and the material contained within them may be isolated from the contents of the stem canal at certain times and be continuous with it at other times.

In the subsequent course of digestion an unusual sort of coöperation occurs between gastrozoöids and palpons. Rhythmical contractions ensue in each of these members, by which fluid is alternately taken in and squeezed out through the basal valve. Cells in the walls of both types of zoöid take up food particles and digest them intracellularly. Although each zoöid seems to have inherent rhythmicity, it is a common observation that a gastrozoöid, being larger than the palpons, comes to dominate several of the latter in its vicinity, filling them when it empties and emptying them when it fills. Thus local, rhythmically coördinated groups are set up. From time to time a palpon may withdraw temporarily from the group by shutting its basal valve and proceeding to expel wastes from the tip. The "integration" of these to-and-fro pumping movements is probably achieved by hydraulic means, and there is no reason to suppose that the neuromuscular mechanisms responsible for the individual rhythms are coördinated by the nervous system.

Turning finally to integration at the highest level, we find that certain activities are organized on a general basis throughout the colony by the integrative action of through-conduction systems. The response to strong stimulation of the siphosomal appendages and posterior nectophores is one of general contraction of the stem accompanied by a burst of forward-swimming movements by the nectophores (medusoid locomotory members). Stimulation of the float and anterior nectophores causes reverse swimming. Each nectophore has two muscle systems: the system of circular fibers lining the subumbrellar cavity, whose contraction causes the swimming jet; and a set of radial fibers at the upper corners of the velum (fig. 24-1, "fibers of

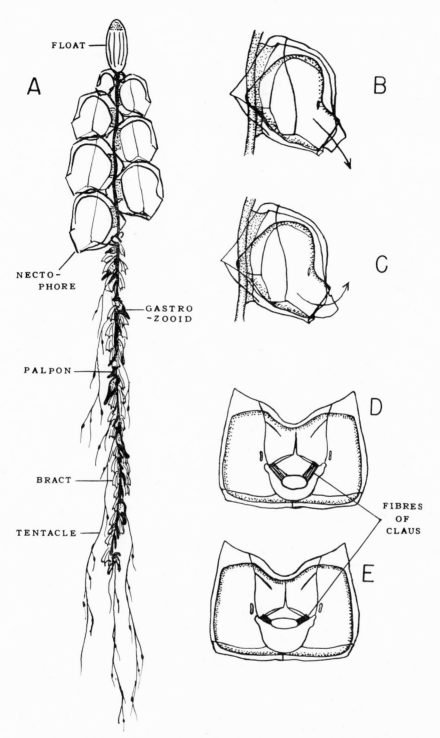

FIGURE 24-1. *Nanomia cara:* A, whole colony—a young specimen; B, lateral view of a nectophore in forward-swimming response; C, the same, reverse swimming; d, frontal (abaxial) view of nectophore, velar fibers of Claus relaxed, as in forward swimming; E, the same, fibers of Claus contracted, as in reverse swimming.

Claus"), which alter the shape of the velum, diverting the water jet forward. In forward locomotion, only the circular system contracts; in reverse, both systems contract simultaneously. Numerous observations and experiments (Mackie, in press) go to show that: (1) the nectophores act together as a group both in forward and in reverse swimming, showing either general activity or general quiescence at any given time; (2) the nectophores active at any time are either all swimming forward or all backward; (3) forward and reverse swimming responses are through-conducted by separate systems and can, to some extent, be selectively eliminated by surgical operations on the nervous system or by controlled levels of anesthesia.

We are not here concerned with the details of these responses and the three characteristics listed are simply given to show that, in locomotion, the activities of the individual members of the colony are completely controlled by, and subordinated to, the "colonial will" (*volonté commune*—Vogt, 1853). Not only is the morphology of the nectophore meaningless unless seen in the context of the colony, but its activity is useful only in the sense that it is useful to the colony.

The Colonial Individual

In locomotion and in some other activities, the siphonophore behaves as a well-integrated unit. It darts around in a rapid and agile manner, going into reverse on striking a resistant object, showing perfect coördination and "unity of purpose" throughout. The fact that certain other activities are carried on more or less locally does not mean that the organism is poorly integrated. There is no need for all activities to be integrated at the highest possible level; much can be left to local action systems. Even in man himself an important set of activities—the gut movements—is organized on a largely autonomous basis. No one would suggest that the siphonophores are "higher animals," but they are the most complex celenterates and the only ones to have explored fully the possibilities of colonialism. They have developed colonialism to the point where it has provided them with a means of escaping from the limitations of the diploblastic body-plan. The higher animals escaped these limitations by becoming triploblastic and using the new layer, the mesoderm, to form organs. The siphonophores have reached the organ grade of construction by a different method—that of converting whole individuals into organs. It is interesting to speculate that, had it not been for the invention of the mesoderm in some remote, diploblastic era, the highest animals on earth might now be, if not the Siphonophora, something similar to them in principle.

REFERENCES

Beklemishev, V. N. [Beklemischew, W. N.]
    1958   Die Grundlagen der vergleichenden Anatomie der Wirbellosen. Vol. I. Dtsch. Verlag. Wissensch., Berlin.
Emerson, A. E.
    1939   Social coordination and the superorganism. Amer. Midl. Nat. 21:182–206.

Fulton, C.
    1961   The development of Cordylophora. Pp. 287–295 in: The Biology of
            Hydra and of some other Coelenterates. Lenhoff, H., and W. F. Loomis
            Eds. Univ. Miami, Coral Gables, Florida.
Horridge, G. A.
    1957   The coordination of the protective retraction of coral polyps. Phil. Trans.
            675B 240:495–529.
Josephson, R. K.
    1961   Colonial responses in hydroid polyps. J. exp. Biol. 38:559–577.
Knight-Jones, E. W., and J. Moyse
    1961   Intraspecific competition in sedentary marine animals. Symp. Soc. exp.
            Biol., Cambridge 15:72–95.
Loomis, W. F.
    1961   Feedback factors affecting sexual differentiation in *Hydra littoralis*. Pp.
            337–362 in: The Biology of Hydra and of some other Coelenterates.
            Lenhoff, H., and W. F., Loomis, Eds. Univ. Miami, Coral Gables,
            Florida.
Lucas C. E.
    1961   On the significance of external metabolites in ecology. Symp. Soc. exp.
            Biol. Cambridge 15:190–206.
Lüscher, M.
    1955   The termite and the cell. Pp. 68–74 in: First Book of Animals. Eds. of
            Scientific American. Simon and Schuster, New York.
Mackie, G. O.
    1960   Behavior and Histology. In: Studies on Physalia. Totton, A. K., and
            G. O. Mackie, Eds. "Discovery" Rep. 30:371–407.
    1962   Pigment effector cells in a cnidarian. Science 137:689–690.
  In press. Analysis of locomotion in a siphonophore colony. Proc. roy. Soc. B.
Mackie, G. O., and D. A. Boag
            [Unpublished observations on fishing, feeding, and digestion in siphono-
            phores.]
Nursall, J. R.
    1962   On the origins of the major groups of animals. Evolution 16:118–123.
Parker, G. H.
    1919   The Elementary Nervous System. Lippincott, Philadelphia, London.
Perrier, E.
    1898   Les Colonies Animales et la Formation des Organismes. Masson, Paris.
Stern, C.
    1962   Presidential address to American Society of Zoologists, Corvallis meetings.
            Unpublished.
Thomson, Sir J. A., and P. Geddes
    1931   Life: Outlines of General Biology. Williams and Norgate, London.
Vogt, C.
    1853   Recherches sur les animaux inférieures de la Mediterranée. 1: Sur les
            siphonophores de la mer de Nice. Mém. Inst. nat. Genev. 1. 1–164.

25 ◆ Preliminary Toxicologic Studies of Rhodactis howesii (Coelenterata)

EDGAR J. MARTIN

LABORATORY OF COMPARATIVE BIOLOGY,
KAISER FOUNDATION RESEARCH INSTITUTE, RICHMOND, CALIFORNIA

Rhodactis howesii W. S. Kent, 1893, belongs to the phylum Coelenterata, or Cnidaria, order Corallimorpharia, family Actinodiscidae. Records show it occurs in tropical seas from the eastern Indian Ocean to French Oceania and to the Marshall Islands. It grows exposed to sunlight below water on dead coral, rocks, or shells at depths of a few centimeters to about four meters. Its entoderm is crowded with algal cells (Cutress, 1957, personal communication). The present studies were done with *R. howesii* from Tutuila, American Samoa, where this anemone occurs on the reefs. During seasons of very low tides, parts of the reef surface covered with aggregates of the anemone stand above water level for several hours a day during a week or so. It is not known what effect this exposure has on the biological cycle of *R. howesii* and on its marine ecology.

Cooked in water, the anemone is harmless and is commonly eaten by the Samoans. But when ingested raw, it causes a fatal poisoning. I observed three cases of this poisoning in the hospital of Pago Pago. Shortly after the alleged ingestion of the anemone, the patients went into a stupor that lasted from 8 to 36 hours, depending on the case. During this period respiration, heart rate, and blood pressure were regular and within normal limits. All patients finally went into prolonged shock. They died of pulmonary edema. The phase of stupor suggested that the poison either had a curare-like action or affected primarily the central nervous system. The long duration of this phase, with respiration and cardiac functions apparently intact, suggested that further studies of this poison might lead to something useful in pharmacology.

The paucity of research facilities on the island restricted me to a study of general properties of the poison. I hoped to obtain information adequate for comparing it with other "marine poisons" and on the mode of preservation for shipping the perishable anemone to research laboratories overseas with its poison intact. A bioassay had to be worked out using what was available. The toad *Bufo marinus* L., which abounds on Tutuila, was found suitable for a bio-assay.

Experiments and Results

The toads were weighed and injected intraperitoneally with diluted homogenate of anemone, five toads being used at each dose level. When doses were plotted against survival times, a satisfactory dose-effect curve was obtained. Observations were not extended beyond 48 hours after injection. The lowest dose that caused death in a high proportion of toads was found to be 1 $\mu l/g$. The details of the method are described elsewhere (Martin, 1960).

Experiments showed that toads did not die after injection of either sea water, or the clear fluid that spurts from the anemone upon touch and slight pressure, or the jelly-like substance that exudes from lacerated anemones upon prolonged exposure to air. Dialyzed homogenates of the anemone yielded the same dose-effect curves as the fresh material from which they had been taken. Homogenates that had been heated in a boiling water bath for 15 minutes caused no mortality among injected toads.

For evaluation of "fresh" homogenates 12 batches of *R. howesii,* harvested on 9 irregularly spaced days during various seasons of the year over a period of 14 months, were assayed. Included were batches from a dark-blue and a yellow-brown color variety and batches from aggregates that grew in various locations. Their dose-effect curves were found to vary within a narrow range—an indication that the poison content was about the same in all batches (fig. 25-1,C).

For the evaluation of preserving procedures, the dose-effect curves obtained from preserved material were compared with those from controls of fresh material from the same batch. The significance of differences at any one dose-level was estimated at the 2 per cent level of *P*. It was found that storage of the anemones at room temperature with sodium chloride at various pH values (fig. 25-1,A) and storage in 75 per cent ethyl alcohol (fig. 25-1,B) did not yield satisfactory preservation of the poison. But anemones kept at 3° C. for 14 days yielded the same dose-effect curves as the controls.

A batch of *R. howesii* shipped to San Francisco under refrigeration was studied by K. F. Meyer and L. Farber at the George Williams Hooper Foundation, University of California Medical Center. With their permission I report here some of their unpublished data. Diluted homogenates of *R. howesii* were centrifuged, and the supernatant was administered to mice either intraperitoneally or by stomach tube. Both modalities caused death of the mice within 4 hours. The symptoms of the poisoning included decrease or lack of response to tactile stimuli, convulsions, and death by respiratory paralysis. The symptoms suggested that the poison was a neurotoxin. Further experiments showed that heating of the homogenate for 10 minutes at 80° C. caused loss of its toxicity, but heating for 30 minutes at 56° C. did not (L. Farber, to be published).

Discussion

The following discussion is based on the assumption that the poison that caused death of the toads is the same as the one that caused death of humans and mice. Its nature is unknown.

Neither the patients' symptoms nor prevailing environmental conditions suggested infectious agents as cause of the poisoning.

Contact with the anemone caused no lesions of any kind to the human skin. Thus it is uncertain whether the discharge of the nematocysts of *R. howesii* is capable of injuring the human tegument, and whether the poison is contained in the nematocysts or in any other tissue of the anemone. But it is certain that the cutane-

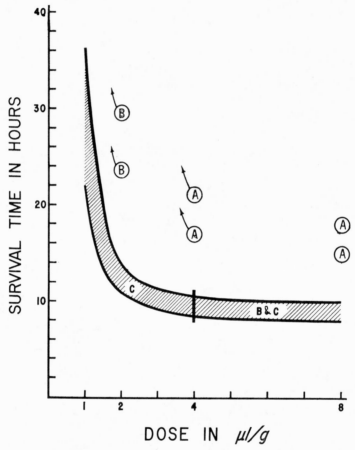

FIGURE 25-1. Relation of dose to survival time of *Bufo marinus* injected with homogenates of *Rhodactis howesii*. A and B are values obtained from inadequately preserved batches. C is the dose-effect curve obtained from the means of fresh and cold-preserved batches of *R. howesii*.

ous allergenic potentialities of *R. howesii* are negligible as compared with those of some other anemones and of squids (Halstead, 1959).

R. howesii contains a paralytic poison. It distinguishes itself from the paralytic poisons of mussels and clams (McFarren *et al.,* 1957) by the long duration of stupor it causes in humans. Furthermore, in contrast to mussels and clams, seasonal variations in toxicity of *R. howesii* have not been noticed so far (Sommer *et al.,* 1937).

The poison has not been found in the secretions of the anemone. This suggests that it occurs intracellularly. We have no indication, however, as to whether it is proper to the tissue of the anemone itself or is derived from ingestion of poisonous plankton (Abbott and Ballantine, 1957), or if it is formed by a symbiote (McLaughlin and Zahl, 1959).

Since *R. howesii* loses its toxicity when heated, but not when dialyzed, the poison may be related to proteins. It can be speculated that its absorption through the lining of the mammalian alimentary tract is made possible by the dissociation of the molecule in the intestine. Such a process has been postulated for another toxic protein, the type A toxin of *Clostridium botulinum* (Wright, 1955).

Summary

The paralytic poison of *Rhodactis howesii* is inactivated at 80° C. It is non-diffusible in dialysis, and it can be stored unchanged at 3° C. These characteristics suggest that it is related to proteins. Instances of poisoning caused by ingestion of raw anemone were observed in humans. A phase of stupor lasting 8 to 36 hours, during which the patients showed normal pulmonary and circulatory functions, preceded the terminal shock. The poison of *R. howesii* differs from the known paralytic poisons in other marine organisms.

REFERENCES

Abbott, B. C., and D. Ballantine
1957   The toxin from *Gymnodinium veneficim* Ballatine. J. mar. biol. Assn. U. K. 36:169–189

Halstead, B. W.
1959   Dangerous Marine Animals. Cornell Maritime, Cambridge, Maryland.

Martin, E. J.
1960   Observations on the toxic sea anemone, *Rhodactis howesii* (Coelenterata.) Pacif. Sci. 14:403–407.

McFarren, E. F., M. L. Schafer, J. E. Campbell, and K. H. Lewis
1957   Public health significance of paralytic shellfish poison. Proc. nat. Shellfish Assn. 47:114–141.

McLaughlin, J. J. A., and P. A. Zahl
1959   Axenic zooxanthellae from various invertebrate hosts. Ann. N. Y. Acad. Sci. 77:55–72.

Sommer, H., W. F. Whedon, C. A. Kofoid, and R. Stohler
1937   Relation of paralytic shell-fish poison to certain plankton organisms of the genus *Gonyaulax*. Arch. Path. 24:537–598.

Wright, G. P.
1955   The neurotoxins of *Clostridium botulinum* and *Clostridium tetani*. Pharmacol. Rev. 7:413–465.

C. PLATYHELMINTHES-RHYNCHOCOELA

26 ◆ Some Aspects of Nutrition in the Turbellaria, Trematoda, and Rhynchocoela

J. B. JENNINGS

DEPARTMENT OF ZOÖLOGY,
UNIVERSITY OF LEEDS, LEEDS

The Turbellaria, Trematoda, and Rhynchocoela show a variety of structural and physiological adaptations concerned with nutrition that allow them to utilize a wide range of food materials and so contribute much toward their biological success.

The Turbellaria and Rhynchocoela are carnivorous, and, with mechanisms for either the capture or pre-ingestion treatment of the food as their fundamental nutritional adaptations, they have available a variety of prey ranging from protozoa to annelids, arthropods, molluscs, and tunicates (Jennings, 1957, 1959a, 1960). These mechanisms are elaborated to varying degrees within the two groups, and, since they determine the physical condition in which food enters the gut, they exert a profound influence upon subsequent digestive processes. In particular, the particle size of the ingested food determines the relative amounts of extracellular and intracellular digestion. Thus physiological adaptations concerning the site and course of digestion are present, but these can be regarded as essentially secondary features correlated with particular feeding mechanisms.

In contrast to this, the variations that exist in the digestive processes of the Trematoda cannot be related to feeding mechanisms, which are relatively simple and constant in character throughout the group. There is, however, a relationship between the type of digestion and the nature of the chosen food, and varying degrees of adaptation to diets of blood, other tissues, or the host's own semidigested food can be recognized (Jennings, 1959b). Thus in the Trematoda the fundamental nutritional adaptations seem to be physiological rather than morphological as in the Turbellaria and Rhynchocoela.

These points can be illustrated by briefly reviewing feeding mechanisms and digestive processes in the three groups under consideration. The review is based upon personal observations (*op. cit.*) unless otherwise stated.

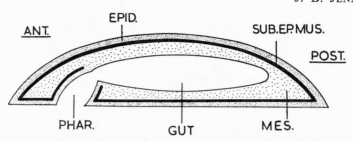

FIGURE 26-1. Diagrammatic longitudinal section of the rhabdocele *Macrostoma* to show the simple pharynx. ant. = anterior; epid. = epidermis; mes. = mesenchyme; phar. = pharynx; post. = posterior; sub.ep.mus. = subepidermal muscles. (Reproduced by courtesy of the Editorial Board of the *Biological Bulletin*.)

Feeding Mechanisms

In the Turbellaria the prey is encountered by chance, except in the fresh-water triclads where mucus "snares" may be used, and in this group the emphasis is upon mechanisms for the treatment of the food before or during ingestion. The prey is seized and held by the anterior portion of the body while being dealt with by the pharynx. This latter organ forms the basic element of the feeding mechanism, and its degree of elaboration determines the type of animal that can be attacked. Where the pharynx consists of a simple ciliated tube, as in the aceles and some rhabdoceles (fig. 26-1), the flatworm is restricted to preying upon protozoa, small rotifers, crustacean larvae, etc., which can be drawn in by the pharynx and swallowed whole. The aceles also feed by protruding a portion of the digestive syncytium through the mouth and using it as a large pseudopodium to engulf bacteria, diatoms, and similar minute organisms. In all other turbellarians the pharynx becomes an organ that

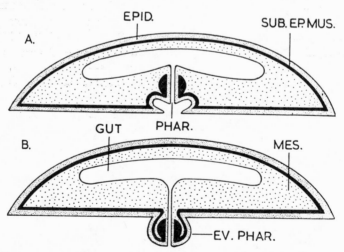

FIGURE 26-2. Diagrammatic longitudinal sections of the rhabdocele *Mesostoma* to show the bulbous pharynx: A, normal condition with pharynx retracted; B, pharynx everted for feeding. Ev.phar. = everted pharynx. (Reproduced by courtesy of the Editorial Board of the *Biological Bulletin*.)

enables the flatworms to extend their range of food to include many animals too large to be ingested intact. The modification of the pharynx follows one of two courses. In the remaining rhabdoceles and some alleoceles it thickens into a muscular bulbous structure—the so-called bulbous pharynx—that can be protruded through the mouth by eversion (fig. 26-2). Turbellarians with this type of pharynx feed on the smaller annelids and crustaceans by seizing them and thrusting the everted pharynx through their integument to draw out internal organs and body fluids. The pharynx does not cause a great deal of fragmentation of the food during ingestion, but its eversible nature and the elaboration of its musculature allows animals too large for ingestion intact to be utilized as food.

In the alternative modification of the pharynx the pharyngeal tube develops an

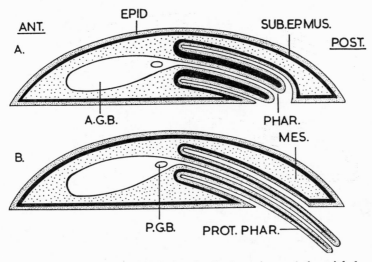

FIGURE 26-3. Diagrammatic longitudinal sections of the triclad *Polycelis* to show the cylindrical plicate pharynx: A, normal condition with pharynx retracted; B, pharynx protruded for feeding. a.g.b. = anterior gut branch; p.g.b. = origin of posterior gut branches; prot.phar. = protruded pharynx. (Reproduced by courtesy of the Editorial Board of the *Biological Bulletin.*)

internal muscular fold that can be protruded through the mouth by simple elongation. This gives the plicate type of pharynx that may remain a simple cylindrical tube, as in a few alleoceles, all triclads, and the cotylean polyclads (fig. 26-3), or become much expanded, ruffled, and funnel-shaped as in the acotylean polyclads (fig. 26-4). In the triclads the cylindrical plicate pharynx is extremely muscular and extensible and, after being thrust into the prey, extends to penetrate every part of the body. The internal organs are withdrawn piecemeal, and, as they pass up the pharynx, the waves of muscular contraction propelling them toward the flatworm gut cause them to break up into extremely small fragments. This mechanical breakup is supplemented by proteolytic juices poured onto the food from glands in the pharyngeal wall (Jennings, 1962b), and the development of these glands represents a further elaboration of the pharynx into a highly efficient feeding organ. When feeding is completed, only the empty exoskeleton or integument of the prey remains. Aquatic triclads feed in this way upon insect larvae, crustaceans, or other invertebrates, and the terrestrial species on earthworms or slugs (fig. 26-5). In cotylean polyclads the cylindrical pharynx is less well developed, but functions in a similar manner to that of the triclad. The cotyleans prey on sessile animals such as colonial tunicates by plunging the pharynx into the colony to withdraw individual zoöids. The pharynx does not cause extreme disruption of the food, as in the triclads, but is otherwise admirably suited to this type of feeding. During withdrawal of zoöids the cotyleans use their small ventral sucker to adhere to the tunicate colonies, and such may well be the primary function of this structure. Many cotyleans such as *Cycloporus* also possess "anal chambers" that connect distal gut ceca with the exterior. Food or fecal matter has never been found in these chambers, and personal observations suggest that they are used during feeding to allow escape of sea water

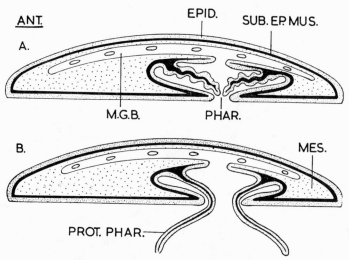

FIGURE 26-4. Diagrammatic longitudinal sections of the acotylean polyclad *Leptoplana* to show the ruffled plicate pharynx: A, normal condition with pharynx retracted; B, pharynx protruded. m.g.b. = median gut branch. (Reproduced by courtesy of the Editorial Board of the *Biological Bulletin.*

passing into the gut with the food. The chambers, therefore, are probably further structural adaptations to this type of feeding.

The ruffled plicate pharynx of the remaining polyclads, the Acotylea, is used in a totally different manner from that of either the cylindrical plicate or bulbous types. Instead of being inserted into the prey to withdraw body contents, it is extended over the captured animal until the latter is completely enveloped. Digestive juices from the gut are then poured over the prey to break it up, and the resulting semi-digested fragments ingested. Small prey are swallowed whole, but this use of the pharynx as an external "stomach" allows quite large crustaceans or annelids to be used as food.

Thus the majority of the Turbellaria are able to prey on animals often larger and more complex than themselves by virtue of simple but effective feeding mechanisms. These mechanisms are remarkable in that their basic element is the anterior portion of the gut, which has assumed functions performed in higher animals by modified appendages or skeletal elements. The large body-size attained by the triclads and polyclads is perhaps an indication of the success and value of their feeding mechanisms, and the subdivision of the gut in these flatworms may be a consequence of this increase in body size and the need to distribute food in the absence of a vascular system.

In the Rhynchocoela the emphasis is upon devices for the capture of prey, rather than methods for reducing its size before ingestion. There is no elaboration of the anterior region of the gut into an organ comparable in form or function to the various types of turbellarian pharynges and hence the food must be swallowed whole. This, however, does not restrict the Rhynchocoela to feeding on animals much smaller than themselves, as is the case in the lower rhabdocele Turbellaria, for the presence of an eversible prehensile proboscis, separate from the gut, allows capture of relatively large annelids and crustaceans. Where the proboscis is simple and unarmed, as in the genus *Lineus,* it is used merely to grasp the prey, which is then drawn back toward the mouth and ingested alive. A disadvantage of this method of feeding is that the prey occasionally escapes from the gut before it can be killed by the digestive juices. In other rhynchocelans, in which the proboscis is

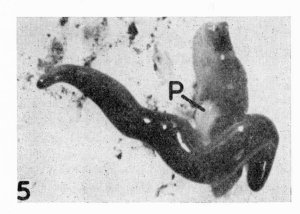

FIGURE 26-5. The terrestrial triclad *Orthodemus terrestris* attacking a slug. The pharynx, P, is protruded and is being thrust into the slug to withdraw body fluids and internal organs. × 7. (Reproduced by courtesy of the Editorial Board of the *Biological Bulletin.*)

more highly evolved and armed with stylets and poison glands, escape is no doubt prevented by death or paralysis of the prey at the moment of capture.

The Trematoda feed largely upon fluids or semi-fluids such as the blood or semi-digested food of the host. This uniformity in the physical condition of the food before ingestion is reflected in the lack of variation in feeding mechanisms, and a bulbous pharynx similar to that of the rhabdoceles is present in the majority of the group. In some representatives, however, this organ is much reduced or even absent. When present the pharynx is only rarely eversible, and little is known of how it operates. In gut-living trematodes such as *Cercorchis* it probably draws in semi-digested food by simple suction. Blood-feeding trematodes such as *Haplometra, Fasciola,* and *Polystoma* need to rupture the host's tissue, and individuals are often found with a papilla of tissue drawn up into the pharynx. Simple localized suction may be sufficient to rupture the host epithelium and capillaries, but current work upon *Haplometra* indicates that proteolytic enzymes produced by glands in the oral sucker and anterior region of the body assist in the breaching of the host tissues (Halton, unpublished work). This method of obtaining food has been described in strigeids by Szidat (1929) and may be of wider occurrence in the Trematoda than has been previously believed.

Digestion

Methods of digestion in the three groups under consideration vary, but the particular type adopted can usually be related to either the method of feeding or the nature of the chosen food. The only exceptions to this general rule are the acele Turbellaria, wherein the condition is anomalous because no true gut is present and digestion occurs in temporary vacuoles in the endodermal syncytium. It is not clear whether these vacuoles represent a temporary gut lumen or true intracellular food vacuoles.

Where the food is swallowed whole or in large pieces, there is of necessity a large amount of extracellular digestion. Thus in rhabdoceles and polyclads digestion is initiated in the gut lumen and may even be completed there, as in the polyclad *Cycloporus.* In the majority of cases, however, once extracellular digestion has reduced the food to particles of suitable size, the semidigested material is either phagocytized or absorbed, and digestion is completed within the gut cells. In the triclads, for example, the proteolytic breakdown of the food that begins in the pharynx is continued and extended in the gut lumen. Digestion in the triclads was long believed to be exclusively intracellular (see Jennings, 1957, for a review of previous accounts), but recent work with histochemical techniques for the detection of proteases has shown that there is some degree of intraluminar proteolysis. Certain cells of the gastrodermis—the "granular clubs" of Hyman (1951) and the "sphere cells" of Jennings (1957)—discharge into the gut lumen an endopeptidase similar to mammalian chymotrypsin, and this is responsible for the lumen proteolysis (Jennings, 1962b). These cells were believed to be protein reserves, since their number shows a progressive reduction during starvation, but in view of their undoubted glandular nature it is likely that one is observing a simple regression such as occurs in other animal digestive organs during starvation. In the triclads this intraluminar proteolysis is followed by phagocytosis of the semidigested food by the gastrodermis, and digestion is completed intracellularly by endo- and exopeptidases, lipases, and diastases (fig. 26-6).

Rhynchocelan digestive processes resemble those of the Turbellaria in that both extra- and intracellular stages occur. The food is swallowed whole, and the total absence of pre-ingestion treatment of the food necessitates a large amount of extracellular digestion. In the genus *Lineus* this is effected by an endopeptidase similar to that of the triclad and produced by gland cells in the gastrodermis. Ciliated columnar cells take up the food when digestion is well advanced and complete the process within their cytoplasm. Again, as in the triclads, the intracellular digestion is effected by a combination of endo- and exopeptidases, lipases, and diastases (Jennings, 1962a).

Digestion in the Trematoda differs from that in the free-living groups in being influenced by the nature of the selected food rather than the manner of ingestion (Jennings, 1959b). The two subgroups forming the Monogenea, for example, differ in diet, and this is reflected in their digestive processes. The Monopisthocotylea feed on fragments of the host's food, tissues other than blood, and mucus or similar secretions. Digestion in these trematodes is largely or perhaps even exclusively extracellular, and the gastrodermis shows no particular adaptive features. In contrast to this, members of the other subgroup, the Polyopisthocotylea, feed exclusively on blood and digestive processes and the form of the gastrodermis are both modified in consequence. In the polyopisthocotylean *Polystoma* a small amount of extracellular digestion renders the blood meal completely soluble, and this is followed by absorption and completion of digestion within the gastrodermis. The intracellular digestion yields large amounts of the insoluble pigment hematin, from the degradation of hemoglobin, and the product accumulates in the gut cells during the course of several meals. The hematin is eliminated eventually, either by extrusion in spherical masses or by the breakdown of entire cells. The degenerating cells are replaced by smaller, younger cells, and the entire gastrodermis is in a

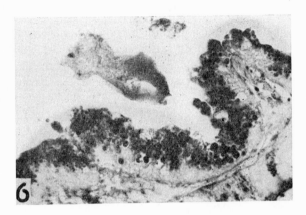

FIGURE 26-6. Transverse section of a portion of the gut in the aquatic triclad *Polycelis cornuta* prepared four hours after a laboratory meal of boiled liver. Material lying in the gut lumen (top left) shows endopeptidase activity resulting from secretions poured into the lumen from the "sphere cells" of the gastrodermis. The part of the latter shown here consists of columnar cells that have phagocytized material from the lumen, and the resulting food vacuoles also show intense endopeptidase activity. This represents activity carried over from the lumen supplemented by intracellularly produced enzyme. × 200. (Reproduced by courtesy of the Editorial Board of the *Biological Bulletin*.)

state of constant degeneration and renewal. Llewellyn (1954) reports the presence of hematin in the gut of a variety of other Polyopisthocotylea; it would seem, therefore, that this deciduous type of gastrodermis is typical of the subgroup— presumably as the result of a diet of blood and a digestive process involving production of hematin, which must be eliminated at the cost of constant renewal of gut cells.

In the Digenea a similar situation exists in certain of the blood feeders, notably *Fasciola* (Stephenson, 1947) and *Schistosoma* (Rogers, 1940), and here, as in the Polyopisthocotylea, there seems to be incomplete physiological adaptation to a diet of blood, since a deciduous gastrodermis loaded with hematin is present. Other blood-feeding Digenea, however, such as *Haplometra*, *Gorgodera*, and *Gorgoderina*, have achieved a more complete adaptation to a blood diet. In these genera digestion is almost entirely extracellular, and hematin is not produced during degradation of the hemoglobin. Unwanted iron is eliminated, presumably, in a soluble form, and the gastrodermis is non-deciduous, with no cell wastage. Digenea feeding on the host's food (*e.g., Cercorchis*) have digestive processes similar to the Monopisthocotylea and show no particular adaptive features.

In conclusion, the various food reserves formed by the Turbellaria, Trematoda, and Rhynchocoela may be mentioned. In each of these groups adaptive features in either the feeding mechanism or the digestive process fit members for various ways of life, and there are appropriate adustments in the nature of the food reserves. The two free-living groups form reserves of fat, stored in the gut cells and parenchyma, to offset adverse conditions when prey may be scarce. The triclad turbellarians also have the ability to utilize gonads and general body tissues as sources of fat and protein, and this contributes a great deal toward the well-known ability of these animals to withstand prolonged starvation. The Trematoda, on the other hand, form no significant reserves of fat or protein, probably because food is constantly available in the parasitic habitat. Wilmoth and Goldfischer (1945) and Axmann (1947), however, have shown that some Digenea form large deposits of glycogen in the parenchyma. This may well be an adaptation to parasitic life in partially or totally anaërobic habitats and could represent the beginning of an emphasis on carbohydrate metabolism, which reaches a climax in the cestodes.

Summary

1. The fundamental nutritional adaptations in the Turbellaria and Rhynchocoela are morphological and take the form of various mechanisms for either the capture or pre-ingestion treatment of the food. These make available an extremely wide range of prey drawn from the majority of the invertebrate phyla.

2. The feeding mechanisms affect the physical condition in which food is ingested and consequently exert a profound influence upon digestive processes.

3. The Trematoda, in contrast to the two free-living groups, show little variation in feeding mechanisms, and in this group the fundamental nutritional adaptations seem to be physiological and to concern the site and course of digestion. Varying degrees of adaptation to a diet of blood, in particular, can be recognized, and the most complete adaptation to this is found in certain of the Digenea.

4. In each group the adaptive features concerned with feeding and digestion are paralleled by adjustments in the nature of the food reserves appropriate to either a predatory or parasitic mode of life.

REFERENCES

Axmann, M.
    1947   Morphological studies on glycogen deposition in schistosomes and other flukes. J. Morph. 80:321–343.
Halton. D. W.
            Unpublished work.

Hyman, L. H.
    1951   The Invertebrates. Vol. II: Platyhelminthes and Rhynchocoela—the Acoelomate Bilateria. McGraw-Hill, New York, Toronto, London.

Jennings, J. B.
    1957   Studies on feeding, digestion and food storage in free-living flatworms (Platyhelminthes: Turbellaria). Biol. Bull. 112:63–80.

    1959a   Observations on the nutrition of the land planarian *Orthodemus terrestris* (O. F. Müller). *Ibid.* 117:119–124.

    1959b   Studies on digestion in the monogenetic trematode *Polystoma integerrimum.* J. Helminth. 33:197–204.

    1960   Observations on the nutrition of the rhynchocoelan *Lineus ruber* (O. F. Müller). Biol. Bull. 119:189–196.

    1962a   A histochemical study of digestion and digestive enzymes in the rhynchocoelan *Lineus ruber* (O. F. Müller). *Ibid.* 122:63–72.

    1962b   Further studies on digestion in the triclad Turbellaria. *Ibid.* 124:571–581.

Llewellyn, J.
    1954   Observations on the food and gut pigment of the Polyopisthocotylea (Trematoda: Monogenea). Parasitology 44.428–437.

Rogers, W. P.
    1940   Haematological studies in the gut contents of certain nematode and trematode parasites. J. Helminth. 18:53–62.

Stephenson, W.
    1947   Physiological and histochemical observations upon *Fasciola hepatica.* Parasitology 38:123–127.

Szidat, L.
    1929   Beiträge zur Kenntnis der Gattung *Strigea* (Abildg.). Z. Parasitenk. 1: 612–687.

Wilmoth, J. H., and R. Goldfischer
    1945   On the distribution of glycogen in the trematode *Ostiolum* sp. J. Parasit. 31, Suppl: 22.

D. ECTOPROCTA

27 ◆ Normal and Phototropic Growth Reactions in the Marine Bryozoan *Bugula avicularia*

DIETRICH SCHNEIDER

ABTEILUNG FÜR VERGLEICHENDE NEUROPHYSIOLOGIE,
DEUTSCHE FORSCHUNGSANSTALT FÜR PSYCHIATRIE,
MAX-PLANCK-INSTITUT, MÜNCHEN

The Bryozoa Ectoprocta are a relatively small class (or phylum) consisting mostly of marine invertebrates, growing in colonies. A sexually produced larva settles down on a suitable substratum and develops into the primary individual. All the others of the many hundreds or thousands of animals composing the colony are asexually produced by budding from the first individual and its descendants (fig. 27-1). Growth is continuous (provided that climatic changes and hazards are eliminated, as in the laboratory). This, as well as the small size of the individual and its transparency, is of great advantage in a study of morphogenetic and physiological processes. Before it is possible to understand the phototropic reactions of the growing buds, it is necessary to consider the mechanism of growth in general as well as the histology and fine structure of the growing system.

The species studied most intensely is *Bugula avicularia*. As reported earlier, this species and some of its relatives can be cultivated successfully over long periods under laboratory conditions (Schneider, 1959). For this it is necessary to provide the colorless flagellate *Oxyrrhis marina,* which lives on the green flagellate *Dunaliella* sp. *Bugula* will ingest both these flagellates, but is only able to digest *Oxyrrhis*. *Dunaliella* leaves the intestinal tract of *Bugula* intact.

The normally feeding individuals of the *Bugula* colony are called zoöids. Each zoöid consists, according to the zoölogists of the nineteenth century, of a cuticular case with an underlying epithelium, the cystide, which encloses the tentacle crown, and a digestive tract, the polypide. In spite of the fact that modern zoölogists have found this bipartition untenable, it has proved to be very useful, since cystide and polypide are to a remarkable degree independent of one another. The polypide may

This chapter was presented as a paper at the "Symposium on Biological and Physical Effects of Light in the Sea," during the Tenth Pacific Science Conference in Honolulu, 1961. The investigations reported here have been supported by the Deutsche Forschungsgemeinschaft.

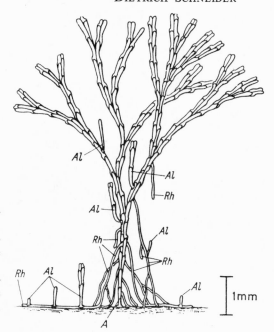

FIGURE 27-1. *Bugula avicularia*. Colony at the age of nearly two months. The colony is attached to the substratum by the adhesive disc of the primary individual (ancestrula-A) and the many rhizoöids (Rh). Regenerative buds (Al) grow out of the older zoöids and the rhizoöids. (From Schneider 1959a.)

degenerate and regenerate or not appear at all during development. The shape of the whole colony is only dependent upon the specific processes taking place during the apical growth of the cystide. Consequently, we are dealing here only with the cystide and need not pay further attention to the polypide.

Fine Structure of the Cuticle

The cuticle or integument of the Bryozoa is considered to be chiefly chitinous. This is to some extent true, because we have checked many different species and always found strong chemical evidence for the glucosamine that forms chitin in its polymerized form. This, however, is not the whole story, as has already been demonstrated by gross chemical analysis of *Bugula* with a number of topochemical methods. The bulk of *Bugula* cuticle is made of protein. The quantitative analysis of whole colonies of *Bugula* avicularia allows the statement that only 10 per cent of the organic components of the cuticle is chitin; 90 per cent is protein. We do not have many data about the quantitative relations in other species, but, as far as we see, protein *and* chitin are always present. In any case, it seems clear that it is as incorrect to call bryozoan cuticle a "chitin-cuticle" as it is to call the cuticle of arthropods a chitin-cuticle.

In a preliminary examination it was possible to demonstrate a foliate ultramicroscopic texture of the cuticle protein in teased preparations under medium power of the electron microscope (fig. 27-2). If, however, the cuticle is treated with hot potassium hydroxide and water repeatedly, most of the protein is washed out, and electron micrography shows a network of chitin fibrils, which was invisible before (Schneider, 1957b, and fig. 27-3).

In addition, *Bugula* cuticle is impregnated with calcium carbonate, with the exception of the apical growth area of the buds, the frontal shield, and the pores where the zoöids communicate with each other. With chemical, optical and physical methods it is possible to identify the calcium carbonate incorporated as calcite, which forms bands of rather uniform optical orientation in the cuticle. Each band is composed of numerous crystal threads nearly parallel to each other and contacts the neighboring band with a xenomorphic zigzag borderline (figs. 27-4 and 27-6). The birefringence of the threads is either positive or negative in relation to their longitudinal axis (Schneider, 1957a,b, and 1958).

Calcification of the colony with crystal spherites starts early in the primary

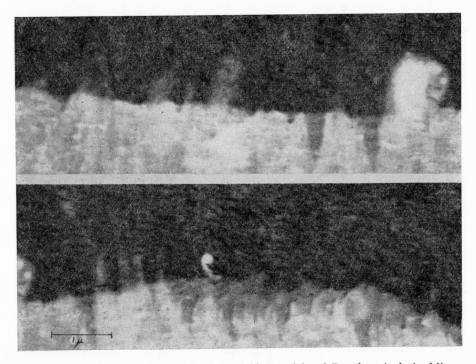

FIGURE 27-2. Electron micrograph of decalcified cuticle of *Bugula avicularia*. Microscopic magnification: 5,000 ×. The suspensive collodium membrane and the cuticle piece broke during the electron bombardment and revealed the foliate structure of the protein component. The preparation was exposed to Pt-Rh vapor under vacuum at an angle of 25°.

zoöid. The band pattern is formed later. This secondary calcification in the form of a continuous growth of the calcite bands follows the growth of the zoöid buds through the whole colony.

Normal Growth of Bugula

The shape of a *Bugula* zoöid is roughly cylindrical, with a cupula-like apex. This, however, holds only for the most apically located, and therefore youngest, zoöids. There is a continuous chain of zoöids, from each of the apical individuals down to the primary zoöid that started the colony. The branches of *Bugula avicularia* grow biserially, with two zoöid chains side-by-side. Bifurcation of such a branch follows strict morphogenetic rules (Schneider, 1959).

As mentioned earlier, the colonies grow continuously by apical processes in the tip area of each bud. Consequently, zoöid formation is a kind of "story-building in a chimney-shaped building, where the bricklayers work on the top level in the cupula."

The question we have to consider now is: how can a system grow that is covered by a cuticle? If we look at the cupula-like apex of a *Bugula* bud, we see a group of spherical cells below the cuticle and a rather dense, but not more than

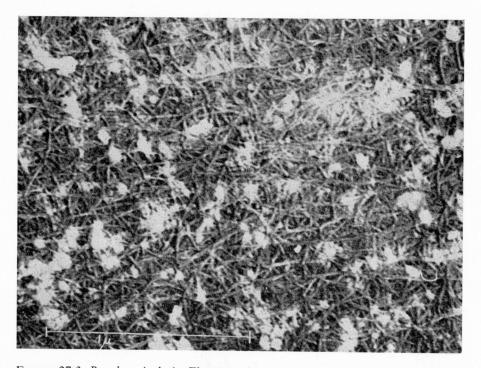

FIGURE 27-3. *Bugula avicularia*. Electron micrograph, technical data as in figure 2. In this case not only was the cuticle decalcified, but the protein was washed out by potassium hydroxide and hot water. The fibrils are chitin; the white patches are protein residues.

unicellular, layer of spindle-shaped cells lining the cylindrical part of the bud. Between these two cell complexes one can sometimes observe a cell-free space (figs. 27-5 and 27-6).

If the bud grows, it can only do so when the cuticle also grows. Such a surface growth of membranes is called intussusceptive growth. Theoretically the *Bugula* bud could grow by cuticle expansion either in the cupula zone or in the cylindrical zone above the lime-impregnated area, or in both zones simultaneously.

In spite of the fact that markings could not be made on the cuticle, it was possible to show that the cuticle area increases in the cupula zone above the spherical cells. This is best shown in a phototropical experiment (see fig. 27-9). Since a cuticle is not "living" in the strict sense, we have to look for the cells responsible for its surface expansion. The best answer comes again from the same experiment: the spherical cells in the cupula itself are the wall-constructing elements.

These cells have been observed continuously for periods up to two days and have not divided during these periods. This means that they are attached to the cupula wall they are constructing and that they move forward with the site of their activity, while the mantle of spherical cells glides forward in the cylindrical part of the bud. Farther down in the layer of spindle cells there is some mitotic activity. Spherical and spindle cells are the epidermal epithelium. This epithelium, however, becomes progressively thinner, farther down the zoöid. Older zoöids have only a

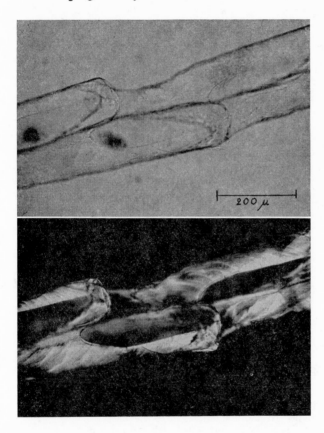

FIGURE 27-4. *Bugula avicularia.* Calcification pattern, photomicrograph. Frontal view of a biserially grown branch. Upper picture: parallel polarizers. Lower picture: crossed polarizers.

very thin cell lining below the cuticle. The whole system seems to be organized with extreme economy, using only a minimum of apical cells for the cystide formation. During wall construction there is a very high metabolic activity to be seen in a number of cell strands passing through the lumen of the bud and transporting material to the construction zone in the bud's cupula.

The bud elongates at a rate of about 12 μ/h in normal zoöids and up to, maximally, 25 μ/h in regenerating (ancestruloid) zoöids. With the bud's diameter of about 100 μ, this is a surface gain of about 3,600, or 7,500 μ^2/h respectively.

The unexpected lack of mitotic activity in the area forming the cystide is a unique phenomenon in multicellular animals, because volume increase is normally accompanied by cell divisions. Here a constant quantity of cells and protoplasmic mass is directly and over a long term associated with expansive integument formation. This is similar to the volume growth in some plant cells with a big vacuole and protoplasm lining the cell wall (Ekdahl, 1957). While apical growth of a system covered by an integument is well known from hyphae of some fungi and from plant root hairs, it is not clear whether the actively wall-forming protoplasm in such instances keeps its mass constant too, as in *Bugula*.

Theoretically, a single row of *Bugula* zoöids could grow with the one constant set of spherical cells in the cupula. There is, however, some exchange of cells between the spherical and spindle cells. The thin layer of epithelial cells in older zoöids possibly originates from the spindle cells, which show some mitotic activity as described before. New spherical cells are recruited from the spindle-cell pool. This is most markedly necessary when a very young bud is dividing to form a

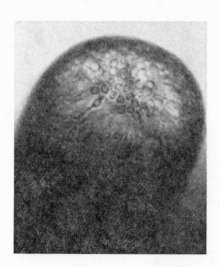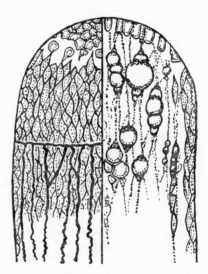

FIGURE 27-5. *Bugula avicularia*. Photomicrograph of a growing zoöid bud. The spherical cells in the bud's apex are surrounded by a cell-free space. The spindle cells may be seen further back from the tip. Diameter of the bud, 100μ.

FIGURE 27-6. *Bugula avicularia*. Semi-schematic drawing of the cells in a growing bud. Left side: superficial view with spherical and cylindrical cells and the calcite band pattern. Right side: optical section with the same cells and celomic supply tissue in the inner part of the bud.

double bud, thus starting a biserially growing branch, or during such a bud division before branch bifurcation (Schneider, 1959).

Mitotic activity is very intense in the polypide-forming blastematic tissues lying in the inner lumen of the growing cystide.

So far, no information is yet available about the biochemical mechanism of cuticle secretion or the calcification of the organic material. An interesting paper dealing with an anologous problem has been recently published by Falcone and Nickerson (1958). The wall of yeast cells is prepared for expansion by the activity of mitochondria. These assemble at the place under the wall where the hernia-like budding will later take place, and soften the old wall, presumably by the secretion of special enzymes. Cell turgor suffices then to start the budding. New wall material has to be added to the expanded wall rapidly, so that the new surface area shall not break (see Schneider, 1960).

In the *Bugula* bud cupula, the spherical cells are inferred to be responsible for similar processes, softening the cuticle and adding new material as well. The whole bud actually shows some turgor, which is necessary for such a system to work.

The spherical cells are very active in moving about under the cuticle of the cupula. This has been revealed by time-lapse cinemicrography (Schneider, 1958). While there is only a limited amount of random movement of the individual cells, the degree of cell coördination is remarkable. All these cells are somehow oriented to the center of the cell plate, which is rhythmically expanding and contracting or even twisting. How this locomotive activity and coördination is brought about is quite unknown. But it is explained further on that these movements play an important role as soon as the bud changes its direction of growth.

Phototropic Growth

The direction of bud growth in *Bugula avicularia* and some other cheilostomatous Bryozoa is regulated by the incidence of light. This has been observed independently by Aymes (1956) and Schneider (1955, 1958, 1959, 1960). Zoöid buds turn toward the source of light and rhizoöid buds turn away from it (Schneider, 1955, 1959) (fig. 27-7). While the mechanism of positive phototropism has been an-

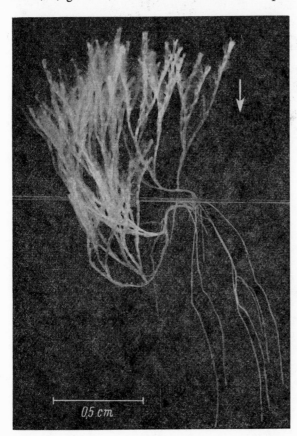

Figure 27-7. *Bugula avicularia.* Photomicrograph of a colony mechanically fixed with a glass capillary onto a glass plate. After illumination for five weeks from one side (arrow), the zoöid branches turned toward the light, while the rhizoöid branches turned away from it (see also Schneider 1959a).

alyzed to some degree, negative phototropic growth of the rhizoöid buds has not yet been studied. Preliminary observations, however, indicate that the only difference between the two types of reactions is the difference in sign.

As mentioned before, the spherical cells are a rather active group moving somewhat under the cuticle in the cupula. The movements of an individual cell seem

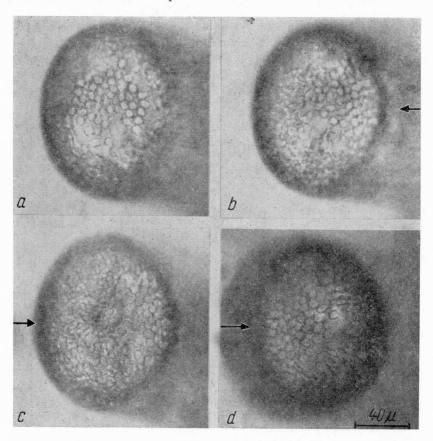

FIGURE 27-8. *Bugula avicularia.* Movement of the cell plate in the apex of a zoöid bud, under the influence of a permanent light stimulus from the side: *a,* cell pattern before the side stimulus; *b,* 100 minutes after the onset of the stimulation from the right side (arrow). The apical cells moved to the right side. The stimulation was now interrupted for 66 minutes: *c,* 61 minutes after the onset of the new stimulus from the left side (arrow); *d,* 86 minutes after picture *c,* with continuation of the illumination from this side. The apical cells moved to the left side of the cupula. A cell-free space appears on the shadow side (see Schneider 1959b).

to be random, but definitely show a relationship to the other cells in the apical cell plate. Sometimes the cell plate is densely packed, but still practically a monocellular layer; sometimes it expands so that the individual cells scarcely touch one another. These movements may go on rhythmically for 30 to 60 minutes.

The first reaction to illumination of a zoöid bud kept in the dark is sometimes an early contraction of the cell plate; the cells rush together. Later they begin rhythmical movements again. If light is not diffuse, but comes from one side only,

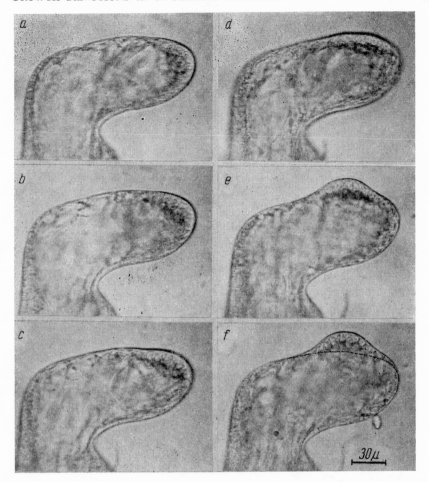

FIGURE 27-9. *Bugula avicularia.* Under the influence of diluted sea water, the zoöid bud's diameter was reduced. Before the beginning of this experiment, the light came from the right. The apical cells are arranged in the narrow apex, facing the light. *a,* End of illumination from the right, onset of continuous illumination from above; *b,* 65 minutes after *a*—the cells started to move to the newly illuminated site; *c,* 110 minutes after *a; d,* 227 min. after *a; e,* 400 minutes after *a*—the apical cell group arrived at its new site and continued wall construction (growth) at this place; *f,* 450 minutes after *a*—the hatched line marks the outline of state *a.* The speed of growth is remarkably reduced under these conditions. This makes the cell movements appear more clearly (Schneider 1959b).

the center of the cell plate is progressively shifted to the illuminated side (figs. 27-8 and 27-9). Since these cells of the phototactically reacting apical cell-plate are the cuticle builders as well, growth of the bud automatically follows the incidence of light. In classical terminology (Kühn, 1919; Koehler, 1950), a taxis is an orientation resulting from muscular or protoplasmic movements, and tropisms are growth movements. Therefore *Bugula* phototropism actually seems to be brought about by a phototaxis of the apical cells.

In addition to the movement of the cell plate toward the illuminated side of the bud's cupula, a light-induced orientation can be observed. The cells we call spherical have actually a somewhat prismatical shape. In a normally, orthotropically growing bud, one can see that the longitudinal axes of these cells are not oriented perpendicularly to the tangent of the cupula, but are, rather, parallel to the longitudinal axis of the whole bud. Finally, after a phototropic turn is completed, we are able to see that again this rule is followed. In other words, the cells in the cupula tend to orient in a way to let the light pass along their full length (figs. 27-6, 27-9, 27-10).

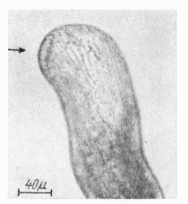

FIGURE 27-10. *Bugula avicularia.* Photomicrograph of a zoöid bud that was illuminated for several hours from above and subsequently from the left side (arrow). The apical cells shifted to the left side. Their longitudinal axes are almost parallel to the light beam. (From Schneider, 1959b.)

Physiology of Phototropism

For a further analysis of light-induced reactions, a special method has been developed (Schneider, 1959). A number of branches of *Bugula* were arranged in parallel and mechanically fixed on a glass plate. This set of growing branches was at first illuminated so that the former growth direction was maintained. Subsequently the whole preparation was put in the dark for approximately one hour, and then the test stimulus was given at a right angle to the former growth direction.

As test stimuli, white lights of different intensities and duration as well as spectral lights of equal quantal intensity were used. After stimulation, the experimental colony was kept in the dark for about ten hours and then checked. Angular growth was measured with a microscope turntable (fig. 27-11).

The enormous variability of the light reaction is related to a number of factors that are only partly understood. One factor is a normally occurring bending (morphogenetic bend) during the growth of each zoöid. This bending is independent of illumination, but its effect is additive (see standard deviation of control in fig. 27-13). Since morphogenetic bending is not systematically controlled, each phototropic response must be based on the average of many experiments.

Preliminary experiments with white light indicated that the reaction has a maximum at an intensity of approximately 100 lux. Below this value the response is proportional to the logarithm of the intensity; at higher intensities the reaction suddenly decreases to values not significantly different from zero (fig. 27-12). A graph illustrating the relation between scotopic vision in humans and light intensity has not only a similar shape, but also an abrupt decrease at almost the same intensity (Dodt and Wadenstein, 1954; Dodt and Walther, 1958).

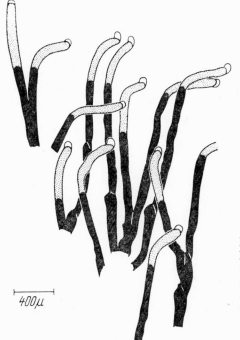

400μ

FIGURE 27-11. *Bugula avicularia.* Set of long zoöid buds under the influence of different light directions: black, permanent illumination from above (in the picture); stippled, 41 hours' illumination from the right side; white: 5 hours' illumination from above. This picture shows the great variability of the response. (From Schneider, 1959b.)

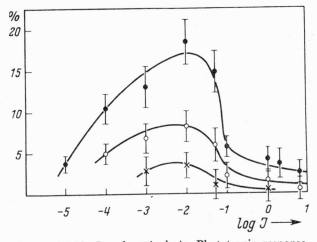

FIGURE 27-12. *Bugula avicularia.* Phototropic response of zoöid buds is a function of the intensity of white light. Light stimulus given at 90° from the former light and growth direction. Ordinate: turn of the buds in per cent of 90°. Abscissa: intensity of $CuSO_4$-filtered, parallel light. The intensities of the incandescent bulb were calibrated with a thermopile; logarithmic scale, $0 = 1,450$ lux. The exposure times in the three curves were 15 minutes (upper curve), 7.5 minutes (middle curve), and 3.25 minutes (lower curve). The vertical bars at each point on the curves show the ± 3 times the standard deviation of the mean (± 3 m). The curves are based on 8,367 measurements on individual zoöid buds.

The first information about the range of the action spectrum was given in a preliminary report (Schneider, 1955). It was stated there that the upper limit of the effective wave-length lies between 650 and 700 mµ, while the lower limit was not reached at 380 mµ.

A detailed analysis of the action spectrum was recently carried out by Kaissling

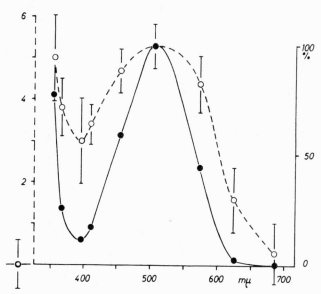

FIGURE 27-13. *Bugula avicularia,* action spectrum (from Kaissling, 1962). Spectral lights from double interference filters, calibrated with a thermopile. Intensity less than one tenth of the intensity necessary to elicit the maximal bending in figure 27-12; 15 minutes' illumination. The filters had a width between 6 and 14 mµ (at one-half transmission amplitude) and were adjusted with neutral filters to equal quantal intensities. *Hatched curve* (left ordinate): response of the zoöid buds in angular degrees of deviation from the original growth direction toward the 90°-side stimulus. The vertical bars indicate ±2 times the standard deviation of the mean (±2 m). The curve is derived from a total of 9,383 measurements on individual buds. *Full-drawn curve* (right ordinate): physiological efficiency of spectral lights. 506 mµ response equals 100 per cent; values calculated according to the intensity-response function shown in figure 27-12. Control experiment on the left-hand side of the left ordinate.

(in press, 1962). He found that the zoöid buds of *Bugula avicularia* are most sensitive to wave lengths of approximately 500 mµ. The reaction ceases somewhere beyond 700 mµ and is minimal (but significantly different from zero) at about 400 mµ. There is, however, a second rise in the ultraviolet toward 356 mµ (fig. 27-13). Shorter wave lengths were not checked and are, moreover, not available to marine animals.

The *Bugula* action spectrum is in its general appearance very similar to the spectra of well-known visual systems in vertebrates (see reviews of Crescitelli, 1958;

Wald, 1959; Autrum, 1961) and in some invertebrates—*e.g.,* in a sea anemone (North and Pantin, 1958), a flatworm (Marriott, 1958), insects (Goldsmith, 1958, a, b; Walther and Dodt, 1959; Autrum and Burkhardt, 1961; Hoffmann and Langer, 1961), crustaceans (Kampa, 1955; Wald and Hubbard, 1957; Stieve, 1960; Kennedy and Bruno, 1961), a snail (Medioni, 1958), cephalopods (Hubbard and St. George, 1958), and a sea urchin (Millott and Yoshida, 1957; Yoshida and Millott, 1960). Most interestingly, the phototactical action-spectrum of the melanophores of a sea urchin is of a similar type (Yoshida, 1957). The position of the maxima and minima in the *Bugula avicularia* action spectrum indicates that the phototropic growth reaction of this animal is probably initiated by a photosensitive system of the retinene type.

Unfortunately, there is no pigmentation to be seen in the bud area of *Bugula avicularia.* The amount of photosensitive substance in the cupula cells must be very small indeed. Aymes (1956), working with the reddish-brownish species *Bugula neritina,* assumed the pigment of this animal to be responsible for its light-directed growth. This seems to be very unlikely, since phototropism is observed in the unpigmented *B. avicularia,* as well as in a number of other colorless Bryozoa. Moreover, the action spectrum of *B. avicularia* is not at all similar to the absorption spectrum of *B. neritina* extracts.

The spectral sensitivity of *B. avicularia* fits very well the type of photobiological processes that are generally called "vision," and not the other group of processes called "general or dermatoptic light sensitivity." Reactions of the latter type mostly show a rather gradual increase of response from the visible to the ultraviolet. This indicates that protoplasmic proteins are mainly responsible for photosensitive reactions (see Viaud, 1950).

Summary

Organic components of the cuticle in *Bugula avicularia* (Bryozoa Cheilostomata) are protein (90 per cent) and chitin (10 per cent). About 70 per cent of the total dry cuticle is $CaCO_3$ in the form of calcite. Growth of the zoöid buds is brought about by a group of cells in its cupula-shaped apex. Growth of the chain of cylindrical individuals is continuous; formation of the outer case of the zoöid is finished by the formation of a complicated transverse wall below the growing bud. The apical bud cells are responsible for the intussusceptive growth of the subsequently calcified organic cuticle: growth is purely apical. Calcification follows strict rules and begins in the primary zoöid of the colony by formation of calcite spherites. Secondary calcification is effected by continuous growth of crystal bands with a calcite frontier below the bud apex.

If the direction of light is shifted to the side of the zoöid bud, the plate of apical wall-building cells moves to the now maximally illuminated area. Consequently, the zoöid buds show positive phototropism. Rhizoöid buds demonstrate a negative phototropism.

The phototropic response is a function of intensity and spectral composition of the incident light. During stimulation with white light, the response is maximal at about 100 lux and ceases (like human scotopic vision) with higher intensities. The action spectrum is similar to the absorption spectrum of rhodopsin, with a maximum at about 500 mμ, a minimum at about 400 mμ, and a second rise toward 356 mμ. The reaction ceases at about 700 mμ.

REFERENCES

Autrum, H.
  1961   Physiologie des Sehens. Fortschr. Zool. 13:257–302.
Autrum, H., and D. Burkhardt
  1961   Spectral sensitivity of single visual cells. Nature 190:639.
Aymes, Y.
  1956   Croissance phototropique chez les Bryozoaires du genre *Bugula*. C. R. Acad. Sci., Paris 242:1237–38.
Crescitelli, F.
  1958   The natural history of visual pigments. Ann. N. Y. Acad. Sci. 74:230–255.
Dodt, E., and L. Wadenstein
  1954   The use of flicker electroretinography in the human eye. Observations on some normal and pathological retinae. Acta ophthal., Kbh. 32:165–180.
Dodt, E., and J. B. Walther
  1958   Der photopische Dominator im Flimmer-ERG der Katze. Pflüg. Arch. ges. Physiol. 266:175–186.
Ekdahl, I.
  1957   On the growth mechanism of root hairs. Physiol. Plant. 10:798–806.
Falcone, G., and W. J. Nickerson
  1958   Enzymatic reactions involved in cellular division of microorganisms. 4th int. Congr. Biochem. (Vienna), Sympos. VI, Preprint 9:1–6.
Goldsmith, T. H.
  1958a   On the visual system of the bee (*Apis mellifera*). Ann. N. Y. Acad. Sci. 74:223–229.
  1958b   The visual system of the honeybee. Proc. nat. Acad. Sci. 44:123–126.
Hoffman, C., and H. Langer
  1961   Die spektrale Augenempfindlichkeit der Mutante "chalky" von *Calliphora erythrocephala*. Naturwissenschaften 48:605.
Hubbard, R., and R. C. C. St. George
  1958   The rhodopsin system of the squid. J. gen. Physiol. 41:501–528.
Kaissling, K. E.
  In press. Die phototropische Reaction der Zoide von *Bugula avicularia* L. Z. f. vergl. Physiol.
Kampa, E. M.
  1955   Euphausiopsin, a new photosensitive pigment from the eyes of euphausiid crustaceans. Nature 175:996–998.
Kennedy, D. A., and M. S. Bruno
  1961   The spectral sensitivity of crayfish and lobster vision. J. gen. Physiol. 44:1089–1102.
Koehler, O.
  1950   Die analyse der Taxisanteile instinktartigen Verhaltens. Symp. Soc. Exp. Biol. 4:269–304.
Kühn, A.
  1919   Die Orientierung der Tiere im Raum. Fischer, Jena.
Marriott, F. H. C.

1958   The absolute light-sensitivity and spectral threshold curve of the aquatic flatworm *Dendrocoelum lacteum*. J. Physiol. 143:369–379.

Medioni, J.
1958   Étude de la sensibilité visuelle de *Limnaea stagnalis* L. par la méthode de la réaction skioptique. C. R. Soc. Biol., Paris 152:840–43.

Millott, N., and M. Yoshida
1957   The spectral sensitivity of the echinoid *Diadema antillarum* Philippi. J. exp. Biol. 34:394–401.

North, W. J., and C. F. A. Pantin
1958   Sensitivity to light in the sea-anemone *Metridium senile* (L.): adaptation and action spectra. Proc. roy. Soc. London 148B:385–396.

Schneider, D.
1955   Phototropische Wachstum der Zoide und Rhizoide von *Bugula avicularia*. Naturwissenschaften 42:48–49.

1957a   Orientiertes Wachstum von Calcit-Kristallen in der Cuticula mariner Bryozoen. Verh. dtsch. zool. Ges., Graz (1957) (Zool. Anz., Suppl. 21): 250–255.

1957b   Zur Analyse des Feinbaues der Cuticula mariner Bryozoen. Zeiss-Werkzeitschrift (Oberkochen, Württ.) 5:60–63.

1958   Calcitwachstum und Phototropismus bei *Bugula* (Bryozoa). Inst. f. d. wiss. Film, Göttingen, Wiss. Film B762, with Text, pp. 1–14.

1959   Der Aufbau der *Bugula*-Tierstöcke und seine Beeinflussung durch Aussenfaktoren. Biol. Zbl. 78:250–283.

1960   Über den Mechanismus des phototropischen Knospenwachstums bei marinen Bryozoen. Verh. dtsch. zool. Ges., Münster/Westf. (1959) (Zool. Anz., Suppl. 23) 238–247.

Stieve, H.
1960   Die spektrale Empfindlichkeitskurve des Auges von *Eupagurus bernhardus* L. Z. vergl. Physiol. 43:518–525.

Viaud, G.
1950   Recherches experimentales sur le phototropism des Planaires. Behaviour 2:163–216.

Wald G.
1959   The photoreceptor process in vision. Pp. 671–692 in: Handbk. of Physiol., Sect. 1. Vol. I. American Physiological Society, Washington, D.C.

Wald, G., and R. Hubbard
1957   Visual pigments of a decapod crustacean: the lobster. Nature 180:278.

Walther, J. B., and E. Dodt
1959   Die spectrale Sensitivität von Insekten-Komplexaugen im Ultraviolet bis 290 mμ. Z. Naturf. 14b:273–278.

Yoshida, M.
1957   Spectral sensitivity of chromatophores in *Diadema setosum* (Leske). J. exp. Biol. 34:222–225.

Yoshida, M., and N. Millott
1960   The shadow reaction of *Diadema antillarum* (Philippi). III. Re-examination of the spectral sensitivity. J. exp. Biol. 37:390–397.

III. Other Disciplines of Comparative Biology

A. DEVELOPMENT: Porifera

28 ◆ Gastrulation and Larval Phylogeny in Sponges

CLAUDE LÉVI

LABORATOIRE DE BIOLOGIE GÉNÉRALE,
FACULTÉ DES SCIENCES DE STRASBOURG, STRASBOURG

As is known, the Porifera include three classes, the Calcispongiae, Hyalospongiae, and Demospongiae, defined in terms of the nature and the structure of their skeleton. The histology and development of sponges of the three classes are rather unequally known, because of the difficulties encountered in collecting and observing the Hyalospongiae.

The Calcispongiae have a particularly simple anatomy, and the asconoid forms are rightly considered to be the most primitive sponges, from which the heteroceles are derived. The present-day Demospongiae, always leuconoid, have all attained a higher level of organization. Histological studies immediately reveal differences between the Calcispongiae and the Demospongiae, such as the important development in the latter of an ectomesenchyme with numerous cytological differentiations and marked fibrogenesis. Nevertheless, these differences diminish in importance when we compare certain leuconoid heteroceles to the Demospongiae with reduced mesenchyme, such as *Oscarella*. The segmentation of the egg leads to the formation of two larval types: amphiblastula and parenchymella. In the asconoid calcareous sponges, the two larval types produce similar homocelic individuals after fixation. The parenchymella of reticulate asconoids derives from a simple celoblastula or preamphiblastula, as defined by Brien (1943), by uni- or multipolar migration of the blastula cells.

The amphiblastula, whose life history is so complex in all the Calcispongiae that have been studied (especially in the ramified asconoids), differentiates into its two typical parts as early as the stomoblastula stage and even before.

In the Demospongiae, the parenchymella develops from a stereoblastula composed of blastomeres often very unequal in size and, as a result of cellular movements, equivalent to morular delamination. The few amphiblastulae found among the Demospongiae derive from a morula, certain blastomeres of which cytolyse. The cells of both parts of the larva are morphologically similar, but are separated by enigmatic cells, which underline the amphiblastular nature of these larvae.

These four types of larvae have axial symmetry and even tetraradial symmetry in the amphiblastula type of calcareous sponges. They swim spirally. The anterior swimming pole is choanoblastic and the posterior pole, like the internal cells, is ectoblastic. Nevertheless, the cytological differentiation of the amphiblastula or the parenchymella is already comparable in large measure to that of the adult, except in a few details—the principal one being, certainly, the absence of the collar in the choanoblastic cells. In the Demospongiae, as in certain of the heterocele Calcispongiae, the cells of the mesenchyme and the skeletal products are already noticeably differentiated.

Following fixation the outline of adult histogenesis appears. This consists largely in the organization of the choanoblastic cells and the development of the water-channel system, characteristics that are peculiar to sponges and lead to the formation of the asconoid organism.

A study of larvae and their development led Delage and Maas to elaborate their theory of the inversion of layers, which has since been rejected by Duboscq and Tuzet (1937) and by Brien (1943). Zoölogists, in discussions of sponge classification and the phylogeny of the group, have taken into full consideration all the ontogenetic events. At the International Congress of Zoology of 1898 [1] this problem was attacked by Delage, Minchin, Haeckel, Vosmaer, and Saville Kent; it was taken up again in 1907 [2] by Kemna, Sollas, Delage, Maas, Van Beneden, and others. Apparently, all the embryological data were studied carefully and were used to support opposing opinions, identity in vocabulary often masking divergent interpretations of the data. This was particularly true in the description of pre- or post-larval cell movements. If the terminology employed for embryonic movements in celomates is satisfactory, it should be applied to those of sponges, and especially to the problem of gastrulation.

Gastrulation in Sponges

In the celomates, where gastrulation by invagination has been studied in detail by embryologists, it has been accepted that morphogenetic movement results in the formation of the endoblastic layer and the development of a diploblastic individual, while the major embryonic fields either are being outlined progressively or are already developing. This is the first active phase of embryogenesis, and its onset coincides with an important period of synthesis. The invagination of the endoblastic region is often accompanied by the migration of mesenchyme cells. Cytological differentiation remains limited from the time the cilia or flagella appear until the beginning of gastrulation, even if cellular determination occurs early. (Fig. 28-1).

In all sessile celomates with free-living larvae, gastrulation normally takes place before fixation, and generally even before full development of the larva, which is an organized and differentiatated organism. The same is true for the Anthozoa, in which gastrulation also precedes fixation. The planula of the Hydrozoa is another gastrula type of larva, whose endoderm is established and whose gastrulation there-

---

[1] See *Proc. 4th int. Congr. Zool.* (1898) 1899:56–67.

[2] See *Ann. Soc. zool. malac. Belg.* 42:72–97, 129–147.

fore is completed before fixation. In the planula, however, cytological differentiation takes place particularly early and corresponds to that of the polyp that derives from it. In all these cases the blastopore opens at the posterior end of the larva.

Embryologists have easily grasped the sequence of the embryonic morphological stages, but they have covered by the single term, *gastrulation,* two phenomena that, although seemingly occurring simultaneously in Cnidaria, are clearly disconnected in sponges. These are the development of the diploblastic state and the formation of an archenteron or digestive cavity.

If we examine development in *Clathrina* or *Halisarca,* we observe the uni- or multipolar migration of external cells, which associate and become an internal cellular mass. The free larva is then diploblastic without having gastrulated, and gastrulation is not completed until after fixation, generally following events con-

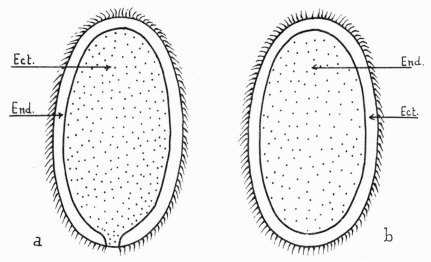

FIGURE 28-1. (*a*) Parenchymella of Porifera with internal ectomesenchyme (Ect.) and external endoblast (End.). (*b*)Parenchymula of Cnidaria, with internal endoblast (End.) and external ectoblast (Ect.).

nected with fixation. Parenchymellae of *Halisarca* (fig. 28-2) sometimes contain one or two internal cavities limited by migrated flagellated cells (Lévi, 1956). Such cells have a marked tendency to an epithelial grouping, even before fixation. This limited gastrulation is always transitory, and the young sponge, immediately after fixation, never contains such internal cavities. If we now consider the amphiblastula larval type, its two parts, the anterior and the posterior, are equivalent to the external and internal parts of the parenchymella and are so well differentiated (even separated by special cells) that one cannot help considering the organism at this stage (as its name suggests) to be amphi- or diploblastic, the two layers being set end to end. As is true for the parenchymella, gastrulation in the Demospongiae is only completed after fixation, although in the heteroceles it begins before fixation through invagination or epiboly.

Thus it would be desirable to follow one of two courses: (1) group under the same term, gastrulation, the formation of a diploblastic larva with subsequent formation of the archenteric cavity, or (2) dissociate the two phenomena, reserving the term *gastrula,* as traditionally, to larvae whose endoblast is already in place and applying the proposed name *diploblastula* to the appropriate larval stages of sponges.

Embryonic development of sponges is complicated, therefore, by the presence of a complementary stage, lacking in the development of other metazoa. Or we may say, following Brien (1943), that gastrulation takes place in a modified way because of certain peculiarities of the embryo and that it is unusually prolonged owing to complex cellular movement. If we accept Weiss's (1939) definition of gastrulation as "a movement of the endoderm toward the interior" we note that this process occurs in sponges generally at the time of fixation and is correlated with metamorphosis. Such a timing of the events of gastrulation is peculiar to sponges.

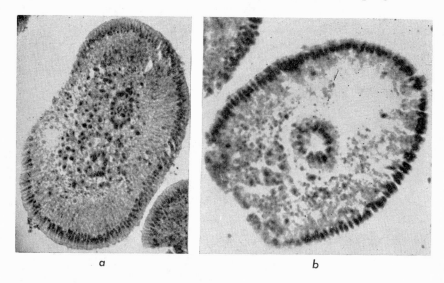

a   b

FIGURE 28-2. Parenchymella of *Halisarca,* with internal cavities limited by migrated flagellated cells: (*a*) *Halisarca metschnikovi* Lévi. (*b*) *Halisarca dujardini* Johnston.

Palingenetic and Cenogenetic Development

Much has been written about gastrula and parenchymella larvae in phylogenetic discussions. In the Porifera, as in the Cnidaria, both types of larvae are found—with this restriction, that in sponges one finds not a true gastrula, but a diploblastula. Duboscq and Tuzet (1937), in their extensive study of development in heterocele calcareous sponges, indicate that here one is confronted with a palingenetic development whereby one observes consecutive stages that are presumably all primitive; the gastrula comes before the parenchymula and the planula and is preceded by a blastula with external flagella, itself preceded by a blastula with internal flagella. This succession of stages is indeed remarkable and seems conclusive. The gastrula is a transitory stage, but it does exist. Mechnikov (1874) and Schulze (1875) have clearly indicated that during the development of *Sycon* the epibolic gastrula precedes fixation and the formation of a mass of cells of a parenchymuloid or planuloid type. If the development of *Sycon* is palingenetic and very "dilated," that of the

Demospongiae with a parenchymella is cenogenetic in being characterized by multiplication and immigration of the posterior ectoblastic cells. This is the opinion held by Brien (1943). In *Halisarca,* the particularly simple parenchymella develops by multipolar migration (Lévi, 1956). In the other Demospongiae, the formation of the parenchymella comes about through early cellular movement equivalent to delamination. This represents the most condensed form of development found in sponges. The cells of the morular mass take on a larval topographic arrangement instead of what is to become their permanent (reverse) orientation. But Brien (1943) considers the development of *Clathrina* to be the most extended: the blastula larva tends toward an amphiblastula state that is followed rapidly by early immigration and the formation of a parenchymella.

I do not see any fundamental difference between this development and that of *Halisarca,* whose larvae possess a bipolarity marked by the presence of larger posterior cells and whose internal cellular mass is rudimentary. The cellular proliferation in *Clathrina* cannot be considered to bear any relation to the ultimate development of the adult ectomesenchyme such as is found in *Leucosolenia.*

Contrary to the hypothesis that the parenchymella is derived from an amphiblastula by early proliferation of the ectoblastic cells, Kemna (1907) has suggested the reverse situation: the amphiblastula results from an ectodermal proliferation retarded by early differentiation. The difference in the evolution of the ectoblastic cells remains enigmatic, but probably finds its origin in the structure of the egg and its mode of segmentation. From the sixteenth stage on in heteroceles, the amphiblastula is, in fact, completely formed. In *Clathrina* and *Halisarca,* on the other hand, the blastomeres, as Brien (1943) has pointed out, preserve their totipotency and only lose it individually upon spreading in the blastocele. In Demospongiae with a stereoblastula, this spreading, cell by cell, is replaced by an early determination of cell fate during differentiation.

If the amphiblastula and parenchymella states are mutually exclusive, these two forms are, nevertheless, modified during metamorphosis in such a way as to become more gastrula-like in form, acquiring first the structure of a parenchymuloid, then that of the fixed planuloid. One can, therefore, conceive of the embryogenetic evolution of sponges in the form of cenogenesis by ectoblastic proliferation (the more probable):

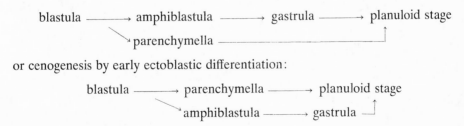

blastula ⟶ amphiblastula ⟶ gastrula ⟶ planuloid stage
  ↘ parenchymella ⟶⟶⟶⟶⟶⟶⟶↑

or cenogenesis by early ectoblastic differentiation:

blastula ⟶ parenchymella ⟶ planuloid stage
  ↘ amphiblastula ⟶ gastrula ⟶↑

But the first stages of the development in the heteroceles complicate the scheme still further. The stomoblastula stage with internal flagella does not exist among the reticulate asconoid calcareous sponges, in which the blastula is formed immediately with external flagella. One can conclude logically, as Duboscq and Tuzet (1937) have done, that the stomoblastula stage is skipped, in which case the development of *Clathrina* is not the most dilated. It is interesting in this respect to compare the respective polarity of the endoblastic cells in the two types of larvae.

During the development of *Clathrina* (fig. 28-3,*a*), the nuclei of the blastomeres and the blepharoplasts are oriented toward the periphery of the morular mass, and in the emergent blastula, not yet freed, the nuclei are in an apical position if we consider as apical the flagellated pole. After metamorphosis the flagellated choanocytes have a basal nucleus clearly separate from the apical blepharoplast. Thus the position of the nucleus in the cell is shifted after gastrulation.

In the embryonic history of *Leucosolenia* or *Sycon* (fig. 28-3,*b*), the nucleus of the endoblastic cells maintains its same apical position from the stomoblastula stage to the olynthus stage, although the apical region of the cell is first turned toward the center of the embryo, then toward the exterior, and finally again toward the spongocele. In such instances the amphiblastula can be considered as a tran-

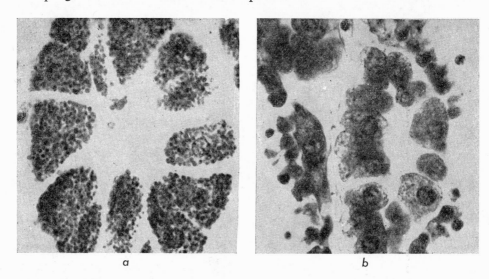

a   b

FIGURE 28-3. Embryos of (*a*) *Clathrina coriacea* and (*b*) *Sycon* (just before the stomoblastula stage). Nuclei of the posterior cells of the *Sycon* embryo are situated near the blastocele, so that the apical pole of the cell is internal.

sitory stage situated between two stages with internal flagella. The external flagella of the amphiblastula larva enable the new organism to make its way out of the parent sponge. In *Volvox,* as well as in the heteroceles, the initial cellular polarity is difficult to understand. For what reasons do the nucleus and the blepharoplasts turn toward the center of the embryo? Is this orientation determined, as is probable, by the structure of the egg or is it acquired for functional reasons, taking into account the presence of the blastula opening?

The beginning of development in the two lines of calcareous sponges is remarkable, therefore, for a polarity that is the reverse of that of the blastomeres. In the Demospongiae, the nuclei of the choanocytes remain apical, retaining the same position they had earlier in the parenchymella or the amphiblastula.

To conclude, should the stomoblastula be considered a stage of phyletic value? Probably not. The stomoblastula-like stage of *Volvox* is of no greater phyletic value for the Volvocales. Nevertheless, in the heteroceles, the stomoblastula is fed by means of a true intercellular opening, not by intracellular pores; but this mode of feeding seems to be independent of the flagella present in the embryonic cavity. A free stomoblastula seems inconceivable on account of the incompatibility between locomotion and nutrition. It is therefore necessary for it to turn inside out, again posing the problem of nutrition. A more successful mechanism is found in *Clathrina* and all other sponges, where external flagella are acquired immediately.

In the egg and very young embryo of heteroceles, the endoblastic region is posterior and the ectoblastic region anterior, in every way comparable to those of other metazoa. From this point on, however, an inversion of position occurs, and gastrulation takes place in three periods: ectoblast anterior, posterior, and exterior.

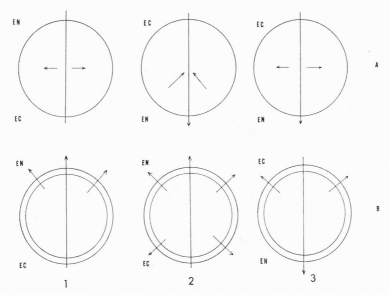

FIGURE 28-4. Cellular polarity (flagellated cells) and ecto-endoblastic (EC *vs.* EN) gradient during development of primitive Porifera and Cnidaria: A, embryo, 16–32 cell stage; B, larva; 1, *Clathrina,* Demospongiae; 2, *Leucosolenia, Sycon;* 3, Cnidaria, Eumetazoa.

It is difficult to say exactly whether the primitive type of egg organization led to a differential cleavage as in *Leucosolenia* or to the establishment of embryonic gradients as in *Clathrina*. It is likely that, following fixation, the most primitive asconoid sponges had a larval type with late differentiation, and it is very possible that these "protosponges" had an amphiblastula rather closely resembling the blastula of *Clathrina*. In agreement with Duboscq and Tuzet (1937), I attribute to the stomoblastula an ancestral character that cannot be, as Marcus (1958) has said, a developmental accident resulting from lack of space. All other sponges have been derived from the original line by early modification of the antero-posterior polarity of the egg and the cellular polarity during segmentation (fig. 28-4).

Without being opposed in principle to the idea of a polyphyletic origin of metazoa, I should like to underline the fact that the ecto-endoblastic polarity of cnidarian eggs is equivalent to that of present-day heterocele eggs and to that of the "protosponges" as defined here.

REFERENCES

Brien, P.
  1943   L'embryologie des Éponges. Bull. Mus. Hist. nat. Belg. 19 (16):1–20.
Duboscq, O., and O. Tuzet
  1937   L'ovogénèse, la fécondation, et les premiers stades du développement des Éponges calcaires. Arch. Zool. exp. gén. 79:157–316.
Kemna, A.
  1907   Les caractères et l'emplacement des Spongiaires. Ann. Soc. zool. malac. Belg. 42:72–97, 129–147.
Lévi, C.
  1956   Étude des *Halisarca* de Roscoff. Embryologie et systématique des Démosponges. Arch. Zool. exp. gén. 93:1–184.
Marcus, E.
  1958   On the evolution of the animal phyla. Quart. Rev. Biol. 33:24–58.
Mechnikov [Metschnikoff], E.
  1874   Zur Entwicklungsgeschichte der Kalkschwämme. Z. wiss. Zool. 24:1–14.
Schulze, F. E.
  1875   Über den Bau und die Entwicklung von *Sycandra raphanus* Haeckel. *Ibid.* 25 Suppl.: 247–280.
Weiss, P.
  1939   Principles of Development. Holt, New York.

Acanthocephala

29 ◆ Embryology, Post-Embryonic Development, and Phylogeny of the Acanthocephala

W. L. NICHOLAS

DEPARTMENT OF ZOÖLOGY, AUSTRALIAN
NATIONAL UNIVERSITY, CANBERRA

H. B. N. HYNES

DEPARTMENT OF ZOÖLOGY,
UNIVERSITY OF LIVERPOOL, LIVERPOOL

The Acanthocephala are a small group of worm-like animals with no unequivocal affinities with any other group. Petrochenko (1956, 1958) lists fewer than a hundred genera, and they exhibit little diversity of form or life history. Indeed, Hyman (1951), though giving the group phylum status, has rejected Van Cleave's (1948) division into two classes, on the ground that the diversity of form is insufficient to warrant such categories, and has instead accepted the division of the phylum directly into three orders.

All the Acanthocephala are parasitic, and their profound specialization for this way of life, which affects every stage of the life cycle, has tended to obscure their phylogenetic affinities. In the past they have, for systematic purposes, been grouped together in various ways with other worm-like animals. Inevitably, the earliest attempts to associate them with other animals in a supposedly natural group were based on inadequate knowledge. Hyman (1951) and Van Cleave (1941) have reviewed such attempts.

Briefly, three views have been expressed. First, they have been treated as a distinct phylum, but showing affinities with the Platyhelminthes, especially the Cestoda (Chitwood, 1940; Van Cleave, 1941). Second, they have been included in a supposedly natural group with the Rotifera, Gastrotricha, Kinorhyncha (= Echinodera), Priapulida, Nematoda, and Nematomorpha as the Aschelminthes (Meyer, 1933). This corresponds with Hyman's concept of the Aschelminthes except for the inclusion of the Acanthocephala. Third, they have been considered as a phylum without clearly recognizable phylogenetic relationships (Hyman, 1951).

Evidence for Meyer's view, which includes the Acanthocephala in the Aschelminthes, came partly from comparative embryology, based on his studies of *Macracanthorhynchus hirudinaceus* (typically of the pig) and *Neoechinorhynchus rutili* (found as adults in sundry fresh-water fishes). This evidence did not convince Hyman—who, on the contrary, pointed to similarities between acanthocephalan and platyhelminth embryology.

The adults of the Acanthocephala are parasites of vertebrates. They are found in the intestine, each with the proboscis deeply embedded in the intestinal wall. They can move about in the intestine, reëmbedding the proboscis, and in this way males find and copulate with the females. Fertilization is internal; the male passes sperm into the female vagina and then seals up the orifice by the secretion of the cement glands. Eggs can only be released after the copulation cap produced by the secretion of the male's cement glands has disappeared (Petrochenko, 1958).

Soon after the female has become established in the alimentary canal of the definitive host, the ovary breaks up into bodies, the ovarian-balls. These float in the dorsal ligament sac in the Archi- and Eoacanthocephala, where fertilization and embryonic development is completed, while in the Palaeacanthocephala, the single sac ruptures and development is completed in the body cavity. An organ associated with the ligament strand, the uterine bell, takes up the embryos from the ligament sac or the body cavity as the case may be. Each fully developed embryo, the *acanthor,* enclosed within a complex shell, is passed by the uterine bell to the uterus and so out into the host's gut. Immature embryos are returned by the uterine bell to the body cavity or ligament sac.

Regrettably, there has been some confusion in the use of Van Cleave's names for the various developmental stages. We use them here in the sense in which they were originally used by Van Cleave (1947) and supplemented by Hyman (1951).

The acanthor is the dispersive phase, which is passed out of the host with its feces. For further development it must be swallowed by an intermediate host, either an arthropod or a mollusc. In the intermediate host it hatches in the alimentary canal and invades the host's tissues. A series of developmental stages, during which it is called an *acanthella,* are passed in the hemocele, terminating, when the adult organs have developed, in another resting stage, the *cystacanth.*

The cystacanth develops into the adult if swallowed by the definitive host. In some species, the cystacanth, when swallowed by an animal other than the definitive host, invades the tissues and remains viable and infective. Such transport hosts may be occasional or integral parts of the life cycle, depending on the species (see review by Petrochenko, 1956).

It is our intention here to describe the embryology and post-embryonic development of *Polymorphus minutus* and to reconsider opinions based on comparative embryology studies with other forms in the light of our investigations with this species. The definitive hosts of *P. minutus* are waterfowl, and the intermediate hosts are fresh-water arthropods. Our methods of experimentally infecting ducks and fresh-water "shrimps" (amphipods) of the genus *Gammarus* to obtain the material for this study have been described elsewhere (Hynes and Nicholas, 1957; Nicholas and Hynes, 1958).

We have also been interested in the structure of the body wall because of its possible phylogenetic significance. We are indebted to Dr. A. F. Bird, of the Waite Agricultural Research Institute, for cutting sections and making electron micrographs of the body wall of another species, *Moniliformis dubius* (obtained from Dr. S. J. Edmonds; parasitic in rats of the genus *Rattus*). The worms were fixed in osmium tetroxide and sectioned in methacrylate.

The structure of the adult male and female is illustrated in figure 29-1, the drawings of which were made from cleared and partly dissected specimens. They do not, therefore, show the superficial system of canals (lacunar system) in the epidermis that is characteristic of these animals, but this system is shown in figure 29-4. Our interpretation of the musculature must be considered as tentative. We are indebted to Mr. J. C. Chubb, of Liverpool University, for making the preparations from which these drawings were made.

Embryology of P. minutus

In *P. minutus,* the ovary begins to give rise to ovarian-balls very soon after the worm has become established in the intestine of the bird, often within two days. The process is seemingly completed in most cases within four days. The male is probably ready to copulate after a week. Fully developed acanthors have not been found before the nineteenth day of infection, but soon after that they become numerous. The whole body cavity becomes distended with ovarian-balls, developing embryos, and fully developed acanthors. The embryonic development probably takes about two weeks from fertilization to the fully developed acanthor.

The embryonic development is not easy to follow. The embryo is very small, about 45 μ by 15 μ, and, when fully developed, contains some hundreds of nuclei. Cell walls disappear early in development, and the observable development is primarily concerned with changes in the nuclei. We have, therefore, used Feulgen's method of staining because of its specificity for nuclei. We have also made some use of hematoxylin, carmine, and other stains, but found it impossible to distinguish individual nuclei with any of these stains. Our technique is being described more fully in another paper (accepted by the *Proc. Zool. Soc. Lond.*).

The ovarian-ball (fig. 29-2) contains some hundreds of nuclei, within a syncytium—at least, we have not been able to detect cell walls within its interior, nor have we observed mitotic figures in these central nuclei. Presumably in the worms we examined (derived from 15- to 30-day-old infections in the duck), the central nuclei were no longer dividing. The surface of the ovarian-ball is covered with maturing oöcytes. Dividing nuclei can be seen in these, and, on the mature oöcyte, two small polar bodies can be seen at one end of the elongated egg. It seems likely that the small central nuclei give rise to the oöcytes. We are not sure whether the ovarian-ball has a bounding membrane. Spermatozoa can be detected on the surface of the ovarian-ball (fertilization, as noted for the Acanthocephala as a whole, being internal). The oöcytes undergo two maturation divisions and are fertilized while on the surface of the ball. They become free from the ovarian-ball, before, or soon after, the first cleavage division. Subsequent developmental stages are shown in figure 29-3.

The first cleavage, which is slightly unequal, gives rise to two cells lying one behind the other. The second cleavage is also slightly unequal. The third is markedly so, giving rise to four large cells (macromeres), lying one behind the other, and four small cells (micromeres), to one side.

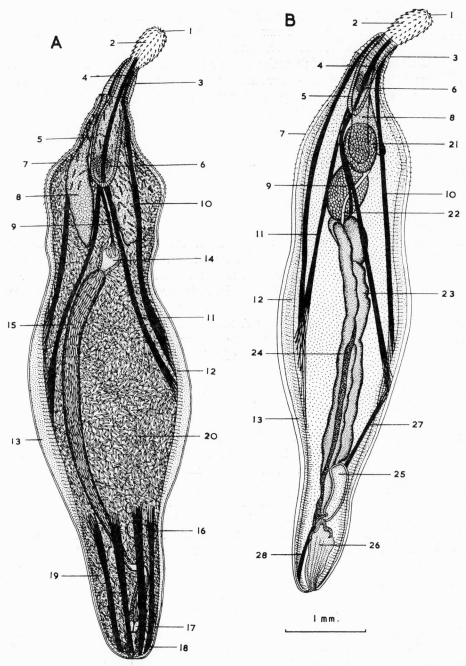

Figure 29-1. General anatomy of A (female) and B (male) adults of
Polymorphus minutus, drawn from specimens stained in aceto-orcein and cleared in
glacial acetic acid. The female worm was partly dissected after staining in order to
remove a large proportion of the acanthors, which otherwise completely obscure the
internal organs of the front two-thirds of the worm. Details of musculature must be
considered tentative. 1, proboscis sense organ; 2, proboscis; 3, neck; 4, proboscis retractor-muscle; 5, proboscis sheath; 6, ganglion; 7, fore-body spines; 8, lemniscus; 9,
central ligament; 10, neck retractor-muscle; 11, proboscis sheath retractor-muscle; 12,
muscles of body wall; 13, cortex; 14, uterine bell; 15, uterus, full of ripe eggs; 16, pos-

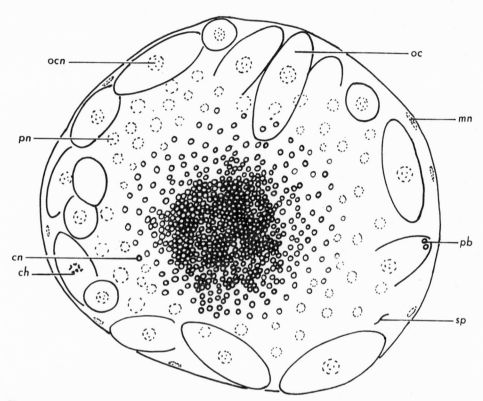

FIGURE 29-2. A diagramatic representation of the appearance of the ovarian-ball of *Polymorphus minutus* after fixation in acetic alcohol (1:3) and staining by Feulgen's method. *ch,* chromosomes of dividing nucleus; *cn,* central nuclei; *mn,* nucleus, possibly associated with ovarian-ball membrane; *oc,* oöcyte; *ocn,* oöcyte nucleus; *pb,* polar-body; *pn,* peripheral nucleus; *sp,* spermatozoan head.

Succeeding divisions of the macromeres are unequal, each cleavage giving rise to a macromere and a micromere. The micromeres also divide. We consider this development (as originally suggested by Meyer) as a distorted form of spiral cleavage. It differs from classical spiral cleavage in that the first four blastomeres lie one behind the other, instead of side-by-side, and the micromeres lie laterally to the macromeres. One macromere, the third from the anterior end, is larger than the others. At the 36-cell stage, we can describe the embryo as consisting of four macromeres, along one side of the embryo, and the progeny of three generations of micromeres. At one end, which we believe to be the anterior, two small polar bodies are still visible. The embryo is enclosed in a viteline membrane.

terior longitudinal muscles of female, which perhaps aid in oviposition; 17, sphincter muscle of uterus; 18, vagina; 19, ovarian-balls, the last of which persist at the hind end; 20, developing eggs; 21, testis; 22, vas deferens; 23, cement gland; 24, lower vas deferens filled with sperm; 25, Saefftigen's pouch; 26, copulatory bursa; 27, bursa retractor-muscle; 28, bursa protractor-muscle.

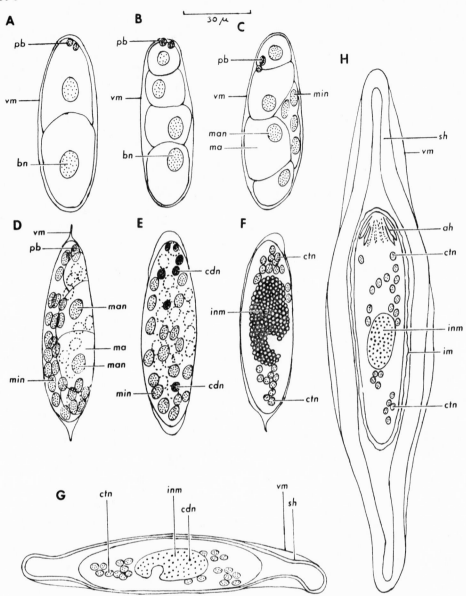

FIGURE 29-3. Embryonic development of *Polymorphus minutus*. The drawings show the appearance of the embryos after fixation in acetic alcohol (1:3) and staining by Feulgen's method. A, two-cell stage; B, four-cell stage; C, eight-cell stage; D, 36-cell stage; E, stereoblastula, nuclear condensation commencing; F, stereoblastula, formation of inner cell mass nearing completion; G, shell beginning to form around the acanthor; H, fully developed acanthor; *ah*, acanthor hooks; *bn*, blastomere nucleus; *cdn*, condensing nucleus; *ctn*, cortical nucleus; *im*, inner membrane; *inm*, inner nuclear mass; *ma*, macromere; *man*, macromere nucleus; *min*, micromere nucleus; *pb*, polar body; *sh*, shell; *vm*, vitelline membrane.

It is consistently difficult to distinguish the cell walls of the micromeres, and, after the thirty-six cell stage, all signs of the cell walls of both the micromeres and the macromeres disappear. A process characteristic of the Acanthocephala now begins. As nuclear division continues, some of the nuclei become smaller and more deeply staining. Gradually, this process involves most of the nuclei, very roughly estimated by us as about 200 for the fully developed embryo. As the nuclei become smaller, they also draw closer together to give a compact inner nuclear mass of tiny nuclei. Some nuclei are not involved in the process of condensation and drawing together. These nuclei, of which we believe there are 14 anteriorly and 10 posteriorly, are to become the cortical nuclei of the acanthella stage.

The macromeres, prominent at the 36-cell stage because they displace the micromere nuclei, gradually become indistinguishable from the micromeres as division proceeds. One of the macromeres, however, the largest, lying third from the anterior end, seems to provide a focus onto which the condensing nuclei draw together. Perhaps this cell is equivalent to the 4D of classical spiral cleavage.

We have referred to "anterior" and "posterior," but we can only assign these terms tentatively. In the mature acanthor we can distinguish the anterior end by the presence of eight hooks (or spines) that develop there. At an earlier stage we can distinguish one end by the small polar bodies. Unfortunately there is a stage, after the disappearance of the polar bodies and before the assumption, by the acanthor, of its final form, when the two ends are almost indistinguishable. Nevertheless, from the shape of the inner nuclear mass, we think we can orientate the embryo, and in this way we have tentatively identified the polar bodies as lying at the future anterior end of the embryo.

The acanthor, excluding its shell, is only very slightly larger than the egg. In addition to the eight hooks or spines, it possesses simple muscle fiber with which it can crawl and move its hooks. The fibers only become apparent when the acanthor is activated in the gut of its intermediate host. It secretes an elongated spindle-shaped shell within the vitelline membrane, the knobs appearing first and growing outwards. Within the shell a further fine membrane is secreted. Though the developing organism is bilaterally symmetrical, we lack any criteria for distinguishing between dorsal, ventral, and lateral.

A more detailed account of the embryonic development of *P. minutus* is to be published elsewhere (Nicholas and Hynes, in press, *Proc. Zool. Soc. Lond.*).

Monné and Hönig (1954) and Monné (1955a,b) have studied the chemical constitution of the egg membrane of *Polymorphus minutus* and *P. botulus* (of the eider duck). The vitelline membrane and the innermost membrane are proteinaceous. The shell has two layers, the outer being of lightly tanned keratinized protein and the inner of keratin-like protein and chitin. Chitin had earlier been reported by von Brand (1939, 1940) in the shell of *Macracanthorhynchus hirudinaceus*.

Comparative Embryology of the Acanthocephala

We can compare the embryology of *P. minutus,* which belongs to the order Palaeacanthocephala, with that of *Neoechinorhynchus rutili* (order Eoacanthocephala— Meyer, 1931) and *Macracanthorhynchus hirudinaceus* (order Archiacanthocephala —Meyer, 1936, 1937, 1938)—thus, one species from each acanthocephalan order.

The position of the polar bodies is unusual for animal eggs in that they (presumably) lie at the future anterior end of the animal instead of at the posterior. The first two cleavages are unequal, one of the blastomeres being distinctly larger. The discrepancy is greatest in *N. rutili.*

The early development can be considered, as suggested by Meyer, to be a distorted form of spiral cleavage. In each species the third cleavage is unequal, giving rise to four macromeres and four micromeres. In subsequent unequal divisions, the four macromeres persist for a time, while the successive generations of micromeres produced also continue to divide. The details of the process, however, differ in the three species. We have already seen that in *P. minutus* the four macromeres lie along one side of the embryo, side-by-side with several generations of micromeres. In *M. hirudinaceus,* the first four macromeres lie obliquely with micromeres in front of and behind them. Eventually each macromere divides more equally to give two macromeres, one behind the other. At this stage, the 34-cell stage, each macromere has given rise to two generations of micromeres posteriorly and, then, one generation anteriorly. In each quadrant there are now two anterior micromeres, two macromeres, and four posterior micromeres. In one quadrant, identified as the D quadrant by Meyer, there are two additional micromeres posteriorly.

In *N. rutili* one of the first four blastomeres is much larger than the others, the D macromere according to Meyer. At the 12-cell stage the D macromere has given off two micromeres anteriorly and the remaining macromeres two each posteriorly.

Cell walls disappear at about the 36-cell stage in *P. minutus* and *M. hirudinaceus* and at the 12-cell stage in *N. rutili.* Thereafter it is difficult to recognize the fate of the individual cells. Most of the nuclei condense and come together to form the inner nuclear mass. We agree with Meyer in considering the formation of this inner nuclear mass to be a kind of gastrulation. The details of the process differ in the three species. In *M. hirudinaceus,* Meyer recognized three groups of nuclei in the inner nuclear mass, representing the primordia of the ganglion, adult muscles, and gonads plus ligament. In addition, he observed, later, separate inpushings of nuclei and cytoplasm, one at the anterior end, the proboscis primordium, and a second, at the posterior end, the primordium of the urinogenital system. In *P. minutus,* we cannot recognize any distinct groups in the inner nuclear mass, and there are no such inpushings. In *P. minutus* the most anterior and the most posterior nuclei remain uncondensed and later form the cortical nuclei of the acanthella.

In *N. rutili* the larger daughter nuclei of the D macromere enclose, by a kind of epiboly, the smaller and more numerous daughter nuclei of the other three cells. The latter become the inner nuclear mass. The daughter nuclei of the D macromere degenerate during the acanthella stage and the cortical nuclei of the adult worm (which in the Eoacanthocephala, unlike in the other two orders, persist in the adult) are derived from a nucleus that separates itself in the acanthor stage from the inner nuclear mass.

In *M. hirudinaceus* the acanthor shell is oval, with a line of weakness at the anterior. The embryo has three pairs of hooks, and its body is covered with smaller spines. The acanthor of *P. minutus* has already been described. The shell is spindle-shaped, and we have not observed the fine body-spines.

Moore (1946a) has described muscle fibers in the acanthor of *Moniliformis dubius* (order Archiacanthocephala). A fine network forms a spiral beneath the cuticule. A band of fibers lies in the region of the blade-like hooks. Retractor muscles, with origin on the body surface some distance back, are inserted at the anterior end. These muscles come into play when the acanthor is activated in the gut of the intermediate host.

In addition to the blade-like hooks, smaller body-spines have been described in some species. In *M. dubius* two more prominent circles lie in the region of the larger hooks, with smaller spines studding other parts of the body (Moore, 1946a). In *Leptorhynchoides thecatus* (De Guisti, 1949) a large number of small spines are present at the anterior end, but larger spines are absent. In the genus *Neoechinorhynchus* (Meyer, 1931; Ward, 1940; Hopp, 1954) there are no spines, and, instead, a tubular depression occurs. In *N. emydis* (found as adults in several chelonians) a large vacuole lies between the inner membrane and the shell anteriorly.

The number of cortical nuclei varies considerably, from only a few, perhaps four to six, in *Neoechinorhynchus,* to more than 36 in *Moniliformis dubius.*

Post-Embryonic Development of P. minutus

The intermediate hosts, fresh-water species of *Gamarus,* are scavengers that readily ingest the eggs of *P. minutus* during feeding. As soon as the acanthor is taken into the proventriculus, it becomes active, moving forward in its shell. (We suspect it is activated by a rise in CO_2 tension.) In the midgut, one end of the shell breaks off (this process taking one to twenty hours to free the acanthor) (fig. 29-4, B). The free acanthor bores its way through the midgut and comes to lie on the latter's outer surface in the hemocele (in about two days). The length of the developmental period is affected by the environmental temperature. Our estimates were made for temperatures of about 17° C.

The embryo swells and becomes more nearly spherical (fig. 29-4,E,F). The cortical nuclei enlarge rapidly, and the nuclei of the inner nuclear mass also begin to enlarge. Soon discrete groups can be seen in the inner mass. The most anterior group is destined to give rise to the proboscis and its sheath. The ganglion primordium can be distinguished anterolaterally to the main body of nuclei, while at the posterior end a genital primordium appears. This stage can be taken as the end of the acanthor stage and the beginning of the acanthella stage (about 20 days after ingestion). The acanthor spines disappear, and a membrane of host cells may surround the embryo.

The acanthella grows and elongates (fig. 29-4,G,H), and further differentiation occurs in the inner nuclear mass. Anteriorly a block of nuclei constitutes the proboscis and proboscis-sheath primordium. Behind lie the primordia of the brain and the retractor muscles and, more posteriorly, a long column comprising the primordia of the body-wall muscles, the gonads, and the ligament. At the extreme hind end are to be found the primordia of some of the genital organs. (This stage is reached by about the 28th day.) The cortex is granular, and a split separates the inner nuclei from the cortex, but this split is ephemeral and does not represent the pseudocele of the adult. (We may note in passing that such a split is sometimes visible in the acanthor stage—*e.g.,* in *N. cylindratus;* see Ward, 1940.)

We may now trace the development of the adult organs separately (fig. 29-4).

The proboscis primordium grows densely granular in appearance. Four nuclei

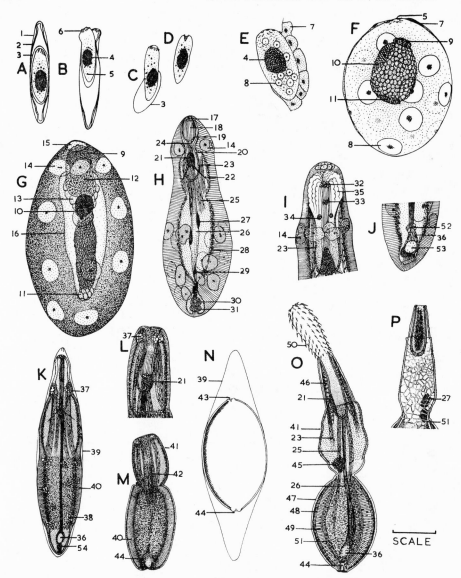

FIGURE 29-4. Developmental stages of *Polymorphus minutus,* drawn from specimens stained in aceto-carmine. A, mature acanthor from body cavity of female worm; B, acanthor hatching in mid-gut of *Gammarus; C,* acanthor free in mid-gut, but still partly inside inner shell; D, acanthor with spines withdrawn; E, 10-day-old acanthor on outer side of gut of *Gammarus;* F, 20-day-old acanthor free in body cavity; G, 28-day-old specimen (early acanthella stage); H, 36-day-old male acanthella; I, 38-day-old acanthella, anterior end; J, 36-day-old female acanthella, posterior end; K, 42-day-old female acanthella; L, 42-day-old acanthella, anterior end, with proboscis withdrawn; M, 50-day-old acanthella/cystacanth, small specimen; N, 60-day-old cystacanth, with fore body and hind end fully retracted, large specimen; O, fully developed cystacanth 24 hours after being fed to a duck, hind end still retracted; P, fully developed cystacanth, front end partly everted by pressure, showing cortical canal system; 1,2,3, acanthor shells; 4, inner nuclear mass; 5, cortical nucleus; 6, acanthor spines; 7, cells of intermediate host; 8, giant nucleus; 9, proboscis primordium; 10, ganglion primordium; 11, genital primordium; 12, proboscis-sheath primordium; 13, retractor-muscle pri-

become distinct posteriorly. In front of them the primordium assumes a balloon-like appearance, with anterio-posterior striations. The posterior lateral surface differentiates to give the sac-like proboscis sheath; the four distinct nuclei rapidly move forward, while the anterior end of the acanthella grows rapidly. As the nuclei move forward, the striations become crenellated, the crenellations later becoming the proboscis hooks. The four nuclei join one of the disintegrating cortical nuclei, which lie at the extreme anterior end. The structure produced by the inversion of the "balloon" is the proboscis itself. As it everts, two nuclei remain at the base, next to the proboscis sheath, and two, lying in the intervening space, give rise to the intrinsic proboscis retractor muscles, with origins on the sheath and insertions on the proboscis. Eversion of the proboscis is complete by about the fortieth day.

The ganglion primordium becomes adherent to the ventral wall of the proboscis sheath; fibers grow out from it to form two lateral nerves to the body wall (apparent on about the 36th day).

The proboscis-sheath and neck-retractor muscles, which grow back to connect with the body wall of the "hind body," develop in association with nuclei lying immediately behind the proboscis sheath. These nuclei have become considerably enlarged and are actively dividing (28th day). They are apparent as discrete muscles on the 36th day and are probably functional by the fiftieth day, when the withdrawal of the "fore body" into the hind body is presumably brought about by their contraction.

The column of nuclei lying around and behind the ganglion and the retractor muscle primordia gives rise to the muscles lining the body wall, to the ligaments, and to the gonads. A cylinder splits off peripherally, leaving a central column (30th day), and expands so that its nuclei come into contact with the body wall (complete by 35th day). Muscle cells develop in association with the nuclei in the cylinder, and these form the muscles of the body wall. The space between the cylinder and the remaining column is the psuedocele.

The central column is the ligament running from the proboscis sheath to the genital primordium. The sexes are distinguishable by the thirty-fifth day. The testes appear as two concentrations of nuclei lying side-by-side in the ligament—

---

mordium; 14, giant nucleus destined to form lemniscus; 15, anterior giant nucleus; 16, boundary between cortex and medulla; 17, divided anterior giant nucleus; 18, proboscis; 19, proboscis nuclei; 20, proboscis sheath; 21, ganglion; 22, lateral nerve; 23, neck-retractor muscle; 24, proboscis-retractor muscle; 25, proboscis-sheath retractor muscle; 26, central ligament; 27, testis; 28, body-wall nucleus; 29, cement glands; 30, muscular cap of bursa primordium; 31, protrusible bell of bursa primordium; 32, anterior proboscis nuclei; 33, proboscis-retractor nuclei; 34, posterior proboscis nuclei; 35, proboscis-hook primordia; 36, uterus primordium; 37, fragmenting lemniscus-nuclei; 38, fragmenting giant cortical nucleus; 39, envelope (shown only in K and N, but present from stage G onward); 40, inner radial layer of epidermis, thickened portion of fore body; 41, spines on fore body; 42, developing proboscis hooks; 43, intucked fore body; 44, intucked hind end; 45, ovary; 46, lemniscus; 47, cuticle; 48, outer layers of epidermis; 49, inner radial layer of epidermis; 50, proboscis hooks; 51 lateral canal; 52, uterine bell primordium; 53, sphincter primordium; 54, vagina primordium, giant nucleus. The scale represents the following measurements: A-F, 0.05 mm.; G, 0.1 mm.; H-J, 0.2 mm.; K-P, 0.4 mm. (Reproduced, with permission of the editors, from *Annals of Tropical Medicine and Parasitology*, Vol. 51, p. 386—Hynes and Nicholas, 1957.)

at this stage a strand of tissue with few nuclei. In the female the nuclei remain scattered through the ligament and do not concentrate to give a discrete ovary until later—*i.e.,* after the contraction of the fore body.

The development of the accessory sexual organs, which are rather complex, is largely obscured by the thickening of the cortex. In the male a group of nuclei, arising from the genital primordium at the hind end of the inner nuclear mass, gives rise to the cement glands, while another group from this primordium gives rise to the muscles of the copulatory bursa. At the extreme hind end a cortical nucleus is associated with the protusable bell of the bursa. In the female a ring of nuclei moves forward to give rise to the uterine bell, while a second group is associated with the development of the uterus and its sphincter muscle. The terminal cortical nucleus, which, like the other cortical nuclei, fragments, is associated with the vagina.

The cortex begins to differentiate on the thirtieth day. It becomes granular and fatty (and takes up an orange carotenoid pigment normally concentrated in the yolk of the host's eggs and in its fat-storage tissues). The giant nuclei increase in size, but not in number. One at the anterior end is associated with the developing proboscis. Four, forming a ring round the body, are associated with the lemnisci. More posteriorly there is a less orderly ring of five or six, followed by eleven to twelve arranged asymmetrically, and, finally, a terminal cortical nucleus at the posterior tip of the body. The anterior nucleus breaks up as the proboscis forms. Elongation of the acanthella (28th to 36th day) separates the anterior ring from the more posterior ring. The enucleated region will form the fore body.

The cortical nuclei fragment (about the 30th day), and their substance disperses in the cortex. Those of the anterior ring are associated with the ingrowth of the lemnisci from the cortex. Their development cannot be clearly followed in *P. minutus* because of the retraction of the fore body into the hind body (60th day), presumably by the contraction of the neck and proboscis-sheath retractor muscles. Later the hind tip of the body is also withdrawn into the hind body. In other species, which do not invert the fore body, nuclei migrate into the lemnisci from the cortex. In *P. minutus* the lemnisci, in a forcibly reëverted fore body, contain many small "nuclei," presumably derived from the breakup of the cortical nuclei.

The cortex of the hind body becomes much thicker than that of the fore body (noticeably by the 35th day). Radial striations appear (35th day), and an outer hyaline "cuticula" appears (50th day). At about the same time the fore body becomes covered with very fine spines (50th day). A reticular system of canals forms in the cortex over the whole body, connected by two lateral canals (fig. 29-4,O,P).

A transparent membrane comes to envelop the developing parasite. We suspect it to be a product of the host's cellular reaction to the parasite. It appears on about the thirty-fifth day and closely invests the animal. In the fully developed pre-adult parasite (within the shrimp), now termed a cystacanth (infective to ducks from about the 60th day), the proboscis, fore body, and hind body are retracted so that the animal takes on an elliptical, almost spherical form, only very loosely invested by the transparent membrane. The cystacanth, unlike the soft and delicate acanthella, has acquired a tough, leathery body-wall and, when fully withdrawn, is quite hard. No doubt this tough construction enables the parasite to pass unharmed through the gizzard of the bird, whereafter it everts in the intestine. Cystacanths can be induced to evert the fore body and the proboscis by immersion in distilled water at 37° C., presumably owing to osmotic forces. Eversion ruptures the envelope. The hind tip does not evert until after several days in the duck.

The adult organ systems are complete in the cystacanth. In the final host the parasite grows in size, and the gonads and accessory sexual organs undergo further development.

Comparative Post-Embryonic Development

The development of the acanthor to the cystacanth stage has been studied in varying detail in a number of species. The development of *Polymorphus magnus* (also of various waterfowl) seems to resemble that of *P. minutus,* although it has been studied in rather less detail (Petrochenko, 1956). De Giusti (1949) has described the development of another member of the order Palaeacanthocephala, *Leptorhynchoides thecatus* (of sundry fish). It follows rather closely the development of *P. minutus,* but one interesting difference lies in the early development of the acanthella from the acanthor. In *P. minutus* the whole of the acanthor becomes incorporated into the acanthella. In *L. thecatus* the developing acanthor bulges out laterally. The lateral outgrowth gives rise to the acanthella while the rest of the acanthor tissue remains undeveloped. As the inner nuclear mass enlarges, it becomes forced into the lateral outgrowth. The outgrowth finally becomes attached to the acanthor by a mere stalk, which eventually breaks, releasing the acanthella into the hemocele. We are, however, somewhat doubtful of the correctness of De Giusti's interpretation of this phase of development in the light of our own unpublished observations on the early stages of *Acanthocephalus ranae* (found as adults in sundry amphibians) and *Metechinorhynchus truttae* (in trout and related fish). In both these species the acanthor shows an initial lopsidedness, but the lateral outgrowth ultimately absorbs the stalk instead of breaking away from it.

Another point of difference is that in *L. thecatus* the cortical nuclei become dendritic before fragmenting, and De Giusti reports that their branches are replaced by the branches of the lacunar system. In *P. minutus* the cortical nuclei are certainly associated with the canals, but only in the sense that they occur in the same general area. That, at any rate, part of the lacunar system develops where there are no nuclei is shown in the fore body (fig. 29-4,K,P), which is devoid of cortical nuclei.

The development of three species of Archiacanthocephala has been described: *Macracanthorhynchus hirudinaceus* (Meyer, 1938; Kates, 1943), *M. ingens* (of various carnivores—Moore, 1946b), and *Moniliformis dubius* (Moore, 1946a). In each of these species there are more cortical nuclei than in *Polymorphus,* and, according to Moore, their number is increased by recruitment from the inner nuclear mass. We suspect that in *M. dubius,* and perhaps in *M. ingens,* Moore has not distinguished between the condensed inner nuclei and the uncondensed nuclei lying next to them. The latter would in our view be the equivalent of cortical nuclei and not of the primordia of the other organs. There are more lemniscal nuclei.

The ligament in *M. dubius* arises from two nuclei at the base of the proboscis sheath and grows posteriorly to join the gonad primordia. In this order the ligament primordium gives rise to two cavities, and ligament sacs, which partially occlude the body cavity. Moore, unlike us, credits the parasites and not the host with the formation of the outer transparent membrane.

The development of two species of *Neoechinorhynchus* (Eoacanthocephala) has been described: *N. cylindratus* (by Ward, 1940) and *N. emydis* (by Hopp, 1954). In this genus six large cortical nuclei are present in the adult, but whether they are derived from the embryonic cortical nuclei, or from the inner nuclear mass as in *N. rutili* (Meyer, 1931), is unknown.

A feature that distinguishes both *P. minutus* and *L. thecatus* from the others and that may be a characteristic of the order Palaeacanthocephala is the initial development of the proboscis in an inverted position. By contrast, in the other species, and in *Metechinorhynchus truttae,* it develops in the everted position. Species of *Polymorphus* differ from all the others in that, at the cystacanth stage, the fore body and the hind tip of the hind body are invaginated. Probably this is an adaptation to survival in the gizzard of birds.

Phylogenetic Affinities of the Acanthocephala

Both Chitwood (1940) and Van Cleave (1941) have drawn attention to the similarities in morphology between the Cestoda and the Acanthocephala. They have suggested that the Acanthocephala are closer to the Platyhelminthes than to any other phylum. Van Cleave has listed a number of undoubted similarities to the Cestoda—*i.e.,* the absence of any trace of an alimentary canal at any stage, a proboscis with hooks (*cf.* the rostellum, especially as seen in the Trypanorhyncha), the presence of circular and longitudinal muscles, and the similarity between the acanthor and the hexacanth embryo of the Cestoda. These comparisons are of varying significance, it seems to us, and some seem farfetched. The protonephridia of the Archiacanthocephala, perhaps, provide a point of similarity to the cestode excretory system, but a comparison between the acanthocephalan cortical-canal system and the cestode "vascular system," between the subcuticula in *Polymorphus* and the parenchyma of cestodes, and between the male cirrus of cestodes and the acanthocephalan proboscis are too conjectural to be very helpful. Van Cleave puts forward these similarities very tentatively and does not claim that there is evidence for true homology.

We have examined one of his comparisons rather more closely. Van Cleave cites both groups as having similar thin cuticles. But Monné (1959) has studied the cuticles of the Cestoda, Trematoda, Nematoda, and Acanthocephala (*P. minutus* and *P. botulus*) and has concluded that the acanthocephalan cuticle consists of a tanned fibrin-like protein somewhat like that of nematodes, but quite unlike that of cestodes and trematodes. In his view the nematodes and acanthocephalans have developed this cuticle as an adaptation to parasitism, the tanning rendering it resistant to digestion. Cestodes and trematodes, on the other hand, have evolved a different mechanism and block digestion by anti-enzymes (acid mucopolysaccharides) that are incorporated into the cuticle.

Kent (1957) has published electron micrographs of the cuticle of several cestodes. It seems probable that the microvilli shown on the outer surface represent the brush border reported by Monné and that they are concerned with assimilation. Dr. Alan Bird, of Adelaide, has prepared electron micrographs of the cuticle of an acanthocephalan, *Moniliformis dubius* (order Archiacanthocephala) for comparison (see fig. 29-5). The functional significance of the structures shown is uncertain, but the cuticle is unlike that of the cestodes.[1] The cuticle is similar in appearance in both longitudinal and transverse sections. Instead of microvilli there

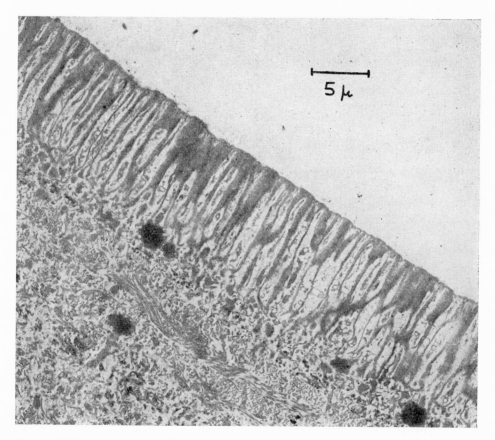

FIGURE 29-5. An electron micrograph, prepared by Dr. A. F. Bird, of a longitudinal section of the body wall of *Moniliformis dubius* (fixed in osmium tetroxide and embedded in methacrylate).

is a homogeneous matrix penetrated by protoplasmic channels. In places these reach the surface, possibly with breaks in the overlying outer osmiophilic membrane. Presumably the matrix is the tanned protein layer described by Monné. It would give mechanical strength, while the protoplasmic channels would provide a route for the assimilation of nutrients. Below the matrix, structures that are probably part of the fibrous "felt" layer are visible, together with lipid droplets.

---

[1] Since this manuscript was written, the ultrastructure of the cestode *Dipylidium caninum* has been described—Threadgold, L. T. (1962, Quart. J. micr. Sci., 103:135–140). The structure, illustrated in electron-micrographs, is perhaps not entirely unlike that of *Moniliformis dubius*. The cuticle, which is cytoplasmic, exhibits microvilli (trichytes) and pore canals.

Another significant difference between the Platyhelminthes and the Acanthocephala is the presence of a body cavity in the Acanthocephala. This body cavity is generally termed a pseudocele, though it is not a remnant of the blastocele as the name implies, but is formed by a split in the inner nuclear mass. A more fundamental criticism of Van Cleave's and Chitwood's view in this connection is that it lays emphasis on the similarities between the Cestoda and the Acanthocephala, both highly modified for a similar way of life, rather than between the Acanthocephala and the primitive free-living Platyhelminthes.

As was noted earlier, Meyer (1933) proposed a grouping of the Acanthocephala, Rotifera, Nematoda, Priapulida, Gastrotricha, Kinorhyncha (Echinodera), and Nematomorpha to form a natural group, the Aschelminthes. Points in common were the division of the body into soma and presoma, eutely (cell or nuclear constancy), and the type of cleavage (especially between the Acanthocephala and the Rotifera). The morphological similarities between these groups are discussed by Lang in this volume (chap. 18).

Hyman (1951) included these same groups, except the Acanthocephala, in the phylum Aschelminthes, though admitting that their common ancestry was not so clearly evident as for members of most other phyla. She has surveyed the evidence for relating the Acanthocephala either to the Platyhelminthes or to the Aschelminthes and concluded that their adult morphology is on the whole closer to that of the Aschelminthes. In particular, she cites, among their common features, the presence of a presoma and metasoma (Priapulida and larval Gordiacea), the invaginable armed proboscis (Priapulida, larval Gordiacea, and Kinorhyncha), a body cavity divided by partitions (Gastrotricha) and the replacement of the alimentary canal by a ligament strand (some male rotifers).

In their embryology, Hyman suggests that the Acanthocephala resemble the Platyhelminthes rather than the Aschelminthes, drawing attention to the cestode embryo. She points out that the epidermis separates early from the inner cell mass, and stresses the formation of shells and the appearance of larval hooks. The same objections can, however, be raised to inferences based on resemblances between the cestode and acanthocephalan embryos as to resemblances between the adults. The features cited may well be convergent adaptations to parasitism.

In the Platyhelminthes, embryonic plasticity is retained in many post-embryonic tissues. The great powers of regeneration in the planarians, the interpolated asexual reproductive stages in the trematodes, the power of growth and differentiation in the neck region of the cestodes, all contrast with acanthocephalan pattern. In the latter, as in the Aschelminthes (*sensu stricto*), cells or nuclei (aside from the gonads) are few in number and rigidly determined in position. Interpolated reproductive stages do not occur. No great powers of regeneration are apparent.

There are similarities in embryology between the Acanthocephala and the primitive flatworms. They resemble the Acoela in the absence of any early separation of the germ layers and in the primary division into an epidermis and an inner cell mass.

Meyer (1931) considered the development of the Acanthocephala to be a modified form of spiral cleavage. We have accepted this view, but do not see such a close correlation as did Meyer between classical "4D" spiral cleavage, such as is seen in the Polycladida, Polychaeta, and Mollusca, and the cleavage pattern of the Acanthocephala. We cannot see any cell that is clearly homologous with cell

4D and gives rise exclusively to the entoderm and mesoderm. Indeed, we cannot recognize any clearly defined entoderm or mesoderm. It is possible that the largest macromere is homologous with the "D" macromere of classical spiral cleavage. One thing is clear, the embryonic development has been so extensively modified that little remains of the typical spiral-cleavage pattern; and, in any case, though such a pattern of cleavage relates the Acanthocephala to the major invertebrate groups, it does not take us any further in determining phylogenetic affinity.

We view a presumptive modification of the spiral-cleavage pattern as an adaptation by the acanthor to its role in dispersal. The acanthor is very small, with a rigid shell. Within the confines of this shell, nuclear division goes on without concomitant cytoplasmic growth and differentiation. These are postponed until the later parasitic phases.

REFERENCES

Brand, T. von
    1939   Chemical and morphological observations upon the composition of *Macracanthorhynchus hirudinaceus*. J. Parasit. 25:329–342.
    1940   Further observations upon the composition of Acanthocephala. *Ibid.* 26:301–307.

Chitwood, B. G.
    1940   Nemic relationships. Pp. 190–204 in: An Introduction to Nematology, Sec. 1, Pt. 3. Monumental Press, Baltimore.

De Giusti, D. L.
    1949   The life cycle of *Leptorhynchoides thecatus* (Linton), an acanthocephalan of fish. J. Parasit. 35:437–460.

Hopp, W. B.
    1954   Studies on the morphology and life cycle of *Neoechinorhynchus emydis* (Leidy), an acanthocephalan parasite of the map turtle, *Graptemys geographica* (Le Sueur). *Ibid.* 40:284–299.

Hyman, L. H.
    1951   The Invertebrates. Vol. III: Acanthocephala, Aschelminthes and Ectoprocta—the Pseudocoelomate Bilateria. McGraw-Hill, New York, Toronto, London.

Hynes, H. B. N., and W. L. Nicholas
    1957   The development of *Polymorphus minutus* (Goeze 1782) (Acanthocephala) in the intermediate host. Ann. trop. Med. Parasit. 51:380–391.

Kates, K. C.
    1943   Development of the swine thorn-headed worm, *Macracanthorhynchus hirudinaceus*, in its intermediate host. Amer. J. vet. Res. 4:173–181.

Kent, H. N.
    1957   Aspect biochemique de la spécificité chez les Cestodes. Pp. 293–308 in: Premier Symposium sur la Spécificité parasitaire des Parasites de Vertébres. First Symposium on Host Specificity among Parasites of Vertebrates. Attinger, Neuchâtel.

Meyer, A.
    1931   Urhautzelle, Hautbahn und plasmodiale Entwicklung der Larve von *Neoechinorhynchus rutili* (Acanthocephala). Zool. Jb. (Anat.) 53:103–126.
    1933   Acanthocephala. Bronn's Klassen 4, sect. 2, book 2:1–582.

1936   Die plasmodiale Entwicklung und Formbildung des Reisenkratzers (*Macracanthorhynchus hirudinaceus* (Pallas). I. Zool. Jb. (Anat.) 62:111–172.

1937   *Idem.* II. *Ibid.* 63:1–36.

1938   *Idem.* III. *Ibid.* 64:131–197.

Monné, L.

1955a   On the nature of Gram basophilia. Ark. Zool., Stockh. (ser. 2) 7:559–575.

1955b   On the histochemical properties of the egg envelopes and external cuticles of some parasitic nematodes. *Ibid.* (ser. 2) 9:93–113.

1959   On the external cuticles of various helminths and their role in the host-parasite relationship. *Ibid.* (ser. 2) 12:343–358.

Monné, L., and G. Hönig

1954   On the embryonic envelopes of *Polymorphus botulus* and *P. minutus* (Acanthocephala). *Ibid.* (ser. 2) 7:257–260.

Moore, D. V.

1946a   Studies on the life history and development of *Moniliformis dubius* Meyer 1933. J. Parasit. 32:257–271.

1946b   Studies on the life history and development of *Macracanthorhynchus ingens* Meyer 1933, with a redescription of the adult worm. *Ibid.* 32:387–399.

Nicholas, W. L., and H. B. N. Hynes

1958   Studies on *Polymorphus minutus* Goeze 1782 (Acanthocephala) as a parasite of the domestic duck. Ann. trop. Med. Parasit. 52:36–47.

In press.   The embryology of *Polymorphus minutus*. (Acanthocephala). Proc. zool. Soc. Lond.

Petrochenko, V. I.

1956   [Acanthocephala of Domesticated and Wild Animals.] Vol. I. Acad. Sci., Moscow. [In Russian.]

1958   *Idem.* Vol. II. [In Russian.]

Van Cleave, H. J.

1941   Relationships of the Acanthocephala. Amer. Nat. 75:31–47.

1947   A critical review of terminology for immature stages in acanthocephalan life histories. J. Parasit. 33:118–125.

1948   Expanding horizons in the recognition of a phylum. *Ibid.* 34:1–20.

Ward, H.

1940   Studies on the life history of *Neoechinorhynchus cylindratus* (Van Cleave, 1913). Trans. Amer. micr. Soc. 59:327–347.

B. GENETICS

30 ◆ Genetics of Reproductive Mechanisms and Chromosome Behavior in Some Fresh-Water Triclads

MARIO BENAZZI

ISTITUTO DI ZOOLOGIA E DI ANATOMIA COMPARATA,
UNIVERSITÀ DI PISA, PISA

A long series of studies with my collaborators (above all with my wife, Dr. G. Benazzi-Lentati), on the cytology and reproductive mechanisms in some fresh-water planarians, has demonstrated micro-evolutionary processes giving rise to different races with peculiar genetic and chromosomal systems.

The fundamental and primitive condition, represented by diploidy, amphimixis, and normal chromosome cycle, has evolved toward polyploidy correlated with pseudogamous development of the eggs (gynogenesis). This evolution has been achieved through two different routes (that is, through ameiotic oögenesis or through a normal meiosis similar to what is known as parthenogenetic reproduction).

Our work deals with some European species forming three species groups: *Dugesia gonocephala* (*sensu lato*), *Dugesia lugubris* (*sensu lato*), and *Polycelis nigra* and *P. tenuis*.

I think it is necessary to discuss briefly chromosomal evolution in the above-mentioned planarians before describing the genetic research that represents the chief subject of my report.

The Chromosome Cycle in Polyploid Biotypes

THE *Gonocephala* GROUP

The superspecies *Dugesia gonocephala* (see Benazzi, 1955) contains many closely related species, with the basic chromosomal number of eight. *D. gonocephala* (*sensu stricto*), *D. etrusca, D. ilvana,* and *D. sicula,* which are diploid ($2n = 16$, $n = 8$) except for frequent cases of polysomics in some populations, show normal meiosis in both male and female germ lines, and development from amphimictic eggs (Benazzi, 1945, 1950, 1955; Benazzi-Lentati, 1957).

D. benazzii, of the same group, starting from a diploid biotype similar to the preceding ones, gives rise to new biotypes with different genetic systems:

    1. Triploid-hexaploid biotype. Here there are a triploid chromosome set in the somatic cells (24 chromosomes), hexaploid oöcytes (24 biva-

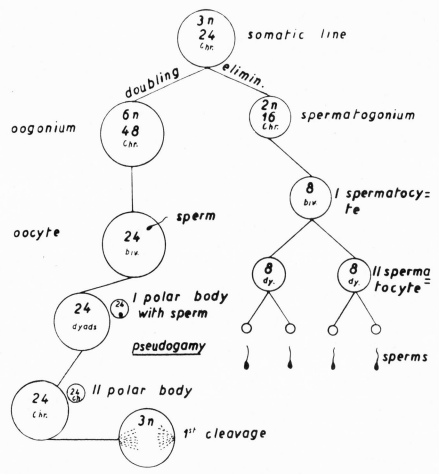

FIGURE 30-1. *Dugesia benazzii:* schematic chromosome cycle of triploid biotype, hexaploid in female germ line, diploid in male germ line, pseudogamous.

lents), which show normal meiosis and develop pseudogamously, and a male diploid line that produces haploid sperm (fig. 30-1). The female germ line becomes hexaploid by means of a chromosomal doubling, which occurs when oögonia arise from the triploid parenchymal cells, while the male germ line is diploid as a consequence of the elimination of a haploid set during the formation of spermatogonia or spermatocytes. The sperm, after having entered the oöcyte and having activated bivalent congression, is eliminated with the first polar body or sometimes degenerates in the egg (Benazzi-Lentati, 1953).

2. Tetraploid biotype asynaptic in the female line. Oöcytes possess 32 chromosomes, which do not pair during oögenesis; there is only one maturation division, which is mitotic in character. The eggs develop pseudogamously (the sperm nucleus being eliminated by the polar body or by means of a cytoplasmatic bud), and therefore the somatic line is also tetraploid. The male germ line is diploid or tetraploid with normal meiosis and produces haploid and diploid sperm respectively (Benazzi, 1950; Benazzi and Benazzi-Lentati, 1950; Benazzi-Lentati and Nardi, 1951). (Fig. 30-2.)

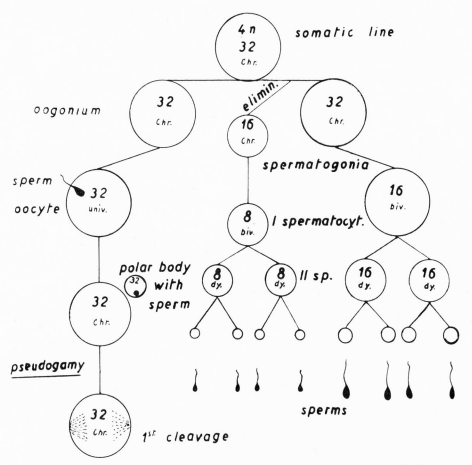

FIGURE 30-2. *Dugesia benazzii:* schematic chromosome cycle of tetraploid biotype, asynaptic in female germ line, diploid or tetraploid in male germ line, pseudogamous.

The basic karyotype of the *gonocephala* group consists of eight chromosomes: two metacentric, four submetacentric (two long, one intermediate, and one short), and two acrocentric (Benazzi-Lentati *et al.,* 1951). The polyploid biotypes are certainly autopolyploids.

THE *Lugubris* GROUP

Dugesia lugubris (*sensu lato*) presents an even more highly differentiated chromosomal system. Thus far I have found (Benazzi, 1951, 1953, 1955, 1957) four biotypes that evidently evolved in the same direction as *D. benazzii,* because from an originally diploid amphimictic biotype (2n = 8, n = 4) three polyploid, pseudogamous biotypes arose.

    1. Triploid-hexaploid biotype. The somatic line is triploid (12 chromosomes); the oöcytes are hexaploid (12 bivalents) with normal meiosis (fig. 30-3).

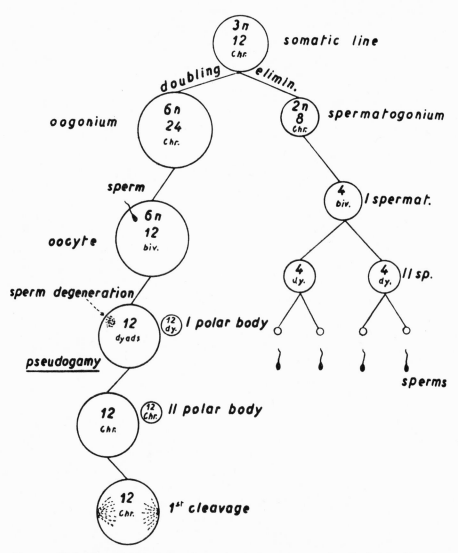

FIGURE 30-3. *Dugesia lugubris:* schematic chromosome cycle of triploid biotype, hexaploid in female germ line, diploid in male germ line, pseudogamous.

2. Triploid biotype asynaptic in the female line. There are 12 univalents in the oöcytes and 12 chromosomes in the somatic cells (fig. 30-4).

3. Tetraploid biotype asynaptic in the female line. Here there are 16 univalents in the oöcytes and 16 chromosomes in the somatic line.

The male germ line is diploid with normal meiosis in all three biotypes (Pieragnoli, 1954). The sperm nucleus, after fertilization, degenerates in the egg.

These four biotypes (indicated by the letters A to D, respectively) are genetically closely related; they are all interbreeding, and their chromosome sets are

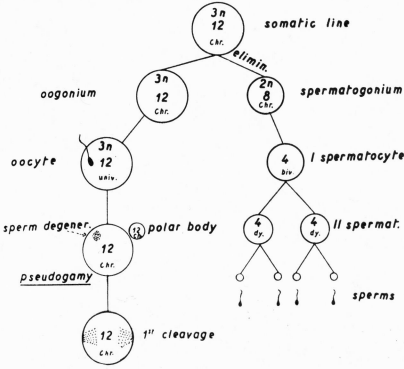

FIGURE 30-4. *Dugesia lugubris:* schematic chromosome cycle of triploid biotype, asynaptic in female germ line, diploid in male germ line; pseudogamous.

homologous. The basic number of four chromosomes contains a heterobrachial metacentric (the longest chromosome) and three acrocentrics of different size. This set is repeated three or four times in the polyploid biotypes; thus they must be autopolyploids that have arisen from biotype A.

Subsequently, I found three other diploid and amphimictic biotypes (Benazzi, 1957, 1960a, 1960b; Benazzi and Puccinelli, 1961) that seem to be distinct because their chromosomes are not related to those of the above-mentioned biotypes. Biotype E possesses four bivalents in oöcytes and spermatocytes; these bivalents do not correspond in size and chiasma frequency to those of biotype A. Biotype F has only three bivalents; the haploid set shows a very long metacentric chromosome, an acrocentric of middle size, and a short chromosome; oöcytes and spermatocytes show normal meiosis with three peculiar bivalents. Biotype G has a diploid number of eight with four bivalents in oöcytes and spermatocytes, but different from those of both A and E biotypes.

The chromosomal differentiation of biotypes E, F, and G is correlated with their reproductive isolation, which allows us to suppose that *D. lugubris* (*sensu lato*) must be regarded as a superspecies containing different sibling or incipient species.

At this point I must recall that the European *D. lugubris* (*sensu lato*) poses an interesting systematic problem, because Schmidt (1860) described, under the names of *Planaria lugubris* and *P. polychroa,* two related species that many subsequent workers have not accepted. As a matter of fact, the two species are not clearly differentiated from the morphological viewpoint and a clear diagnosis does not seem possible.

After the finding of different biotypes, some reproductively isolated, it was of interest to establish whether or not Schmidt's species correspond to some of these biotypes.

Thanks to the kindness of Professor Reisinger, of Graz University, recently I received some specimens coming from the original localities of Schmidt's *P. lugubris* and *P. polychroa*. The results of my cytological studies are very interesting, because they demonstrate that *P. lugubris* corresponds to biotype F with six chromosomes, and *P. polychroa* to the common diploid biotype A.

Therefore I think the old distinction between *P. lugubris* and *P. polychroa* in Schmidt's sense should not be retained, because four sibling or incipient species can be recognized. They are reproductively isolated, but not easily distinguishable on morphological grounds, Examination of the copulatory organs of the different biotypes is now in progress in our laboratory.

THE *Nigra-Tenuis* GROUP

Cytological studies on the *nigra-tenuis* group, which are common European triclads, were accomplished in my laboratory by Dr. N. G. Lepori from 1949 to 1954. He first studied (Lepori, 1949) individuals of *Polycelis nigra* Ehrenberg coming from various Italian localities, which show polyploidy and gynogenesis. The oögonial cells normally possess 24 chromosomes; the oöcytes, 24 bivalents. Meiosis is normal and the eggs develop pseudogamously (the sperm degenerate in the egg), and therefore somatic cells possess 24 chromosomes. The spermatogonial cells normally show 24 chromosomes, but spermatogenesis follows two main lines: one with 48 chromosomes, the other with 24 chromosomes. In both lines the spermatocytes show either the normal number of bivalents, 24 or 12 respectively, or various combinations of bivalents, univalents, and multivalents. Only spermatocytes with bivalents undergo normal spermatogenesis.

Lepori (1950) supposed that the number 24 could be referred to a basic number six, for he found some spermatocytes with 24 chromosomes producing 12 pairs of homologs. Thus triploidy seemed excluded and the tetraploid condition seemed probable. Hence the Italian populations of *P. nigra* should be considered as tetraploid in the somatic cells (24 chromosomes) and octoploid in the oöcytes (24 bivalents), in which a chromosome doubling takes place; the spermatocytes can be either tetraploid or octoploid. Later Lepori (1954a) found a new chromosome complement, in individuals from the Var River near Nice (France), with 36 (or nearly 36) chromosomes in the embryonic cells and 36 (or nearly 36) bivalents in the oöcytes and spermatocytes; the eggs develop pseudogamously and a chromosome doubling takes place in both germ lines. Lepori came to the conclusion that these chromosome complements should be referred to the same basic number six. *P. nigra* of the Var River should then be regarded as hexaploid in the somatic line and dodecaploid in the male and female germ lines.

My own research during the last year does not, however, seem to agree with these conclusions.

In Lake Garda I have found individuals with eight bivalents in oöcytes and a normal development of the male pronucleus in the egg. By crossing these individuals with polyploids from Pavia, I obtained fertile offspring from both parents; this proves that they belong to the same species.

I believe the Garda individuals to represent the diploid and amphimictic biotype of *P. nigra*. Also Schleip (1907) found, in middle Europe, specimens of *P. nigra* with eight bivalents in the spermatocytes; more recently Melander-Hansen, Melander, and Reynoldson (1954) have reported a haploid number of eight for this species. The known diploid populations therefore indicate a basic number of eight. Certainly this number does not easily explain the polyploid complements found by Lepori, especially that of the Var specimens, because 36 is not a multiple of eight. One may suppose that during the evolution of polyploidy the specimens have undergone losses or doubling of some chromosomes, so that a heteroploid assortment arises.

As to *Polycelis tenuis* Jijima, a species closely related to *P. nigra*, Lepori (1954b) found 12 chromosomes (diploid number) in specimens from the Gulf of Finland and 14 chromosomes in specimens from Frankfurt and Monfalcone. Specimens from Aarau, Zurich, and Strasbourg show a polyploid set of 19–22 chromosomes in both oögonial and spermatogonial mitoses and 19–22 tetrads in the oöcytes as a consequence of a chromosome doubling; this polyploid biotype is pseudogamous. I have studied specimens from the Rhone River (near Avignon) and found them polyploid with about 18–20 bivalents in the oöcytes. It is difficult to interpret the number found in *P. tenuis*; Lepori supposed that both *P. nigra* and *P. tenuis* have the same basic number of six, while the number seven may be derived by the doubling of a chromosome in the haploid set (tetrasomic condition).

Melander *et al.*, in the work already cited, have described a new species of the *nigra-tenuis* group, formerly confused with the other two, and named it *Polycelis hepta* because of its haploid number of seven chromosomes; this new species has a penis and a "glandular bursalis" similar to those of *P. tenuis*, but it has no adenodactyls like *P. nigra*.

The three authors hold that the haploid chromosome number is eight in *P. nigra*, six in *P. tenuis*, and seven in *P. hepta*. According to them, *P. nigra* is commonly diploid, whereas *P. tenuis* has established a bisexually reproducing tetraploid form in England. Out of the diploid *P. hepta* have arisen triploids and tetraploids with 21 and 28 chromosomes, respectively; these latter forms are able to propagate either by obligate or facultative parthenogenesis and are very successful, having a larger distribution in western Europe than the bisexually reproducing diploid biotype.

It is evident that the *nigra-tenuis* group affords interesting systematic and cytological problems, which require further studies. The new species *P. hepta* seems doubtful on morphological grounds, because the adenodactyls are lacking in some *P. tenuis* populations as in *P. nigra* (Lepori, 1955; Lender and Le Moigne, 1960); moreover the chromosome number (2n = 14, n = 7) certainly occurs in specimens correctly placed in *P. tenuis* (Lepori, 1954b; Benazzi, in press). Recent studies have shown that *P. nigra* and *P. tenuis* are not reproductively isolated, at least under laboratory conditions, since I was able to obtain fertile offspring by crossing the two species. I think they are to be regarded as species *in statu nascendi* (Benazzi, in press).

Genetic Analysis of the Chromosome Cycle and Reproductive Mechanisms

The different biotypes show that chromosomal evolution in the planarians already considered is characterized by certain events—that is, polyploidy, pseudogamy, ameiotic oögenesis (with, for example, asynapsis in oöcytes), or normal meiosis made possible by the doubling of the chromosome complement during oögonium formation.

It seems very probable that polyploidy succeeded as an evolutionary mechanism because it was correlated with pseudogamous reproduction. A genetic system in-

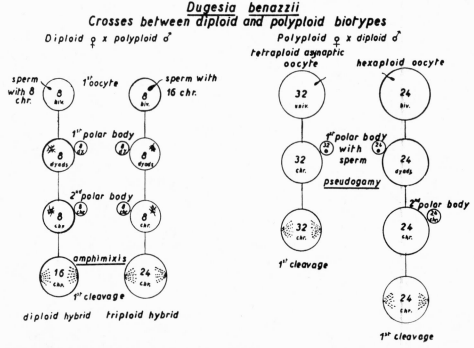

FIGURE 30-5. *Dugesia benazzii:* schematic representation of crosses between diploid and polyploid biotypes. *Left:* oöcytes of the diploid amphimictic biotype fertilized by sperm from tetraploid pseudogamous biotype, with either 8 or 16 chromosomes. *Right:* oöcytes of polyploid pseudogamous biotypes, either tetraploid asynaptic or hexaploid synaptic, fertilized by sperm from diploid biotype.

corporating meiotic pseudogamy seems to be the most advantageous, as indicated by its wide distribution.

We have found many other interesting facts in our attempt at analysing the genetic basis controlling such an evolution; the experimental synthesis of natural biotypes or of new chromosome complements is now a particularly interesting possibility.

In fact, eggs of diploid amphimictic biotypes can be fertilized by sperm of polyploid ones, and some offspring of such crosses inherit maternal characters, namely, asynapsis in the oöcyte, the possibility of chromosome doubling, and pseudogamous development of the egg.

Chromosomal evolution, therefore, can be experimentally analysed, because the cross between diploids and polyploids succeeds in giving normal offspring (Benazzi, 1957, 1960a, 1960b; Benazzi and Benazzi-Lentati, 1956, 1959a, 1959b). I wish to emphasize that such results (previously limited to plant genetics) were here obtained for the first time in the animal kingdom. In other animal groups with polyploid evolution, crosses between different biotypes either are not possible or do not produce viable offspring, or give rise to sterile intersexes.

The basic facts from our research are the four following points:

1. The egg of a diploid amphimictic biotype remains amphimictic even if fertilized by sperm of a pseudogamous biotype (figs. 30-5, 30-6).

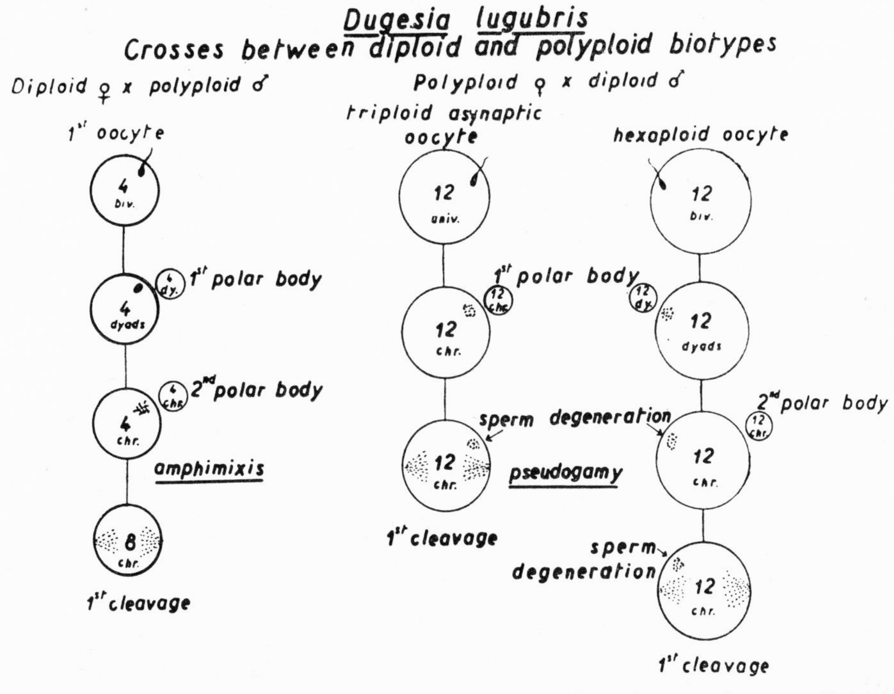

FIGURE 30-6. *Dugesia lugubris:* schematic representation of crosses between diploid and polyploid biotypes. *Left:* oöcyte of the diploid amphimictic biotype fertilized by sperm from a polyploid pseudogamous biotype (in this species the sperm of polyploid individuals are all haploid). *Middle and right:* oöcytes of polyploid pseudogamous biotypes, triploid asynaptic and hexaploid synaptic respectively, fertilized by sperm from the diploid amphimictic biotype.

2. The egg of a polyploid pseudogamous biotype remains pseudog-amous even if fertilized by sperm from a diploid amphimictic biotype (figs. 30-5, 30-6); only in a few cases does amphimixis occur followed by an increase in chromosome number.

3. The fate of the sperm in the egg is therefore established by the properties of the egg, but perhaps an interaction between egg and sperm may be considered. In any case the sperm of a pseudogamous individual always has the capacity of developing into a male pronucleus and of achieving amphimixis; the fusion of the male and female pronuclei occurs at the first cleavage—a phenomenon similar to what occurs in normal amphimictic biotypes (Benazzi-Lentati, 1956).

4. Traits of polyploid and pseudogamous individuals can be trans-mitted by sperm, control by chromosomal genes thus being suggested.

It is necessary to present in some detail the results obtained in *D. benazzii* and *D. lugubris* because, though basically similar, they have distinguishing features. In the *Polycelis nigra-tenuis* group these studies are still at an early stage.

Dugesia benazzii

The main results were obtained by crossing the diploid with the tetraploid biotype asynaptic in the female germ line (fig. 30-5); the male germ line of the latter biotype may be diploid or tetraploid, and accordingly the sperm are either haploid or diploid.

The eggs of the diploid biotype, if fertilized by haploid sperm of the tetraploid biotype, produce diploid offspring, some of which show synaptic oöcytes like the mother, others partially asynaptic oöcytes (that is, with univalents and bivalents), and a few with completely asynaptic oöcytes; the former are amphimictic and fertile, the last two almost sterile because of irregularities of the maturation mech-anisms (Benazzi-Lentati, 1960). A third kind of F_1 individual is characterized by chromosome doubling occurring in the female line; some specimens possess asynap-tic and tetraploid oöcytes (32 univalents) like the paternal biotype; also, in these individuals oögenesis does not take place; other individuals possess oöcytes with 16 bivalents and are fertile (Benazzi-Lentati, 1961).

Even more interesting offspring are obtained when the same type of egg is fertilized by diploid sperm of the tetraploid biotype; such progeny have been carefully studied by Benazzi-Lentati and Puccinelli (1959). The somatic cells of these individuals are triploid, the female germ line becomes hexaploid by means of a chromosome doubling while the male germ line is diploid because of the elimi-nation of a haploid set. Female meiosis is normal because the 48 chromosomes give rise to 24 bivalents; the oöcytes then produce triploid eggs, which develop pseudog-amously, the sperm being discarded with the first polar body. This chromosomal cycle is like that of the natural triploid-hexaploid biotype; therefore a natural race has been obtained experimentally.

In the reciprocal cross (that is, tetraploid individuals fertilized by sperm of diploid ones) the eggs usually develop pseudogamously, as one would expect; some-times, however, amphimixis may take place, and the F_1 then show some paternal characters, such as synapsis in the oöcytes.

Dugesia lugubris

We have studied two different kinds of crosses: diploid ♀ × triploid asynaptic ♂ and diploid ♀ × triploid-hexaploid ♂ (fig. 30-6).

The F_1 from the first cross (Benazzi, 1960a) are mostly diploid and synaptic, like the mother (that is, with four bivalents in the oöcytes); a small number being also diploid but asynaptic (that is, with eight univalents in the oöcytes). Some of these asynaptic F_1 are pseudogamous and maintain their diploid set of eight univalents in the oöcytes. Others are amphimictic and, through repeated crosses or backcrosses, give further generations, each one with an increase of four chromosomes. This latter result is easily explained, for in the asynaptic oöcytes oögenesis occurs without reduction of the chromosome number while sperm are always haploid, even in polyploid individuals. Therefore, the second generation is triploid, the third tetraploid, and the fourth pentaploid. The haploid set of four chromosomes, one metacentric and three acrocentric, is repeated in the corresponding generations, respectively, three, four, and five times; this confirms that all the individuals are autoploid.

In these experimentally synthesized polyploids, asynapsis may be total or partial, for many oöcytes show all univalents; others, univalents and peculiar bivalents having only terminal chiasmata. In still others, even a trivalent may be formed by the union of three metacentric chromosomes. These bivalents and trivalents arise from a synaptic process entirely different from that occurring in normal meiosis; in highly polyploid individuals, however, even bivalents of normal type are sometimes observed.

After the fourth generation chromosomal increase does not proceed regularly; in some individuals of the fifth generation, hexaploid or subhexaploid sets may occur, but in most cases it remains pentaploid or may be reduced to tetraploid. Perhaps tetraploidy represents a more stable condition for, indeed, it is found in the somatic line of natural biotypes. Oögenesis is very irregular in highly polyploid individuals, and their fertility decreases.

Puccinelli (1959, 1961), studying the mechanisms of chromosome diminution in these highly polyploid individuals, has found that both oöcytes and somatic cells show a conspicuous variability, so that in the same individual there is a real mosaic of cells with different chromosome numbers. This phenomenon is owing to a continual and widespread chromosome elimination with irregular effects. The elimination is mainly achieved by mitotic irregularities, such as failure of metaphase congression, deficient chromatid separation, delayed anaphase migration; but even chromosomal elimination by means of cytoplasmic buds may occur.

The second cross, that is, diploid ♀ × triploid-hexaploid ♂, gives mostly diploid individuals and a few that produce two kinds of oöcytes, namely, diploid with four bivalents and tetraploid with eight bivalents. Evidently the paternal polyploid biotype has transmitted to some F_1 specimens the property of doubling the diploid set (Benazzi and Benazzi-Lentati, 1959b; Mirolli and Nocentini, 1959). The somatic line of such individuals is always diploid; when the germ cells arise, some remain diploid and some others double their chromosome complement, giving tetraploid spermatogonia and oögonia. Probably the tetraploid male germ cells are not functional, while the tetraploid oöcytes give oöcytes with eight bivalents.

The ratio between diploid and tetraploid oöcytes varies in the same individual, and the statistical data so far collected do not explain the genetic basis for such a segregation.

Both diploid and tetraploid oöcytes show normal meiosis. The former produce amphimictic eggs and develop a new generation with diploid and tetraploid oöcytes, like the F_1; some haploid eggs, however, do not develop because the sperm is inhibited.

Diploid eggs arising from tetraploid oöcytes develop in most cases pseudogamously, giving offspring that produce diploid and tetraploid oöcytes like the F_1 individuals; only few diploid eggs are amphimictic and produce individuals triploid in their somatic line (12 chromosomes) and hexaploid in their female germ line (12 bivalents in oöcytes), that is, with the characteristics of the natural triploid-hexaploid biotype.

Therefore, a natural polyploid biotype has been experimentally reproduced. The eggs of these individuals develop pseudogamously like the eggs of the natural biotype; an amphimictic process only seldom takes place, with the production of tetraploid individuals, octoploid in their oöcytes (16 bivalents). Even in these highly polyploid individuals chromosome elimination takes place, like that observed in hybrids from the preceding cross (Puccinelli, 1961).

Further Studies on Polyploidy in Triclads

The frequent occurrence of polyploid races in fresh-water triclads has been confirmed by Dahm (1958) in an important contribution to the taxonomy and ecology of five species groups in the family Planariidae. Pointing out the difficulties of triclad taxonomy because of the lack of definite, measurable characters, he acknowledges the importance of cytological research: "From the papers of Professor Mario Benazzi, Pisa, and his co-workers it was apparent that triclads could afford favourable material for cytogenetic and taxonomic investigations." Dahm's research concerns the following species:

1. *Dugesia gonocephala* (*sensu lato*); mostly diploid (2n = 16, n = 8) and a few triploid specimens were found. Dahm summarizes his results as follows (p. 130): "From the papers of the Benazzi team and from my own investigations it appears that *Dugesia gonocephala s.s.* represents the diploid condition while in the remaining species of *D. gonocephala*-like planarians both the diploid and various polyploid conditions are found."

2. *Dugesia tigrina* (Girard); this North American planarian is now distributed in many European watercourses and lakes. Dahm was able to obtain specimens propagating solely by fission, and cytological examination of the specimens showed that their chromosome number varied, being mostly 16 and 24, which represent the diploid and the triploid numbers respectively (a single, probably tetraploid one, was also recorded).

3. *Phagocata vitta* group [*Fonticola vitta* (Dugès) and *F. albissima* (Vejdovsky), two species not clearly differentiated]; eight different chromosome sets were found (the lowest number of chromosomes was 21;

the highest, 70). Dahm was able to identify seven chromosomes of different sizes and shapes, which karyotype was repeated many times to give multiples of seven (21, 28, 35, 42, 49, 56, 63, 70). The conclusion must therefore be that the specimens studied most likely represented ploidy levels ranging from 3n to 10n. A relation seems to exist between chromosome set and reproductive mechanism, which may be (as shown by de Beauchamp, 1939) purely sexual, purely asexual by fission, or both sexual and asexual depending upon environmental conditions. According to Dahm's findings, populations of the first and third groups (that is, with sexual reproduction) were composed of individuals that were probably tetraploid, while populations with purely asexual multiplication were composed of animals showing various degrees of polyploidy—up to chromosome numbers interpreted as decaploids. As to gametogenesis, Dahm found that regular meiosis occurs only in tetraploid populations showing complete synapsis; in the other populations bivalents together with uni- and multivalents are present.

4. *Polycelis felina* (Dalyell, 1814); the mitotic chromosome numbers counted by Dahm varied from 18 to 27, with almost all numbers between these two, but with marked peaks at 18 and 27. A closer study of the morphology of the chromosomes revealed that the genome of *P. felina* is made up of nine chromosomes differing in size and shape. Hence diploid, triploid, and some aneuploid cells, mostly with 21–24 chromosomes, occur in this species; aneuploidy is most likely owing to the triplication of the smaller chromosomes. A mixture of chromosome numbers may be sometimes observed in the same animal. Either regular meiosis with nine bivalents, or somewhat irregular meiosis occurs. In most of the samples the individuals proved to reproduce only asexually, but there were also samples with obligate or facultative sexual reproduction. In the latter group the specimens seemed to be diploid, while in obligate asexually reproducing samples the chromosome numbers were found to range from diploids to triploids, most of the anticipated aneuploid numbers also being recorded.

5. *Crenobia alpina* (Dana, 1766); as the chromosomes are tiny and not well characterized individually, there are difficulties in identifying them and in analysing the metaphase plates. The chromosome numbers varied from 28 to 63; in the plates where a really clear analysis was possible, six chromosome numbers were found (28, 35, 42, 49, 56, 63), all multiples of seven. Dahm came to the conclusion that the material studied by him most probably represented tetra- to nona-ploids, the genome of *C. alpina* being formed by seven chromosomes, of which only the biggest and smallest ones could be individually recognized; neither diploids, triploids, nor aneuploids were identified. In many of the tetraploid and hexaploid specimens, gametogenesis resulted in regular bivalents, but in others, and also in animals characterized by other degrees of polyploidy, gametogenesis was clearly an irregular process. These latter populations never produced fertile cocoons; in the populations producing fertile cocoons, there was presumably amphimixis. Even in this triclad,

three reproductive groups were found: one with only sexual reproduction (interpreted as hexaploid), another with only asexual reproduction but able to produce sterile cocoons, and a third with facultative sexual and asexual reproduction (some samples considered as tetraploids, others as hexaploids).

Dahm's researches are interesting, first, because they confirm and enlarge the field of polyploidy in triclads, and, second, because they suggest a possible causal relationship between polyploidy and asexual reproduction. After having reported my conclusions on the importance of pseudogamy for the existence of polyploid biotypes, Dahm writes (p. 123): "However, the existence of the various chromosome numbers found in the planarians treated in the present study might also be considered in the light of the common occurrence of asexual reproduction. All viable deviation will have the chance to build up clones as a result of the ability of fission. The chromosomal mosaics which occur will also be able to maintain themselves and spread if cells with different chromosome numbers do not differ too much in their rate of multiplication."

Doubtless Dahm's statements are acceptable for the species having the capacity to reproduce by fission; one must not forget that in plants some polyploids have been able to persist and to spread by means of asexual reproduction.

The primary importance of pseudogamy, however, is shown by the evolutionary success of polyploidy in triclads such as *Dugesia lugubris* and *Polycelis nigra-tenuis*, groups that never reproduce by fission. This reproductive mechanism has undertaken the same function as parthenogenesis in other animal groups with polyploid evolution.

A last cytological question that needs further consideration is aneuploidy. From our and Dahm's investigations it seems to be of frequent occurrence in different planarian species, both in diploid and polyploid biotypes. In *D. gonocephala* (*sensu stricto*) and in *D. etrusca*, normal diploid (2n = 16, n = 8) and aneuploid populations are known, the latter with higher chromosome numbers (up to 34); the excess chromosomes are homologous to those of the normal set, but their number varies in different individuals as well as in cells of the same one. Benazzi-Lentati (1957) found, in aneuploid races of *D. etrusca*, that these variations are owing to the abnormal movement of the daughter chromatids, so that after mitosis one cell receives two chromatids and the other none. Aneuploidy occurs in both germ lines; spermatocytes and oöcytes of these aneuploids show, besides the eight normal bivalents, excess bivalents or multivalents as well as univalents. But in the course of spermatogenesis the extra chromosomes are eliminated so that all sperm are haploid, whereas during oögenesis some of them remain in the egg; aneuploidy in *D. etrusca* is therefore transmitted only through the mother. In other species of the *gonocephala* group, such as *D. benazzii,* however, even the sperm can be aneuploid (Papale, 1956).

Discussion

Our studies on different planarian species have demonstrated cytological mechanisms that control the chromosome cycle in polyploid biotypes, namely: (1) pseudogamous development of the egg; (2) asynapsis in oöcytes, or (3) chromosome doubling in the female germ line when oögenesis is accomplished with normal meiosis; and (4) chromosome elimination in the male germ line, or in a part of it.

The results obtained by crossing amphimictic diploid biotypes with pseudogamous polyploid ones show that the above-mentioned cytological mechanisms may be transmitted through the sperm of polyploid biotypes and therefore can be considered as traits controlled by chromosomal genes. Unfortunately the numerical data so far collected do not allow any definitive conclusion from the viewpoint of Mendelian genetics, and our investigations still remain in a largely descriptive stage.

About the origin of pseudogamy, three interesting points emerge from our work: (1) it is not associated with an unreduced oögenesis, because it occurs both in synaptic and in asynaptic oöcytes; (2) it is controlled by the egg, but probably not by its cytoplasm, because some F_1 descended from an amphimictic mother may be pseudogamous and the presence of two phenotypes in the F_1 is difficult to explain on a cytoplasmic basis; (3) the ploidy level is not a determinative factor so far as the experimentally produced individuals are concerned. In natural biotypes the diploids found up to now are amphimictic and the polyploids are pseudogamous; but in hybrid individuals some diploid oöcytes may inhibit the function of the sperm. For instance, in *D. lugubris* some diploid and asynaptic F_1 specimens are amphimictic, others are pseudogamous; the first ones may produce offspring remaining amphimictic even at a high ploidy level. Also the diploid synaptic oöcytes of F_1 specimens may be either amphimictic or pseudogamous, but the latter do not develop, because they become haploid after meiosis. Even at a high ploidy level (4n, 6n, 8n), meiotic oöcytes may be either pseudogamous or amphimictic, with normal development.

The different behavior of the sperm after penetrating a primary oöcyte of an F_1 individual results in either amphimixis or pseudogamy. As a matter of fact, if the sperm degenerates or is expelled, pseudogamy occurs; on the contrary, if the sperm develops into a pronucleus, amphimixis occurs. According to Benazzi-Lentati (in press) the different position of the sperm head in the oöcyte seems to determine whether the first or second mode of development occurs. The following cases were found: (1) the same individual produces either exclusively amphimictic oöcytes or exclusively pseudogamous ones; (2) the same individual has oöcytes that are amphimictic when diploid and pseudogamous when tetraploid; (3) the same individual gives diploid pseudogamous and tetraploid amphimictic oöcytes; and (4) the same individual produces diploid and tetraploid oöcytes, which may both develop either through amphimixis or pseudogamy. The fourth case is very peculiar, since the two types of development seem to be already determined in prometaphase or metaphase I, even though in every individual, all the oöcytes have the same genotype.

As to "oöcyte asynapsis," strong genic control is indicated by all our research. Hybrids with total or partial asynapsis remain such for all their life and are not influenced by environmental conditions; even in specimens obtained by regenerated pieces of such individuals, the character remains constant. It seems quite probable that some genes, perhaps together with modifiers, account for asynapsis or for reduced chromosome pairing in oöcytes. The ratio between synaptic and asynaptic specimens in the progeny of synaptic individuals fertilized by sperm of asynaptic ones shows considerable variation in different crosses, but the frequency of asynap-

tics is always lower than that of synaptics. We are inclined to conclude that sperm
produced by an individual of asynaptic biotype carry different numbers of genes
dealing with asynapsis and that a certain number of them is required for the pheno-
typic expression of the character. According to this hypothesis, asynaptic individuals
might be heterozygous, but with a number of "asynapsis" genes always in a super-
threshold quantity. Totally synaptic hybrids of *D. benazzii* may carry genes for
asynapsis, because asynaptic specimens are sometimes present in their offspring
(Benazzi-Lentati and Bertini, 1961); this also seems to be consistent with our
interpretation.

It will be noted that chromosomal factors controlling the behavior of chromosomes themselves during specific stages of nuclear division are known in several
species, the first case being discovered by Beadle (1930) in maize.

Even for chromosome doubling, genic control is in evidence, as shown by the
occurrence of tetraploid oöcytes in individuals produced by diploids crossed with
polyploids. I also wish to mention that, in normal diploid individuals, oögonia
showing chromosome doubling are of frequent occurrence, but the corresponding
oöcytes do not develop. It seems reasonable to assume that genes are carried by the
sperm of polyploid individuals and that these function to make possible normal
development and meiosis of oöcytes with doubled chromosome number.

If we look at the totality of our observations on reproductive mechanisms and
chromosome behavior in planarians, we must admit that some facts have been
elucidated, but that their genetic interpretation still remains in a primitive stage.
I emphasize the need of new investigations in order to explain the several crucial
questions still unanswered.

REFERENCES

Beadle, G. W.
    1930   Genetical and cytological studies of Mendelian asynapsis in *Zea mays*.
            Mem. Conn. agric. Exp. Sta. 129:1–23.
Beauchamp, P. de
    1939   La systématique et l'éthologie des *Fonticola* (Turb. Triclades). Mém.
            Soc. zool. tchécosl. (Věst. česk. zool. Spolneč.) 6–7:91–96.
Benazzi, M.
    1945   Mutazione genomica in una razza di *Dugesia* (*Euplanaria*) *gonocephala*
            (Dugès). Boll. Soc. Biol. sper. 20:270–271.
    1950   Ginogenesi in tricladi di acqua dolce. Chromosoma 3:474–482.
    1951   Peculiare mutazione genomica in popolazioni di *Dugesia lugubris* (O.
            Schm.). Mem. Soc. tosc. Sci. nat. (ser. B) 58:3–8.
    1953   Matazioni genomiche in *Dugesia lugubris* (Tricladida Paludicola). Ric.
            Sci., Suppl. (Convegno di Genetica) 23:33–41.
    1955   L'evoluzione della poliploidia nelle planarie appartenenti alla superspecie
            "Dugesia gonocephala". R. C. Accad. Lincei. (ser. 8) 18:527–533.
    1957   Cariologia di *Dugesia lugubris* (O. Schmidt) (Tricladida Paludicola).
            Caryologia 10:276–303.
    1960a   Ulteriori ricerche sui poliploidi sperimentali della planaria *Dugesia lugu-
            bris* (O. Schmidt). *Ibid.* 12:414–438.

1960b   Evoluzione cromosomica e differenziamento razziale e specifico nei tri-
         cladi. In: "Evoluzione e Genetica, Colloquio Internaz. (1959)" Prob.
         att. Sci. Cult. Acc. naz. Lincei. 47:273–297.

In press. Il problema sistematico delle *Polycelis* del gruppo *nigra-tenuis* alla luce di
         ricerche citologiche e genetiche. Monit. zool. ital.

Benazzi, M., and G. Benazzi-Lentati
1950   Ulteriori osservazioni sulla ovogenesi e sul ciclo cromosomico del biotipo
         G di *Dugesia benazzii* della Sardegna. Arch. zool. (ital.), Napoli 35:251–
         263.

1956   Ricerche su incroci tra biotipi diploidi e poliploidi di Planarie. Mem. Soc.
         tosc. Sci. nat. (ser. B.) 62:129–138.

1959a   Corredo cromosomico e meccanismi della ovogenesi e della fecondazione
         in ibridi fra biotipi diploidi e poliploidi di Planarie. Ric. Sci., Suppl. (Con-
         vegni di Genetica) 29:3–10.

1959b   Ricerche su ibridi tra i biotipi diploide e triplo-esaploide della Planaria
         Dugesia lugubris (O. Schmidt). Mem. Soc. tosc. Sci. nat. (ser. B.) 66:
         45–57.

Benazzi, M., and I. Puccinelli
1961   Analisi comparativa del cariogramma dei biotipi di *Dugesia lugubris*
         (Tricladida Paludicola). Atti Ass. genet. ital. 6:419–426.

Benazzi-Lentati, G.
1953   Nuove ricerche sulla riproduzione pseudogamica e sul ciclo cromosomico
         in biotipi poliploidi di *Dugesia benazzii* (Tricladida Paludicola). Caryo-
         logia 5:223–236.

1956   Anfigonia in Tricladi diploidi e comportamento dello spermio in incroci
         fra biotipi diploidi anfigonici e poliploidi pseudogamici. Arch. zool.
         (ital.), Napoli 41:113–128.

1957   Sul determinismo e sulla ereditarietà della aneuploidia in *Dugesia etrusca*
         Benazzi, Planaria a riproduzione anfigonica. Caryologia 10:352–387.

1960   Condizionamento dei processi maturativi in ovociti sinaptici ed asinaptici
         di Planarie. Atti Ass. genet. ital. 5:199–206.

1961   Considerazioni sul determinismo dei cicli cromosomici in ibridi di Pla-
         narie. Caryologia 14:271–277.

In press. Due modalità di sviluppo nello stesso tipo di uova in ibridi di Planarie.
         Acta Embryol. et Morph. Exp. 5.

Benazzi-Lentati, G., and V. Bertini
1961   Sul determinismo della "asinapsi femminile" in ibridi di *Dugesia benazzii*.
         (Triclade paludicolo). Mem. Soc. tosc. Sci. nat. (ser. B.) 68:83–112.

Benazzi-Lentati, G., A. Curini, and M. J. Piegaja
1951   Studi cariologici su alcune specie di triclidi di acqua dolce. *Ibid*. 58:85–
         93.

Benazzi-Lentati, G., and O. Nardi
1951   La spermatogenesi in due biotipi di *Dugesia benazzii* della Sardegna.
         Caryologia 3:181–199.

Benazzi-Lentati, G., and I. Puccinelli
1959   Ulteriori ricerche sugli ibridi fra biotipo diploide a biotipo tetraploide di
         Dugesia benazzii: produzione di individui triplo-esaploidi. *Ibid*. 12:110–
         131.

Dahm, A. G.
1958   Taxonomy and Ecology of Five Species Groups in the Family Planariidae
         (Turbellaria Tricladida Paludicola). Nya Litografen, Malmö.

Dalyell, J. G.

422   MARIO BENAZZI

  1814 Observations on some Interesting Phaenomena on Animal Physiology
       Exhibited by Several Species of Planaria. Constable, Edinburgh.

Dana, J. P. M.
  1766 De hirudinis nova species, noxa, remediisque adhibendis (*H. alpina*).
       Mélanges de Philosophie et de Mathém. de la Soc. roy. de Turin (1762–
       1765) 3:199–205.

Lender, T., and A. Le Moigne
  1960 Les organes musculo-glandulaires de *Polycelis tenuis* Jijima (Turbel-
       larié Triclade). Bull. Soc. zool. Fr. 85:90–99.

Lepori, N. G.
  1949 Ricerche sulla ovogenesi e sulla fecondazione nella Planaria *Polycelis
       nigra* Ehrenberg con particolare riguardo all'ufficio del nucleo spermatico.
       Caryologia 1:280–295.
  1950 Il ciclo cromosomico con poliploidia, endomitosi e ginogenesi, in popo-
       lazioni italiane di *Polycelis nigra* Ehrenberg. *Ibid.* 2:301–324.
  1954a Nuova mutazione genomica in *Polycelis nigra* Ehrenberg. *Ibid.* 6:90–102.
  1954b Prime ricerche cariologiche su alcune popolazioni europee di *Polycelis
       tenuis* Jijima. *Ibid.* 6:103–115.
  1955 La differenziazione specifica di *Polycelis nigra* Ehr. e *Polycelis tenuis*
       Jijima (Tricladida, Paludicola) e la loro distribuzione geografica in Eur-
       opa. Mem. Soc. tosc. Sci. nat. (ser. B.) 62:50–71.

Melander-Hansen, E., Y. Melander, and T. B. Reynoldson
  1954 A new species of freshwater triclad belonging to the genus *Polycelis*.
       Nature 173:354–355.

Mirolli, M., and A. M. Nocentini
  1959 Evoluzione delle linee germinali in esemplari diplo-tetraploidi e triplo-
       esaploidi della Planaria *Dugesia lugubris* (O. Schmidt). Mem. Soc. tosc.
       Sci. nat. (ser. B.) 66:58–69.

Papale, S.
  1956 Sulla trasmissione della aneuploidia in alcune specie di Tricladi. *Ibid.* 63:
       29–34.

Pieragnoli, U.
  1954 Il ciclo cromosomico in un biotipo poliploide di *Dugesia lugubris* (O.
       Schmidt) (Triclade paludicolo). *Ibid.* 61:3–19.

Puccinelli, I.
  1959 Variazioni del numero cromosomico in poliploidi sperimentali della
       Planaria *Dugesia lugubris* (O. Schmidt). Boll. Zool. 26:311–317.
  1961 Variazioni del numero cromosomico e meccanismi di eliminazione cromo-
       somica in poliploidi sperimentali della Planaria *Dugesia lugubris* (O.
       Schmidt). Acta Embryol. et Morphol. Exp. 4:1–17.

Schleip, W.
  1907 Die Samenreifung bei den Planarien. Zool. Jb. (Anat.) 24:129–174.

Schmidt, O.
  1860 Die Dendrocoelen Strudelwürmer aus den Umgebungen von Gratz. Z.
       wiss. Zool. 10:24–33.

C. IMMUNOLOGY

31 ◆ Immune Mechanisms in the Phylum Coelenterata

JOHN H. PHILLIPS

HOPKINS MARINE STATION OF STANFORD UNIVERSITY,
PACIFIC GROVE, CALIFORNIA

Immunology is usually defined as the study of relative resistance to infectious disease. For the most part, emphasis has been placed upon the study of relative resistance of a few kinds of vertebrates to microbial parasites. When a less restricted group of organisms is considered, however, associations other than those of host and parasite become of interest because of their obvious ecological importance. It may be expected that an organism can be modified in at least two ways so as to resist the deleterious effects of its associates. The selection of mutant forms possessing greater resistance could lead to the establishment of populations with a particular set of "native," constitutive, or genetically determined immune mechanisms. A second observed type of modification can occur within the life of an individual and results in acquired or induced mechanisms of immunity. Finally it may be expected that the modifications may result in either anatomical, physiological, or behavioristic alterations.

It is hoped that the investigations described here will contribute to the understanding of immune mechanisms in general and that the comparison of resistance mechanisms operating in different kinds of associated organisms will be extended.

The phylum Coelenterata consists of a collection of relatively simple yet highly successful animal forms. Its members live in a variety of kinds of associations with other organisms, and many thrive in crowded environments.

At least in the case of anemones, individuals with extremely long life-spans have been observed (Hyman, 1940). Longevity, exposure to large populations of other organisms, and interesting associations make the celenterates a particularly interesting group for the study of immune mechanisms.

The studies reported here were supported by grants from the National Science Foundation and the U.S. Public Health Service. They were carried out while the author was on the staff of the Department of Bacteriology, University of California, Berkeley.

Two possible defense mechanisms directed at larger organisms should be mentioned. First, the nematocysts formed by this group of animals probably play an important role in resisting antagonistic organisms large enough to be hit by the discharge of these structures. It is interesting that there is a correlation between certain taxonomic features and nematocyst type. This suggests that such constitutive structures have been subjected to considerable selective pressure. Second, the facilitated response of some anemones (Pantin, 1935) has been suggested by Ross (1957) to restrict the closing response of the animal to events in which the stimulus suggests danger from a large antagonist.

I would now like to describe some of our observations on defense mechanisms directed against smaller organisms. The intertidal anemone *Anthopleura elegantissima* was used in these studies. The examination of this animal from its outer surface to its interior reveals a number of protective barriers. The mucoid secretions of the surface can be observed to form a constantly replenished barrier against the invasion of microörganisms. This property of the mucus can be readily demonstrated by the

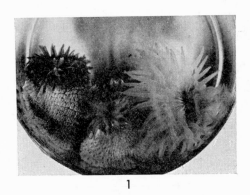 

1   2

FIGURE 31-1. *A. elegantissima,* before exposure to carbon particles.
FIGURE 31-2. *A. elegantissima,* immediately after exposure to carbon particles.

use of finely divided carbon particles as is illustrated in figures 31-1–31-4. Figure 31-1 shows the anemones before exposure to carbon. Figure 31-2 shows the same animals immediately after exposure to the particles. In figure 31-3, obtained 1½ hours later, the mucus-trapped carbon has been rolled up into strands that are pushed toward the base of the animal as is shown in figure 31-4. The slow rhythmic contractions of the animal and the action of the cilia result in clearance of the mucus-trapped particles, and it may be expected that many microörganisms landing on the surface of the animal meet a similar fate. An essentially identical process has been described by Florey (1933) with respect to clearance of particles and bacteria from the lumen surface of the vertebrate intestine. The essential difference between the two situations is one of geometry. Peristalsis effects the movement of the mucus in the intestine.

A study of the bacterial flora of *Anthopleura elegantissima* was made in order to determine whether the microörganisms of this constantly cleaned surface possess unique properties. A medium containing half-strength sea water, .05 per cent yeast extract, .05 per cent peptone, and 1 per cent agar was used for isolations. This dilute medium was selected because it allowed the growth of the greatest number of bacteria from sea-water inocula. Sea water and the surface of anemones were used as inocula. In addition, enrichments of live anemones in small amounts of sterile sea water held at 5°, 22° and 37° C. were sampled until decomposition of the animal was all but complete. One hundred and twenty colonies were picked and purified through the preparation of first and second plates. There was no attempt to identify the isolates on the basis of preëxisting descriptions. Instead the cultures were subjected to the 62 different tests, including ones for morphology and tinctorial properties; ability to digest chitin, cellulose, agar, and gelatine; ability to ferment a variety of carbohydrates; ability to grow in a variety of simple defined media; temperature and salinity tolerances; and sensitivity to 27 different antibiotics and chemotherapeutic agents. On the basis of these 62 different properties no unique bacterial flora could be ascertained. That is, for every bacterium isolated from the surface or from the enrichments a very similar organism could be isolated from sea water. Although the surface of anemones can be demonstrated to be highly

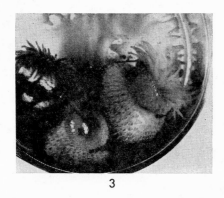
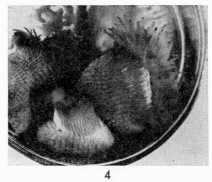

3   4

FIGURE 31-3. *A. elegantissima*, 1½ hours later—mucus-captured carbon particles rolled up into strands.
FIGURE 31-4. *A. elegantissima*, sometime later—mucus with carbon now at base of anemones.

contaminated with bacteria, this collection would seem to be derived from the surrounding sea water. In the intertidal zone the population of bacteria per ml. of sea water can reach levels as high as 10^5 bacteria/ml. as determined by direct counts of stained organisms collected on millipore filters.

It might be expected that mucinase-producing microörganisms would be selected from this population of bacteria surrounding the anemones, and that this selection would result in their establishment on the surface of these animals. Through the use of elective cultures it is possible to obtain from marine sediments bacteria capable of breaking down not only the mucus but the intercellular cementing material of the animal as well. Some studies have been carried out in this connection for the purpose of obtaining enzymes that would allow the preparation of suspensions of single cells for tissue culture. The existence of such bacterial forms in the marine environment and the lack of a unique bacterial flora of the anemone would suggest that resistance to microbial invasion evokes a number of immune mechanisms. Two other such properties of the anemone surface have been observed. Beneath the coat of older secreted mucus a pH of 5.9 can be demonstrated by applying the electrodes of a pH meter directly to the scraped surface of the animal. The secretions responsible for this comparatively acid surface would seem to be the mucus itself, because titrations of freshly collected mucus indicate that it behaves like a weak acid. A test of the earlier-described collection of bacteria revealed that 43 per cent were unable to grow at this low pH. Like the mucus of vertebrates, collections of mucus from the anemone contain an enzyme that resembles lysozyme in its ability to lyse the bacterium, *Micrococcus lysodeikticus*. Further studies are anticipated to determine the properties of this enzyme and its effect on the culture collection. The protective effects of the mucoid secretions of anemones are strikingly similar to the known effects of mucus from vertebrates. It will be interesting to determine whether this similarity holds for mucus from other invertebrate types.

In the internal tissues of anemones no antibiotic materials can be demonstrated. Such substances have been observed by Jakowska and Nigrelli (1960) in sponges. Extracts prepared from living anemones using a variety of solvents have not contained these agents. A very active phagocytic system has long been known to be present in these animals and was originally described from the immunologic point of view by Mechnikov (1905). Particulate materials introduced into the celenteron or directly into the tissues are rapidly taken up by phagocytic cells. These cells seem to be the final site of food digestion as well. The detection of opsonizing agents, such as specific antibody, in these animals has been described (Phillips, 1960; Phillips and Yardley, 1961). Briefly, the observations have been the following: The injection of Armour's Bovine Serum Albumin Fraction V (BSA), or Cutter Human Plasma Albumin (HuPA), into anemones induces the animals to produce non-enzymatic materials that combine with their homologous antigens. These antibody-like materials, which show a high degree of specificity, are present in tissue extracts. Because they are non-precipitating, they must be detected by observing their effect on rabbit precipitating-antibodies specific for the antigens studied. In low concentration anemone antibody is able to add on to the rabbit antibody-antigen complex, and this results in a greater amount of precipitate. At higher concentrations the anemone substance is inhibitory and decreases the amount of precipitate formed.

No observations have been made of the effect of this antibody-like material at the cellular level—that is, whether or not it does facilitate phagocytosis. Some preliminary observations have been made, however, of the response of whole immunized animals to subsequent exposure to the antigen. These experiments were suggested by an observation of Dr. Leonard Muscatine of the Zoölogy Department of the University of California, who noted interesting food preferences in these anemones. The experiments were performed in the following way. Protein-rich extracts of sardine and mackerel were prepared by mascerating whole fish in sea water in a Waring Blendor. The amount of protein in these extracts was determined, and dilutions were prepared in 1 per cent agar. BSA and HuPA were used to prepare similar protein-agar mixtures. Small cylinders with a diameter of 3.5 mm. and a length of 4.5 mm. were cut, using a cork borer. The piece of agar containing extract or protein was dropped onto the tentacles of anemones and their response was observed. Depending upon the preparation, animals either ignored the material or grasped and swallowed it. For convenience a 15-minute time limit was imposed, and anemones that swallowed the preparation within this time interval were scored as acceptors. Table 31-1 shows the results of initial tests on thirty animals. With respect

TABLE 31-1

ORIGINAL GROUP OF THIRTY UNTREATED ANEMONES

Protein concentration in agar cylinder	Response to			
	Sardine	Mackerel	BSA	HuPA
7.2 mg/ml	30/30	17/30	0/30	0/30
3.6 mg/ml	25/30	12/30	0/30	0/30
1.8 mg/ml	21/30	4/30	0/30	0/30
0.9 mg/ml	16/30	0/30	0/30	0/30
0.45 mg/ml	11/30	0/30	0/30	0/30

to the sardine and mackerel extracts it can be seen that there is a relationship between concentration of the extract in the agar cylinders and acceptance. Also, there are indications of a greater response to sardine than to mackerel. There was no acceptance of either BSA, HuPA, or plain agar. There is, of course, an important difference between the purified proteins and the extracts. The latter contain a variety of materials including small-molecular-weight substances, such as amino acids and possibly glutathione.

These thirty anemones were divided into six groups of five, and five of these groups were given injections of BSA as shown in table 31-2. They were then re-

TABLE 31-2

RESPONSE TO 7.2 MG/ML PROTEIN IN AGAR TEST CYLINDERS

Groups of anemones	BSA						HuPA
	Days after treatment						
	1–3	4–5	6	7	8	9	9
I. Injected with 1.0 mg. BSA	0/5	. . .[a]	1/5	2/5	3/5	3/5	0/5
II. Injected with 0.1 mg. BSA	0/5	. . .	1/5	1/5	1/5	3/5	0/5
III. Injected with 0.01 mg. BSA	0/5	. . .	1/5	1/5	3/5	3/5	0/5
IV. Injected with 0.001 mg. BSA	0/5	. . .	1/5	1/5	1/5	1/5	0/5
V. Injected with 0.0001 mg. BSA	0/5	. . .	0/5	0/5	0/5	0/5	0/5

[a] No tests on fourth and fifth days.

tested at intervals. An acceptance of BSA was noted on the sixth day in all groups except the one receiving the least amount of BSA. There was some increase in acceptance in the following days. In studies on the time of appearance of a rise in titer of the antibody-like material, it was observed that at least six days are required for the production of significant amounts of this reactive material. On the ninth day these same animals were tested, using HuPA. There was a complete lack of response. This suggests a similar specificity in this altered behavior to that observed with the antibody.

The five anemones of the remaining group were not given an injection of BSA, but were tested and observed in the same manner as groups I–V. The results of these tests are shown in table 31-3. On the ninth day they received an injection of

TABLE 31-3

RESPONSE TO 7.2 MG/ML PROTEIN IN AGAR TEST CYLINDERS

Groups of anemones	BSA						HuPA
	Days after treatment						
	1–3	4–5	6	7	8	9	9
VI. Anemones not injected with BSA	0/5	. . .[a]	0/5	0/5	0/5	0/5	0/5
Anemomes injected with extract prepared from an accepting anemone of Group I; response after 24 hours	3/5	. . .	. . .	. . .	. . .	. . .	0/5

[a] No tests on fourth and fifth days.

a cell-free extract prepared from one of the acceptors of group I. Twenty-four hours later they were tested, and three out of the five were found to be acceptors of BSA and not of HuPA. These results indicate that the altered response can be passively transferred. As was mentioned earlier, these are only preliminary observations and will require further quantitation and repetition with larger numbers of animals. They do, however, seem to indicate at least one possible role played by the antibody-like material of these animals. The last few years have been filled with theories of antibody formation, and I do not feel it is desirable to add further to this burden of theory. Nevertheless, antibody as a recognition system is not a new concept. Burnet and Fenner (1949) suggested this activity of antibody some years ago. They focused on a recognition of foreign materials within the organism; our observations would suggest that there may be recognition at the surface of the organism as well. Antibody may assist in the detection and acquisition of desirable materials as well as in clearance of foreign and undesirable substances.

In way of summary, I feel that our observations indicate that, in the phylum Coelenterata, there are immune mechanisms not essentially different from those believed to be important in vertebrates.

REFERENCES

Burnet, F. M., and F. Fenner
    1949   The Production of Antibodies. Macmillan, Melbourne.
Florey, H. W.
    1933   Observations on the functions of mucus and the early stages of bacterial invasion of the intestinal tract. J. Path. Bact. 37:283–289.
Hyman, L. H.
    1940   The Invertebrates. I: Protozoa through Ctenophora. McGraw-Hill, New York, Toronto, London.
Jakowska, S., and R. F. Nigrelli
    1960   Antimicrobial substances from sponges. In: conference on "Biochemistry and Pharmacology of Compounds Derived from Marine Organisms." Ann. N. Y. Acad. Sci. 90:913–916.
Mechnikov [Metchnikoff], E.
    1905   Immunity in Infective Diseases. Cambridge Univ., London.

Pantin, C. F. A.
 1935 The nerve net of the Actinozoa. I. Facilitation. J. exp. Biol. 12:119–138.
Phillips, J. H.
 1960 Antibodylike materials of marine invertebrates. In: conference on "Biochemistry and Pharmacology of Compounds Derived from Marine Organism." Ann. N. Y. Acad. Sci. 90:760–769.
Phillips, J. H., and B. J. Yardley
 1961 Detection in invertebrates of inducible, reactive materials resembling antibody. Nature 188:728–730.
Ross, D. M., and G. A. Horridge
 1957 Responses of *Cerianthus* (Coelenterata). *Ibid.* 180:1368–1370.

D. ECOLOGY: General

32 ◆ Ecological Affinities and Origins of Free-Living Acelomate Fresh-Water Invertebrates

ROBERT W. PENNAK

DEPARTMENT OF BIOLOGY,
UNIVERSITY OF COLORADO, BOULDER

Compared with that of most other contributions to this volume, my topic is broad and necessarily generalized and speculative. Some parts of my discussion will draw only upon the American literature; other parts will use appropriate literature at large. Incidentally, it should be emphasized at the outset that our knowledge of the taxonomy, ecology, and distribution of fresh-water metazoan invertebrates of the United States is in a notably retarded state (Pennak, 1958). We are probably twenty-five years behind the situation in Europe, where the fauna is relatively well known. At the moment I am making a sincere plea for my American colleagues to devote much more effort to our fresh-water invertebrates in the way of field collections, taxonomy, and zoögeography.

In a discussion of this nature we might easily become bogged down in a welter of literature citations covering many interrelated endeavors, and I am therefore intentionally including only certain few essential and recent references with no citations being listed for many obvious and well-known aspects of my topic.

For example, there is no need to document the general consensus that the free-living, non-celomate groups being considered are all ancient, and that, with the exception of one or two phyla, they all originated in the sea, although specific remarks about their evolutionary migratory paths are admittedly highly speculative.

I should like to consider three intermingled general problems. (1) From the standpoint of number of species involved, how does our modern fresh-water acelomate metazoan invertebrate fauna compare with that of the seas? (2) What is unique or peculiar about the distribution, physiology, behavior, and ecology of

Contribution No. 37, Limnology Laboratory, University of Colorado. This is an expanded version of a paper read at the Second Annual Symposium on Comparative Biology sponsored by the Kaiser Foundation Research Institute at Asilomar, Pacific Grove, California, Sept. 6–10, 1960. The author is grateful to Dr. Donald J. Zinn, of the University of Rhode Island, who gave the manuscript a critical reading.

these invertebrates as compared with their marine counterparts? (3) What can be said about the present and past highways of migration into fresh waters and the relative speed of migration? Perhaps these matters can be best approached by means of a phylum-by-phylum consideration. The Ctenophora, Kinorhyncha, and Priapulida can be dismissed without comment, since, to our knowledge, they have never successfully colonized fresh waters.

Table 32-1 gives a census of lower metazoan species in various habitats.

TABLE 32-1

ESTIMATED ENVIRONMENTAL CENSUS OF FREE-LIVING NON-CELOMATE INVERTEBRATES

Major taxon	Total number of species	Number of marine species	Number of species occurring in brackish waters ($7^0/_{00}$–$25^0/_{00}$)	Number of species restricted to brackish waters ($7^0/_{00}$–$25^0/_{00}$)	Number of species in fresh waters
Porifera	4,500	4,350	Few	0	150 (28 in U.S.)
Coelenterata	10,000	10,000	Few	0	(17 in U.S.)
Ctenophora	90	90	Few	0	0
Turbellaria	1,500	Many	Few	Very few	Many
Nemertea	750	700	Few	?	About 8 (1 in U.S.)
Rotatoria	1,800	50	200	70	1,680
Gastrotricha	500	210	?	?	250
Nematoda	14,000	Many	Few	Very few	Many
Kinorhyncha	50	50	Few	0	0
Priapulida	6	6	?	0	0
Entoprocta	60	58	?	0	2 (1 in U.S.)

NOTE: Parasitic species are included only in the second column. Uncertain items are indicated by question marks.

The Porifera

One of the most clear-cut phylogenetic and ecological cleavages between a marine fauna and a fresh-water fauna is found in the Porifera. Of the 4,500 modern species of sponges, about 150 (the entire family Spongillidae) are restricted to fresh waters, the other 4,350 being found only in marine and strongly brackish waters. Significantly, the Spongillidae occur in *clean* inland waters only—never in silty waters, never in estuaries where suspended sedimentary loads are usual.

Some species, such as *Spongilla lacustris,* are cosmopolitan and occur all over the world in suitable habitats, but others are highly restricted and have been taken only from single localities. In the United States, for example, *Spongilla heterosclerifera* is known only from Oneida Lake in New York, *Meyenia subdivisa* is known from the St. Johns River in Florida, and *Heteromeyenia conigera* from Early County, Georgia. Certain genera are restricted to single continents or parts of single continents. Thus, *Corvomeyenia* and *Dosilia* occur only in a few places in North America. Africa has several endemic genera; South America has *Uruguaya* and *Parmula;* and Lake Baikal in Asia and Lake Ohrid in Europe are widely known for their endemic genera and species. Many other examples could be cited. In spite of the fact that there are only about 150 species of Spongillidae, speciation seems to be of common occurrence and sharply defined.

A unique feature of fresh-water sponges is the production of gemmules, especially in the late summer and early autumn. Such stages are highly resistant to adverse temperature, chemical, and moisture conditions, and it is notable that Rasmont (1954) goes so far as to consider gemmule production a "diapause" mechanism. Basically, a true gemmule is a mass of archeocytes surrounded by two or three organic membranes and a layer of compacted spicules of various design, but the term "gemmule" has also been applied to structures produced by some marine Demospongiae. These "gemmules" are, however, nothing more than small masses of archeocytes, each surrounded by a poorly-defined membrane of living cells; they develop into flagellated larvae, and it seems doubtful that they are phylogenetically or developmentally similar to true gemmules.

Hadžišče (1953) believes that *Ochridospongia rotunda* of Lake Ohrid does not form gemmules, and it is also said that endemic genera of Lake Baikal (*Lubomirskia, Swartschewskia,* and *Baicalospongia*) do not form gemmules either. Since Baikal and Ohrid are ancient lakes, one may then speculate as to whether these genera are primitive or whether their gemmule-forming habit has been more recently lost. Perhaps their endemism is, indeed, a reflection of the fact that these forms have been unable to become more widely dispersed because of the *lack* of resistant, easily-transportable gemmules.

During early embryology a stereoblastula is formed only in the Spongillidae among sponges. No free-swimming larvae are known for this family, in striking contrast to the situation in marine species.

In view of the pronounced osmoregulatory differences between marine and fresh-water invertebrates, it is significant that little seems to have been written about osmoregulation in fresh-water sponges. No special mechanisms are known, and it is presumed that contractile vacuoles and the cell membranes of individual sponge cells function in maintaining a proper intracellular salt/water balance. Zeuthen (1939) has noted that in summer the osmotic pressure in gemmules is 25 to 30 mM NaCl; before fall dissemination it is 110 mM NaCl; and, after dissemination, but before germination, it is back down to 25 to 30 mM NaCl.

The Coelenterata

Although there are more than 10,000 modern species of the Coelenterata, the number restricted to the fresh waters of the world is quite small, only 17 species, for example, being reported from the United States. These include 15 species of the familiar hydras (family Hydridae), the common fresh-water jellyfish *Craspedacusta sowerbyi* (family Petasidae), and a single colonial hydrozoan, *Cordylophora lacustris* (family Clavidae). Like the Porifera, therefore, the fresh-water celenterates are represented by only a few "adventitious" species.

Hyman (1940) is of the opinion that the hydras are not a primitive group, owing to their four types of nematocysts and relatively high degree of histological differentiation. The group has probably been in fresh waters for a very long time and has lost all traces of a medusa stage.

The United States seems to have a larger hydra fauna than other continental areas. Some species, such as *Chlorohydra viridissima* and *Hydra oligactis,* are widely distributed both in the United States and elsewhere, but several other American species are known only from type localities. It is my conviction that there are still many undescribed species in this country awaiting more careful and systematic field collecting.

Craspedacusta sowerbyi is probably not a modern immigrant into fresh waters, in view of its widespread but sporadic occurrence on all continents. On the other hand, the fact that it is a euryokous species taken predominantly in quarry ponds and other types of man-made bodies of water is puzzling. In addition, it appears most commonly in warm waters and in warm months (Pennak, 1956). The hydroid phase is branching and without tentacles, and, because of its microscopic size and sessile habits, it is usually overlooked by collectors in the field. Undoubtedly it is much more common than most aquatic zoölogists are inclined to believe. Several other species of *Craspedacusta* are known from China and Japan, and several additional species of the closely related *Limnocnida* have restricted distributions in India and Africa.

Cordylophora lacustris is the only known fresh-water colonial hydroid, and in certain respects its ecology is most interesting. This form is probably indistinguishable from *C. caspia,* the common species of Europe and other continents. Many investigators have cited *C. lacustris* as the classical example of a typical euryokous brackish species, and most records in the literature indicate that it thrives in water having a salinity ranging from 5 to 20 per mil. Kinne (1956), for example, found that it had an optimum at 16.7 per mil. This celenterate is most frequently collected in brackish estuaries and brackish ponds along coastlines of all continents, and the fact that most of the inland records describe collections from *streams* and *rivers* (rather than ponds) is therefore difficult to rationalize. Davis (1957) lists the following strictly fresh-water records for *Cordylophora lacustris* from the United States:

> Benson Creek, Kansas
> Rivers near Philadelphia, Penn.
> Illinois River near Havana, Illinois
> Mississippi River near East St. Louis, Illinois
> Arkansas River near Little Rock, Arkansas
> Red River, Louisiana
> Near mouth of Chagrin River, Ohio

It might be argued that *Cordylophora* could be carried to these areas on the bottoms of coastal and river vessels, but several of these locations are not on such navigable rivers. Then, too, if colonies were being spread actively upstream from coastal areas, there should be many records from locations nearer the coast rather than from such isolated upstream inland areas.

This celenterate has a richer and denser growth in brackish water than in fresh water. In the former habitat the female gonophore produces 6 to 20 ova, while in fresh water there are only 3 to 6 ova. The medusa stage is everywhere absent.

Most investigators assume that *Cordylophora* is not a modern immigrant, particularly in view of its world-wide distribution. It is my own conviction that we are dealing with a highly euryokous species or with a physiological complex. Kinne (1956) supports this contention in his discovery that individual colonies vary greatly in their salinity preferences.

Unlike marine celenterates, the fresh-water hydras enclose the fertilized egg in a sclerotized yellowish shell, the embryonic theca. Such thecae are resistant to adverse environmental conditions and endure drying and freezing. Normally, after a dormant period of three to ten weeks, the theca "cracks open" and releases the embryo, which by this time has a gastrovascular cavity. No theca is known for *Craspedacusta* or *Cordylophora*. During cold weather, however, the *Craspedacusta* polyp contracts and secretes a protective sclerotized coating. In *Cordylophora* the colony regresses and only a few horizontal and upright parts winter over in a semidormant state.

Typical marine celenterates are more or less isotonic with sea water, but hydras are in a habitat obviously requiring considerable osmotic adjustment. Lilly (1955) found that *Hydra* cells are highly permeable to water, but are nevertheless capable of maintaining an internal salt concentration well above that of the external medium. This must require some form of regulation of water and salt content, but the mechanisms seem to be completely unknown.

The Turbellaria

Free-living flatworms are richly represented in both fresh and salt waters, but relatively few species are restricted to brackish waters. It is clear that most groups of fresh-water flatworms are derived from marine ancestors (probably in very early times). Hyman (1951) points out that "only Catenulida and Temnocephalida are typically fresh-water, with no evident marine ancestors."

The average zoölogist often thinks of the conspicuous "planarians" (triclad turbellarians) as being most typical and abundant in fresh water, but from both qualitative and quantitative standpoints, the substrates of lakes, ponds, and stagnant waters support a much greater population of small and microscopic lower turbellarians.

Although there is a large turbellarian literature (especially European), no one has recently gone to the trouble of working it over with the idea of arriving at an estimate of how many fresh-water, brackish, and marine species are found in various parts of the world. Needless to say, the fresh-water turbellarian fauna of the United States is very poorly known; about 45 genera have been reported (Pennak, 1953; Ward and Whipple, 1959), but the number of species represented is very uncertain, and undoubtedly many undescribed forms await collection and study. A few generalizations, however, may be suggested. First, there are relatively few species of turbellarians that are *restricted* to brackish waters—perhaps 40 or 50 in European waters. The actual number likely to be collected in brackish waters may, neverthe-less, be quite large, chiefly because typical marine and fresh-water species often stray into brackish estuaries and ponds. Fresh-water flatworms found in brackish waters commonly belong to the following categories: triclads, *Macrostomum, Dalyellia, Castrada, Phaenocora, Catenula,* and *Otoplana.* Hyman (1951) states that fresh-water species usually become smaller and develop denser tissues when they enter brackish waters, and marine species that invade brackish waters are larger and have looser tissues. A very few turbellarians, including *Gyratrix her-maphroditus* and *Breslauilla relicta,* have evolved such an efficient osmoregulatory system that they thrive equally well in fresh, brackish, and marine waters.

In general, fresh-water species are not abundant in the tropics and subtropics, and some investigators have maintained that the scarcity of calcium is an effective ecological barrier in such areas. I have collected large numbers of fresh-water turbellarians, however, in many temperate and cold lakes having only a trace to 2.0 mg. of calcium per liter, and I am inclined to think that calcium inadequacy is only a part of the explanation in the tropics. Invasion of the land in the tropics has been accomplished by a few triclads and lower turbellarians.

Unlike the other phyla whose biology is treated in this volume, the turbellarian flatworms are well represented by modified subterranean and cave species. *Phago-cata subterranea, Sorocelis americana, Proctyla typhlops,* and the Kenkiidae, for example, are American triclads occupying such habitats.

The United States has a relatively large triclad fauna, with about 30 species represented, but none of these are true alpine forms like the common *Dugesia gonocephala* and *Crenobia alpina* of Europe. Although North America has many endemic species of lower turbellarians, as well as species that have been collected in only one locality, this continent does not have important primitive elements. There is nothing to compare with, for example, the primitive rhabdoceles of Lake Ohrid in Jugoslavia (summary in Stanković, 1960), where some species are clearly related to the marine Acoela.

Eggs of marine and terrestrial turbellarians are commonly deposited in gelatinous masses, capsules, or cocoons, and these are not especially resistant to environmental adversities. Most fresh-water turbellarians deposit similar so-called "summer eggs," but, in addition, are capable of producing "winter eggs," which are enclosed in tough capsules or thick sclerotized shells. Such resistant eggs may remain dormant for weeks or months, in contrast to summer eggs and eggs of marine species, which hatch promptly.

The conspicuous flame-bulb system of fresh-water turbellarians acts in conjunc-tion with body cells that are specialized for salt retention. This specialization is exhibited to a remarkable degree in turbellarians that can thrive in waters in which the total quantity of dissolved salts is as little as 2 to 10 mg. per liter. In marine forms, on the other hand, the flame-bulb system is less well developed, and in the Acoela it is lacking.

The Rhynchocoela (=Nemertea)

Like the Porifera and Coelenterata, the phylum Rhynchocoela is represented by a small adventitious fauna. Only about eight species of *Prostoma* are known from fresh waters; *P. graecense* and *P. eilhardi* are the most common European species; *P. rubrum* is the one species known from North America, and it also occurs in Central and South America.

Marine nemertines are found abundantly in the mud, stone, sand, and débris substrates of the intertidal and littoral zones of the oceans, but fresh-water nemertines occupy a space-niche that is not commonly present in marine habitats. Especially during the late summer and early autumn, *Prostoma* are found creeping about on submerged rooted aquatic vegetation and in floating masses of filamentous algae in ponds and lakes—the finely divided leaves of *Myriophyllum* and *Ceratophyllum* are favored places. The occurrence of *Prostoma* is sporadic, and sometimes specimens cannot be found even by assiduous collecting in likely places. Indeed, many fresh-water biologists never have the opportunity of observing live specimens in spite of the fact that they are easily seen (10 to 20 mm. long) in their natural habitat. Commonly only small numbers can be found, but sometimes they occur in great abundance in localized areas in ponds and stagnant bays of lakes. The ecological factors responsible for the sporadic distribution and abundance of *Prostoma* are unknown.

Under adverse conditions, such as lack of food, insufficient oxygen, and high temperature, *Prostoma* encysts by rounding up within a secreted layer of mucus, which soon hardens. The worm is viable for a few days to a few weeks and emerges when environmental conditions are again suitable. Such cysts, however, cannot withstand drying and are of limited value in dissemination. Lacking appropriate disseminules, *Prostoma* must be a very old genus in fresh water, which is perhaps the logical explanation of its widespread distribution. Cysts are unknown in marine species. A few investigators have concluded that *Prostoma* produces thick-shelled winter eggs, but modern workers do not concur in this opinion.

Excretion and osmoregulation are effected by a protonephridial system consisting of many branched tubules with clusters along each side of the body. A protonephridial system is present in most marine species also, but it is well developed in only a small minority of species. It seems that the physiological mechanisms of the protonephridial system of fresh-water species are quite different from those in marine forms.

The Rotifera (= Rotatoria)

Undoubtedly the rotifers must be designated as the one major taxonomic category characteristic of fresh waters. Of the 1,800 species in this phylum, only about 50 are restricted to the salt-water environment. By all ordinary criteria, the rotifers have attained a major degree of "biological success." They are abundant and can withstand wide ranges of ecological conditions; they are easily spread from place to place; they are pelagic, littoral, and associated with the substrate; they are found in all waters, from the smallest puddle to the largest lakes and rivers; they swim, "jump," creep, and crawl, or are sessile; they are specialized for consuming many types of food; they represent many morphological types. In short, to borrow terminology usually reserved for vertebrate biology, the rotifers exhibit an amazing array of adaptive radiations.

Of the 50 marine species, about 15 (mostly *Synchaeta, Trichocerca,* and *Keratella*) are pelagic, and only two species occur in the mid-Atlantic. The other 35 are more or less restricted to the littoral zone. A few species (possibly 70) are specialized for a brackish-water existence, especially in the genera *Proales, Synchaeta, Pedalia, Cephalodella, Erignatha,* and *Encentrum.* This fauna is presumed to be an immigrant fauna, with some forms being derived from marine ancestors and some from fresh-water ancestors. Remane and Schlieper (1958) state that 75 to 80 per cent of these brackish species have been derived from immediate marine ancestral forms. It seems that no bdelloid rotifers are restricted to brackish waters.

In spite of these small numbers of species typical of salt and brackish waters, a much longer list, perhaps 200 species, has actually been *reported* from these environments. The majority of these forms, however, are merely fresh-water species that have been washed into brackish and salt waters from rivers and estuaries. Many fresh-water rotifers can easily withstand up to 8 per mil salinity, although they cannot reproduce in anything but fresh water. *Brachionus plicatilis,* however, is unique in that it is found in both the sea and in strongly alkaline inland waters.

Bērziņš (1951) classifies rotifers according to their ecological preferences as follows:

	Per cent
Normally found only in fresh water	94.0
Found in fresh water and brackish water	8.0
Normally restricted to brackish water	3.5
Found in brackish and salt water	5.0
Normally restricted to salt water	2.5

Almost all of the brackish and marine species are members of the order Ploimida. No marine Collothecida are known, and only *Testudinella* among the Flosculariida has marine representatives. The Bdelloidida, a primitive order of leech-like rotifers, is restricted to fresh waters with the exception of a single genus, *Zelinkiella,* which occurs on sea cucumbers. The order Seisonida is marine, but it includes only one genus, *Seison,* which is epizoic on *Nebalia.*

Little has been published about the probable ecological origins of the Rotifera, but, in view of the preceding paragraphs, it is tempting to postulate fresh water as the ancestral environment for this group. For it is in fresh water that the group has had its great success and demonstrated its enormous adaptive radiation. For the most part, the marine and brackish faunas are composed of derivatives from a few scattered fresh-water genera.

During much of the year female rotifers in the class Monogononta produce haploid, thin-shelled "summer eggs" by parthenogenesis. These eggs hatch almost immediately and are incapable of withstanding adverse environmental conditions. For a period of one to several weeks during the year, however, males appear, and the females that are fertilized by males produce large, diploid, thick-shelled "winter eggs" or "resting eggs." Such eggs are remarkably resistant to desiccation, temperature extremes, and adverse chemical conditions, and it is thought that they represent the chief means of rotifer dispersal. Very little seems to have been written about the production of winter eggs by marine and brackish-water species; the production of these eggs presumably is a rare event.

Except for *Seison* (order Seisonida), the rotifers in the class Digononta (order Bdelloidida) have no males. All eggs are therefore parthenogenetic, and though they may be more or less thin- or thick-shelled, they hatch soon after deposition and are incapable of withstanding environmental adversities.

On the other hand, the Bdelloidida (not normally found in salt water) have evolved a distinctive method of tiding over such conditions. Especially when the habitat dries up, a bdelloid loses much of its body water and shrinks into an oval mass surrounded by its crinkled cuticle. A very few species also secrete an outer gelatinous layer which quickly hardens. Such desiccated forms may be frozen or blown about as dust for months or years. Upon being deposited in suitable water again, they quickly absorb water and become extended and normally active. One individual may survive several alternating periods of activity and desiccation.

The salt/water balance of a rotifer is maintained chiefly through the activities of the flame-bulb system, and, although this system can be seen to operate in a lively fashion in fresh-water species, few observations seem to have been made on the relative activity and efficiency of the flame-bulb system in marine species.

The Gastrotricha

Many elementary textbooks still insist that gastrotrichs are "restricted to" or "characteristic of" fresh waters, but most aquatic biologists are aware that only about 50 per cent of the 500 described species are fresh-water. Both marine and fresh-water gastrotrichs are found in similar habitats, especially in débris of the littoral zone, in the capillary interstitial waters of sandy beaches, and in masses of filamentous algae and rooted aquatics.

Taxonomically, on the other hand, there is a sharp cleavage between marine and fresh-water species. The class Macrodasyoidea is almost exclusively marine; a flame-bulb system is absent, there are adhesive tubes along the body, and individuals are hermaphroditic. In the class Chaetonotoidea there is a pair of flame bulbs, two to four posterior adhesive tubes ("toes"), and, since only females are known (except in *Xenotrichula*), reproduction is parthenogenetic. The Chaetonotoidea are almost entirely fresh-water, with only two small marine genera (*Neodasys* and *Xenotrichula*).

There are five common and three rare fresh-water genera, and about 35 genera are known to inhabit salt water. Four genera (*Aspidiophorus, Chaetonotus, Ichthyidium,* and *Polymerurus*) have both fresh-water and marine representatives, or both fresh-water and brackish representatives. In addition, many marine genera also have certain species in brackish waters. A very few species of *Chaetonotus* are said to occur in both fresh and salt water, but this contention seems questionable.

In contrast to most other groups of fresh-water micro-invertebrates, few species of gastrotrichs are generally distributed or cosmopolitan. Of the 35 species known from American fresh waters, for example, only about five are also known from Europe. On the other hand, so little work has been done on American forms that, of most species on this continent, nothing can be said in a definitive way about the ecology and zoögeography.

Brunson (1949) recognizes two types of eggs among fresh-water gastrotrichs. Thin-shelled eggs that develop and hatch immediately after deposition are called *tachyblastic* eggs. *Opsiblastic* eggs are thick-shelled, resistant to adverse environmental conditions, and may persist over an interval of up to two years before hatching. Such eggs are formed in old cultures and under natural conditions when ecological factors become highly unfavorable; they are undoubtedly important in the geographic spread of fresh-water species. So far as is known, marine species produce only tachyblastic eggs.

The presence of osmoregulatory flame-bulbs in fresh-water gastrotrichs and their absence in marine species is a striking distinction and unlike the situation in the Rotifera, Rhynchocoela, and Turbellaria. This fact, coupled with the fact that the Gastrotricha are about equally represented in marine and fresh-water environments, makes any speculation difficult as to their ecological origin. On the other hand, it is significant that marine species (Macrodasyoidea) are hermaphroditic, while fresh-water species (Chaetonotoidea) are parthenogenetic females. Presumably the former condition is more logically ancestral, and one is therefore inclined to postulate a marine origin for the phylum.

The Nematoda

The great majority of nematode publications deal with soil, parasitic, and plant-infesting species. Those that are concerned with free-living marine and fresh-water species are generally devoted to taxonomy and minute morphological characters with little attention being accorded to ecological relationships. Free-living aquatic nematodes are, in fact, poorly known by almost any major ecological criterion, and perhaps the chief reason is the great difficulty involved in making species identifications, together with the fact that there are thousands of undescribed species in existence.

In general, the free-living nematodes form a rather homogeneous group, and there seems to be little obvious morphological or physiological distinction between those that occur in terrestrial soil, fresh waters, and brackish waters; some oceanic forms are, however, markedly specialized. Although marine species are generally more ornamented and bristly than fresh-water species, there are numerous exceptions.

Nematodes are enormously abundant in and on all types of aquatic substrates, but especially where there is no dearth of organic matter. They are, in fact, usually the most abundant of all semi-microscopic metazoa to be found on aquatic substrates.

Hyman (1951a) states that terrestrial nematodes have arisen directly from marine ancestors and have then spread directly into fresh-water habitats. There is, moreover, no sharp distinction between terrestrial "soil" nematodes and "fresh-water" nematodes, since more than half of the species found in fresh-water soils and substrates are likewise found in terrestrial soils.

Brackish areas seem to constitute an ecotone between marine species on the one hand and fresh-water and terrestrial species on the other hand. Many marine nematodes may be collected in brackish areas, and many fresh-water and soil forms may be collected in brackish areas, but marine species are never found in fresh waters and soils, nor are fresh-water and soil species ever found in marine habitats. Relatively few forms seem to be restricted to brackish waters. There are, nevertheless, certain genera that include some marine species and some fresh-water and soil species, notably *Mononchus, Oncholaimus, Dorylaimus,* and *Enoplus.*

In spite of the pronounced difference in the osmoregulatory problem in salt as opposed to fresh water, no corresponding anatomical differences can be found in the two groups of nematodes. It is thought that osmoregulation is governed by the differing physiological activities of the hypodermis, and perhaps also by the renette system, unicellular hypodermal glands, and excretory canals.

In contrast to the situation in all other groups discussed here, the fresh-water nematodes have never evolved any special resistant cysts or winter eggs, although some species have a "resistant" third larval stage.

The Entoprocta

The marine species *vs.* fresh-water species situation in the phylum Entoprocta is remarkably similar to that in the Porifera, Coelenterata, and Rhynchocoela—namely, that of a fresh-water adventitious fauna consisting of a negligible number of species having no near marine relatives. Only two fresh-water entoprocts are known, of which *Urnatella gracilis* is by far the more familiar. This species forms scanty mosslike growths on stones and other submerged objects in rivers in scattered localities in the eastern half of the United States and in Texas (summary in Weise, 1961). Several recent and surprising Old World records have also been published, especially from the Berlin area, the Maas River in Belgium, the Danube in Hungary, and the Dniester River in the Ukraine (Lüdemann and Kayser, 1961; Damas, 1938; Koloshvari and Abrikosov, 1960). Its occurrence only in *running* or moving waters is puzzling in view of the fact that none of the marine Entoprocta seem to have evolved such an ecological requirement. Another peculiarity is the fact that it commonly occurs in rivers that may be somewhat polluted and carry considerable silt in suspension. *Urnatella* seems to be derived from very remote marine ancestry, since it does not occur in brackish waters and is regularly found in drainages distant from the seacoast.

The only other fresh-water entoproct is *Urnatella indica,* which was first reported from India in 1946 and is fully described by Seshaiya (1949).

Although marine species have a free-swimming ciliated larval stage, *Urnatella* has none.

Nothing resembling winter eggs has ever been found in *Urnatella,* but in the autumn and early winter the basal segments become filled with vitelline inclusions and serve the role of statoblasts or hibernacula.

The Brackish Barrier

Pearse (1927, 1950) summarized much of the earlier discussion of evolutionary migration pathways of marine groups into fresh waters, and there is no point in reviewing these matters at length in the present paper. Briefly, such migration paths include: (1) active migrations up rivers into inland drainages, (2) gradual dilution of an embayment or other cut-off part of the ocean, (3) entry into fresh

waters via coastal marshes and swamps, and (4) migration through large subterranean drainages, especially in areas of karst topography, and into underground
streams and thence to caves (see also Absolon and Hrabé, 1930).

As brought out by Pearse, however, all of these pathways present serious ecological and physiological difficulties. For one thing, each involves the migration
of ancestral forms through a barrier of brackish water even before the more
difficult fresh-water habitat is penetrated. Many papers and textbook accounts
take a rather superficial viewpoint, and one is led to believe that the salt-brackish-
fresh transition is only a matter of time and that it is frequently being traversed
by many modern species that are evolving new fresh-water forms.

Unfortunately, a close examination of the evidence indicates that quite the
contrary situation exists. If, for example, the brackish environment were being
constantly penetrated by species "on their way" from the sea to fresh water, one
would expect to find a very rich population of species that had undergone sufficient mutations to have become genuine brackish species restricted to brackish
waters. But, as emphasized in the foregoing sections, the brackish fauna is an
impoverished fauna, and the great majority of species found in brackish waters
are either marine or fresh-water forms that are found fortuitously and are usually
incapable of reproducing there. Segerstråle (1949) comments significantly on
this point: "The fact that aquatic animals (and plants) thrive well on the one
hand in the highly salt ocean and on the other in the almost saltfree fresh water,
whereas the [great] majority cannot tolerate transitional salinities, is in ecological
respect a very strange phenomenon."

Perhaps a major difficulty inherent in the brackish-water barrier is the fact that
the salt concentration at any particular small area in a brackish habitat is in a
constant state of flux, depending on rainfall, tides, currents, and the amount of
water being brought in by rivers and direct surface drainage. Estuarine temperature
conditions are likewise quite variable. Under such circumstances it must be difficult for a marine species to become adjusted and established. Further difficulties,
especially in upper estuarine habitats, are the rapid currents and the shifting
substrate of the river or stream, since so few marine species are preadapted to
cope with such problems.

The wide expanse of the Baltic with its gradual salt-fresh transition is often cited
as an ideal place for the formation of fresh-water species from marine ancestors,
but Ekman (1953, p. 117) comments: "The Baltic in spite of its size, possesses
no endemic brackish-water animals. It is obviously too recent to have been able
to evolve new species." Perhaps the same comment may be made for other extensive brackish areas in view of the important changes in sea level during and
since Pleistocene times. Some investigators are opposed to a strict interpretation
of the Ekman generalization and point out that the Baltic fauna includes species
inhabiting brackish waters of Europe in general. These and other problems of
brackish waters are reviewed by Segerstråle et al. (1959).

Pearse (1950) has written: "An estuary has been called the doorway by which
marine forms have populated fresh water. This statement is perhaps in part true,
but an estuarine doorway is not wide open and easily passed. There are many
difficulties to be surmounted. Many animals struggle long ages to get through and
fail. Only a few attain fresh water by this route." I would speculate still further
and contend that the many ecological difficulties operating in most estuaries are

much less surmountable than most ecologists are willing to concede. As an alternative, it should be pointed out that large, semi-enclosed basins and extensive areas of salt marshes on flat, gradually sloping coasts offer fewer ecological disadvantages than a typical estuary, and I feel that this migration path is a much more logical one. At any rate, we must agree that those fresh-water groups that are definitely derived from marine ancestors must have attained fresh waters in very ancient times.

Psammolittoral and Phreatic Habitats as Pathways for Colonization of Fresh Waters

At this point it seems appropriate to discuss another possible pathway from marine to fresh water that, until recently, has been completely neglected. Especially since about 1940, a large literature has accumulated dealing with the biology of the complex community of microörganisms living in the interstitial waters of fresh-water and marine sandy beaches (psammolittoral). Also, beginning about 1900, but more particularly since 1920, a very few investigators have been studying the biology of the ground-water fauna, that is, the assemblage of microörganisms found in the ground water, either at a depth of a meter or more along the edges of bodies of water, or (Husmann, 1956) in the circulating ground water away from any ocean, stream, or lake. Recently Motaş (1958) has referred to the ground-water habitat as the *phreatic* habitat. Unfortunately, these two lines of research have been largely ignored by ecologists, but recently Delamare Deboutteville (1960) has summarized much of the work and provided a bibliography of more than 800 titles (nearly all European). There is no sharp dividing line between the psammolittoral and phreatic habitats, and the rich and surprisingly dense faunas of the two are somewhat similar. Major groups of micrometazoa represented are: minute hydra-like Coelenterata, Turbellaria, Rotifera, Gastrotricha, Nematoda, Annelida, Tardigrada, Crustacea, and Acarina. Some species are adapted to the interstitial habitat by means of exceptional elongation of the body, and others seem to have no special morphological peculiarities. Although the majority of species seem to be restricted to this habitat, there are others that are regularly found in the shallows of lakes, streams, ponds, and the ocean. Perhaps the most striking aspect of the psammolittoral and phreatic faunas is the large number of primitive forms.

The taxonomic and ecological work on these two environments now has reached the point where the evidence indicates that micrometazoa could possibly move from intertidal and subtidal zones into the marine psammolittoral and (1) thence into the phreatic ground water and thereafter inland to distant ponds or lakes via their psammolittoral, or (2) into the psammolittoral of an estuary, and thence progressively "upstream" in the river psammolittoral or deeper phreatic zone to inland fresh-water localities. Porous substrates below typical stream beds have long been known to have well-defined phreatic currents. Remane and Schlieper (1958) suggest the importance of the interstitial highway: "viele Vorposten mariner Gruppen im Süsswasser subterran lebe, vor allem in Spaltengewässern und im interstititiellen Wasser und kiesigen Sand." Orghidan (1959) and Ruffo (1961) also emphasize the rich fauna and ease of migration through this hyporheic zone below river beds.

The migration of micrometazoa through the interstitial waters of the phreatic zone is possible only where the subsurface deposits are sufficiently porous materials, such as gravels and coarse sand. Clay and bedrock formations naturally inhibit migrations. Odum (1953) has shown how important ground water is in the problem of marine invasion into fresh waters in low-lying areas of porous soils and heavy rainfall or arid conditions: "a foot of fresh water above sea level can support a displacement of the salt-water–fresh-water boundary downward 40 feet [into the ground] according to the Ghyben-Herzberg approximation."

As shown in figure 32-1, any organism moving from the marine psammolittoral into the phreatic ground water must usually first traverse a narrow intermediate zone of brackish water in the sand and gravel. This brackish water, however, is not so much of an ecological barrier in the sand as is brackish water in an open

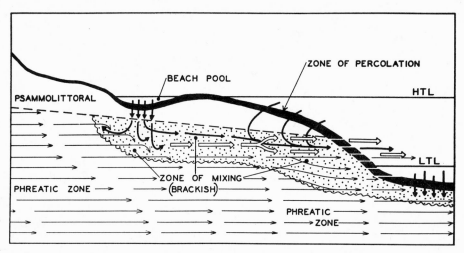

FIGURE 32-1. Diagrammatic section of marine shoreline. HTL, high tide level; LTL, low tide level; brackish zone of mixing shown by stippling. Thick, open, and thin arrows show relative amounts of salt, brackish, and fresh waters, respectively. (After Delamare Deboutteville, 1960, greatly modified.)

estuary. Currents are not strong enough to dislodge organisms and eggs, temperatures do not vary greatly, and food supply is comparatively constant. To be sure, there are variations in the thickness of this gradient, depending on tides, rains, and relative velocity of seaward seepage of phreatic fresh water, but the brackish stratum is usually so thin that animals can easily migrate about locally and remain in the particular brackish concentration to which they happen to be adapted. Such local migrations in the psammolittoral have already been demonstrated, and, as a matter of fact, there are many records of species being collected from restricted horizontal zones in the psammolittoral, a fact indicating that, for example, at a depth of 50 or 100 cm. they are concentrated in a zone of a particular salinity (or fresh water). To summarize, any animal migrating from the sea to fresh water via the interstitial route must first become adapted to a narrow transition stratum of interstitial brackish water, but certainly the physical and chemical conditions obtaining in the wet sand and gravel are much less rigorous and less variable than in an open estuary or salt marsh.

There is, of course, a whole field of speculation involving migratory paths in the opposite direction. That is, fresh-water species (with proper adaptations) could, theoretically, pass through the phreatic-psammolittoral zone and into the salt water of the littoral.

Genetics and the Origin of the Fresh-Water Fauna

As outlined earlier, fresh-water acelomate faunas differ generally from their close marine relatives in several significant respects:

1. They have almost invariably lost the motile larval stages.

2. They are much more euryokous and are able to withstand wide ranges in (*a*) hydrogen-ion concentration, (*b*) temperature, (*c*) dissolved oxygen, and (*d*) other chemical and physical conditions.

3. They have become adapted to a habitat in which there is a low salt concentration, with the chief soluble ions being calcium, carbonate, and bicarbonate rather than sodium and chlorine.

4. They have developed new morphological and physiological sets of osmoregulatory mechanisms to cope with the hypotonic fresh-water environment. Such adaptations are undoubtedly especially critical for sperm, eggs, and early embryos.

5. With few exceptions, they produce unique resistant structures or disseminules at some stage in the life history, including (*a*) gemmules, (*b*) embryonic thecae, (*c*) protective sclerotized or mucus coatings, (*d*) winter and opsiblastic eggs, (*e*) desiccation stages.

Since the great majority of lower fresh-water metazoa are specialized in *all* of these five respects, and since each such specialization is undoubtedly the result of a complicated series of evolutionary adaptations engendered by many mutations, the picture, from a genetic standpoint, becomes formidable indeed. Accordingly, we can be genuinely skeptical about postulating the *de novo* and simultaneous appearance in a marine species of whole clusters of preadaptations to its "new" fresh-water environment. The transition from marine to fresh water is therefore a far cry from the hop-skip-jump process, and is, rather, a long, slow course of mutation, selection, and adaptation. To put it another way, I believe that the successful invasion of fresh water is an evolutionary rarity.

Summary

The physiological and ecological peculiarities of acelomate fresh-water metazoa are summarized, with special reference to their marine counterparts. The difficulties confronting marine species in overcoming the brackish-water barrier and becoming further adapted to fresh-water habitats are of enormous importance, but the psammolittoral-phreatic pathway from salt to fresh waters offers a much less difficult ecological migration route than estuarine waters. Since the great majority of acelomate fresh-water metazoa have lost the motile larvae, are remarkably euryokous, are adapted to low concentrations of dissolved electrolytes, have developed effective osmoregulatory devices, and produce special resistant structures or disseminules, it must be concluded, on the basis of genetics, that the successful colonization of fresh waters by any taxonomic group is a rare evolutionary achievement.

REFERENCES

Absolon, K. and S. Hrabé
  1930   Uber einen neuen Süsswasser-Polychaeten aus der Hohlengewässern der Herzegowina. Zool. Anz. 88:249–264.

Bērziņš, B.
  1951   Contributions to the knowledge of the marine Rotatoria of Norway. Univ. Bergen Årb. naturv. R. 6:1–11.

Brunson, R. B.
  1949   The life history and ecology of two North American gastrotrichs. Trans. Amer. micr. Soc. 68:1–20.

Damas, H.
  1938   Sur la présence dans la Meuse belge de *Branchiura sowerbyi* (Beddard), *Craspedacusta sowerbyi* (Lancaster), et *Urnatella gracilis* (Leidy). Ann. Soc. zool. Belg. 69:293–310.

Davis, C. C.
  1957   *Cordylophora lacustris* Allman from Chagrin Harbor, Ohio. Limnology Oceanogr. 2:158–159.

Delamare Deboutteville, C.
  1960   Biologie des Eaux souterraines littorales et continentales. Hermann, Paris.

Ekman, S.
  1953   Zoogeography of the Sea. Sidgwick and Jackson, London.

Hadžišče, S.
  1953   Beitrag zur Kenntnis der Spongillidenfauna der grossen mazedonischen Seen (Dojran, Prespa and Ohridsee). Rec. Trav. Stat. Hydrobiol. Ohrid 1:73–103.

Husmann, S.
  1956   Untersuchungen über die Grundwasserfauna zwischen Harz and Weser. Arch. Hydrobiol. 52:1–184.

Hyman, L. H.
  1940   The Invertebrates. I: Protozoa through Ctenophora. McGraw-Hill, New York, Toronto, London.
  1951   *Idem.* II: Platyhelminthes and Rhynchocoela—the Acoelomate Bilateria. McGraw-Hill, New York, Toronto, London.
  1951a   *Idem.* III: Acanthocephala, Aschelminthes, and Entoprocta—the Pseudocoelomate Bilateria. McGraw-Hill, New York.

Kinne, O.
  1956   Über den Einfluss des Salzgehaltes und der Temperatur auf Wachstum, Form und Vermehrung bei dem Hydroid-polypen *Cordylophora caspia* (Pallas), Thecata, Clavidae. I. Mitteilung über die Einfluss des Salzgehaltes auf Wachstum und Entwicklung mariner, brackischer und limnischer Organismen. Zool. Jb. (Allg. Zool.) 66:565–638.

Koloshvari, G., and G. G. Abrikosov
  1960   [Finding a representative of the class Kamptozoa (*Urnatella gracilis* Leidy) in the fresh waters of Hungary.] Zool. Zh. 39:1735–1737. [In Russian.]

Lilly, S. J.
    1955   Osmoregulation and ionic regulation in *Hydra*. J. exp. Biol. 32:423–439.
Lüdemann, D., and H. Kayser
    1961   Erster Fund einer Süsswasser-Kamptozoe, *Urnatella gracilis* Leidy, in
              Deutschland, zugleich mit einer kurzen Mitteilung über das Auftreten
              von *Cordylophora caspia* Pall. im Berliner Gebiet. S. B. naturf. Fr. Berl.
              (n.s.) 1:102–108.

Motaş, C.
    1958   Freatobiologia, o noura ramura a limnologiei. Natura, Bucareşti 10:95–
              105.

Odum, H. T.
    1953   Factors controlling marine invasion into Florida fresh waters. Bull. mar.
              Sci. Gulf and Carib. 3:134–156.

Orghidan, T.
    1959   Ein neuer Lebrensraum des unterirdischen Wassers: Der hyporheische
              Biotop. Arch. Hydrobiol. 55:392–414.

Pearse, A. S.
    1927   The migration of animals from the ocean into freshwater and land habi-
              tats. Amer. Nat. 61:466–476.
    1950   The Emigrations of Animals from the Sea. Sherwood, Dryden, New York.
Pennak, R. W.
    1953   Fresh-water Invertebrates of the United States. Ronald, New York.
    1956   The fresh-water jellyfish *Craspedacusta* in Colorado with some remarks
              on its ecology and morphological degeneration. Trans. Amer. micr. Soc.
              75:324–331.
    1958   Some problems of freshwater invertebrate distribution in the Western
              States. Zoogeography (Publ. 51, A.A.A.S.):223–230.

Rasmont, R.
    1954   La diapause chez Spongillides. Bull. Acad. Belg. Cl. Sci. (5) 11:288–304.
Remane, A., and C. Schlieper
    1958   Die Biologie des Brackwassers. Die Binnengewässer 22:1–348.
Ruffo, S.
    1961   Problemi relativi allo studio della fauna interstiziale iporreica. Boll. Zool.
              28:273–319.
Segerstråle, S. G.
    1949   The brackish-water fauna of Finland. Oikos 1:127–141.
Segerstråle, S. G., *et al.*
    1959   Symposium on the classification of brackish waters. Arch. Oceanogr.
              Limnol., Roma. Suppl. 11:1–248.
Seshaiya, R. V.
    1949   On *Urnatella indica* Seshaiya, a freshwater entoproctan from South India.
              Rec. Indian Mus. 45:283–389.
Stanković, S.
    1960   The Balkan Lake Ohrid and its Living World. Junk, The Hague.
Ward, H. B., and G. C. Whipple
    1959   Fresh-water Biology. Edmondson, W. T., Ed. 2d ed. Wiley, New York.
Weise, J. G.
    1961   The ecology of *Urnatella gracilis* Leidy: phylum Endoprocta. Limnol.
              Oceanogr. 6:228–239.
Zeuthen, E.
    1939   On the hibernation of *Spongilla lacustris* (L.). Z. vergl. Physiol. 26:537–
              547.

Platyhelminthes

33 ◆ Observations on the Habitats of Platyhelminths, Primarily Turbellaria

MARIETTA VOGE

DEPARTMENT OF MEDICAL MICROBIOLOGY AND IMMUNOLOGY,
SCHOOL OF MEDICINE, UNIVERSITY OF CALIFORNIA, LOS ANGELES

The purpose of this report is to discuss the habitat distribution of platyhelminths. Knowledge of the place where an animal lives provides at least some indication of tolerance of a given species to its environment. An attempt will therefore be made to present information on tolerance ranges indicated from data gathered in the field by different workers. There are several reasons for discussing the flatworms from this point of view. One of them is that we know far too little about the ecology of flatworms. This is unfortunate, because even from the scanty and haphazardly collected data it is apparent that among the lower Metazoa, possibly with the exception of the nematodes, the platyhelminths have become adapted to or are able to tolerate the greatest variety of habitats and environmental extremes. This applies particularly to the free-living turbellarians, but also to the parasitic trematodes and cestodes. Another reason for presenting this information is to remind us that the trematodes and cestodes have received little attention from those invertebrate zoölogists primarily interested in free-living organisms. Conversely, the parasitologists have neglected the study of free-living turbellarians. As the greater majority of species in the phylum Platyhelminthes live in close association with other animals, and because many symbiotic species are also found among the turbellarians, the flatworms represent an ideal group of organisms for the study of different aspects of symbiosis. Symbiosis is here defined as "living together" and thus includes such close and protracted associations as commensalism, mutualism, and parasitism. Investigation of the phenomenon of symbiosis has been much neglected by biologists (Read, 1958). The parasitic trematodes and cestodes are usually considered to be far removed from the turbellarians, and their study in general invertebrate zoölogy is minimized or neglected. It is true that relationships among the different classes of flatworms seem to be indeed remote on the basis of morphology and life cycles, and the separation of the parasitic groups from their free-living ancestors very distant. If, however, one examines the free-living turbellarians, one must conclude that this group is one of the most versatile and, in habitat tolerance, most generalized among the metazoa. These features of turbellarians, together with their ability to adapt to extreme environments, might aid in our understanding the manner of transition from free-living to symbiotic forms within the phylum. We know, furthermore, that a large number of turbellarian species live in more or less close association with other organisms, although precise information on the degree of dependency in these associations is for the most part unavailable. It is proposed that the transition from a free-living to a symbiotic mode of existence may not represent many barriers to organisms exhibiting a wide range in tolerances and great adaptability in the free-living state.

The information to be presented below includes a general review of the occurrence of the Turbellaria in water and on land, followed by more detailed reports on their vertical distribution, temperature tolerances, and associations with other organisms. The discussion of the symbiotic trematodes and cestodes is by necessity limited because too little is known about the environments provided by the hosts in which they live. It must be emphasized that all data were gathered from numerous, primarily taxonomic studies, usually containing no more than a few sentences about the collection site of the species discussed. Therefore, the term "habitat" as used here refers to the place or places from which the species was recovered, the extent of useful information varying with each author or collector. Complete coverage of all references on flatworms was not attempted. References cited were selected to illustrate certain phenomena and do not, of course, represent a complete list of studies dealing with the habitat distribution of flatworms.

Distribution of Free-Living Turbellaria

The major habitats of the orders of Turbellaria are shown in table 33-1. The aceles and the polyclads are restricted to the sea, while species of alleoceles,

TABLE 33-1

DISTRIBUTION OF TURBELLARIA

Order	Marine	Fresh-water	Terrestrial
Acoela	X		
Polycladida	X	one species	
Alloeocoela	X	X	X
Rhabdocoela	X	X	X
Tricladida	X	X	X

rhabdoceles, or triclads also occur in fresh water or on land. Marine turbellarians are mostly littoral in distribution, occurring on or under rocks, in sand, on or in other animals, or on plants. Pelagic species are found in the orders Acoela, Rhabdocoela, and Polycladida (Bresslau, 1928–1933). Some turbellarians occur at relatively great depths of the sea and will be discussed further on.

The fresh-water and terrestrial turbellarians have invaded all areas of the earth containing readily available moisture during at least a part of the year. Some species occur in the arctic and antarctic regions, others in the tropics. Among the permanent bodies of fresh water, they occur in lakes and ponds, in swiftly flowing streams and rivers, and in wells and springs. Temporary pools and puddles may contain adult turbellarians which often survive the dry period in an encysted state. Certain species are abundant in swiftly flowing clear streams; others seem to thrive in stagnant waters rich in decaying matter.

On land, turbellarians may be found on different types of soil, under rocks, in moist sand or mud, on vegetation including trees, and in moist leaf litter. Briefly, turbellarians may occur wherever there is some moisture, be this near the poles or in the jungle, in the desert, or in caves. The wide altitudinal and temperature tolerances shown by the group are discussed in more detail further on. Some species exhibit a remarkable tolerance for varying salinity. The marine species *Coelogynopora biarmata* has been reported from fresh-water warm springs, *Prorhynchus stagnalis* from fresh-water and brackish water (Bresslau, 1928–1933). *Macrostomum thermale* was found in hot springs in Java with a salt-content of 32 per mil (Bresslau, 1928–1933) and the ubiquitous *Dugesia tigrina* in warm springs in Death Valley, California, at a salinity of 30 per mil.

With reference to desert-inhabiting turbellarians, it should be emphasized that they are by no means as rare as one might suppose. Dr. John Belkin, of University of California, Los Angeles, and I have collected *Dugesia tigrina* from several isolated springs in the Death Valley desert. Hyman (1956) described *Dugesia diabolis* from a pool (fresh-water hot spring) in the Devil's Hole in the Nevada desert. Further search should reveal additional desert localities for turbellarians. More extensively known than the desert forms are the cave planarians occurring in limestone and other caves in different parts of the world. The European species belong to several genera of triclads that exhibit loss of eyes and pigmentation (Bresslau, 1928–1933). In North America, species of the family Kenkiidae are cave dwellers and also show loss of eyes and pigment. Of the numerous records of cavernicolous triclads, *Sorocelis americana* is of interest because many thousands of individuals of this species were found on a guano deposit in a bat cave in Oklahoma. The species was also collected from springs outside this cave (Hyman, 1939b). *S. americana* reminds one of another coprophilous triclad, *Microplana humicola,* described from dunghills in Bohemia (Gamble, 1910). An example of a cave dweller from the western United States is *Kenkia rhynchida* from Malheur Cave, Oregon, located in dry, sage-covered lava hills (Hyman, 1937).

From the foregoing it is evident that turbellarians can occur wherever there is moisture. Some species, however, have become adapted to environments with relatively little moisture and are able to withstand considerable desiccation. This may be accomplished by encystment of the organism, by survival of the unencysted adult, or by resistant eggs. The ability to encyst is found in terrestrial rhabdoceles, alleoceles, and triclads. Among the alleoceles, *Geocentrophora applanata* remains alive in dried bromeliads by means of mucous cysts (Marcus and Marcus, 1951), and *G. marcusi* may survive the drying of temporary pools in the same manner. Darlington (1959) states that between rains the exposed substrate of these temporary pools is bare granite or a thin layer of detritus which becomes severely desiccated and very warm. Survival of adults in the unencysted state for many days in dryness has been reported for the triclad *Procerodes* (von Graff, 1908).

Oxygen content of the environment may be very important for some turbellarian species. Steinböck (1926) describes the occurrence of large numbers of 15 different species of turbellarians on moss growing on rocks in rapidly flowing alpine streams, particularly in areas where the water cascades most swiftly downward. The same species were also found in less rapidly flowing water and on moist vegetation outside the water. One of these was found 9 feet above the ground, on the branch of a tree overgrown with moss. Other species, however, seem to require or tolerate environments with relatively low oxygen content. For example, species of *Phaenocora* may occur in badly smelling water, rich in decaying matter (von Graff, 1908).

Vertical Distribution of Turbellaria

The known species of free-living turbellarians occur primarily at sea level or close to sea level. This is particularly true for the orders Acoela and Polycladida, which do not have representatives in fresh water or on land. Certain aceles and polyclads, however, have been reported from relatively great ocean depth. The acele *Rimicola glacialis* has been collected at a depth of 1,000 feet as well as in ice holes at sea level (Bresslau, 1928–1933), thus showing considerable pressure tolerance. Several other species of aceles, as well as alleoceles and rhabdoceles, have been reported to occur at a depth of 1,000 feet or more. The species of Polycladida occur primarily at sea level or to a depth of 300 feet, except for *Polyposthides caraibica,* which has been recovered at 3,000 feet. At present one cannot be certain that this is an exceptional situation, owing to insufficient collecting for flatworms at comparable depths.

The triclads and the rhabdoceles, with large numbers of species in fresh water or on land, have numerous representatives at high altitudes. Some of these species have a wide vertical range and also occur in a great variety of habitats. The rhabdocele *Gyratrix hermaphroditus* has been collected at sea level, at an altitude of 7,000 feet, and at a depth of approximately 180 feet (von Graff, 1908). Other species have comparable distributional ranges. Rhabdoceles and triclads have been found at high altitudes in different parts of the world. Thus de Beauchamp (1936) found the rhabdocele *Phaenocora chappuisi* at an elevation of 12,000 feet in Uganda, and Ruebush (1939) described *Mesostoma lingua baoensis* and *Phaenocora alticola* from Tibet as occurring at 13,000 feet and 15,000 feet respectively. Another altitudinal record of distribution is that of the rhabdocele *Mesostoma togarmensis* in Tibet reported by Ferguson and Hayes (1941) to occur at 15,000 feet. In Peru, numerous species of triclads have been reported from altitudes up to 12,000 feet (Marcus, 1957) and several species of rhabdoceles from comparable elevations (Marcus, 1955). Triclads have been collected in the state of Colorado at an altitude of 13,500 feet by Dr. Robert W. Pennak, of University of Colorado (personal communication).

From these data it is apparent that many species of turbellarians have become successfully adapted to high altitudes and to the considerable fluctuations in temperature which are characteristic for such areas. A summary of the vertical distribution of the orders of the Turbellaria is shown in figure 33-1. According to our

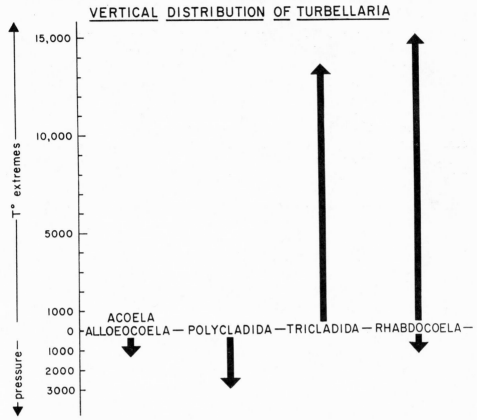

FIGURE 33-1. Vertical distribution of the orders of the Turbellaria.

present knowledge, the class as a whole ranges from 3,000 feet below sea level to approximately 15,000 feet above sea level. This represents a total vertical range of 18,000 feet.

Temperature Tolerance of Flatworms

Many free-living turbellarians are able to withstand wide ranges of temperatures, and some species have become adapted to extreme cold or heat. Examples of cold-adapted species are *Crenobia alpina* in alpine streams, surviving (air?) temperatures of $-40°$ to $-50°$ C., *Procerodes* in ice water of mountain streams (Bresslau, 1928–1933), *Mesostoma arctica* occurring in fresh-water pools dry or frozen during the greater part of the year (Hyman, 1938), and species of rhabdoceles collected beneath a 2-inch layer of ice in the state of Virginia (Jones and Ferguson, 1941).

Among the heat-adapted or heat-tolerant species is the triclad *Dugesia tigrina,* which, in addition to a wide variety of fresh-water habitats, also occurs in warm springs in Death Valley, California, at a water temperature of 30° C. *Dugesia diabolis* (Hyman, 1956) has been described from a warm spring in Nevada, living in water of 33° C. It should be noted that the water temperature of these desert springs remains fairly constant throughout the year. Well-known examples of extreme heat tolerance are the rhabdoceles *Macrostomum thermale,* living in water of 45° C. in hot springs in Java (Bresslau, 1928–1933), and *Microstomum lineare,* in hot springs at 40° to 47° C. (von Graff, 1908).

Perhaps more surprising than the extreme examples cited above, is the tolerance of individuals of a species to extreme daily fluctuations in water temperature. Kenk (1953) found mature specimens of *Polycelis borealis* in water of 3° to 15° C., rarely up to 22.4° C., at an altitude of 3,800 feet where relatively great diurnal temperature fluctuation would be expected. Darlington (1959) reports the rhabdocele *Mesostoma georgianum,* the triclad *Phagocata bursaperforata,* and the alleocele *Geocentrophora marcusi* from temporary pools having a diurnal water temperature range of 9° to 20° C. at the time the turbellarians were present. The greatest water-temperature range recorded was 0° to 18° C. In these pools, *Mesostoma georgianum* was observed to be active through a wide range of temperatures and also at a time when pools were covered with ice.

Ruebush (1939) recovered *Phaenocora alticola* and *Mesostoma lingua baoensis* from ponds measuring 11.8° C. and 20.6° C. respectively during the day, and states that these waters probably freeze over at night.

While relatively few precise measurements are available, it is reasonable to assume that most alpine species are exposed to similar diurnal fluctuations in water temperature. One would therefore expect that *Microstomum lineare* is able to tolerate temperatures ranging from 3° to 47° C. since this species occurs in alpine lakes as well as in hot springs. The above data pertain to adult specimens of the species cited and represent nearly the total known range in temperature tolerance of the Turbellaria (*i.e.,* 0° to 47° C.). Almost nothing is known about survival of eggs or of encapsulated stages at different temperatures, or about the effect of diurnal or seasonal temperature variations on the growth of very young individuals. The possibility of the existence of different strains within a species adapted to different habitats requires investigation.

Temperature tolerance of parasitic flatworms (trematodes, cestodes) is partly dependent on the tolerance of the host in which they live and grow. The range of host tolerance, however, does not necessarily coincide with the tolerance range of the parasite. Furthermore, the different stages in the life cycle of the parasitic species may have different temperature requirements and different ranges of tolerance. In the cestode *Hymenolepis diminuta* the cysticercoid larva in the insect host *Tribolium confusum* can develop and grow normally at temperatures ranging from 15° to 37° C., and when fully grown can survive 40° C. for several days. The adult cestode in the intestine of rodents normally matures at temperatures of 38° or 39° C., which are deleterious to the developing cysticercoid (Voge and Turner, 1956; Voge and Heyneman, 1958).

More field as well as experimental data are needed on temperature tolerance of free-living as well as parasitic flatworms, particularly information concerning tolerances at different stages of the life cycle of any one species.

Associations of the Turbellaria with Plants

Numerous turbellarian species have been collected from the surface of a variety of plants, primarily marine algae. Whether such occurrences are primarily fortuitous or represent specific relationships between the worms and the plants other than just the physical provision of a holdfast is not known. There is no doubt that plants help provide the moisture essential to terrestrial turbellarians, and indirectly, perhaps the food used by the species in question. Both alleoceles and triclads have numerous representatives occurring in leaf litter, in moss, and in marshy areas. Many of these species, however, may also be found in moist areas almost devoid of plants. The alleocele *Geocentrophora applanata* occurs in bromeliads and remains alive by encystment during the dry period. This species, however, also occurs in permanent waters (Marcus and Marcus, 1951).

Many marine turbellarians have been collected from the surface of marine algae. Thus, species of *Oligocladus* and *Eurylepta* have been found on red algae at a depth of more than 300 feet (Meixner, 1938). The polyclads *Stylochoplana gracilis, S. longipenis,* and *Notoplana saxicola* have been recovered from floating kelp or kelp holdfasts (Hyman, 1953). The triclad *Procerodes pacifica* was collected from *Macrocystis* that had been washed ashore (Hyman, 1954). Similar records may be found in the numerous publications by E. Marcus. The acele *Amphiscolops sargassi* was collected on floating sargassum, and *A. bermudensis* on rooted seaweed (Hyman, 1939a).

Although many of these records may reflect the idiosyncrasies of the collector rather than those of the flatworm, other data suggest that in certain instances the association between algae and turbellarians may be of a less tenuous nature. Riedl (1953), in a very fine ecological study of marine turbellarians, made repeated collections from seaweeds as well as other locations in the intertidal zone and reports 24 species of flatworms on coralline algae. On brown algae (*Halopteris scoparia*) as many as 62 flatworms, including 18 species, were recovered from a surface area of 20 cm.^{2} Certain species that occurred on brown algae were not found on corallines. One wonders whether factors other than the physical situation of these algae or availability of shade or light determine or favor the differential distribution of the flatworm species. The question of specificity of associations between turbellarians and marine algae could be advantageously subjected to laboratory experimentation.

Associations of Flatworms with Animals

Marine turbellarians.—It is well known that many species of marine turbellarians occur in close association with a variety of marine animals. The precise nature of these associations in most instances is unknown, and very little information is available on the degree of dependency of the turbellarians on their associates. There also exists a miscellaneous assemblage of turbellarian species that may be found more or less fortuitously among a variety of animals. An example of the type of association to be discussed is illustrated by Gamble (1910) in his description of the polyclad *Leptoplana*: "At low water *Leptoplana* may be found buried in mud or on the under surface of stones, in pools where darkness and dampness may be ensured till the return of the tide. It is, however, by no means easy to detect and remove it from the encrusting Polyzoa, ascidians or sponges with which it is usually associated. The flat, soft, unsegmented body is so closely appressed to the substratum that its presence is usually only betrayed by its movement. . . ." Gamble further states that certain species of *Leptoplana* do not endure removal from their animal associates.

From available information on the types of associations not yet proved to be obligatory for the turbellarians, it has been assumed that many of these "symbioses" fall into the following categories: (1) temporary and fortuitous, (2) non-specific as to type of animals selected, (3) for shelter only, (4) for feeding-scavenging, (5) to escape dehydration or light. Only extensive collecting and careful ecological studies can resolve these problems and prove or disprove the correctness of these assumptions for each species.

Examination of existing collecting records shows that species of all orders of the Turbellaria may be found associated with other animals. Examples among the polyclads are recorded by Pearse and Littler (1938), who described several species found in association with sponges, barnacles, and oysters and among ascidians. According to these authors, the oysters served as food for the turbellarians; availability of food may in this instance be the basis of this association. Hyman (1953) described *Stylochus californicus* from burrows of the rock-boring clam *Barnea pacifica* and *S. exiguus* from the burrows of *Upogebia pugetensis*. *Parviplana californica* was collected among sponges and bryozoans, and *Notoplana sanjuania* from the back of crabs or from the inside of barnacles growing on the crabs. Meixner (1938) describes *Notoplana atomata* from corals taken at a depth of 600 feet, and Hyman (1953) records *Leptoplana limnoriae* from burrows of the wood-boring isopod *Limnoria*. Polyclads were also found in association with corals in Hawaii. *Notoplana saxicola* was found on *Mytilus*, but also on masses of algae (Hyman, 1953).

Other associations seem to be more specialized and possibly obligatory. *Taenioplana teredini* spends its entire life cycle in burrows of *Teredo* and lays its eggs there (Hyman, 1944). *Stylochoplana inquilina* is found on hermit crabs bearing sea anemones and uses the snail shell as a retreat (Hyman, 1950). Another association with hermit crabs is exemplified by the acele *Ectocotyla paguri*, which also possesses a caudal adhesive disk (Hyman, 1951a). It would be interesting to know whether these species also can occur in other situations.

Among the alleoceles, Gamble (1910) describes *Monotus fuscus* as living among limpets, barnacles, and chitons. At low tide, it creeps between the mantle folds "to obtain moisture and darkness"; upon return of the tide it leaves and swims about freely.

Associations of triclads with other animals seem to be less common than of other groups of the Turbellaria. Domantay (1955) describes an association of "tiny triclad flatworms" with a species of tube-dwelling amphipod. This association occurred in relatively large masses and, in different collection sites, contained different transient inhabitants. The species of amphipod and triclad, however, were always the same and in each location represented the bulk of the material composing the mass.

The rhabdoceles, which contain relatively large numbers of obligatory symbionts, to be discussed below, also have species associated with animals in what seems to be a more tenuous relationship. For example, at the Hawaii Marine Laboratory, a small white rhabdocele was repeatedly found attached by its posterior end to the white and red hydroid *Pennaria*. In color and in shape it blended so well with parts of the hydroid that its presence was at first detected only through movement. This rhabdocele, however, was also collected, although in lesser numbers, from various algae growing next to the hydroid on the same float.

From the few examples presented here it may be seen that members of all orders of the Turbellaria may live in relatively close association with other animals. That this represents a definite trend for the phylum Platyhelminthes rather than an exceptional situation is obvious from the wholly symbiotic Trematoda and Cestoda, as well as from the many examples of varied associations to be found among the Turbellaria. It is, of course, very difficult and often impossible to draw lines and neatly pigeonhole the many different types of associations existing between animals. A division into facultative and obligatory associates is helpful in that it may indicate the extent of specialization undergone by the species so classified. A species that is an obligate associate of another animal species may be a parasite, a commensal, or a mutualist. Yet these terms, while convenient, are often misleading because there may exist many transitional states. Furthermore, one type of relationship may shift to another, depending on the environment of the associates. It is unfortunate that so little is known about the factors predisposing any one species toward an obligate association with another organism. There is no doubt, however, that the turbellarians as a group are predisposed if not preadapted for a symbiotic existence and that all types of associations intermediate between a free-living and a parasitic existence can be found among them.

A brief review of the host distribution of symbiotic turbellarians is shown in table 33-2. Except for a few species of triclads, which occur on selachians, all symbiotic turbellarians are found on or in various invertebrates. Aside from the temnocephalans, which occur on fresh-water hosts, the symbiotic turbellarians are primarily marine. One wonders why larger numbers of fresh-water and terrestrial

TABLE 33-2

Symbiotic Turbellaria and Their Hosts

Major taxon		Hosts
Acoela	Endosymbiotic in	Echinoids Holothurians
Polycladida	Ectosymbiotic on	Molluscs Crustaceans Echinoderms
Alloeocoela	Ectosymbiotic on	Molluscs Crustaceans
Rhabdocoela	Endosymbiotic in	Turbellarians Molluscs Echinoderms Sipunculids Crustaceans Annelids
(Temnocephalida	Ectosymbiotic on	Crustaceans, molluscs, and turtles)
Tricladida	Ectosymbiotic on	*Limulus* Selachians

rhabdoceles have not become adapted to a symbiotic existence. Although the rhabdoceles contain the largest number of symbiotic species, such species are found in all the other orders as well. As previously stated, the degrees of dependency upon the host or the precise natures of some of these associations have not been adequately determined, and the very general listing in Table 33-2 probably includes facultative as well as obligate symbiotes.

The Trematoda.—The trematodes are all obligate symbionts. Table 33-3 briefly

TABLE 33-3

Trematoda and Their Hosts

Order		Hosts
Monogenea	Ectosymbiotic (1-host cycle)	Cold-blooded vertebrates, crustaceans, cephalopods
Aspidogastrea	Endosymbiotic (1- or 2-host cycle)	Cold-blooded vertebrates, molluscs, crustaceans
Digenea	Endosymbiotic	Cold- and warm-blooded vertebrates
	(2- or 3-host cycle)	Molluscs, crustaceans, insect larvae, fish, amphibians

reviews the host distribution of the orders and the types of life cycles characteristic for each. The monogenes have a one-host cycle and are therefore the least complex in their life history. The aspidogastrids, considered by some not to deserve ordinal rank, are essentially endosymbiotic, but inhabit the same major host groups as do the monogenes. From the point of view of degree of specialization for a symbiotic existence one might consider the aspidogastrids to be intermediate between the monogenes and the digenes. The digenetic trematodes are all endosymbiotic and occur as adults in all major groups of vertebrates; the larval stages occur in molluscs. Crustaceans, insect larvae, fish or amphibia are used as additional, intermediate hosts by some species only. These seem to serve, as do plants, as a means of transport only. Within the Digenea, a molluscan host is, of course, obligatory for the development of the larval stages. With regard to habitats, the adult digenetic trematodes have become adapted to live in many different environments within the body of their hosts. Unfortunately, very little precise information is available about the characteristics of these environments. For example, adults of different species of digenes may occur subcutaneously, in the blood vessels, in the lungs or brain, in the gall bladder or liver tissues, in the stomach or intestines, or in the urinary bladder in a variety of host species. In a general way one knows that the lungs and the brain have at least one feature in common—namely, that both are well supplied with oxygen. Therefore it is not surprising to find that the lung fluke *Paragonimus westermanii* may also occur in the brain. Very little is known about the other features of these two environments as they relate to the growth of the parasite. There are many different environments within any one host-species to which different digenes have become adapted. In addition, each of these tissue sites must differ physiologically in various hosts. This leads to the problem of host specificity, about which there has been much written although little specific information has been accumulated. It is now generally conceded, however, that most species of trematodes are not limited to one vertebrate host-species, although host-group specificity does exist. At the intermediate-host level, specificity may be more or less strict, depending on the species of digene. Thus the range of habitat tolerance is represented by the environment of the host or hosts a given species is able to use for growth and reproduction. Complete knowledge of this range of tolerance for any species of digene is not available and can only be acquired through extensive laboratory investigations.

The Cestoda.—The cestodes that occur as adults in all groups of cold- or warm-blooded vertebrates are, with very few exceptions, limited in occurrence to the intestine of their vertebrate hosts. The various larval stages, however, have a very wide host distribution and occur in molluscs, in arthropods, in a few annelids, and in cold- or warm-blooded vertebrates. As in the digenetic trematodes, host specificity of cestodes has been much overrated by taxonomists in their desire to describe new species. As will be shown further on, many species of cestodes are able to utilize a variety of intermediate as well as definitive hosts. What this means in terms of tolerance or adaptation to different environments is as yet largely unknown because the features of these host environments have not been carefully investigated and the specific requirements of the parasites for the most part have not been determined.

Habitat Variation and Tolerance of Single Species

Demonstration of the existence of wide ranges in habitats of the platyhelminths as a group, tells us very little, if anything, about the adaptability or tolerances of single species. In selecting examples among those species about which we have more than the usual limited knowledge, one is tempted to choose extreme examples and neglect the seemingly conservative majority. Unfortunately, there are so few data on tolerance ranges of different flatworm species to their environment that one can do nothing more than report the information at hand, selecting examples from the different major groups of flatworms whenever possible. For some of the groups, particularly the endosymbiotic ones, the ideas presented are largely based on extrapolation from miscellaneous facts because we know too little about what constitutes a host environment.

The Turbellaria.—Among the triclads, the well-known *Dugesia tigrina* is ubiquitous, ranging from Canada to southern Brazil (Hyman, 1951b). While this is essentially a fresh-water species, occurring in ponds, lakes, and rivers, on vegetation, and under stones, it is also found in warm springs with a high salt content (see above). It thus exhibits considerable tolerance with respect to salinity as well as temperature.

The alleocele *Prorhynchus stagnalis* occurs in brackish water as well as in fresh water, in the mud of rivers and lakes, in deep wells, in moss of springs, and in moist soil (at a depth of more than 300 feet), and is found in Europe, Asia, and North America (Steinböck, 1927).

One of the most remarkable species is the rhabdocele *Gyratrix hermaphroditus,* which may occur in all types of bodies of fresh water at sea level, as well as at altitudes of 7,000 feet, in dark wells, and in marine tide pools. In these different habitats, which encompass a wide range in salinity, temperature, exposure to light, as well as other aspects of the environment, *G. hermaphroditus* shows very little morphological variability. A detailed study of this species is essential to substantiate these remarkable observations.

The Trematoda.—Among the endosymbiotic species having a complex life-history that involves two or more obligatory hosts, each developmental stage of the worm has become adapted to a set of environmental conditions represented by the internal environment of the host as well as by the features of the external environment that must be tolerated between hosts. For example, the adult lung fluke *Paragonimus westermanii* lives in the lungs or brain of a mammal; the miracidium larva hatches in fresh water and enters the fresh-water molluscan host, where further larval development occurs. The resultant cercariae leave the snail and must spend at least a brief time in fresh water to penetrate a crab or crayfish, where they remain in an encysted state until ingested by the mammal. In the mammalian intestine, digestion of the cyst enables the young worm to escape confinement, to penetrate the wall of the gut, and to pass by way of the celom and the diaphragm into the pleural cavity. Thus during the course of its life cycle *P. westermanii* is exposed to habitats comprising two different kinds of invertebrate hosts, one warm-blooded vertebrate host, as well as fresh water for short periods between hosts. Within the vertebrate host, penetration and migration through several different tissues must be accomplished.

The Cestoda.—Within the limits of the specialized host requirements of different growth stages, different species of parasitic flatworms have considerable tolerance with respect to the vertebrate or the invertebrate host. Many examples of this lack of close "host specificity" are found among the tapeworms. The rat tapeworm *Hymenolepis diminuta,* for instance, occurs not only in brown rats or Norway rats, but also in man. It can be experimentally introduced into a variety of rodents. The cysticercoid stages which require an invertebrate host for development may grow successfully in at least 30 different species of insects belonging to several different orders. Unfortunately the life cycles of several major groups of cestodes are still unknown, and the full range of physiologically suitable hosts for any one species has not been determined. For example, few attempts have been made to introduce species habitually found in mammals into birds or into cold-blooded vertebrates. With few exceptions, the species of cestodes are exposed to one invertebrate host and to one or two vertebrate hosts during their life cycles. In contrast to the digenetic trematodes, adult cestodes are limited to the intestine or bile ducts of the vertebrate host, but their larval stages, which are as a rule extraintestinal, usually have much less stringent host requirements than those of the trematodes.

Discussion

In the preceding account an attempt has been made to show that members of the phylum Platyhelminthes have succeeded in invading almost every type of habitat which provides some moisture during at least a part of the year. Furthermore, many flatworms show great tolerance or adaptation to a variety of environmental extremes, as well as to fluctuations in the physical characteristics of their habitat. In addition, flatworms have been highly successful in becoming associated with other animals and have entered many different types of symbiotic relationships. This adaptability or tolerance seems to be a characteristic of the phylum as a whole rather than of a few species only. It was stated at the outset that the Nematoda comprise the only other group among the lower Metazoa showing comparable diversity. The habitat distribution of other metazoa shows that the sponges, celenterates and ctenophores, kinorhynchs and priapulids are primarily or exclusively marine, with few or no symbiotic species. The Mesozoa and Acanthocephala have no free-living representatives, and the small group of Nematomorpha are primarily fresh-water forms with parasitic larval stages. Two other phyla, the Nemertinea (Rhynchocoela) and the Rotifera, show a relatively great variety in habitats and tolerance of extreme conditions. The Nemertinea have representatives in fresh water and on land, as well as a few symbiotic members. The rotifers have numerous species in salt and in fresh water. They also include terrestrial forms and a few that are parasitic, and may exhibit remarkable temperature tolerance. In their range of habitat adaptation, the rotifers closely resemble the free-living turbellarians. It is therefore of interest that Hyman (1951c), on the basis of morphology, states that the rotifers "show a greater resemblance to Turbellaria than to any other group."

The flatworms, in addition to their success as free-living organisms, are unique in their varied adaptations to a symbiotic existence. One wonders what characteristics, other than small size, predispose any one group of animals toward symbiosis. In the flatworms, perhaps an initial wide tolerance with respect to certain environmental features, such as oxygen tension, temperature, and pH, is one of the essential predisposing features, as suggested by Osche (1955) for the nematodes. Of all the animal phyla with large numbers of free-living species, the flatworms, the roundworms, and the arthropods also contain the greatest number of symbiotic species.

Regarding the host environments, especially those of invertebrates and cold-blooded vertebrates, one would want to know much more about factors such as temperature, availability of oxygen, etc., to gain some understanding of tolerance of the different symbiotic flatworms. In addition, the purely physical properties inherent in host environments and their effects on the symbiont have thus far been given very little attention. The physical aspects of the environment—for example, the types of holdfasts, clinging surfaces, or any properties permitting adhesion or partial compression of the worm—may be very important for the performance of the various biological functions and require study.

A superficial view of any one symbiotic species requiring an invertebrate as well as a vertebrate host would suggest that the larval stages in the invertebrate host are exposed to an environment radically different from that of the vertebrate host in which the adult develops. One wonders to what extent a two-host cycle is merely an adaptation to a convenient mode of transportation? What are the factors that limit the occurrence of certain larval stages to a molluscan or to an insect host? Aside from purely physical factors such as entry into a host, what, for example, are the physiological barriers to development of a sporocyst in a host other than a mollusc? Surely differences in temperature, oxygen tension, or pH would not be the decisive barriers for organisms showing relatively wide ranges in tolerance with respect to these features. It is more likely that the nutritional means and requirements of the symbiont are the most important factors in a host environment. The different requirements and different tolerances at different stages of the life history of any one species deserve careful study.

With regard to our present state of knowledge about the ecology of flatworms, the glaring deficiencies lie in our understanding of symbiotic relationships. Among the free-living turbellarians, the marine species have been much neglected, and, by comparison with terrestrial or fresh-water forms, little is known about them. Perhaps this is a reflection of the distribution of marine biologists and marine stations rather than of a lack of interest in marine turbellarians. One wonders whether free-living marine turbellarians are potentially capable of tolerating as wide a range of environmental conditions as are the fresh-water forms, or whether they are much more specialized and less adaptable.

In conclusion, it should be stressed that the gaining of more precise information about the ecology and physiology of free-living turbellarians might greatly further our understanding of the symbiotic species and perhaps suggest new approaches for study of the symbiotic forms. Important areas for investigation include the nutritional mechanisms and requirements, the influence of the physical environment upon nutrition and growth, and the requirements and tolerances of individuals at different stages of development. The relative simplicity of free-living flatworms should enable us to gain much valuable information that might contribute greatly toward the development of new approaches in the study of the complex symbiotic species.

REFERENCES

Beauchamp, P. de
    1936   Turbellariés et Bryozoaires. Mém. Mus. Hist. nat. Paris. (n.s.) 4:141–153.
Bresslau, E.
    1928–
    1933   Turbellaria. Handb. Zool., Berl. 2, sect. 1:52–304. [1928:52–112; 1930:113–192; 1933:193–304.]
Darlington, J.
    1959   The Turbellaria of two granite outcrops in Georgia. Amer. midl. Nat. 61:257–294.
Domantay, J. S.
    1955   Rectification of *Oscarella malabonensis,* a spongiomorphic mass formed by myriad of tiny animals, mostly tube-dwelling amphipods, polychaetes and turbellarians. Philipp. J. Sci. 84:335–339.
Ferguson, F. F., and W. J. Hayes, Jr.
    1941   A synopsis of the genus *Mesostoma* Ehrenberg 1935. J. Elisha Mitchell sci. Soc. 57:1–52.
Gamble, F. W.
    1910   Flatworms and Mesozoa. Pp. 1–91 in: Cambridge Natural History, Vol. II. Macmillan, London.
Graff, L. von
    1904–
    1908   Acoela und Rhabdocoelida. Bronn's Klassen 4, Sect. Ic (Turbellaria,

Sect. 1): I–XXII, 1733–2599. [1904–1905, pp. 1733–1984; 1907, pp. 1985–2192, 2193–2256; 1908, pp. 2257–2599.]

Hyman, L. H.

1937   Studies on the morphology, taxonomy, and distribution of the North American Turbellaria. VIII. Some cave planarians of the United States. Trans. Amer. micr. Soc. 56:457–477.

1938   North American Rhabdocoela and Alloecoela. III. *Mesostoma arctica,* new species. Amer. Mus. Novit. 1005:1–8.

1939a   Acoel and polyclad Turbellaria from Bermuda and the Sargassum. Bull. Bingham oceanogr. Coll. 7:1–26.

1939b   North American triclad Turbellaria. X. Additional species of cave planarians. Trans. Amer. micr. Soc. 58:276–284.

1944   A new Hawaiian polyclad flatworm associated with *Teredo.* Occ. Pap. Bishop Mus. 18:73–75.

1950   A new Hawaiian polyclad, *Stylochoplana inquilina,* with commensal habits. Occ. Pap. Bishop Mus. 20:55–58.

1951a   The Invertebrates. Vol. II: Platyhelminthes and Rhynchocoela—the Acoelomate Bilateria. McGraw-Hill, New York, Toronto, London.

1951b   North American triclad Turbellaria. XII. Synopsis of the known species of fresh-water planarians of North America. Trans. Amer. micr. Soc. 70:154–166.

1951c   The Invertebrates, Vol. III: Acanthocephala, Aschelminthes, and Ectoprocta—the Pseudocoelomate Bilateria. McGraw-Hill, New York, Toronto, London.

1953   The polyclad flatworms of the Pacific Coast of North America. Bull. Amer. Mus. nat. Hist. 100:269–392.

1954   A new marine triclad from the coast of California. Amer. Mus. Novit. No. 1679:1–5.

1956   North American triclad Turbellaria. XV. Three new species. Amer. Mus. Novit. 1808:1–14.

Jones, R. E., Jr., and F. F. Ferguson

1941   Studies on the turbellarian faunas of the Norfolk area. VI. Anatomy of *Macrostomum appendiculatum* var. *stirewalti* new variety. J. Elisha Mitchell sci. Soc. 57:53–57.

Kenk, R.

1953   The fresh-water triclads (Turbellaria) of Alaska. Proc. U. S. nat. Mus. 103:163–186.

Marcus, E.

1955   Turbellaria. Pp. 101–151 in: South African Animal Life. Results of the Lund University expedition in 1950–1951. Vol. I. Hanstrom, B., *et al.,* Eds. Almqvist and Wiksell, Stockholm.

Marcus, E. duB.-R.

1957   On Turbellaria. Ann. Acad. bras. Sci. 29:153–191.

Marcus, E. duB.-R., and E. Marcus

1951   Contributions to the natural history of Brazilian Turbellaria. Communic. Zool. Hist. nat. Montevideo, 3:1–25.

Meixner, J.

1938   Turbellaria (Strudelwürmer) I. Tierwelt N.- u. Ostsee. Lief 33, Teil 4:1–146.

Osche, G.

1955   Die Präadaptation freilebender Nematoden an den Parasitismus. Verh. dtsch. zool. Ges., Tübingen (1954) (Zool. Anz., Suppl. 18):391–397.

Pearse, A. S., and J. W. Littler
    1938   Polyclads of Beaufort, North Carolina. J. Elisha Mitchell sci. Soc.
           54:235–244.

Read, C. P.
    1958   A science of symbiosis. A.I.B.S. Bull. 8:16–17.

Riedl, R.
    1953   Quantitativ-ökologische Methoden mariner Turbellarienforschung. Öst.
           zool. Z. 4:108–145.

Ruebush, T. K.
    1939   Report on the rhabdocoele Turbellaria collected by the Yale North
           India Expedition. Zool. Anz. 126:4–67.

Steinböck, O.
    1926   Zur Ökologie der alpinen Turbellarien. Z. Morph. Ökol. Tiere 5:424–446.
    1927   Monographie der Prorhynchidae (Turbellaria). *Ibid.* 9:538–662.

Voge, M., and J. A. Turner
    1956   Effect of temperature on larval development of the cestode, *Hymenolepis
           diminuta.* Exp. Parasit. 5:580–586.

Voge, M., and D. Heyneman
    1958   Effect of high temperature on the larval development of *Hymenolepis
           nana* and *Hymenolepis diminuta* (Cestoda: Cyclophyllidea). J. Parasit.
           44:249–260.

Aschelminthes

34 ◆ Aspects of the Natural History and Ecology of the Gastrotricha

ROYAL BRUCE BRUNSON

DEPARTMENT OF ZOÖLOGY,
MONTANA STATE UNIVERSITY, MISSOULA

More work has been done on the taxonomy of the Gastrotricha than on any other aspect of their study. At our current state of knowledge an outstanding taxonomic question is whether or not cosmopolitanism of species exists. Cosmopolitanism is assumed by many workers, even though it has never been systematically investigated. The systematic position of the Gastrotricha is also a matter of conjecture, and no one taxonomic category will be agreed to by all systematists. The internal anatomy and physiological functions have been investigated by the very efficient German workers. A remaining area to be more thoroughly studied, then, is the ecology of gastrotrichs. My intention here is to present some of the problems that face the ecologist dealing with fresh-water forms.

Eggs and Egg Production

Fresh-water gastrotrichs (order Chaetonotida) produce two types of eggs. Tachyblastic eggs normally start cleavage as soon as they are laid and cannot survive freeze-thawing or drying. Opsiblastic eggs must undergo a period of dormancy before development begins; they can be dried or frozen for several months or even years and hatch out when put in a favorable medium. It is not yet known for the chetonotides whether either or both types of eggs are produced parthenogenetically or by union of gametes. Even though the covering of a tachyblastic egg is much thinner than that of an opsiblastic egg, it is quite evident that, if fertilization occurs, it must be internal. The exact mechanism of fertilization in marine gastrotrichs (order Macrodasyida), which are monecious, is problematical.

Regardless of the type of egg produced, a minimal amount of food material must be present in order that eggs may be produced. In one experiment 39 mature animals (*Lepidodermella squamata*) were taken from a growing culture and placed in clear well-water. One animal produced an egg soon afterwards, and this was the only egg produced in three days. With the addition of food (malted-milk solution) eight of the 39 produced an egg within 23 hours. In cultures with food present the gastrotrichs produced an average of 3.67 eggs. The range was from one to five, and the largest percentage of animals produced four eggs each.

In growing cultures most gastrotrichs produce only tachyblastic eggs. If an opsiblastic egg is produced by an individual, it is usually the last oviposition by that animal even if it is also the first. A sole observed exception to this rule has been with the species *Chaetonotus tachyneusticus*. An experiment was set up with individuals of this species so that animals that had produced an opsiblastic egg were given a fresh amount of food. In an isolated instance an individual produced a tachyblastic egg after the food was added. None of the others produced another egg. The exact mechanism that triggers the production of opsiblastic eggs is not yet known. No opsiblastic eggs have occurred in cultures maintained at 6° and 25° C. as long as food has been present. By contrast, most gastrotrichs will produce opsiblastic eggs if the culture is allowed to stand after the population peak is reached and food is ostensibly depleted. Furthermore, if an animal carrying an ovum is taken from a growing culture and put in water from a "spent" culture, the ovum will become an opsiblastic egg. One must assume, therefore, that the fate of an intrabody ovum may not be determined until near oviposition.

Hatching and Post-Embryonic Development

In *Lepidodermella* the period from laying to hatching varies for different eggs, despite the fact that environmental conditions are ostensibly uniform and that the cleavage stages for the first 12 hours are closely parallel. The period of intra-egg development, at 19° C., varies from 36 to 50 hours. A greater percentage of hatching occurs from 45 to 50 hours. In more than 50 cases observed, no hatchings occurred between 41 and 45 hours. Unfortunately this significant statistical difference between a short and long sequence of embryonation was not recognized in time to develop clones from animals of the two periods. One can only conjecture as to the cause of this difference. Furthermore, no differences were evident in the young of the two groups.

The period of intra-egg development of *Chaetonotus tachyneusticus* varies from 36 to 40 hours, which is similar to the shorter periods in *Lepidodermella*. The longer period leading to hatching found in *Lepidodermella* is absent in *Chaetonotus*. There is, however, one interesting feature found, so far, only in *Chaetonotus tachyneusticus*. This species often produces a second type of tachyblastic egg. Whereas the usual tachyblastic egg is spiny, the second type is covered with numerous low, rounded elevations, which give the egg an appearance much like that of *Ascaris*. The significance of the second type of tachyblastic egg is undetermined.

The newly-hatched young are much like the adults except that they are 20 per cent smaller. Growth is at the rate of 4 micra per hour until adult size is attained. There is no shedding of the cuticule.

Length of Life

Fifty members of the species *Lepidodermella squamata,* which were isolated in depression slides, lived an average of 16 days. The oldest animals lived for between 21 and 22 days, and one died only 8.5 days after hatching. Most of the gastrotrichs lived between 14 and 20 days. The exact moment of death was difficult to determine, because in these experiments it was a slow process. Various inner tissues disintegrated, one after the other, until only the ventral ciliated epithelium, which was attached to the cuticular outer covering, remained alive. An animal might swim around in this condition for 12 to 24 hours.

Interspecific Associations

During twenty years of study on the Gastrotricha, I have never recognized a parasite of gastrotrichs. In that time I have studied many hundreds of individuals from collections made in the field, and tens of thousands of gastrotrichs included in 45 clones. This does not imply, however, that parasites do not exist among the gastrotrichs.

Individuals of the genus *Chaetogaster* have been observed feeding on the eggs of gastrotrichs and rotifers (*Lepadella*). *Amoeba spumosa* can depopulate a culture of gastrotrichs in a very short time, even though the ameba has scarcely enough protoplasm to encircle the gastrotrich. If an ameba catches a gastrotrich by the caudal prongs, the gastrotrich can soon free itself. If the head is caught first, the gastrotrich dies after threshing around wildly for a short time. If gastrotrichs were able to reverse the direction of their cilia and back up, predation by amebae might be greatly lessened. (Hypotrichs have been observed to free themselves from amebae by backing up.)

A weird instance of predation on gastrotrichs (also on rotifers and small annelids) was exhibited by an unidentified predaceous fungus that developed in several gross cultures. The fungus developed until it spread throughout the culture medium. If an animal moved close to the tip of a mycelium, it suddenly was stuck and could not free itself. Within a few minutes all internal tissues would pass into the fungus, with only the cuticular covering remaining. The fungus could destroy all the animals in a culture in a short time.

Culturing

During the process of culturing *Lepidodermella* it seemed, on general inspection, that in well-established clones the reproductive rate increased with the number of individuals present. This surge of reproduction also seemed to be correlated with the size of the container (both 1-inch and 2-inch Stender dishes were used) and the availability of food materials. Preliminary experiments were designed to test this impression by placing different numbers of individuals in containers of the same size for a given length of time. Old-style individual salt dishes with dimensions of 21 mm. in diameter and 8 mm. in depth were used as culture dishes. Animals, ranging in number from one to 200, were placed in culture medium for 14 days, then killed and counted. The results are shown in table 34-1.

TABLE 34-1

REPRODUCTION EXPERIMENT COVERING PERIOD OF 14 DAYS

Number of animals at start	Number of animals at end	Number of eggs at end	Eggs plus animals	Increase per animal	Ratio of animals to eggs
1	10	5	15	15	2:1
5	49	14	63	12.6	3.5:1
10	89	14	103	10.3	6.3:1
50	223	25	248	5.0	9:1
100	388	25	413	4.1	15.5:1
200	612	41	653	3.3	15:1

By adding the number of eggs, which were potential individuals, to the number of animals present at the end of the two-week experiment, it can be seen that the greatest increase from the original number occurred when the starting number was one. The rate of increase decreased with the greater numbers so that the lowest increase was found where the original number was 200. Whether this pattern of increase would be repeated in larger culture dishes is not yet known. Obviously these data do not verify the original impression, even though my observations on 1,500 cultures had seemed to support it.

In initiating an experiment like that summarized in table 34-1, there are certain variable factors one must consider. In the first place, the container used should be large enough so that more food can be added from time to time. Although no opsiblastic eggs (which might indicate a lack of food) were present in the experiment just described, it is obvious that food was relatively depleted where there were higher numbers. In the experiment no food was added in 14 days, whereas in good growing-cultures food must be added every 48 hours. Thus this experiment may well be regarded as having suggested a correlation between reproductive rate and availability of food. A second variable operates in the process of "picking up" animals by means of a mouth micro-pipette. In some gastrotrichs a definite "shock" effect can be observed. This may be severe enough that, if the animal is carrying an ovum, the ovum is resorbed and no further ova are produced regardless of the amount of food. There are, of course, lesser effects from the moving. A third variable seems intrinsic to the animal itself. Brunson (1949, p. 13) has shown that, under uniform conditions, one individual may produce an ovum 49 hours after hatching, whereas at the other extreme an animal's first oviposition may require 189 hours. Further: "a great variation was also evidenced in the age of the individual at the time of its last oviposition. This age ranged from 5.8 days to 14.3 days." It is possible, then, for one individual to produce four eggs within six days after hatching, whereas another may take 14 days to produce the same number of eggs.

To check individual variability, several animals were isolated singly in depression slides, each with the same amount of food. All animals were near the same stage in development and, in a first experiment, were left for ten days. At the end of that period all progeny and eggs were counted. The total counts were as follows: 8 animals, no eggs; 9 animals, 1 egg; 12 animals, 1 egg; 13 animals, no eggs; 13 animals, no eggs; 18 animals, 1 egg; 22 animals, no eggs. A second experiment lasted for two weeks with the following results (number of animals given first and eggs second): 9,0; 12,5; 22,5; 25,5; 28,12; and 33,13. All animals in these experiments were members of the same clone and presumably, therefore, genetically alike. Inasmuch as all other conditions (*i.e.,* food, temperature, etc.) were ostensibly very similar, it would follow that these differences were the result of individual variation. If the highest biotic potential (*i.e.,* all eggs hatching in 36 hours; oviposition occurring 39 hours after hatching; every animal producing 5 eggs; and eggs being produced every 23 hours) were realized in the foregoing experiment, the total number of animals and eggs at the end of the 14 days would have been twice the greatest number.

In several species of *Chaetonotus* all attempts to develop clones have failed, despite the fact that "gross" cultures have flourished. Although on occasion an isolated animal has produced one or two eggs, the second generation has produced none. When the starting number has been two animals, cultures have developed slowly. When the starting number has been six, cultures have developed more than three times as rapidly as when the starting number was two. Inasmuch as the gross culture throve on the culture medium, some other explanation has to be found for this failure to develop clones. Some explanations suggested are: (a) Allee's theory of protection of numbers, and (b) the presence of a "male factor."

Future Work

In addition to extending the many problems presented in this paper, there are other areas of future work. These include: (1) experimental embryology, such as destroying or marking cells in early development; (2) chromosomal studies; (3) the problem of males or "maleness"; (4) whether or not cosmopolitanism of species exists; and (5) the variability of taxonomic characters.

REFERENCES

Brunson, R. B.
    1949   The life history and ecology of two North American gastrotrichs. Trans. Amer. micr. Soc. 68(1):1–20.
    1950   An introduction to the taxonomy of the Gastrotricha with a study of eighteen species from Michigan. Trans. Amer. micr. Soc. 69(4):325–352.
    1959   Gastrotricha. Pp. 406–419 in: Fresh-Water Biology. Ward, H. B., and G. C. Whipple, Eds. Wiley, New York.
Hyman, L. H.
    1951   The Invertebrates. Vol. III: Acanthocephala, Aschelminthes, and Entroprocta—the Pseudocoelomate Bilateria. McGraw-Hill, New York, Toronto, London. [Gastrotricha: pp. 151–170.]

Packard, C. E.
  1958–
  1959   Studies on the Gastrotricha. [A series of papers in Turtox News.]
Pennak, R. W.
  1953   Fresh-Water Invertebrates of the United States. Ronald, New York.
            [Gastrotricha: pp. 148–158.]
Remane, A.
  1935–
  1936   Gastrotricha und Kinorhyncha. Bronn's Klassen 4, Sect. 2, book 2, pt.
            1:1–385. [1935, Lieferung 1:1–160; 1936, Lieferung 2:161–385.]
Sacks, M.
  1955   Observations on the embryology of an aquatic gastrotrich, *Lepidodermella
            squammata* (Dujardin, 1841). J. Morph. 96(3):474–496.
Varga, L.
  1954   Die Gastrotrichen der Ozberek-Quelle bei Diósjenő. Acta Zoologica.
            Academia Scientiarum Hungaricae. 1(1–2):171–175.
Voigt, M.
  1958   Gastrotricha. Tierwelt Mitteleur. 1, no. 4a:1–74.
Wilke, U.
  1954   Mediterrane Gastrotricha. Zool. Jb. (Syst.) 82:497–550.